Liposomes
in
Biological Systems

Liposomes in Biological Systems

Edited by

Gregory Gregoriadis and **Anthony C. Allison**

Clinical Research Centre, Watford Road, Harrow, UK and International Laboratory for Research on Animal Diseases, Nairobi, Kenya

A Wiley–Interscience Publication

JOHN WILEY & SONS

Chichester · New York · Brisbane · Toronto

British Library Cataloguing in Publication Data

Liposomes in biological systems.
  1. Liposomes
  I. Gregoriadis, Gregory
  II. Allison, Anthony Clifford
  574.8'734   QH601   79-40507
  ISBN 0 471 27608 1

Typeset by Preface Ltd., Salisbury, Wiltshire
Printed by Page Bros. (Norwich) Ltd., Norwich

List of Contributors

A. D. Bangham
Biophysics Unit, Agricultural Research Council, Institute of Animal Physiology, Babraham, Cambridge CB2 4AT, UK.

T. de Barsy
Laboratoire de Chimie Physiologique, Université de Louvain, and International Institute of Cellular and Molecular Pathology (ICP), 1200 Bruxelles, Belgium.

J. T. Dingle
Tissue Physiology Department, Strangeways Research Laboratory, Worts' Causeway, Cambridge CB1 4RN, UK.

J. H. Fendler
Department of Chemistry, Texas A&M University, College Station, Texas 77843, USA.

M. Finkelstein
Division of Rheumatology, Department of Medicine, New York University School of Medicine, New York, NY 10016, USA.

G. Gregoriadis
Clinical Research Centre, Watford Road, Harrow, Middlesex HA1 3UJ, UK.

D. Hoekstra
Laboratory of Physiological Chemistry, University of Groningen, Bloemsingel 10, Groningen, The Netherlands.

G. M. K. Humphries
Stauffer Laboratories for Physical Chemistry, Stanford University, Stanford, California 94305, USA.

H. K. Kimelberg
Division of Neurosurgery and Department of Biochemistry, Albany Medical College of Union University, Albany, New York, USA.

W. E. Magee
Division of Allied Health and Life Sciences, University of Texas at San Antonio, San Antonio, Texas, USA.

I. R. McDougall
Division of Nuclear Medicine, Stanford Medical Center, Stanford, California 94305, USA.

G. Poste
Department of Experimental Pathology, Roswell Park Memorial Institute, Buffalo, New York 14263, USA.

Y. E. Rahman
Division of Biological and Medical Research, Argonne National Laboratory, Argonne, Illinois, USA.

F. Roerdink
Laboratory of Physiological Chemistry, University of Groningen, Bloemsingel 10, Groningen, The Netherlands.

G. Scherphof
Laboratory of Physiological Chemistry, University of Groningen, Bloemsingel 10, Groningen, The Netherlands.

I. H. Shaw
Tissue Physiology Department, Strangeways Research Laboratory, Worts' Causeway, Cambridge CB1 4RN, UK.

Present address:
Corpus Christi College, Cambridge, UK.

F. Van Hoof
Laboratoire de Chimie Physiologique, Université de Louvain, and International Institute of Cellular and Molecular Pathology (ICP), 1200 Bruxelles, Belgium.

G. Weissmann
Division of Rheumatology, Department of Medicine, New York University School of Medicine, New York, NY 10016, USA.

E. Wisse
Laboratory of Electron Microscopy, University of Leiden, Rijnsburgerweg 10, Leiden, The Netherlands.

Present address:
Laboratory for Cell Biology and Histology, Free University of Brussels, Laarbeeklaan 101 1090 Brussels-Jette, Belgium.

J. Zborowski   *Laboratory of Physiological Chemistry, University of Groningen, Bloemsingel 10, Groningen, The Netherlands.*

Present address:
Nencki Institute of Experimental Biology, Department of Cellular Biochemistry, 3 Pasteur Street, 02–093 Warsaw, Poland.

Contents

Preface   xi

1. **Development of the Liposome concept**   1
   A. D. Bangham

2. **The liposome drug-carrier concept: its development and future**   25
   G. Gregoriadis

3. **Optimizing drug entrapment in liposomes. Chemical and
   biophysical considerations**   87
   J. H. Fendler

4. **The interaction of lipid vesicles (liposomes) with cultured cells
   and their use as carriers for drugs and macromolecules**   101
   G. Poste

5. **Uptake of enzyme-bearing liposomes by cells *in vivo* and *in vitro*** 153
   G. Weissmann and M. Finkelstein

6. **Stability of liposomes in presence of blood constituents: consequences
   of uptake of liposomal lipid and entrapped compounds by rat liver
   cells**   179
   *G. Scherphof, F. Roerdink, D. Hoekstra, J. Zborowski, and E.
   Wisse*

7. **Effect of antibodies administered in liposomes**   211
   T. de Barsy and F. Van Hoof

8. **Liposomes as carriers for methotrexate**   219
   H. K. Kimelberg

9.   **Liposomes as carriers of polynucleotides**   249
     W. E. Magee

10. **Liposomes and chelating agents**   265
     Y. E. Rahman

11. **Liposomes as steroid carriers in the intra-articular therapy of
     rheumatoid arthritis**   299
     I. H. Shaw and J. T. Dingle

12. **Liposomes as diagnostic tools**   325
     I. R. McDougall

13. **The use of liposomes for studying membrane antigens as
     immunogens and as targets for immune attack**   345
     G. M. K. Humphries

14. **Recent progress in liposome research**   377
     G. Gregoriadis

Subject Index   399

Preface

It has become evident in recent years that problems associated with direct drug use in pharmacology and medicine may be resolved by the use of carrier systems. These are expected, at least in theory, to optimize the action of drugs by transporting them to target areas, thus circumventing drug waste and inactivation and also anatomical barriers preventing drugs from entering such areas. In other situations a carrier system could serve as a mechanism for the slow release of locally applied drugs. Among the various carrier candidates proposed to date, liposomes stand out as the most promising, not only because they are biodegradable and easy to prepare, but also because their remarkable versatility in terms of composition, size, and other structural characteristics provide for a variety of mechanisms by which liposomes can interact with living entities. Indeed, within a few years since their role as membrane models was extended to that of a drug carrier, numerous investigators have adopted liposomes in their respective fields of work, all requiring a means of controlling drug action. Application of liposomes as such or in association with active agents in biological systems can now be classified into two broad but interrelated areas, one dealing with the use of the system in the study or modification of the behaviour of biological entities (e.g. cells) and the other with the application of knowledge from such work in improving drug action in the treatment or prevention of disease.

This book is the first attempt to bring together research work which is exclusively related to these two aspects of liposomes as a carrier system. Authors who are leaders in their particular disciplines have contributed experiences in attempting to use liposomes for the systemic and local administration of biologically active molecules in diseases (mostly animal model) as diverse as cancer, enzyme and hormonal deficiencies, arthritis, and metal storage diseases. Other chapters deal with methodology, and uses in diagnostic medicine and immunology. The important aspect of the way liposomes interact with the biological environment *in vitro* or *in vivo* is also covered (either diffusely or in separate chapters) since information gained from such studies will form the backbone for the successful application of liposomes in man. Preliminary investigations with patients have already revealed the type of problems one can expect in the future from the clinical application of the system. It is hoped that this book will be of considerable help to all scientists and clinicians attempting to translate knowledge from basic science to means for the alleviation of disease.

We would like to thank Mrs. Dorothy Seale for excellent secretarial work and the staff of John Wiley and Sons Limited for their cooperation.

Gregory Gregoriadis
Anthony C. Allison

Liposomes in Biological Systems
Edited by G. Gregoriadis and A. C. Allison
© 1980, John Wiley & Sons, Ltd.

CHAPTER 1

Development of the Liposome Concept

A. D. Bangham

The idea that isolated and purified phospholipids of cellular origin could spontaneously re-form, in the presence of water, into closed membrane systems, probably emerged during the course of an electron microscopic study which Horne and I carried out during 1961–1963 shortly after Robertson (1960) had postulated his universal unit membrane theory. In our study we deliberately used the electron-dense, potassium phosphotungstate salt as a 'negative' stain on the grounds that it offered several important advantages for the visualization of lipids in aqueous media. Firstly, the rigid and abrupt setting of the salt *in vacuo* in the form of an electon-dense glass, we believed, would preserve any structures as though they were still in the presence of water, no 'fixation' in the histological sense, being required. Secondly, it was argued, but incorrectly assumed, that a neutral salt such as potassium phosphotungstate would not exhibit any special affinity towards molecules whose collective structure depended uniquely upon its physical environment, and thirdly, the negative-stain technique gave a degree of three-dimensional perspective. Figure 1 was indeed the first figure of our paper (Bangham and Horne, 1964) and depicted the expected variations in density (lower graph) of an electron beam illuminating a structure consisting of concentric lamellae of high (potassium phosphotungstate) and low (phospholipid) electron-dense material. It was derived from an X-ray picture taken of a model prepared with concentric sleeves of cardboard and lead! It seemed to account for the structure seen in Figure 2, a now classic portrait of a multilamellar liposome. Saunders, who was kind enough to supply us with samples of his ultrasonically irradiated lecithin and lecithin/cholesterol (Saunders *et al.,* 1962) was clearly surprised at its membranous, as opposed to micellar, nature (Saunders, 1963).

Shortly after these particular pictures were published Horne and I obtained some really bizarre evidence which encouraged us to believe that equimolar mixtures of ovolecithin and cholesterol spontaneously

1

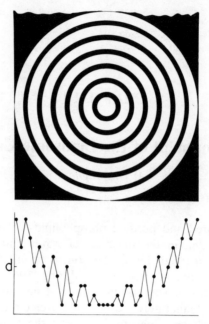

Figure 1 Diagram illustrating the variations in density of an electron beam illuminating a structure consisting of concentric lamellae of high and low electron-dense material. The graph was obtained by summing the contributions of all the high-density lamellae in a vertical plane

aggregated in water to form rather natural-like membranes. The evidence concerned the extraordinary similarity in the electron microscopic appearance of saponin treated natural membranes (Dourmashkin *et al.*, 1962) and of liposomes (Bangham and Horne, 1962; Glauert *et al.*, 1962).

By late 1962, phospholipids of various species were relatively abundant and available in our laboratory, thanks to the preparative methods developed by Lea *et al.*, 1955 and Dawson, 1958). With such largesse it became a permissible and fascinating pastime to place a drop of water, salt or sugar solution on a dried deposit of a few milligrams of phospholipid on a glass slide and then observe the sequence of events under the microscope. Every field would remind a microscopist of some feature, characteristic of one form of living cell or another (Holtfreter, 1948), but alas, as Frey-Wyssling (1953) points out, 'The myelin forms "grow" at random and aimlessly in the substrate and the final outcome is a chaos rather than an illustration of organized life.' But observing these colourless spheroids and cylinders with the knowledge of their electron microscopic image caused one to wonder whether they might not, indeed, share some feature with a dead and/or living cell membrane. Greater insight as to the

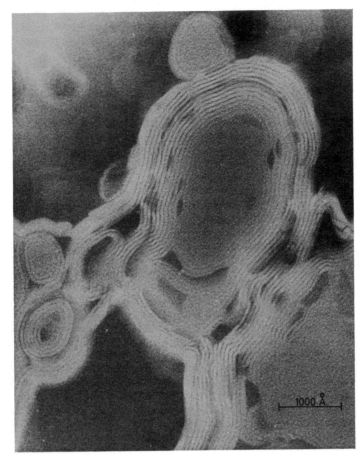

Figure 2 Electron micrograph of ovolecithin treated by ultrasound and mixed with an equal volume of 2% potassium phosphotungstate. Droplet deposited on to substrate

degree of order exhibited by these structures is further obtained if a polarizer and analyser are placed at right angles above and below the specimen. For these weakly birefringent structures it also helps to introduce a first-order red compensator or near equivalent in the form of a sheet (0.75 mm thick) of mica. The sign and magnitude of the birefringence exhibited by these smectic mesophases of phospholipids, as with other crystals, depend on the sum of two components: an intrinsic component (due to the parallel array of lamellae intercalated by sheets of water) which is likewise positive and negative. The intrinsic birefringence is a characteristic of the species and orientation of the individual molecules, whereas the form

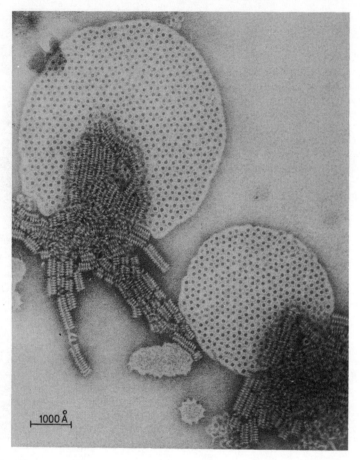

Figure 3 The micrograph shows a dispersion of 1 mol of lecithin and 1 mol of cholesterol in water, treated with an equal volume of 0.2% (w/v) saponin, and finally mixed with an equal volume of 2% potassium phosphotungstate

component can and does vary in magnitude as a function of the relative thickness and refractive index of the two parallel lipid and aqueous phases. If the equilibrium distance between two adjacent lamellae depends on the balance of attractive and repulsive forces, absence of any net charge, as, for example, with pure lecithin, will result in close apposition and strong positive birefringence. The presence of a net charge at the interface, whether positive or negative, will cause a separation of adjacent lamellae and an intensification of the negative-form birefringence, ultimately resulting in an overall loss or even reversal in the sign of the observed birefringence (Bangham *et al.*, 1965a). Such a relationship between the degree of swelling (hydration) of lipid smectic mesophases in electrolytes arises because of the interplay of fixed charges and ionic strength, and was first pointed out by Palmer and Schmitt (1941) using X-ray diffraction studies of mixed brain lipids. More recently, the present author together with colleagues (Bangham *et al.*, 1967a) confirmed in a qualitative fashion the correlation between the optical appearances, the sequestered and pellet volumes, the X-ray spacings, and the fixed charge densities of smectic mesophases. Pure phosphatidylcholine, with no net charge, had an invariant pellet volume, exhibited a constant intensity of birefringence, and gave a constant lamellar spacing. Thus not only are individual membrane molecules shuffled around by favourable energetic forces and/or unfavourable entropic changes, but longer-range forces ensure that the evolving lamellae of the smectic mesophase are accurately spaced.

The realization that the electron microscopic organization of closed and concentrically arranged lamellae of bimolecular dimensions now extended to much larger structures, visible by light microscopy or even the naked eye, came about by the simple expedient of stressing the structures osmotically, and observing the simple shape changes. That these events were reversible and provoked by both simple univalent salts and sugars persuaded the author that the membranous system under test was significantly more permeable to water than to simple solutes, including salts, and therefore was behaving like an osmometer. For example, a few micromoles of mixed brain or egg lipids dissolved in chloroform can be placed, as a smeared-out drop, on the bottom of a shallow 100 ml beaker. The chloroform is removed by evaporation with N_2 or air, and the beaker is placed in a microscope stage. While dry, the smear of lipids will appear as a colourless mass unless crossed polarizers and a first-order compensator are incorporated into the optical path; a × 10, or better, a × 20, objective with a long working distance is recommended, the anisotropic liquid crystalline lipids will show spectral colours due to the random, domain structure and birefringence of the material. If now the smear is gently covered with a thin layer of a dilute salt solution, say 10 mM, smectic mesophases will rapidly form, and the observer will be beguiled by the subsequent events. However, if after a few minutes one adds a quantity of a saturated univalent salt solution to the beaker and mixes, rapid shape changes will be seen to take place. Finally, one can remove by suction most of the hypertonic liquid from the beaker while keeping the same field in view, and replace it once more with a large volume of the original (10 mM) swelling fluid. Under the right conditions, reversible shape changes will occur.

It became crucial to establish, first, that the shape changes were a consequence of water moving *across* a semi-permeable membrane and, second, that the forces were osmotic and electrostatic. Identical behaviour with dilute and concentrated non-electrolytes, e.g. glucose, eliminated the latter consideration. Although the evidence presented by Bangham *et al.*, (1965b) and Papahadjopoulos and Watkins (1967) was more compatible with a closed membrane than a Swiss roll or Schwann cell structure, it was not until valinomycin had been shown to facilitate selectively the more rapid diffusion of K^+ over Na^+ from liposomes containing equal concentrations of K^+ and Na^+ that the closed membrane theory could be finally claimed as proven (Bangham *et al.*, 1967b). Perhaps it was fortunate that the author had previously noted that the presence of a charged component exaggerated the interlamellar aqueous compartment and therefore the volume of osmotically active water in the structure. The shape changes brought about by osmotically driven water are extremely small with pure samples of lecithin. It is not entirely without significance that during the summer of 1962, at which time these qualitative microscopic observations were being made, a preprint of Rudin and Mueller's first full paper describing the successful preparation of a useful (black) lipid membrane model was circulating around the laboratories in Cambridge (Mueller *et al.*, 1962).

Membrane molecules are characteristically amphiphile which is to say that they are sufficiently large for different regions of each molecule to behave, so to speak, in a discrete fashion; thus each molecule behaves as though it were oil soluble at one end and water soluble at the other. Typical examples of membrane compounds which exhibit amphiphile properties to the extent that they form highly ordered phases in equilibrium with a water phase (liposomes) are the class II polar lipids (Small, 1970); e.g. phosphatidylcholines, ethanolamines, and serines; sphingomyelins, cardiolipins, plasmalogens, phosphatidic acids and cerebrosides, and cholesterol. These compounds, when confronted with an encroaching aqueous environment, undergo a sequence of assemblages which reflect the thermodynamic perturbations of increasing water–water, water–oil and oil–oil interactions. Kavanau (1965) analysed these thermodynamic considerations and accounted for the paradoxical emergence and sustained existence of highly ordered structures from within a system containing polar lipids and water. These quasi-equilibrium structures, colloquially referred to in the title of this book as 'liposomes' should, more correctly, be termed 'smectic mesophases'.

Smectic mesophases, whether formed gently on a microscope slide or harshly by swirling lipids on an aqueous phase together, are layer lattices of alternating bimolecular lipid sheets, intercalated by aqueous spaces. When formed from highly water-insoluble amphiphiles such as those mentioned above, they persist even in the presence of excess water. Their usefulness as model system derives from the fact that, as the dry phospho- and/or other lipids of biological origin undergo their sequence of molecular rearrangements, there is an opportunity for an unrestricted entry of solutes, e.g. isotopically labelled salts and proteins, between the planes of hydrophilic head groups before the unfavourable entropy situation of an oil–water interface intervenes. Subsequently, and because of the unfavourable entropy associated with immiscibility of hydrocarbon and an encroaching aqueous phase, a further arrangement of molecules takes place which yields a series of concentric closed membranes, each membrane representing an unbroken, bimolecular sheet of molecules. From this it follows that every aqueous compartment is discrete and isolated from its neighbour by one such closed membrane and that the outermost aqueous compartment of the whole structure (Figure 1) would be isolated from the continuous aqueous phase. The solutes and water originally entering the system are therefore sequestered and can only diffuse between compartments or into the bulk aqueous phase by crossing one or more bimolecular membrane(s).

Thus, the concept of liposomes emerged and the early permeability data (Bangham *et al.*, 1965a) set out to show that phosphatidylcholine membranes were selectively permeable to ions. However, three visitors to the laboratory in the summer of 1964 were to play a decisive role in the ultimate acceptance of the liposome model. Two were anxious to have their respective compounds examined with a view to establishing that their biological action was mediated via the lipid or membranous part of a cell, the third, Papahadjopoulos, was on a longer visit in which he hoped to pursue the role of phospholipids in blood clotting (Bangham, 1961; Papahadjopoulos *et al.*, 1962). Chappell brought samples of valinomycin and gramicidin, and Weissmann brought a range of lysosomal lytic agents. Both were persuaded to forego the monolayer penetration technique which my laboratory had initiated for a similar study with Vitamin A (Bangham *et al.*, 1964). Both readily and successfully exploited the, by then, newly developed liposome model (Chappell and Crofts, 1966; Henderson *et al.*, 1969; Weissmann *et al.*, 1965; Sessa and Weissmann, 1968).

As events unfolded, the liposome model prospered exceedingly in the laboratories of all three visitors. Weissmann was the first to recognize and exploit the similarities between these man-made and man-filled organelles and cell lysosomes (Sessa and Weissmann, 1968), to use them to understand the pathology of certain conditions, e.g. gout (Weissmann, 1971; Weissmann and Rita, 1972) and to attempt to remedy others (Sessa and Weissmann, 1970; Cohen *et al.*, 1976). Weissmann has also initiated a sensible shorthand system or notation to describe the nature and content of liposomes (Weissmann *et al.*, 1975), but not yet, alas, for his co-authors!

Papahadjopoulos elected to investigate the special properties of differing phospholipids, arguing that liposomes prepared from a homogeneous lipid type might reveal archetypal behaviour (Papahadjopoulos and Miller, 1967;

Papahadjopoulos, 1968). Subsequently his endeavours founded a veritable school devoted to the use of the liposome model in many branches of experimental biology and medicine. His group have researched on the ability of liposomes to induce cell fusion (Papahadjopoulos *et al.*, 1973b; Papahadjopoulos *et al.*, 1974b); on the mechanism of action of local anaesthetics on membrane structure and function (Papahadjopoulos, 1972), and the use of liposomes as packages for the delivery of toxic drugs (Papahadjopoulos *et al.*, 1974a) and many other aspects which will be, I feel sure, referred to later in this volume.

Chappell, helped by the ingenuity and research skill of McGiven, 1968, used the liposome to test the proposition, required by Mitchell, that a simple bilayer of typical cell-organelle composition would provide a closed, homogenous osmotic barrier phase of low permeability to ionic solutes in general and to hydrogen and hydroxyl ions in particular. For his hypothesis, Mitchell required just such a structure to plug into his three other functional systems to complete the chemiosmotic mechanism (Mitchell, 1961; Mitchell, 1966; Greville, 1969; Mitchell, 1976). The findings and conclusion of Chappell's group concerning the properties of the antibiotics valinomycin, monactin, enniatin, gramicidin, nigericin, dianemycin, monensin, and various uncoupling agents like dinitrophenol and carbonyl cyanide *p*-trifluoromethoxy phenylhydrazone in liposomes fully support the chemiosmotic mechanism and represent a landmark in an understanding of the manner by which ions cross hydrophobic barriers (Henderson *et al.*, 1969; Henderson, 1971).

Summarizing the principal properties of liposomes at a symposium on Biophysics and Physiology of Biological Transport in 1965 (Bangham *et al.*, 1967b) I reported as follows:

(1) The model membrane systems may be formed from egg lecithin with or without cholesterol, long-chain anions or cations, as well as from whole lipid extracts from RBCs etc.

(2) Solvent molecules are not required and are not present.

(3) The model systems are compound structures of bimolecular sheets intercalated by aqueous spaces, based upon EM birefringence and X-ray data.

(4) They are permeable to water (^3H_2O).

(5) Positively charged membranes are impermeable to cations. Negatively charged membranes are relatively permeable to Li, Na, K, Rb, Ca (50% exchange diffusion time 100 hours at 22 °C). The kinetics are probably not Fick, but are linear for the first 24 hours. $E = 15$ kcals/mol. Cation permeability increases steeply with increasing surface charge density. No selectivity between K and Na, but preliminary results suggest that the incorporation of certain cyclic polypeptides enables the membranes to distinguish between Li^+ or Na^+ and K^+ or Rb^+.

(6) They are osmotically sensitive.

(7) The membranes appear to be about 10^5 times more permeable to anions than cations (50% exchange diffusion time, ~ 1 minute at 22 °C). Positive, negative, and pure lecithin (net uncharged) membranes exhibit rapid anion diffusion rates. The membranes are selectively permeable to anions, those with the smallest hydrated ion radius diffusing most rapidly.

(8) Steroids, which cause lysis of lysosomes increase the diffusion rate of cations. Steroids that protect lysosomes against various physical or chemical insults reduce the cation diffusion rate.

(9) The membranes respond to alcohol, chloroform, and ether by increasing the cation diffusion rate in a manner related to their thermodynamic activity. The effects are measurable at narcotic concentrations.

(10) The membranes respond to local anaesthetics by showing a reduction in the cation diffusion rate. At high concentration this trend is reversed, even though the zeta potentials continue to become more positive.

A clearer picture of the model system and of its potentialities then emerged following a collaborative study with Greville and De Gier (Bangham *et al.*, 1967a). In particular, the application of mitochondrial light-scattering techniques to measure permeation of water and a range of other solutes into and out of liposomes, greatly helped to establish the validity of the system as a model for, at least, the passive areas of cell membranes. De Gier all too quickly returned to Utrecht and has since successfully adapted the shrinking and swelling technique to aid his and Van Deenen's herculean endeavours to correlate the permeability properties of cell membranes with their chemical composition. (De Gier *et al.*, 1968; De Gier *et al.*, 1971; Demel *et al.*, 1972; McElhaney *et al.*, 1970; Van Dennen, 1972; McElhaney *et al.*, 1973, and for a review, see Van Deenen and De Gier, 1974.)

The Utrecht school, under the leadership of Van Deenen, had already innocently exploited the liposome model, as used for electron microscopy, to establish the necessary prerequisite of a sterol, e.g. cholesterol, in membranes for their susceptibility to molecular injury by polyene antibiotics (Kinsky *et al.*, 1966). Subsequently, and prompted by Weissmann's explicit use of liposomes as model cells whose integrity could be tested (Weissmann and Sessa, 1967), Kinsky and Van Deenen re-tested the system by filling liposomes with glucose and then developing an ingenious way of detecting its subsequent leakage out of the system (Kinsky *et al.*, 1967; Kinsky *et al.*, 1968). Cohen, in my laboratory, modified the earlier shrinkage and swelling technique and extended the spectrum of solutes to include homologous series of ureas and amides as well as groups of compounds of approximately equal molecular weights but having various affinities (hydrogen bonds) for water. This survey was undertaken to obtain a greater insight as to the nature of the resistive forces preventing the free diffusion of molecules across a membrane (Cohen and Bangham, 1972; Hill and Cohen, 1972; Cohen, 1975a and b). Recently, the Utrecht school have refined the Hill and Cohen (1972) technique and its subsequent analysis and now claim to account for most of the irreversible thermodynamic parameters for non-electrolytic permeation through liposomes (Van Zoelen *et al.*, 1976). They have also revised the relative permeability of liposomes, in the gel phase, to water (Blok *et al.*, 1976).

As a visitor to Van Deenen's department in Utrecht in the mid-sixties, Kinsky, too, was clearly persuaded that liposomes were useful objects for study, particularly since they had gone quite a long way to reveal how polyene antibiotics might be working. Indeed, it might well have been because of the superficial similarities between the lecithin/cholesterol–filipin lesions, as seen by negative stain, and the similarly stained lesions produced in erythrocytes by complement lysis (presented by Borsos *et al.*, 1964) that Kinsky embarked upon his remarkable series of experiments upon complement. His conclusions, based upon a dozen or more detailed papers, were excellently reviewed by him in a paper entitled 'Antibody–Complement Interaction' (Kinsky, 1972) and paraphrased again in a meeting of the New York Academy of Sciences (Kinsky, 1972). Since then he has investigated the possibilities of using liposomes as vehicles for the immunogenicity of lipids and/or haptens which are covalently linked to amphiphiles instead of high molecular weight, water soluble carriers, such as proteins. Indeed, Kinsky now has a system in which both the immunogen and test cell are one and the same liposome. (Uemura *et al.*, 1974). The mystique for the Kahn serological reaction for syphilis may soon be explained.

Meanwhile, mixtures of purified phospholipids and water, not all as two-phase systems, but nevertheless frequently being referred to as liposomes, were being examined by various new and not-so-new physical techniques (for review see Bangham *et al.*, 1974); the declared aim being in most cases, simply to describe the physical properties of these unusual molecules in water. For example, by microcalorimetry (Chapman and Collin, 1965; Chapman *et al.*, 1967; Ladbrooke and Chapman, 1969); ultracentrifugation (Saunders *et al.*, 1962; Huang, 1969; Huang and Charlton, 1971; Johnson and Buttress, 1973; Johnson *et al.*, 1973); temperature jump (Hammes and Tallman, 1970; Owen *et al.*, 1970); by nuclear magnetic resonance (Chapman and Morrison, 1966; Chapman and Salsbury, 1966; Penkett *et al.*, 1968; Salsbury and Chapman, 1968; Birdsall *et al.*, 1971; Metcalfe *et al.*, 1971; Lee *et al.*, 1972; Horwitz *et al.*, 1973; Cullis and de Kruyff, 1976); electron spin resonance (Waggoner *et al.*, 1969; McConnell and McFarland, 1970; Huang *et al.*, 1970; Hubbell and McConnell, 1971); X-ray diffraction (Palmer and Schmitt, 1941; Finean and Millington, 1955; Luzzati and Husson, 1962; Small, 1967; Chapman, *et al.*, 1967; Levine and Wilkins, 1971); surface properties (Bangham and Dawson, 1960; Bangham, 1963; Papahadjopoulos, 1968; McDonald and Bangham, 1972); electron microscopy (Stockenius, 1962; Bangham and Horne, 1964; Fluck *et al.*, 1969; Junger and Reinauer, 1969; Deamer *et al.*, 1970; Johnson *et al.*, 1971; Papahadjopoulos *et al.*, 1975); and by light scattering (Saunders *et al.*, 1962; Abramson *et al.*, 1964a,b; Attwood and Saunders, 1965; Bangham *et al.*, 1967a; Seufert, 1970; Yi and MacDonald, 1973; Hill, 1974; Chong and Colbow, 1976). All these techniques helped to consolidate the idea that membrane lipids self-assembled to form stable bilayer structures in aqueous media, liquid–crystalline unless cooled below certain characteristic temperatures and that are probably a remarkably good model for the passive areas of cell membranes.

The most studied, pure, phospholipid of recent years has been dipalmitoyl lecithin which undergoes a phase transition between 32 and 42 °C when in equilibrium with water in excess of 50% by weight, i.e. as liposomes in an aqueous media (Oldfield and Chapman, 1972). Even with the naked eye it is possible to perceive the increase in light scattered by such liposomes as they cool through the critical temperature range. Looking down the microscope and poking the liposomes with a probe it is possible to contrast their pultaceous consistency when cold compared with their extreme liquidity when hot.

The 'melting' of a gram molecular weight of dipalmitoyl lecithin as liposomes has a latent heat of 8.66 kcals at 41°C (Chapman *et al.*, 1967). From bulk thermodynamics it would be calculated that the colligative property of an ideal solute dissolving in the membrane would cause a 1° depression in the melting temperature at a concentration of 0.0442 mol/mol of phospholipid. Surprisingly, liposomes, notwithstanding their highly specialized structure, seem to give such a result and can therefore be used as a rather good system for measuring partition coefficients of various compounds (Hill, 1974). The solid-to-liquid phase change for 'transition' as it is sometimes referred to corresponds to an abrupt increase in the rotational motion of the hydrocarbon portions of the molecule (Trauble, 1972). The transition is accompanied by a decrease in thickness of the membrane as perceived by X-rays (Chapman *et al.*, 1967); a change in membrane volume as observed by dilatometry (Trauble and Haynes, 1971); a marked decrease in the proton NMR line width (Chapman *et al.*, 1967; Lee *et al.*, 1972); a decrease in the order parameter of ESR probes (Hubbell and McConnell, 1971); a decrease in the fluorescence polarization of various probes (Cogan *et al.*, 1973); an increase in the fluorescence of 1-anilino-8-napthalene sulphonic acid

(ANS), 2,2,6,6-tetramethyl piperidine-1-oxyl (TEMPO) and perylene (Hubbell and McConnell, 1971; Sackman and Trauble, 1972; Papahadjopoulos *et al.*, 1973a); and finally, changes in light scattering (Abramson, 1971; Trauble, 1972; Yi and MacDonald, 1973; Hill, 1974; Chong and Colbow, 1976).

One of the attractions of using the multilamellar liposome models is that they are exceedingly easy to prepare; indeed, it is no exaggeration to say they form themselves spontaneously! All that is required is that a sufficient quantity of a stock solution in chloroform of the phospholipid and/or sterols is placed in a round-bottomed flask and the solvent chloroform removed *in vacuo* in a rotary evaporator so that the lipids are left as a thin film on the surface of the flask. The aqueous phase, containing any labelled solute, is then added, together with a glass bead or two, and the flask is shaken. One recognizes that lyotropic mesomorphisms have taken place, i.e., smectic mesophases of liposomes have formed, by noticing that the lipid film whitens and disperses into the excess aqueous phase. Useful quantities of ingredients for experimental purposes may be obtained by reference to our most recent review (Bangham *et al.*, 1974). An idea of the diversity of the compounds that have been used to form liposomes may also be gained by a perusal of papers by Bangham and Dawson, 1958, 1959, 1960, and 1962, who added long-chain cations and ions in order to alter the surface charge; Papahadjopoulos and Bangham, 1966, who made liposomes with phosphatidylserines; by Papahadjopoulos and Miller, 1967, who prepared liposomes with a variety of acidic phospholipids; Demel *et al.*, 1968, who used liposomes of natural and synthetic phosphatidylcholines with and without cholesterol; and by Lester *et al.*, 1972, and Hill and Lester, 1972, who examined the effects of introducing gangliosides into phosphatidylcholine liposomes. Failure to produce characteristic liposomes, assuming that appropriate lipid mixtures have been used, is most likely because the predominant lipid is below its transition temperature and is not at all penetrated by water and solute The emphasis on distributing the lipid out of chloroform as a *thin film* is related to a less than desirable phenomenon for sizeable amounts of dry phospholipid to become wrapped up within a concentric system of solute-permeated lamellae, the closed membranes effectively preventing further ingress of both water and salt.

Multilamellar liposomes, as models for study, have been criticized for a number of reasons (by Johnson and Bangham, 1969a) sometimes, but not always, with justification. Undeniably, the most valid criticism is that it is not easy to prepare a suspension of liposomes having a uniform size population, thus the kinetics of efflux are more complex than, for example, the efflux of heat from the uniform 'solid-sphere' (Carslaw and Jaeger, 1947) model first discussed by Bangham *et al.*, 1965a, because of the magnitude of the size range. Recent work of Chowhan *et al.,* 1972, however, seems to indicate that the heterogeneity of these preparations is not of great importance.

A doubtful criticism, based on an interpretation of freeze-fractured preparations, is that the multilamellar, coplanar structures contain inclusion spaces of considerable volume. It is true that the amount of a given solute sequestered is greater in multilamellar liposomes than in microvesicles per micromole of membrane components, but this is because the outer surface area of the sonicated microvesicles is as much as five or six times that of the hand-shaken preparation. As the outermost surface area increases, so will the proportion of membrane molecules facing outward. Indeed, the small discrepancy in trapping ratios between multilamellar and microvesicular liposomes, when related to the proportion of lipid molecules in the outermost skin, may be accounted for by the concensus that microvesicles are usually spherical with a minimum surface/volume ratio, whereas the multilamellar liposomes are oblate or prolate cylinders and/or spheroids.

Despite these criticisms, the multilamellar liposome can be used as a helpful and informative model system for the simple reason that not all experiments require absolute permeability coefficients. Thus, by normalizing a response, e.g. release of a labelled permeant of a rate of swelling, to control aliquot of a given preparation of liposomes, a great deal of information can be gained. From the literature, it is evident that multilamellar liposomes have been useful in a variety of studies: for example, in the effect of surface charge on their cation and anion permeability (Bangham *et al.,* 1965b); and of their susceptibility to hydrolysis by some phospholipases (Bangham and Dawson, 1958, 1959, 1962; Dawson *et al.,* 1976 and a review by Kimelberg, 1976); the properties or ion carriers in membranes (Henderson *et al.,* 1969; Johnson and Bangham, 1969a); Kinsky, 1970; Saha *et al.,* 1970; Ovchinnikov *et al.,* 1974, a review; Cohen, 1975a and b; Singer, 1975); the effect of lytic reagents on biological membranes, including some polyene antibiotics (Kinsky *et al.,* 1966; Weissmann and Sessa, 1967; Kinsky *et al.,* 1968; Gent and Prestegard, 1976); entrapment of enzymes into liposomes (Sessa and Weissmann, 1970; Gregoriadis *et al.,* 1971; Gregoriadis and Ryman, 1972; Weissmann *et al.,* 1975; see also reviews by Ryman, 1975, Colley and Ryman, 1976 and Tyrrell *et al.,* 1976); as immunological adjuvants (Allison and Gregoriadis, 1974); their interaction with immunoglobulin Weissmann *et al.,* 1974; as stimulants of interferon production (Straub *et al.,* 1974); for the quantitative, automatic measurement of complement (Knudson *et al.,* 1971); the binding of soluble basic proteins such as cytochrome *c* (Kimelberg and Papahadjopoulos, 1971; Kimelberg *et al.,* 1970; Kimelberg and Lee, 1970 and a review by Kimelberg, 1976); and mellitin (Sessa *et al.*, 1969); interaction with crystals of monosodium urate (Weissmann, 1971; Weissmann and Rita, 1972); with steroids Bangham *et al.*, 1965b; Sessa and Weissmann, 1968; Heap *et al.*, 1970 and 1971); with retinal and retinaldehyde (Bonting and Bangham, 1967); with thyroid hormones (Hillier, 1970); with lyso- and short-chain phosphatidylcholines (Reman *et al.*, 1969); with chlorophyll (Chapman and Fast, 1968; Tropser *et al.*, 1970; Nicholls *et al.*, 1974; Ritt and Walz, 1976; Walz, 1976); interaction with basic polypeptides (Hammes and Schullery, 1970); as a model for studying the complement lysis of erythrocytes (Kinsky, 1972; see also this volume, Chapter 13); action of local and general anaesthetics (Papahadjopoulos, 1972); effect of membrane composition on small non-electrolyte permeabilities (De Gier *et al.*, 1968, 1969, 1971); amino acid permeabilities related to liposome composition (Klein *et al.*, 1971); as catalytic surfaces for blood clotting reactions (Bangham, 1961; Papahadjopoulos *et al.*, 1962); total salt permeabilities (Singer and Bangham, 1971); as a means of depleting plasma cell membranes of sterols (Bruckdorfer *et al.*, 1969); and for the attachment of viruses and viral fragments (Haywood 1974a,b,c, and 1975; Almeida *et al.*, 1975).

Interest in the microvesicle version of the smectic mesophase has arisen for a number of reasons. For example, Saunders and his group (Saunders *et al.*, 1962; Gammack *et al.*, 1964) were motivated by a pharmaceutical requirement to 'solubilize' cholesterol. They found (Saunders *et al.*, 1962) that ultrasonic irradiation of phospholipids in an atmosphere of nitrogen would give rise to stable, optically clear sols, provided that the hydrocarbon chains were of an appropriate length or degree of unsaturation. The implications of this early work, together with that of Lawrence 1968 and 1969 pertaining to the temperature of water penetration into fatty acid and fatty alcohol mixtures, are only now being appreciated, and their papers are worthy of further study. Out laboratory, too, became interested in Saunders' preparations because, when mixed with dilute aqueous solutions of sodium phosphotungstate, they yielded excellent electron microscopic images (Bangham, 1963; Saunders, 1963; Bangham and Horne, 1964). Indeed, it was from these early negatively stained images that the idea of the entity of closed membranes developed. Looking back over the prints, taken some 10 years ago, it is quite clear that in some of the preparations, but not in others, the negative stains penetrated into the vesicle. An artefact which was to deceive us for some time was the apparent 'double'-membraned microvesicle explained to most people's satisfaction in a paper by Johnson *et al.*, 1971.

Abramson *et al.*, ultrasonicated brain phosphatidylserine (1964a) and phosphatidic acid (1964b) in aqueous media because they wanted to study the ionic structure and ionic exchange capabilities of purified acidic lipids. However, their data were interpreted at the time as though the phosphatidylserine molecules were aggregated as spherical pincushion micelles.

Papahadjopoulos and Watkins (1967), in a wider ranging study of the smectic mesophase of membrane phospholipids, came to the conclusion that phosphatidylserine and phosphatidylcholine formed microvesicles when sonicated. They pointed out that a vesicular structure need not contradict the results obtained by Abramson *et al.*, because rupture of the vesicle would be expected to occur following the changes of pH.

Johnson and Bangham (1969a) switched to using ultrasonicated smectic mesophases of egg phosphatidylcholine and egg phosphatidic acid in an effort to obtain true permeability coefficients and to simplify kinetic analysis. Nevertheless we managed to misinterpret the microscopic evidence and inadvertently introduced a compensating error in our surface area measurements which exactly corrected our data. Our laboratory is, nevertheless, alert to the possibility that the constraints on the membrane of the microvesicle are more severe than on multilamellar liposomes, possibly with some consequent alteration of properties. (See the comparative nuclear magnetic resonance studies of Finer *et al.*, 1972, and Frigenson and Chan, 1974.)

Huang (1969) introduced the method of molecular sieve chromatography on Sepharose 4B columns for the purpose of obtaining a completely uniform population of microvesicles. Huang's procedure, in effect, separated residual multilamellar liposomes as a void volume fraction of the bead bed, recovering ultimately, a population of vesicles small enough to occupy the internal volume of the gel. Although these preparations are, by all criteria, rather homogenous, it requires to be shown that the prolonged and intimate exposure of the vesicles to a solid surface does not alter their properties; one wonders whether a brief ultracentrifugation (Seufert, 1970) might not achieve the same result more rapidly.

Microvesicles may be produced in two ways, namely, solvent evaporation or ultrasonication of multilamellar smectic mesophases. Solvent evaporation (Robinson, 1960; Papahadjopoulos and Watkins, 1967), curiously enough, has not proved a popular method, and the present author is not sure why.

Deamer, in my laboratory, has recently prepared some much larger single-walled vesicles by injecting an ethereal solution of phospholipids into a hot aqueous medium. A variety of lipids were tried successfully and they sequestered a variety of markers (Deamer and Bangham, 1976). Batzri and Korn, 1973, injected an ethanolic solution of phospholipids into water and then concentrated the microvesicles in, as it were, their original juice. Microscopically they were extremely homogenous and were subsequently used for a variety of most interesting interactions with amoebae (Batzri and Korn, 1975). Unfortunately, no practical criteria exist to establish the degree to which the solvent molecules have been removed from the system; any residue would in some experiments be quite unacceptable.

Ultrasonication presents technical difficulties, too, not least that of being able to measure, and therefore meter, the amount of energy actually being imparted to the smectic mesophases (Hammes and Roberts, 1970). Since it has been a consistent, and in our view, correct policy to avoid immersion of a metallic probe into the aqueous phase, we have, of necessity been concerned with effective energy transfer. Metallic probes certainly deliver the energy where it is required, but they erode and the fragments of the metal contaminate the microvesicular preparation; more seriously, they are likely to dissolve and to promote oxidative degradation. Hauser (1971), using such a probe, claims that prolonged exposure at low intensity or short exposure at high intensity causes appreciable chemical degradation, yielding lysolecithin, fatty acids, glyceryl phosphorylcholine, and phosphoryl-choline. Because it is also desirable to sonicate in an atmosphere of nitrogen and to provide a heat sink, we advocate the use of a simple waterbath sonicator (Kerry's KB 80/1). The sample, say, up to 50 μmol in 1.0 ml, is sealed in a glass or plastic ampoule after thorough flushing with nitrogen and located in the focal point of radiant energy within the bath. The resonant volume depends on the geometry of the bath and quantity of water in it. The bath temperature can be controlled by draining unwanted heat away via water circulating in a copper coil. The most important trick of all, however, is to reduce the surface tension of the water in the bath to minimize the dissipation of sonic energy for cavitation of the water in the bath itself; any good aqueous detergent is effective. Finer *et al*. 1972 have studied in detail the fragmentation of multilamellar liposomes by sonication.

Oxidation during ultrasonication is always a hazard, particularly when the vulnerable, polyunsaturated lipids are being used. Saha *et al*., 1970, noted the microvesicles, for example, prepared from cardiolipin, were particularly sensitive to degradation by oxidation because of the high percentage of unsaturated fatty acids. Huang (1969) monitored the development of absorption maxima between 265 and 285 nm in the ultraviolet spectrum, but, as Klein (1970), pointed out, while undertaking a PhD, the appearance of such maxima indicates peroxidation of fatty acids containing only three or more double bonds (i.e. linolenate and higher), whereas the increase in diene conjugation as judged by absorbance changes at 233 nm would measure changes in linoleate as well as the higher polyunsaturated chains. Klein reported a simple technique for detecting oxidation in microvesicular preparations based on the absorption ratio: A_{233}/A_{215}.

Microvesicles have been exploited to measure, among other parameters, the ion-exchange capabilities of biological phospholipids (Abramson *et al*., 1964a,b); differential permeability of differing phospholipids to ions (Papahadjopoulos and Watkins, 1967; Papahadjopoulos, 1971); absolute permeabilities to K^+ at various temperatures with and without valinomycin and in the presence and absence of some anaesthetics (Johnson and

Bangham, 1969a,b); the dielectric properties of phospholipid bilayers (Redwood *et al.*, 1972); reconstitution of membrane enzymes (see review by Kimelberg, 1976); the reversal effect of pressure on anaesthesia (Johnson and Miller, 1970; Johnson *et al.*, 1973); inside–outside transition of phospholipid molecules (Kornberg and McConnell, 1971); inside–outside distributions of phospholipids (De Kruyff *et al.*, 1976); the thickness of a lipid bilayer in an excess aqueous phase (Wilkins *et al.*, 1971); the partial specific volume, diffusion, and sedimentation coefficients and molecular weight of phospholipids (Saunders *et al.*, 1962; Huang, 1969; Johnson and Buttress, 1973); the reflective index of microvesicle bilayers (Seufert, 1970); high-resolution NMR spectroscopy (Penkett *et al.*, 1968; Kaufman *et al.*, 1970; Birdsall *et al.*, 1971; Metcalfe *et al.*, 1971; Less *et al.*, 1972); the partition coefficients and other effects of certain steroids (Heap *et al.*, 1970 and 1971), with added N-acetylneuraminic acids as possible serotonin binding sites (Ochoa and Bangham, 1976) and many studies involving fusion of microvesicles to each other (Taupin and McConnell, 1972; Papahadjopoulos *et al.*, 1974b; Lau and Chan, 1974; Kantor and Prestegard, 1975; Van der Bosch and McConnell, 1975) and perhaps of more interest, the fusion of cells by microvesicles and of microvesicles into cells (Papahadjopoulos *et al.*, 1973b; Grant and McConnell, 1973; Martin and McDonald, 1974; Papahadjopoulos *et al.*, 1974a; Pagano *et al.*, 1974; Batzri and Korn, 1975 and Almeida *et al.*, 1975). In 1969 Reeves and Dowben reported an interesting variation on the smectic mesophase model. It might be suggested that they be called 'macrovesicles' despite the fact that they are purported to be about 1 μm in diameter. They are formed as follows: a chloroform–methanol (2 : 1) solution of egg lecithin is taken to dryness in a flat-bottomed flask; the amount of phospholipid (5 μmol) is small and requires to be thinly distributed on the bottom of a 2 litre flask. Thereafter, the dry lamellae of phospholipid are exposed to water-saturated nitrogen until they, too, become swollen and saturated with water. Parenthetically, this stage of the preparation would correspond to that X-rayed by Levine and Wilkins (1971) where a multilayer periodicity of 51.5 Å was measured, equivalent to a 'wet' region of 17.6 Å. Finally, a 0.2 M sucrose solution at 42 °C is gently added to the flask, which is then left standing for a few hours. The important property of these macrovesicles, once formed and harvested, is that their walls consist of only a few bimolecular sheets. Thus they rather resemble a biological cell or cell organelle. However, for reasons which are not clear, the vesicles do not form when electrolyte or solute protein is added in the place of the non-electrolyte. It should, however, be possible to treat the vesicles as though they were erythrocytes and to lyse and reseal them with selected marker solutes. Reeves and Dowben (1970), using their preparations, reported some elegant stop–flow measurements on their osmotic water permeability consistent with the view that water permeates by dissolution and diffusion in the bimolecular membrane(s). It seems a pity that this method has not been further developed or explored.

It is inevitable and right that liposomes should now find an increasing function when placed back into the organism from which their parent molecules were obtained. Interest has spread rapidly into the realms of using liposomes for practical medicine and therapeutics and the present volume testifies to such an assessment. These are exciting areas of development and to the obvious, high priority problems of delivering specific drugs, viruses, antigens and/or enzymes to specific biological targets might be added the possibility of parcelling up waste, animal haemoglobin for universal short-term transfusion. Alternatively, liposomes of some internationally agreed composition could be used as a substitute for the ubiquitous, but variable, animal erythrocyte in a variety of clinico-pathological test systems (Knudson *et al.*, 1971).

Finally, it would be appropriate to quote from the Foreword to the classic book on membrane structure and function, Davson and Danielli's *The Permeability of Natural Membranes*, first published in the bleak wartime days of 1943.

> Just as chemistry could not have developed without test tubes to hold reacting substances, so organisms could not have evolved without relatively impermeable membranes to surround the cell constituents. This barrier between the inside and the outside, the inner and external world of each living unit, has been and always must be considered one of the fundamental structures of a cell. No one can fail to be impressed with the great difference in properties of living and dead cells. The dead are ultimately permeable to diffusible substances, while the living retain one material and pass another. This difference, selective permeability, is so marked that it becomes the surest test to distinguish the living from the dead, holding where all other methods fail. It can truly be said of living cells, that by their membranes 'ye shall know them'.

Notwithstanding Newton Harvey's implied irrelevance of the properties of dead cell membranes it might now be true to claim that smectic mesophases of membrane constituents (now referred to as liposomes) have, nevertheless, greatly helped out understanding of how dead cell membranes function and thereby those of living cells. Paraphrasing Newton Harvey's Foreword to Davson and Danielli's classic, this present book is about 'Liposomes, and by their properties ye shall know them'!

Acknowledgements

It is a pleasure to acknowledge the secretarial help of Mrs. B. Rector and the technical expertise of N. G. A. Miller during the completion of this chapter.

REFERENCES

Abramson, M. B. (1971). *Biochim. Biophys. Acta*, **225**, 167.

Abramson, M. B., Katzman, R. and Gregor, H. P. (1964a). *J. Biol. Chem.*, **239**, 70.

Abramson, M. B., Katzman, R., Wilson, C. E. and Gregor, H. P. (1964b). *J. Biol. Chem.*, **239**, 4066.

Allison, A. C. and Gregoriadis, G. (1974). *Nature*, **252**, 252.

Almeida, J. D., Brand, C. M., Edwards, D. C. and Heath, T. D. (1975). *Lancet*, **7941**, 899.

Attwood, D. and Saunders, L. (1965). *Biochim. Biophys. Acta*, **98**, 344.

Bangham, A. D. (1961). *Nature*, **192**, 1197.

Bangham, A. D. (1963). *Advan. Lipid. Res.*, **1**, 65.

Bangham, A. D. and Dawson, R. M. C. (1958). *Nature*, **182**, 1292.

Bangham, A. D. and Dawson, R. M. C. (1959). *Biochem. J.*, **72**, 486.

Bangham, A. D. and Dawson, R. M. C. (1960). *Biochem. J.*, **75**, 133.

Bangham, A. D. and Dawson, R. M. C. (1962). *Biochim. Biophys. Acta*, **59**, 103.

Bangham, A. D. and Horne, R. W. (1962). *Nature*, **196**, 952.

Bangham, A. D. and Horne, R. W. (1964). *J. Mol. Biol.*, **8**, 660.

Bangham, A. D., Dingle, J. T. and Lucy, J. A. (1964). *Biochem. J.*, **90**, 133.

Bangham, A. D., Standish, M. M. and Watkins, J. C. (1965a). *J. Mol. Biol.*, **13**, 238.

Bangham, A. D., Standish, M. M. and Weissmann, G. (1965b). *J. Mol. Biol.*, **13**, 253.

Bangham, A. D., De Gier, J. and Greville, G. D. (1967a). *Chem. Phys. Lipids*, **1**, 225.

Bangham, A. D., Standish, M. M., Watkins, J. C. and Weissmann, G. (1967b). *Protoplasma*, **63**, 183.

Bangham, A. D., Hill, M. W. and Miller, N. G. A. (1974). *Methods in Membrane Biology*, **1**, 68, Plenum Press, New York.

Batzri, S. and Korn, E. D. (1973). *Biochim. Biophys. Acta*, **298**, 1015.

Batzri, S. and Korn, E. D. (1975). *J. Cell. Biol.*, **66**, 621.

Birdsall, N. J. M., Lee, A. G., Levine, Y. K. and Metcalfe, J. C. (1971). *Biochim. Biophys. Acta*, **241**, 693.

Blok, M. C., Van Deenen, L. L. M. and De Gier, J. (1976). *Biochim. Biophys Acta*, **433**, 1.

Bonting, S. D. and Bangham, A. D. (1967). *Exp. Eye Res.*, **6**, 400.

Borsos, R., Dourmashkin, R. R. and Humphrey, J. H. (1964). *Nature*, **202**, 251.

Bruckdorfer, K. R., Demel, R. A., De Gier, J. and Van Deenen, L. L. M. (1969). *Biochim. Biophys. Acta*, **181**, 334.

Carslaw, H. S. and Jaeger, J. C. (1947). *Conduction of Heat in Solids*, Oxford University Press.

Chapman, D. and Collin, D. T. (1965). *Nature*, **206**, 189.

Chapman, D. and Fast, P. G. (1968). *Science*, **160**, 188.

Chapman, D. and Morrison, A. (1966), *J. Mol. Biol. Chem.*, **241**, 5044.

Chapman, D. and Salsbury, N. J. (1966), *Trans. Faraday Soc.*, **62**, 2607.

Chapman, D., Williams, R. M. and Ladbrooke, B. D. (1967). *Chem. Phys. Lipids*, **1**, 445.

Chappell, J. B. and Crofts, A. R. (1966). 'Regulation of metabolic processes in mitochondria', *Biochim. Biophys. Acta Library* **7**, 293, Elsevier Pub. Co., Amsterdam.

Chong, C. S. and Colbow, K. (1976). *Biochim. Biophys. Acta*, **436**, 260.

Chowan, Z. T., Yotsuyanagi, T. and Higuchi, W. (1972). *Biochim. Biophys. Acta*, **266**, 320.

Cogan, U., Shinitsky, M., Weber, G. and Nishida, T. (1973). *Biochemistry*, **12**, 521.

Cohen, B. E. (1975). *J. Membrane Biol.*, **20**, 205 (a) and 235 (b).

Cohen, B. E. and Bangham, A. D. (1972). *Nature*, **236**, 173.

Cohen, C., Weissmann, G., Hoffstein, Sylvia, Awasthi, Y. C. and Srivastava, Satish, K. (1976). *Biochemistry*, **15**, 452.

Colley, C. M. and Ryman, B. E. (1976). *TIBS.*, **1**, 203.

Cullis, P. R. and De Kruyff, B. (1976). *Biochim. Biophys. Acta*, **436**, 523.

Dawson, R. M. C. (1958). *Biochem. J.* **70**, 559.

Dawson, R. M. C., Hemington, N. L., Miller, N. G. A. and Bangham, A. D. (1976). *J. Membrane Biol.*, **29**, 179.

Deamer, D. W. and Bangham, A. D. (1967). *Biochim. Biophys. Acta*, **443**, 629.

Deamer, D. W., Leonard, R., Tardieu, Annette and Branton, D. (1970). *Biochim. Biophys. Acta*, **219**, 47.

De Gier, J., Mandersloot, J. G. and Van Deenen, L. L. M. (1968). *Biochim. Biophys. Acta*, **150**, 666.

De Gier, J., Mandersloot, J. G. and Van Deenen, L. L. M. (1969). *Biochim. Biophys. Acta*, **173**, 143.

De Gier, J., Mandersloot, J. G., Hupkes, J. V., McElhaney, R. N. and Van Beek, W. P. (1971). *Biochim. Biophys. Acta*, **233**, 610.

De Kruyff, B., Cullis, P. R. and Radda, G. K. (1976). *Biochim. Biophys. Acta*, **436**, 729.

Demel, R. A., Bruckdorfer, K. R. and Van Deenen, L. L. M. (1972). *Biochim. Biophys. Acta*, **255**, 321.

Demel, R. A., Kinsky, S. C., Kinsky, C. B. and Van Deenen, L. L. M. (1968). *Biochim. Biophys. Acta*, **150**, 655.

Dourmashkin, R. R., Dougherty, R. M. and Harris, R. J. C. (1962). *Nature*, **194**, 1116.

Finean, J. B. and Millington, P. F. (1955). *Trans. Faraday Soc.*, **51**, 1008.

Finer, E. G., Flook, A. G. and Hauser, H. (1972). *Biochim. Biophys. Acta*, **260**, 49.

Fluck, D. J., Henson, A. F. and Chapman, D. (1969). *J. Ultrastructure Res.*, **29**, 416.

Frey-Wyssling, A. (1953). *Submicroscopic Morphology of Protoplasm*, Elsevier Pub. Co., Amsterdam.

Frigenson, G. W. and Chan, S. I. (1974). *J. Amer. Chem. Soc.*, **95**, 1312.

Gammack, G. B., Perrin, J. H. and Saunders, L. (1964). *Biochim. Biophys. Acta*, **84**, 576.

Gent, M. P. N. and Prestegard, J. H. (1976). *Biochim. Biophys. Acta*, **436**, 17 (1).

Glauert, A. M., Dingle, J. T. and Lucy, J. A. (1962). *Nature*, **196**, 953.

Grant, C. W. M. and McConnell, H. (1973). *Proc. Nat. Acad. Sci. USA*, **70**, 1238.

Gregoriadis, G. and Ryman, B. E. (1972). *Europ. J. Biochem.*, **24**, 485.

Gregoriadis, G., Leathwood, P. D. and Ryman, B. E. (1971). *FEBS. Lett.*, **14** (2), 95.

Greville, G. D. (1969). *Current Top. Bioenerg.*, **3**, 1.

Hammes, G. G. and Roberts, P. B. (1970). *Biochim. Biophys. Acta*, **203** (2), 220.

Hammes, G. G. and Schullery, S. E. (1970). *Biochemistry*, **9** (13), 2555.

Hammes, G. G. and Tallman, D. E. (1970). *J. Amer. Chem. Soc.*, **92**, 6042.

Hauser, C. (1971). *Biochim. Biophys. Res. Commun.*, **45**, 1049.

Haywood, A. M. (1974a). *J. Mol. Biol.*, **83**, 427.

Haywood, A. M. (1974b). *J. Mol. Biol.*, **87**, 625.

Haywood, A. M. (1974c). *Model Membranes and Sendai Virus Surface–Surface interactions. Negative Strand Viruses*, Academic Press, London.

Haywood, A. M. (1975). *J. gen. Virol*, **29**, 63.

Heap, R. B., Symons, A. M. and Watkins, J. C. (1970). *Biochim. Biophys. Acta*, **218** (3), 482.

Heap, R. B., Symons, A. M. and Watkins, J. C. (1971). *Biochim. Biophys. Acta*, **233**, 307.

Henderson, P. J. F. (1971). *Ann. Rev. Microbiol.*, **25**, 393.

Henderson, P. J. F., McGivan, J. D. and Chappell, J. B. (1969). *Biochem. J.*, **111**, 521.

Hill, M. W. (1974). *Biochim. Biophys. Acta*, **356**, 117.

Hill, M. W. and Cohen, B. E. (1972). *Biochim. Biophys. Acta*, **290**, 403.

Hill, M. W. and Lester, R. (1972). *Biochim. Biophys. Acta*, **282**, 18.

Hillier, A. P. (1970). *J. Physiol.* (London), **211**, 585.

Holtfreter, J. (1948). *Ann. N.Y. Acad. Sci.*, **49**, 709.

Horwitz, A. F., Klein, M. P., Michaelson, D. M. and Kohler, S. J. (1973). *Annals, N.Y. Acad. Sci.*, **222**, 468.

Huang, C. (1969). *Biochemistry*, **8**, 344.

Huang, C. and Charlton, J. P. (1971). *J. Biol. Chem.*, **246**, 2555.

Huang, C., Charlton, J. P., Shyr, C. I. and Thompson, T. E. (1970). *Biochemistry*, **9** (17), 3422.

Hubbell, W. L. and McConnell, H. M. (1971). *J. Amer. Chem. Soc.*, **93** (2), 314.

Johnson, S. M. and Bangham, A. D. (1969). *Biochim. Biophys. Acta*, **193**, 82 (a) and 92 (b).

Johnson, S. M. and Buttress, N. (1973). *Biochim. Biophys. Acta*, **307**, 27.

Johnson, S. M. and Miller, K. W. (1970). *Nature*, **288**, 75.

Johnson, S. M., Bangham, A. D., Hill, M. W. and Korn, E. D. (1971). *Biochim. Biophys. Acta*, **233**, 820.

Johnson, S. M., Miller, K. W. and Bangham, A. D. (1973). *Biochim. Biophys. Acta*, **307**, 42.

Junger, E. and Reinauer, H. (1969). *Biochim. Biophys. Acta*, **183**, 304.

Kantor, H. and Prestegard, J. H. (1975). *Biochemistry*, **14**, 1790.

Kaufman, S., Steim, J. M. and Gibbs, J. H. (1970). *Nature*, **225**, 743.

Kavanau, J. L. (1965). *Structure and Function in Biological Membranes*, Vols. I and II, Holden-Day Inc., San Francisco.

Kimelberg, H. K. (1976). *Mol. Cell. Biochem.*, **10** (3), 171.

Kimelberg, H. K. and Lee, C. P. (1970). *J. Membrane Biol.*, **2**, 252.

Kimelberg, H. K. and Papahadjopoulos, D. (1971). *J. Biol. Chem.*, **246**, 1142.

Kimelberg, H. K., Lee, C. P., Claude, A. and Mrena, E. (1970). *J. Membrane Biol.*, **2**, 235.

Kinsky, S. C. (1970). *Ann. Rev. Pharmacol.*, **10**, 119.

Kinsky, S. C. (1972). *Biochim. Biophys. Acta*, **265**, 1.
Kinsky, S. C., Haxby, J., Kinsky, C. B., Demel, R. A. and Van Deenen, L. L. M. (1968). *Biochim. Biophys. Acta*, **152**, 174.
Kinsky, S. C., Luse, Sarah, A. and Van Deenen, L. L. M. (1966). *Fed. Proc.* **25**, 1503.
Kinsky, S. C., Luse, Sarah, A., Zopf, D., Van Deenen, L. L. M. and Haxby, J. (1967). *Biochim. Biophys. Acta*, **135**, 844.
Klein, R. A. (1970), *Biochim. Biophys. Acta*, **210**, 486.
Klein, R. A., Moore, M. J. and Smith, M. W. (1971). *Biochim. Biophys. Acta*, **233**, 420.
Knudson, K. C., Bing, D. H. and Kater, L. (1971). *J. Immunol.*, **106**, 258 (1).
Kornberg, R. D. and McConnell, H. M. (1971). *Biochemistry*, **10** (7), 1111.
Ladbrooke, B. D. and Chapman, D. (1969). *Chem. Phys. Lipids*, **3**, 304.
Lau, A. L. Y. and Chan, S. J. (1974). *Biochemistry*, **13**, 4942.
Lawrence, A. S. C. (1968). Soc. of Chem. Indust., London, *Monograph* **29**, 67.
Lawrence, A. S. C. (1969). *Mol. Crystals and Liquid Crystals*, **7**, 1.
Lea, C. H., Rhodes, D. N. and Stoll, R. D. (1955). *Biochem. J.*, **60**, 353.
Lee, A. G., Birdsall, N. J. M., Levine, Y. K. and Metcalfe, J. C. (1972). *Biochim. Biophys. Acta*, **255**, 43.
Lester, R., Hill, M. W. and Bangham, A. D. (1972). *Nature*, **236**, 32.
Levine, Y. K. and Wilkins, M. H. F. (1971). *Nature New Biology*, **230**, 69.
Luzzati, V. and Husson, F. (1962). *J. Cell. Biol.* **12**, 207.
McConnell, H. M. and McFarland, B. G. (1970). *Quart. Rev., Biophys.*, **3**, 91.
McDonald, R. C. and Bangham, A. D. (1972). *J. Membrane Biol.*, **7**, 29.
McElhaney, R. N., De Gier, J. and Van Deenen, L. L. M. (1970). *Biochim. Biophys. Acta*, **219**, 245.
McElhaney, R. N., De Gier, J. and Van der Neut-Kok, E. C. M. (1973). *Biochim. Biophys. Acta*, **298**, 500.
McGivan, J. D. (1968). *Ph.D. Res. Thesis*, Bristol University.
Martin, F. and McDonald, R. (1974). *Nature*, **252**, 166.
Metcalf, J. C., Birdsall, N. J. M., Feeney, J., Lee, A. G., Levine, Y. K. and Partington, P. (1971). *Nature*, **233**, 199.
Mitchell, P. (1961). *Nature*, **191**, 144.
Mitchell, P. (1966). *Chemiosmotic Coupling in Oxidative and Photosynthetic Phosphorylation*, Glynn Res. Lab., Bodmin, Cornwall, UK.
Mitchell, P. (1976). *B. Soc. Trans.*, **4**, 399.
Mueller, P., Rudin, D. O., Tien, H. T. and Wescott, W. C. (1962). *Circulation*, **26**, 1167.
Nicholls, P., West, J. and Bangham, A. D. (1974). *Biochim. Biophys. Acta*, **363**, 190.
Ochoa, E. L. M. and Bangham, A. D. (1976). *J. Neurochem.*, **26**, 1193.
Oldfield, E. and Chapman, D. (1972). *FEBS. Lett.*, **23**, 285.
Ovchinnikov, Yu. A., Ivanov, V. T. and Shkrob, A. M. (1974). *Biochim. Biophys. Acta Library*, **12**, Elsevier Scientific Pub. Co., Amsterdam.
Owen, J. D., Hemmes, P. and Eyring, E. M. (1970). *Biochim. Biophys. Acta*, **219**, 276.
Pagano, R. E., Huang, L. and Wey, C. (1974). *Nature*, **252**, 166.
Palmer, K. J. and Schmitt, F. O. (1941). *J. Cell. Comp. Physiol.*, **17**, 385.
Papahadjopoulos, D. (1968). *Biochim. Biophys. Acta*, **163**, 240.
Papahadjopoulos, D. (1971). *Biochim. Biophys. Acta*, **241**, 254.
Papahadjopoulos, D. (1972). *Biochim. Biophys. Acta*, **265**, 169.

Papahadjopoulos, D. and Bangham, A. D. (1966). *Biochim. Biophys. Acta*, **126**, 185.
Papahadjopoulos, D. and Watkins, J. C. (1967). *Biochim. Biophys. Acta*, **135**, 639.
Papahadjopoulos, D., Hougie, C. and Hanahan, D. J. (1962). *Proc. Soc. Exp. Biol. Med.*, **111**, 412.
Papahadjopoulos, D. and Miller, N. G. A. (1967). *Biochim. Biophys. Acta*, **135**, 624.
Papahadjopoulos, D., Jacobson, K., Nir, S. and Isac, T. (1973a). *Biochim. Biophys. Acta*, **311**, 330.
Papahadjopoulos, D., Poste, G. and Schaeffer, B. E. (1973b). *Biochim. Biophys. Acta*, **323**, 23.
Papahadjopoulos, D., Mayhew, E., Poste, G., Smith, S. and Vail, W. J. (1974a). *Nature*, **252**, 163.
Papahadjopoulos, D., Poste, G., Schaeffer, B. E. and Vail, W. J. (1974b). *Biochim. Biophys. Acta*, **352**, 10.
Papahadjopoulos, D., Vail, W. J., Jacobson, K. and Poste, G. (1975). *Biochim. Biophys. Acta*, **394**, 483.
Penkett, S. A., Flook, A. G. and Chapman, D. (1968). *Chem. Phys. Lipids*, **2**, 273.
Redwood, W. R., Takashima, S., Schwan, H. P. and Thompson, T. E. (1972). *Biochim. Biophys. Acta*, **255**, 557.
Reman, F. S., Demel, R. A., De Gier, J., Van Deenen, L. L. M., Eibl, H. and Westphal, O. (1969). *Chem. Phys. Lipids*, **3**, 221.
Reeves, J. P. and Dowben, R. M. (1969). *J. Cell. Physiol.*, **73**, 4960.
Reeves, J. P. and Dowben, R. M. (1970). *J. Membrane Biol.*, **3**, 123.
Ritt, E. and Walz, D. (1976). *J. Membrane Biol.*, **27**, 41.
Robertson, J. D. (1960). *Progress in Biophysics and Biophysical Chemistry*, **10**, 343.
Robinson, N. (1960). *Trans. Faraday Soc.*, **56**, 1260.
Ryman, B. E. (1975). *Proc. 6th Int. Congr. Pharm., Helsinki (Mattila, Med.)*, **5**, 91, Pergamon Press.
Sackman, E. and Trauble, H. (1972). *J. Amer. Chem. Soc.*, **94**, 4482.
Saha, J., Papahadjopoulos, D. and Wenner, C. E. (1970). *Biochim. Biophys. Acta*, **196**, 10.
Salsbury, N. J. and Chapman, D. (1968). *Biochim. Biophys. Acta*, **163**, 314.
Saunders, L. (1963). *J. Pharm. Pharmacol.*, **15**, 155.
Saunders, L., Perrin, J. and Gammack, D. B. (1962). *J. Pharm. Pharmacol.*, **14**, 567.
Sessa, G. and Weissmann, G. (1968). *Biochim. Biophys. Acta*, **150**, 173.
Seesa, G. and Weissmann, G. (1970). *J. Biol. Chem.*, **245**, 3295.
Seesa, G., Freer, J. H., Colacicco, G. and Weissmann, G. (1969). *J. Biol. Chem.*, **244** (13), 3575.
Seufert, W. D. (1970). *Biophysik*, **7**, 60.
Singer, M. A. (1975). *Can. J. Physiol. Pharmacol.*, **53** (6), 1072.
Singer, M. A. and Bangham, A. D. (1971). *Biochim. Biophys. Acta*, **241**, 687.
Small, D. M. (1967). *J. Lipid. Res.*, **8**, 551.
Small, D. M. (1970). *Federation Proceedings*, **29**, No. 4, 1320.
Stockenius, W. (1962). *J. Cell. Biol.*, **12**, 221.
Straub, S. X., Garry, R. F. and Magee, W. E. (1974). *Infection and Immunity*, **10**, 783.
Taupin, C. and McConnell, H. (1972). *FEBS. Symp.*, **28**, 219.
Trauble, H. (1972). In *Biomembranes*, Vol. 3, p. 197, Plenum Press, New York.
Trauble, H. and Haynes, D. H. (1971). *Chem. Phys. Lipids*, **7**, 324.

Trosper, T., Raveed, D. and Ke, B. (1970). *Biochim. Biophys. Acta*, **223**, 463.

Tyrrell, D. A., Heath, T. D., Colley, C. M. and Ryman, B. E. (1976). *Biochim. Biophys. Acta* (in press).

Uemura, K., Nicolotti, R. A., Six, H. R. and Kinsky, S. C. (1974). *Biochemistry*, **13**, 1572.

Van Deenen, L. L. M. (1972). *Chem. Phys. Lipids*, **8**, 366.

Van Deenen, L. L. M. and De Gier, J. (1974). In *The Red Blood Cell*, **1**, p. 147, Academic Press, New York.

Van Der Bosch, J. and McConnell, H. (1975). *Proc. Nat. Acad. Sci. USA*, **72**, 4409.

Van Zoelan, E. J. J., Blok, M. C. and De Gier, J. (1976). *Biochim. Biophys. Acta*, **436**, 301.

Waggoner, A. S., Kingzett, T. J., Rottshaefer, S., Griffith, O. H. and Keith, A. D. (1969), *Chem. Phys. Lipids*, **3**, 245.

Walz, D. (1976). *J. Membrane Biol.*, **27**, 55.

Weissmann, G. (1971). *Hospital Practice* (July), 43.

Weissmann, G. and Rita, Giuseppe, A. (1972). *Nature New Biology*, **240**, 167.

Weissmann, G. and Sessa, G. (1967). *J. Biol. Chem.*, **242**, 616.

Weissmann, G., Sessa, G. and Weissmann, S. (1965). *Nature*, **208**, 649.

Weissmann, G., Brand, A. and Franklin, E. C. (1974). *J. Clin. Invet.*, **53**, 536.

Weissmann, G. Bloomgarden, D., Kaplan, R., Cohen, C., Hoffstein, S., Collins, T., Gottlieb, A. and Nagle, D. (1975). *Proc. Nat. Acad. Sci.*, **72**, 88.

Wilkins, M. F. H., Blaurock, A. E. and Engelman, D. M. (1971). *Nature*, **230**, 72.

Yi, P. N. and MacDonald, R. C. (1973). *Chem. Phys. Lipids*, **11**, 114.

these will depend on particular needs (Gregoriadis, 1977; Gregoriadis, 1979). It is, however, apparent that most known carriers are limited in the range and quantity of drugs which they can accommodate and also on their ability to prevent contact of their drug moiety with the normal biological environment or to promote its access to areas in need of treatment. In addition, there are difficulties related to the toxicity of the carrier's components, to their availability or cost and to the preparation of the carrier-drug unit. Consequently, extensive efforts have been made, especially during the last decade, towards the development of the ideal drug carrier. As discussed elsewhere (Gregoriadis, 1977) such a carrier should be capable of delivering a wide variety of agents into the precise site of action within the biological entity with no untoward effects on the (normal) remainder of the entity. It is now evident that liposomes are endowed with many of the qualities expected from a multifunctional carrier and success in applying them to membrane research has, more recently, been extended to biology and pharmacology.

In spite of the commitment of numerous membrane biologists to the liposome system in the years that followed its discovery (A. D. Bangham, this volume), it was left to those interested in drug targeting to unfold its other, perhaps more glamorous side (Gregoriadis *et al.*, 1971; Gregoriadis and Ryman, 1971, 1972a, 1972b). These initial reports, dealing with the fate of protein-containing liposomes administered into animals, established some of the principles governing liposomal behaviour when in contact with the biological environment. For instance, it was found that the latency of liposomal enzymes (which is related to the structural integrity of the carrier) is largely retained in the blood circulation after intravenous injection and that liposomal contents are taken mostly by hepatic and splenic cells through endocytosis of the carrier to end up in the lysosomal apparatus. It thus became apparent that the system was particularly attractive as a means of delivering agents into the intracellular environment, especially the lysosomes from which agents could gain access to other cell compartments (Gregoriadis and Ryman, 1972b; Black and Gregoriadis, 1974). The ability of liposomal agents, transported by the carrier into the cell's interior, to act on relevant targets was demonstrated in cell culture (Gregoriadis and Buckland, 1973). It thus became possible to suggest that liposomes presented to cells *in vitro* or *in vivo* are endocytosed and eventually localized in the lysosomal apparatus where, following their disruption, active contents are free to act (Gregoriadis and Buckland, 1973). Further work from this laboratory and from numerous others has now uncovered an intriguing variety of aspects related to the transport potential of the system (Gregoriadis, 1978b). Some of these aspects are discussed in this volume and there are others which will undoubtedly be revealed as more and more disciplines in need of a drug carrier adopt liposomes. Attempts will be made here to summarize some of the basic facets of the interaction of the liposomal carrier with living systems and to discuss possibilities and problems related to its application in biology and medicine.

2. FATE OF LIPOSOMES AND THEIR CONTENTS AFTER INJECTION INTO ANIMALS

A considerable amount of information has been amassed regarding the interaction of a wide variety of cells with liposomes *in vivo* (for reviews see Gregoriadis, 1976a,b,c; Gregoriadis, 1977; Gregoriadis *et al.*, 1977c; Tyrrell *et al.*, 1976b; Fendler and Romero, 1977; Kimelberg and Mayhew, 1978; Finkelstein and Weissmann, 1978). It has been observed by several investigators that after the intravenous injection of liposomes composed of one or more bilayers and containing radiolabels in both their lipid and aqueous phase the ratio of the two labels in the blood plasma often remains similar to that in the injected preparation. From this it is inferred that the carrier retains its structural integrity in the circulation although the possibility exists that a labelled agent can form a complex with the labelled lipid marker and circulate in the blood as such even after disruption of liposomes. However, because of the variety of paired markers used [cholesterol and albumin (Gregoriadis and Ryman, 1972b); dipalmitoyl phosphatidylcholine and albumin (Juliano and Stamp, 1975); cholesterol and bleomycin (Gregoriadis *et al.*, 1977b); cholesterol and methotrexate (Kimelberg *et al.*, 1978] such a possibility is unlikely. On the other hand, *in vitro* experiments by Zborowski *et al.* (1977) and Scherphof *et al.* (this volume) support the notion that liposomes can be unstable when in contact with blood.

We have recently carried out wotk (Davis and Gregoriadis, 1979; Gregoriadis and Davis, 1979) which suggests that liposomal stability *in vitro* is related to the proportion of cholesterol relative to the phospholipid present in the lamellae. To avoid possible complex formation between markers of the lipid and aqueous phases we have used a system which reflects liposomal integrity *per se*. This is achieved by measuring the extent to which the latency of a given liposome-entrapped agent changes in the blood of injected animals. Latency is defined as the amount of the agent (% of the total) which cannot be measured in the blood of such animals unless a liposome disrupting agent (e.g. Triton X-100) is added. When, for instance, the latency of a liposomal enzyme after injection is equal to that observed in the injected preparation one can then assume that the integrity of the preparation has not been altered (in a way which will allow interaction of the enzyme with its substrate) as a result of it being in contact with the biological environment. Figure 1 shows that in rats treated with invertase-containing small multilamellar liposomes stability of liposomes in blood (measured by the extent to which the substrate sucrose permeates the bilayers and reaches the enzyme) is nearly equal to that observed in

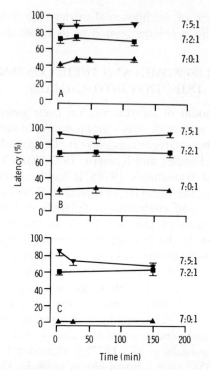

Figure 1 The effect of cholesterol content of liposomes on the latency of entrapped invertase. Small multilamellar liposomes containing invertase and composed of egg phosphatidylcholine (PC) cholesterol (CHOL) (when appropriate) and phosphatidic acid (PA) were injected intravenously into rats (A) or incubated in the presence of whole fresh rat blood (B) or fresh rat serum (C). Invertase latency (Davis and Gregoriadis, 1979) in the blood of injected rats and in the whole blood or serum *in vitro* at time intervals is expressed as % ± SD of the enzyme latency in the injected preparation. The latter (% of total activity in each preparation) was 78.3 ± 14.6 (8 preparations) for 7PC1PA, 82.8 ± 13.0 (5 preparations) for 7PC2CHOL1PA and 89.6 ± 6.2 (7 preparations) for 7PC5CHOL1PA liposomes. (Numbers preceding lipids denote molar ratios). Each point represents values from 4–7 animals (A) or five pooled experiments (B and C). Numbers in Figures are molar ratios for PC, CHOL and PA respectively. (From Gregoriadis and Davis, 1979)

the preparation before injection when the molar ratio of phospholipid to cholesterol is 7 : 5. With the proportion of cholesterol decreasing, liposomal integrity is reduced accordingly (as soon as 2 minutes after injection) and a value of about half the initial latency is reached when liposomes devoid of cholesterol are used. Similar results were obtained with such liposomes exposed to whole blood *in vitro* (Figure 1B) but stability was considerably reduced in the presence of serum only (Figure

1C). If one assumes (Zborowski *et al.*, 1977) that lipoproteins in the blood plasma attract lecithin from liposomes thus upsetting their stability, it may be that the presence of erythrocytes in conjunction with sufficient amounts of liposomal cholesterol may prevent this from happening. Indeed, it is possible that under these conditions there is a preferential donation of erythrocytic phospholipids. Destabilization of cholesterol-poor liposomes as shown in Figure 1 is not necessarily related to a total disintegration of the liposomal structure. It is possible that only 'holes' or fractures are formed, allowing molecules to permeate inwards or outwards (Gregoriadis and Davis, 1979).

In a similar experiment mice were injected intravenously with multi-lamella liposomes containing 0.25 M 6-carboxyfluorescein (Figure 2A). At this concentration the dye is quenched but when, for any reason the dye escapes into the media, ensuing dilution enables it to fluoresce (Weinstein *et al.*, 1977). It again appeared that the presence of a sufficient amount of cholesterol in liposomes (e.g. 7 : 7 or 7 : 5 phospholipid to cholesterol ratio) is essential for the maintenance of their stability (in terms of dye leakage) after they come into contact with blood *in vivo* and also *in vitro* in the presence of whole blood (Figure 2B) or serum (Figure 2C). Work is in progress to establish whether there is retention of a variety of drugs *in vivo* by cholesterol-rich liposomes.

Leakage of liposomal contents *in vivo* may also be prevented by accommodating these within the lipid framework of the carrier, by the use of agents which can interact electrostatically with liposomal lipid components or by linking agents on to already entrapped macromolecules or appropriate acceptors. When for instance the lipid soluble actinomycin D was incorporated into the lipid phase of liposomes, its rate of clearance from the blood of injected rats was very similar to that of the carrier (Gregoriadis, 1973). A similar observation was made with colchicine (Juliano and Stamp, 1975) and with daunomycin and vinblastine (Juliano and Stamp, 1978) all of which are lipid soluble. In other experiments it was shown that ^{111}In-labelled bleomycin can interact with the phosphatidic acid component of liposomes (probably electrostatically) and after injection into animals, most of the radioactivity follows the carrier to its destination (Gregoriadis *et al.*, 1977b). In the 'second carrier' approach (Gregoriadis *et al.*, 1977a) polyglutamic acid is incorporated into liposomes and then allowed to interact with melphalan or methotrexate in the presence of carbodiimide. This leads to the formation of a polyglutamic acid–drug complex and escape of the drug from liposomes, following their injection into rats, is thus prevented. Similar results were obtained when entrapped DNA served as a second carrier to daunomycin or actinomycin D (Gregoriadis *et al.*, 1977a). Finally, according to the technique published by Fendler and co-workers (see this volume) entrapment of 8-azaguanine

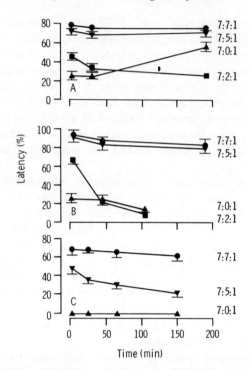

Figure 2 The effect of cholesterol content of liposomes on the latency of entrapped 6-carboxyfluorescein. Small multilamellar liposomes containing 6-carboxyfluorescein (6-CF) and composed of egg phosphatidylcholine (PC), cholesterol (CHOL) (when appropriate) and phosphatidic acid (PA) were injected intravenously into rats (A) or incubated in the presence of whole fresh rat blood (B) or fresh rat serum (C). Latent 6-CF (non-measurable in the absence of Triton X100) in the blood of injected rats and in the whole blood or serum *in vitro* at time intervals is expressed as % ± SD of 6-CF latency in the injected preparations. The latter (% of total 6-CF in each preparation) was 79.5 ± 16.8 (8 preparations) for 7PC1PA, 93.0 and 89.1 for 7PC2CHOL1PA, 94 ± 3.6 (8 preparations) for 7PC5CHOL1PA and 93.8 ± 3.5 (10 preparations) for 7PC7CHOL1PA liposomes. (Numbers preceding lipids denote molar ratios.) Each point represents values for 4–9 animals (A) or 9 (B) and 6 (C) pooled experiments. Incubation of liposomes with 1% NaCl alone or containing 0.63% citrate solution (used as an anticoagulant in B) did not alter initial latencies for the time intervals shown. Numbers in Figure are molar ratios for PC, CHOL and PA respectively.
(From Gregoriadis and Davis, 1979)

and 6-mercaptopurine (donors) into, and their retention by, liposomes was considerably improved in the presence of entrapped chloranil (acceptor) through charge transfer complex formation.

The rate of elimination of liposomes from the blood is controlled by, among other factors, liposomal size and surface charge. For instance, large liposomes are removed more rapidly than small ones. This was anticipated from the biphasic rate of clearance of liposomes of mixed sizes (Gregoriadis and Ryman, 1972a) and eventually confirmed by Juliano and Stamp (1975) and Hinkle *et al.* (1978). Regarding surface charge, it appeared that negative liposomes are removed more rapidly than those which are made to bear positive or neutral charges (Gregoriadis and Neerunjun, 1974; Tagesson *et al.*, 1977). This may be related to the (final) net negative charge which is imposed onto the liposomal surface following contact with plasma proteins (Black and Gregoriadis, 1976) but the way by which such charge controls the affinity of liposomes to cells *in vivo* is unclear. It is possible that the surface charge originally present in liposomes modulates the extent to, or even the fashion by, which plasma components bind onto liposomes and thus cause association of the latter with cell surfaces.

Hepatic Kupffer cells and spleen macrophages are the major sites of liposome localization (Segal *et al.*, 1974; Wisse *et al.*, 1976) and, per unit weight, participation of the two tissues is roughly similar (Gregoriadis and Ryman, 1972b; Gregoriadis *et al.*, 1977b). However, total uptake will depend on the size and charge of liposomes (Gregoriadis and Neerunjun, 1974; Juliano and Stamp, 1975) and on the animal species injected (Gregoriadis *et al.*, 1977b; Gregoriadis *et al.*, 1974b). It has also been observed that even with liposomal preparations made under identical conditions and which are expected to transport entrapped agents to tissues at comparable rates, apparent total uptake of the agents by tissues can differ. This is because agents, depending on their nature, will behave differently intracellularly. Thus, some agents will leak out while others will be degraded or metabolized with products being released extracellularly. It is therefore obvious that an important prerequisite for the estimation of the extent to which a given liposomal preparation transports its contents to a particular tissue is that entrapped substances do not leak from liposomes in the blood, and that they remain within cells (into which they are transported by the carrier) for a period of time long enough to allow quantitative clearance of liposomes from the blood. Assay of the agent in tissues at an appropriate time interval should reveal the true capacity of the tissue for the uptake of liposomes under study. Agents which have proved valuable in this respect include ^{111}In-labelled bleomycin (Gregoriadis *et al.*, 1977b) and ^{125}I-labelled polyvinylpyrrolidone (Dapergolas *et al.*, 1976). In the former case, regardless of the metabolic fate of bleomycin within cells, the ^{111}In label retains its intracellular location and in the latter the polymer is not metabolized and its intracellular levels are maintained for several days.

The participation of hepatic parenchymal cells in the uptake of liposomes is still unclear in spite of extensive investigations (Segal *et al.*,

1974; Rahman and Wright, 1975; Wisse *et al.*, 1976). Initial work (Gregoriadis and Ryman, 1972a) with [^{3}H]cholesterol-labelled liposomes suggested extensive uptake by these cells but the validity of the findings seems now doubtful in view of the possible exchange of hepatic cholesterol with liposomal cholesterol or cholesterol donation to the cells by liposomes directly or via plasma (Gregoriadis *et al.*, 1977c). Electron microscopic studies with horseradish peroxidase-containing liposomes (Wisse *et al.*, 1976) showing localization of horseradish peroxidase in the parenchymal cells of the liver are also subject to the criticism that some of the enzyme leaked out of liposomes and reached parenchymal cells as such. In these experiments the cholesterol content of liposomes composed of egg phosphatidylcholine, cholesterol, and phosphatidic acid was rather low (molar ratio 7 : 2 : 1) and it is possible that, in view of the role of cholesterol on liposomal stability as discussed above, there was indeed some leakage of horseradish peroxidase. On the other hand it is also possible that liposomes smaller than 100 nm in diameter can reach parenchymal cells and be subsequently interiorized by them, probably at a rate greater than that exhibited when the same cells are exposed to liposomes *in vitro* (Scherphof *et al.*, 1978).

While channels leading to the hepatic parenchymal cells are wide enough to allow passage of some liposomes, it is unknown whether liposomes, even at their smallest size (about 15 nm), succeed in diffusing through capillary walls to reach extravascular areas. Liposomes are known, however, to cross membranes lining the peritoneal cavity. For instance, when small or large liposomes containing ^{125}I-labelled polyvinylpyrrolidone are given intraperitoneally, radioactivity is recovered in the blood and liver to an extent which is far above that expected to occur with the free polymer (Dapergolas *et al.*, 1976). Thus, it can be assumed that most of the radioactivity recovered in these tissues is transported there by means of liposomes. Recent work with intraperitoneally given liposomes containing 6-carboxyfluorescein shows that the dye penetrates the blood circulation in its quenched form, supporting passage of intact liposomes (Figure 3). Additional evidence for liposome transport through membranes comes from studies in which the rat testicle was injected with liposomes containing radiolabelled albumin or actinomycin D (Segal *et al.*, 1975). When large liposomes were given they remained quantitatively at the site of injection and disintegrated with released agents diffusing into the blood circulation. The fate of small liposomes was different in that entrapped agents were transported either to the lymph nodes draining the injected tissue or into the blood. Whether entrance in the blood circulation occurred after direct crossing of capillaries or via the lymphatic circulation is not known. Similar findings of lymph node localization of liposomes after local injection have been published recently by Richardson *et al.*

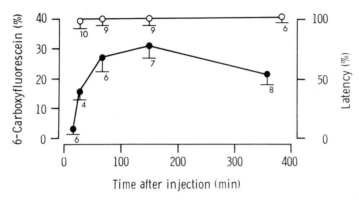

Figure 3 The effect of cholesterol content of liposomes on the latency and blood levels of entrapped 6-carboxyfluorescein. Mice were injected intraperitoneally with small unilamellar liposomes containing 6-carboxyfluorescein (6-CF) and composed of egg phosphatidylcholine (PC) and cholesterol (7PC7CHOL; number preceding lipids is molar ratio) and bled at time intervals. Latency (o) in blood (five pooled experiments) is expressed as % ± SD of that in the injected preparation (90.7 ± 3.9, five preparations). Total blood levels (●) are expressed as % ± SD of the injected dose. Numbers near symbols denote animals used (C. Kirby, J. Clarke and G. Gregoriadis, submitted for publication)

(1977). Further support for membrane crossing comes from experiments with tumor-bearing animals injected intravenously with liposomes containing ^{111}In-labelled bleomycin and these are discussed later.

Regarding intracellular distribution of liposomal agents within cells participating in the clearance of liposomes from the blood, data from liver fractionation show that such agents localize mainly in the lysosomes (Gregoriadis and Ryman, 1972; Gregoriadis *et al.*, 1974a; Black and Gregoriadis, 1974; Steger and Desnick, 1977). However, in recent experiments a significant proportion of glucuronidase was recovered in the 'post-lysosomal-mitochondrial' fraction of the liver of rats injected with glucuronidase-containing positively charged liposomes (Steger and Desnick, 1977). The authors suggest that this arises either from the fusion of hepatic cells with liposomes leading to the release of the enzyme in the cytoplasm or from the destabilization of the lysosomal membranes by the stearylamine component of liposomes effecting loss of lysosomal contents. Since the post-lysosomal-mitochondrial fraction contains the microsomal fraction as well as small pinocytic vacuoles which co-sediment with the microsomes, it is also possible that activity recovered in this fraction represents liposomal enzyme at the stage of being endocytosed. The biochemical data supporting lysosomal localization of liposomes are compatible with electron microscopic studies (Segal *et al.*, 1974; Rahman and Wright, 1975; Wisse *et al.*, 1976). Indeed, lysosomal localization of liposomes is far from being an unusual finding. Fixed macrophages of the liver and spleen are known to endocytose avidly particulate as well as non-particulate matter in the circulating blood and there is no reason to expect that liposomes would be an exception. An even stronger, albeit indirect, argument for lysosomal localization of liposomes is the finding that in rats injected with liposomal radiolabelled albumin, the radioactivity content of the liver declines rapidly presumably as a result of albumin degradation and release of iodinated fragments into the circulation (Gregoriadis and Ryman, 1972a; Gregoriadis and Neerunjun, 1974). Such behaviour, also seen with liposomes containing enzymes (Gregoriadis and Ryman, 1972a,b; Gregoriadis and Neerunjun, 1974; Steger and Desnick, 1977), is not exhibited by liposomal polyvinylpyrrolidone or ^{111}In which cannot be degraded or otherwise metabolized (Dapergolas et al., 1976; Gregoriadis et al., 1977b).

Fusion of liposomes with fixed macrophages or with other cells in the intravascular or extravascular space would present us with the attractive possibility of introducing agents directly into the cytoplasm of cells. However, this is inlikely to occur to any significant extent *in vivo*: (*a*) various studies *in vivo* (Segal et al., 1974; Rahman and Wright, 1975; Wisse et al., 1976) have provided ample morphological evidence for endocytosis but have failed to reveal liposomal material in the cytoplasm not surrounded by membranes. Even a demonstration of this kind would not have automatically implied fusion since lysosomes can break up within cells and release their contents in the cytoplasm. (*b*) Erythrocytes and other blood cells which are in close contact for several hours with intravenously injected liposomes do not incorporate any measurable proportion of liposomal agents.

3. INTERACTION OF LIPOSOMES WITH CELLS *IN VITRO*

The demonstration that liposomes can direct enzymes and other agents into the lysosomes of cells (Gregoriadis and Ryman, 1972a,b) raised the question as to whether agents transported into these organelles could free themselves from the liposomal envelope and survive in the hostile milieu for a sufficient period of time to allow their action on intralysosomal targets. Experiments pertaining to the control of cell metabolism by the use of liposomes were thus carried out (Gregoriadis and Buckland, 1973). Data obtained suggested that cultured cells were capable of taking up liposomes the contents (in this case a hydrolytic enzyme) of which were delivered into the lysosomes where after the disruption of the carrier, agents were set free to act. Cellular uptake of liposomes, their localization in lysosomes and subsequent disruption were expected to occur not only because a similar fate of liposomes had been discovered already *in vivo* but also because cells will, in general, endocytose soluble and particulate matter (up to a certain size) when exposed to it. Uptake will obviously be more rapid with 'professional' endocytosers than with other cells (e.g. fibroblasts, cultured hepatic parenchymal cells etc.). Endocytosis *in vitro* was subsequently shown to occur with a variety of other cells (e.g. Magee *et al.*, 1974; Weissmann *et al.*, 1975; Poste and Papahadjopoulos, 1976a).

The fate and effect of agents entering lysosomes by endocytosis of their liposomal carrier must depend on the physical properties of such agents. Those which are stable in the lysosomal milieu can act within it (e.g. some hydrolytic enzymes, metal chelating agents or certain antimicrobial drugs). Alternatively, agents capable of crossing lysosomal membranes, can reach and act in, other cellular areas. This lysosomotropic action of drugs, discussed by de Duve and co-workers (1974) is from a pharmacologist's point of view of somewhat limited value and a method for the introduction of agents directly into extralysosomal areas would in many ways be preferable.

The suggestion (Grant and McConnell, 1973; Papahadjopoulos *et al.*, 1974a; Pagano and Huang, 1975) that liposomes can fuse with cells opened the way to such a possibility. Papahadjopoulos *et al.* (1974a) for instance attempted to inhibit growth of cells exposed to liposome-entrapped cyclic AMP. They found that growth was inhibited when liposomes were composed of unsaturated phospholipid ('fluid' liposomes) but not when 'solid' dipalmitoyl phosphatidycholine liposomes were used. As fusion of cells was assumed not to occur with 'solid' liposomes, the deduction was made that the latter entered cells by endocytosis and delivered their cyclic AMP into the lysosomes where it was promptly inactivated by enzymes. On the other hand, since there was an inhibitory effect on the growth of cells exposed to 'fluid' liposomes, it was concluded that such liposomes fused with cells to deliver their contents into the cytoplasm where the cyclic AMP could proceed with its effect. That may be so but there are, obviously, other ways to explain such findings. For instance, one could argue that dipalmitoyl phosphatidycholine liposomes are much less vulnerable to lysosomal phospholipases at 37 °C than those made of unsaturated lecithins and although both types of liposomes enter lysosomes by endocytosis, only cyclic AMP from the latter can be liberated rapidly enough to allow its partial diffusion into the cytoplasm. With 'solid' liposomes a slow release of the drug as a result of a gradual breakdown of the carrier would allow relevant enzymes to attack the drug more efficiently. Alternatively, and assuming endocytosis as the principal mechanism of liposome uptake regardless of phospholipid composition, it is possible that some of the endocytic vacuoles carrying 'fluid' liposomes are unable to fuse with lysosomes, either because they are destabilized by, or because they fuse with, their liposome contents. As a result, liposomal agents (e.g. cyclic AMP) are released into the cytoplasm. This event may not occur, at least not to the same extent, with endocytic vacuoles containing 'solid' liposomes. Another possibility is that cell membranes in contact with certain types of liposomes (e.g. 'fluid') are destabilized. In such a case, agents escaping from leaky liposomes can enter equally leaky cells at the points of contact. Similar doubts exist regarding the support given to cell–liposome fusion by the use of inhibitors of energy-dependent endocytosis. Such inhibitors were found to prevent the uptake of 'solid' liposomes by cells almost totally while that of 'fluid' liposomes was affected only modestly (Poste and Papahadjopoulos, 1976a). Again, however, there could have been a similar inhibition of uptake for both types of liposomes but because of destabilization at the cell–'fluid' liposome points of contact, liposomal contents were able to diffuse into cells. Morphological evidence for fusion is also shaky. For instance, 'patches' on cell surfaces alleged to be liposomal membrane regions (Papahadjopoulos *et al.*, 1974a) could be explained as liposome-induced evagination of the plasma membrane. Because of a variety of possible explanations for data obtained from the interacting of cells and liposomes (see chapter 4 for a comprehensive discussion), the term membrane fusion should be applied less generously than it is already. Fusion should not be taken for granted each time that experimental conditions allegedly favouring fusion are used.

4. APPLICATIONS IN BIOLOGICAL SYSTEMS

Liposomes have been applied in biological systems in two different ways. The first concerns *in vitro* or *in vivo* exposure of cells or organs to liposomal agents with the purpose of interfering with cell function in a way which, for various reasons, cannot be accomplished by the agents as such. The second is related to the modifications of drug distribution in the body so as to improve conventional drug action in the treatment or prevention of disease. Both aspects along with problems and possibilities will be discussed here.

4.1. Applications in biology

Understanding of metabolic processes by the use of drugs can be hampered by difficulties associated with poor penetration of drugs into cells or their inability to reach specific cellular sites. The variety of ways by which liposomes are thought to enter, or associate with, cells offer a unique opportunity for the transport of drugs into otherwise inaccessible cellular regions. One of the first instances in which the liposomal carrier was used to bypass membranes for the purpose of studying cell metabolism was in liver perfusion studies in which the organ was exposed to liposomes containing pepstatin (Dean, 1975). This, although an inhibitor of hepatic cathepsin D, cannot act on intact cells because of its inability to cross membranes. Results from these experiments supported a role of lysosomes in the catabolism of intracellular proteins.

Liposomes could offer considerable help in unravelling the mode by which plasma proteins are degraded in tissues. Owing to the long half-life of proteins in the blood, their catabolic products in tissues do not accumulate and cannot thus be identified. In cases where proteins carry prosthetic groups (e.g. glycoproteins, lipoproteins), there is in addition the question of the sequence of hydrolytic steps. Present methods for such studies employing either lysosomal extracts or purified lysosomal hydrolases do not simulate physiological processes and an *in vivo* system would, therefore, seem more appropriate. On the other hand, intravenously injected liposomes containing macromolecules under study could transfer their contents rapidly into the liver lysosomes (believed to be the major catabolic site of catabolism of many plasma proteins (Gregoriadis, 1975b). As there is indirect evidence that the lipid envelope of liposomes is disrupted in the liver within minutes after uptake (Gregoriadis and Ryman, 1972b; Wisse *et al.*, 1976), freed macromolecules could be acted upon by lysosomal enzymes to give catabolites in measurable quantities. Furthermore, one could investigate protein catabolism by the liver in various physiological states, an advantage which is not attainable in the perfused liver system. Indeed, the possibility exists of developing a method for the study of liver function in the intact animal by employing liposomes which retain their contents while in the blood. An example of this has already appeared in work (de Barsy *et al.*, 1976) related to the participation of the lysosomal α-glucosidase in the catabolism of hepatic glycogen in newborn rodents. It was shown that after injection of liposome-entrapped anti-α-glucosidase antibodies, the enzyme was inhibited, presumably as a result of bulk transport of immunoglobulin molecules by the carrier directly into the intracellular target.

Other investigators have taken advantage of the metabolic changes which certain lipid components of liposomes can induce. For instance, after injection of liposomes made of bovine brain lipid extract, glucose distribution in the body was modified. At the same time there was an increase in the metabolism of catecholamines in the brain of injected animals with acetylcholine being released from the brain cortex (Bruni *et al.*, 1976). These changes were attributed to the phosphatidylserine component of the liposomes used. In subsequent work, such liposomes were found to increase both the dopamine-sensitive adenylate cyclase activity and the cyclic AMP content of mouse brain (Leon *et al.*, 1978). The same preparation injected into human subjects affected pituitary function, possibly at the level of dopamine-mediated prolactin regulation

(Masturzo *et al.*, 1977) and it increased homovanillic acid levels in the cerebrospinal fluid (Nizzo *et al.*, 1978).

The use of liposomes in modifying biological systems *in vitro* has been more popular, obviously because of the simplicity in dealing with isolated systems. With regard to altering cell membrane structure and function, work has been carried out on the role of the fluid state of membranes in cellular regulatory mechanisms. Inbar and Shinitzky (1974), for instance, exposed transformed lymphoma cells to cholesterol-containing liposomes and were thus able to enrich the cholesterol content of the cell membrane and increase its rigidity. This, in turn, reduced the tumorgenicity of the cells *in vivo*. Martin and McDonald (1976) on the other hand, used liposomes bearing a specific antigen to introduce a new antigenic determinant on to the surface of red cell membrane. This is, apparently, a two-way process since cell membrane components can also be transferred on to the membranes of liposomes (Dunnick *et al.*, 1976b).

One of the most popular applications of the liposome drug-carrier concept is the 'smuggling' of molecules past selective barriers imposed by membranes. Restrictions in reaching the interior of cells are known to exist for a large variety of drugs and early work showed that liposomes could facilitate the intracellular entrance of such drugs. This, for instance, was demonstrated in the case of antibiotics *in vivo* (Gregoriadis, 1973 [and recently *in vitro* (Bonventre and Gregoriadis, 1978)] and of heavy metal chelators *in vivo* (Rahman *et al.*, 1973). Subsequently, the approach was applied successfully in a variety of other situations. Magee's group (Straub *et al.*, 1974; Magee *et al.*, 1974) made the interesting observation that animals injected with liposomes containing interferon inducers (polynucleotides) produced much more interferon than treatment with the free inducers. In addition, Mayhew *et al.* (1977) were able to show that rIn-rCn incorporated in large unilamellar liposomes was capable of inducing interferon production and protection of cells from vesicular stomatitis virus more than the free inducer. In other experiments, exposure of actinomycin D insensitive DC-3F/ADX cells to liposomes containing the drug, led to the significant inhibition of cellular RNA synthesis and cell growth (Poste and Papahadjopoulos, 1976b). As the liposomal preparation used was composed of phospholipids with a phase transition temperature below the ambient, it was assumed that the drug was introduced into the cytoplasm of the cells. As discussed earlier, this is by no means a correct assumption. Similar liposomes can undergo endocytosis *in vitro* (Gregoriadis and Buckland, 1973; Magee *et al.*, 1974; Weissmann *et al.*, 1975; Poste and Papahadjopoulos, 1976a), and it is possible that at least some of the drug found its way into the cytoplasm following its escape from lysosomes (Black and Gregoriadis, 1974; Gregoriadis and Neerunjun, 1975a). More recently, cell resistance to drugs was circumvented by enriching the membranes of cells (L1210) with ergosterol following their exposure to ergosterol-containing liposomes (Schiffman and Klein, 1977). This structural modification rendered target cells sensitive to amphotericin B the action of which is based on the damage it inflicts to membranes containing certain sterols such as ergosterol. Work along the same lines by Wilson *et al.* (1977) showed that polio virus-resistant Chinese hamster ovary cells could be infected by the virus when the latter was entrapped in large unilamellar liposomes.

One of the more fascinating features of the liposomal carrier is its promising role in genetic engineering where some of the difficulties arise from the poor penetration of information fragments into cells and from their vulnerability to enzymes (e.g. ribonuclease) in the media or blood. This aspect was put forward several years ago (Gregoriadis and Ryman, 1972b; Magee and Miller, 1972) and is now being investigated in a number of laboratories. Following the demonstration that RNA can be incorporated in multilamellar (Ostro, 1977) or large unilamellar (Dimitriadis, 1978a) liposomes, it was, apparently, possible to persuade mammalian cells to produce rabbit globin by exposing them to liposomes containing rabbit mRNA (Ostro *et al.*, 1978; Dimitriadis, 1978b). Work from this laboratory (Wreschner *et al.*, 1978) has now shown that mRNA can be incorporated in large unilamellar liposomes derived from 'hybrid' (Wreschner and Gregoriadis, 1978) liposomes. The latter (Figures 4 and 5) prepared from small positively and negatively charged liposomes, are likely to bear both charges on their surfaces with the positive ones acting as a means of increasing association of the negative mRNA with the vesicles. It is of interest to note that large unilamellar liposomes prepared from hybrids may be composed of a variety of phospholipids and other lipids which is in contrast to the large unilamellar liposomes prepared from phosphatidylserine only (Papahadjopoulos *et al.*, 1975). Work is in progress to investigate possible advantages of using such liposomes in experiments with cells *in vitro* and *in vivo*. Promising results in the use of liposomes in gene transfer have been reported recently by Mukherjee *et al.* (1978). Metaphase chromosomes from hypoxanthine guanine phosphoribosyl transferase (HGPRT)-positive cells (a mouse–human somatic hybrid line) were entrapped in liposomes which were then presented to HGPRT-negative cells. The frequency of transfer (allegedly attained by fusion) of a portion of the X chromosome (3 X-linked genes were transformed) was at least one per 10^5 cells, a minimum of ten fold improvement over other methods.

Liposomes have also been applied in cases where metabolic studies are hindered by technical difficulties. For instance, there is a large number of drugs which are insoluble or unstable in water. One of these is retinol (a precursor of the primary components of visual pigments) which not only is

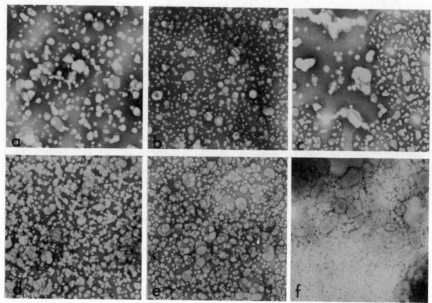

Figure 4 Electron micrographs of mixed negatively and positively charged liposomes. Equal volumes of small positively charged liposomes composed of egg phosphatidylcholine, cholesterol and stearylamine (molar ratio 7 : 2 : 2) (a) and small negatively charged liposomes composed of phosphatidylserine (b) were mixed at room temperature. Immediately after mixing (c) the suspension contained two discrete phases one of which consisted of small aggregates of vesicles. Thirty minutes later the mixture contained small discrete liposomes (d and e) and also aggregates of liposomes with a greater range of size (f) than in the two parent populations. Negatively stained with 1% aqueous sodium silicotungstate ($\times$ 32,500). In previous work (Wreschner *et al.*, 1978) these large structures escaped detection because, owing to the staining procedure used, they tended to aggregate at the edges of the grid (G. Gregoriadis and J. Dorling, submitted for publication)

very sparingly soluble in water, it also is extremely susceptible to oxidation when dispersed in aqueous media. By incorporating the precursor into the lipid phase of small unilamellar liposomes and presenting it to isolated vertebrate retinas, the latter were able to synthesize pigment (Yoshicami and Nöll, 1978). Difficulties related to the microinjection of cells can be resolved by the use of liposomes. For instance, the importance of the intracellular concentration of calcium and sodium in quantal transmitter release from motor nerve terminals has been substantiated by Rahaminoff *et al*. (1978) who used calcium- and sodium-containing liposomes. These authors found that such liposomes increase both evoked and spontaneous acetylcholine release by presynaptic nerve terminals.

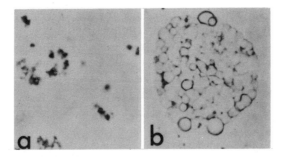

Figure 5 Phase contrast photomicrographs of mixed negatively and positively charged liposomes. Equal volumes of small positively charged liposomes composed of dipalmitoyl phosphatidylcholine, cholesterol and stearylamine (molar ratio 7 : 2 : 2) and of negatively charged liposomes composed of dipalmitoyl phosphatidylcholine, cholesterol and phosphatidic acid (molar ratio 7 : 2 :2) were mixed at room temperature. The aggregates formed (a) persisted for several hours and they were transformed (presumably through fusion, see Wreschner *et al.*, 1978) to aggregates of very large vesicles (b) only after the temperature of the mixture was increased to 45 °C. Liposomes of the parent populations (not shown) were only just visible at the magnification used (× 640) (G. Gregoriadis and J. Dorling, submitted for publication)

4.2. Applications in Medicine

Selective action of drugs is an important prerequisite for their successful application in treating or preventing disease. However, because of the many similarities (e.g. in membrane structure and function, metabolic properties etc.) which exist between cells in need of the drug and normal cells, a specific effect is more often than not the exception rather than the rule. Consequently, side effects occur which hamper or even prevent treatment of a wide variety of diseases ranging from cancer to inherited metabolic disorders. A problem additional to that of poor drug selectivity, is the inability of certain drugs to reach diseased areas. For example, in many parasitic diseases, drugs cannot kill intracellular micro-organisms because of the protection offered to the parasites by cellular membranes in the form of permeability barriers to the drugs. Alternatively, drugs cannot reach the target mainly because of their large size. This is the case with enzymes which are potentially useful in the treatment of some enzyme deficiencies (e.g. lysosomal storage diseases) affecting the central nervous system but are unable to cross the blood–brain barrier. Yet in other instances delivery of a drug, to the area in need of treatment through a particular route which would have benefited the patient, is impracticable because of the drug's properties. Thus, the vulnerability of insulin in the gut prevents its use in the oral treatment of diabetes.

The versatile nature of the liposomal carrier in terms of composition, size, surface properties, and other characteristics warrants its wide (potential) applicability in improving drug selectivity and action and several of the chapters in this book deal with a variety of possible uses. In the following pages I shall discuss some of these and, when possible, speculate on problems and possibilities for success.

4.2.1. Enzyme replacement therapy

Treatment of enzyme deficiences in man with enzymes isolated from human or foreign sources is associated with a host of problems (Desnick *et al.*, 1976). In addition to the immunological reactions which can both inactivate the administered enzyme and endanger the life of the patient, there is the possibility of undesirable enzyme action on substrates in areas other than those in need of treatment (Gregoriadis *et al.*, 1974a). Furthermore, enzymes are prone to premature inactivation in non-target extracellular and intracellular regions.

The transport of active agents by liposomes into the lysosomes offers a unique opportunity to test this carrier system in the treatment of lysosomal storage diseases (Gregoriadis, 1978c). These are characterized by the partial or total absence of a specific lysosomal hydrolase as a result of which substances, normally serving as substrates to the enzyme, are deposited within the lysosomes of tissues (Brady, 1977). It is now widely accepted that liposomes carrying appropriate hydrolases can be effective in 'correcting' model lysosomal storage conditions. Indeed, early work showed that exposure of sucrose-loaded cells to liposomal invertase leads to the entrance of the enzyme into the sucrose-loaded lysosomes and the subsequent hydrolysis of sucrose (Gregoriadis and Buckland, 1973). Encouraging results have also been obtained with fibroblasts from a patient suffering from glycogen storage disease type II (Roerdink *et al.*, 1976) and with the dextran-loaded liver of rats injected with dextranase-containing liposomes (Colley and Ryman, 1976). In both cases there was a considerable reduction of the glycogen and dextran levels, respectively, after exposure to relevant liposomal enzymes. Other researchers, using a cystinotic patient's fibroblasts incubated with liposome-entrapped cysteamine, were able to partially deplete lysosomes from their load of cystine (de Brouhn Butler *et al.*, 1978). More recently, Reynolds *et al.* (1978) published a method for the evaluation of the liposome approach to replacement therapy in a naturally occurring lysosomal storage disease, namely feline GM_1 gangliosidosis in which there is a deficiency in β-galactosidase. Skin fibroblasts from cats with GM_1 gangliosidosis were initially pulse-labelled with radioactive galactose which incorporated itself into the lysosomal glycopeptides of the diseased cells (glycopeptides in these cells are not catabolized over a period of several days). It was found that exposure of the galactose-labelled cells to liposomal β-galactosidase isolated from feline liver was followed by the catabolism of the radiolabelled glycopeptides as a result of enzyme uptake, apparently through endocytosis of the liposomal carrier. Obviously this is an attractive method by which the efficacy of any liposomal enzyme preparation within the lysosomes of diseased cells can be tested and it could be easily applied in a variety of lysosomal storage disorders. There are, however, some limitations in the approach. For instance, degradation of pulse-labelled substrate (which clearly concerns newly synthesized materials) may not be characteristic of hydrolase action on all stored substrate in all intracellular areas. In fact, it is possible that lysosomes which are either aged or excessively loaded may not be able to fuse with the endocytic vacuoles transporting the liposomes or with young secondary lysosomes which have already incorporated the enzyme. In addition, much of the substrate may be in a physical state resistant to enzyme activity. It is therefore important that experiments are carried out to show that such results can be achieved with cells at the centre of a given lysosomal storage disease (as for example macrophages from adult Gaucher's disease patients storing glucocerebroside or cardiac and skeletal muscle cells from glycogen storage disease type II patients) by measuring total accumulated substrate and examining cellular morphology and function before and after treatment.

Extrapolation of results from *in vitro* work to the overall efficacy of the system *in vivo* could, however, be meaningless. For instance, in dealing with animals, one should consider difficulties related to the journey of the carrier to areas in need of treatment. Liposomes must retain their enzyme contents while in the blood circulation and must therefore be designed appropriately. In lysosomal storage diseases involving tissues other than the liver and spleen, liposomes must cross membranes to reach and enter diseased cells (entrance into nerve cells seems improbable at present) and they thus may require control of their size and surface properties (Gregoriadis, 1977). Reduction in size will also ensure less hepatic and splenic interference, although these two tissues are expected to be enzyme-deficient and therefore their participation in uptake is unlikely to be detrimental. Other factors which should be taken into consideration include possible toxicity of the liposomal lipid components and increased immunogenicity of the administered enzymes promoted by the immunological adjuvant properties of the carrier (see later). Even so, transport of enzymes by liposomes into target cells and degradation of the stored material will not necessarily lead to the return of a normal function in the diseased organs.

One of the lysosomal storage diseases, namely adult Gaucher's disease offers a convenient test case for the liposome approach. This disease is characterized by a deficiency in glucocerebroside : β-glucosidase and cells afflicted are predominantly those of the reticuloendothelial system, i.e. the cells which are most active in taking up liposomes. Over the last three years we have treated an adult Gaucher's disease splenectomized patient with numerous intravenous injections of liposome-associated glucocerebroside : β-glucosidase partially purified from human placenta (Braidman and Gregoriadis, 1977). Initial treatment, carried out at irregular time intervals with large amounts of enzyme, was accompanied by transient pain in the abdomen associated with swelling of the liver and subsequent shrinking, and to a lesser extent in the shoulders, spine, hips, and knees. These symptoms were roughly proportional to the amount of β-glucosidase given and were absent with liposomes devoid of enzyme (Belchetz *et al.*, 1977). Because of these complications, enzyme dosage was eventually adjusted to a level [about 500 units (nmoles substrate hydrolysed per minute at 37 °C) bi-weekly] which does not inconvenience the patient and which limits her stay in the hospital to 24 hours. Several months after treatment began, there was a possible clinical improvement in terms of liver size and pressure symptoms in the abdomen and of reticuloendothelial system function. For almost two years of 'mild' but frequent treatment, the clinical picture of the patient has slightly improved with no apparent side reactions. Because of the patient's tendency to bleed and also because of the anticipated variability in the substrate content of the liver (Beutler *et al.*, 1977; Ihler and Glew, 1977) and the small amount of enzyme given, glucocerebroside and β-glucosidase content of serial liver biopsies was not investigated. A number of tests pertaining to the possible toxicity of the treatment were, however, carried out. Serum samples obtained before treatment began and after 4 (three treatments) and 30 months (twenty treatments) were analysed for antibodies against the β-glucosidase-rich preparation (using as a positive control serum from mice immunized with the same preparation) and found negative (Gregoriadis *et al.*, 1979). In addition to a variety of routine clinical and biochemical tests performed throughout the 3 year period, the haemostatic function of the patient has been recently examined. Variables measured before and at time intervals after a number of treatments included clotting factors, fibrinolytic activity, platelet aggregability, and α_2-macroglobulin. None of these appeared to change significantly after the administration of the liposomal enzyme (about 100 mg of total lipid per treatment) (Gregoriadis *et al.*, 1979). In the only other case of lysosomal storage disease treatment with liposomes, some reduction in liver size was also reported. As the patient (an infant with glycogenosis type II injected with liposomal fungal amyloglucosidase) died soon after treatment began, no valid conclusions could be drawn (Tyrrell *et al.*, 1976a).

As mentioned earlier, a major difficulty in therapy with enzymes foreign to the patient is the development of anti-enzyme antibodies which can subsequently interact with the antigen leading to both anaphylactic reactions and loss of enzyme activity. It is hoped that such untoward effects will be avoided when liposomes are used since their lipid bilayers will prevent contact of the circulating immunoglobulins with intraliposomal antigens (Gregoriadis and Allison, 1974; Neerunjun and Gregoriadis, 1976). On the other hand, liposomes are known to act as powerful immunological adjuvants to entrapped antigens (Allison and Gregoriadis, 1974) and caution is, therefore, needed when proteins which are recognized as foreign by the patient are given. This is especially so in the case of a possible disruption of liposomes in the blood circulation as a result of the individual's blood biochemistry and of the preparation's lipid composition. However, recent work by Schwenk *et al.* (1978) suggests that such adverse effects may be circumvented by the use of antigen-containing liposomes in a way which will depress immunogenicity to the antigen. Finally, there is a real possibility of premature enzyme inactivation by the lysosomal cathepsins or other factors within the target organelles. However, extension of the enzyme's life span within lysosomes may be achieved by cross-linking the protein after its entrapment in liposomes (Gregoriadis and Neerunjun, 1974).

4.2.2. Cancer chemotherapy

The possibility of treating cancer by the use of liposomes was one of the first suggestions made regarding the potential of the carrier in medicine. It was anticipated (Gregoriadis, 1973) that transport of cytotoxic agents to malignant tissues would not only circumvent unwanted reactions due to drug action on normal tissues but also prevent drugs from being inactivated or otherwise wasted. Initial work showing leakage of drugs from the carrier, especially after intravenous administration (Gregoriadis, 1973 and 1974b) was disconcerting but methods now exist which can improve drug retention (Gregoriadis, 1973; Fendler, this volume; Gregoriadis *et al.*, 1977a). In addition, our recent work (Figures 1 and 2) on the effect of lipid composition on the permeability of liposomal bilayers *in vivo* indicates that loss of small molecular weight substances may be prevented by increasing the amount of cholesterol in the liposome structure.

Liposomes not only influence the rate of clearance of their cytotoxic contents from the blood and protect these from inactivation (e.g. Kimelberg *et al.*, 1976; Freise *et al.*, 1977) they also determine their fate in the body. As expected liver and spleen take up portions of the injected dose which reflect the extent of uptake of the liposomal carrier. On the other hand, localization of liposomal agents in tissues such as intestinal mucosa, skeletal and cardiac muscle, lungs and kidney is usually less than that obtained with the free agents (Gregoriadis, 1973; Rahman et al., 1975; Juliano and Stamp, 1978). Estimation of the total possible uptake of a liposomal agent by a particular tissue is, however, seldom correct. As discussed earlier, this is because drugs are usually lost, at least in part, from the carrier during its circulation in the blood and also because many drugs spill out of the tissue's cells (Kimelberg et al., 1975) often in the form of metabolites. We have used ^{111}In-labelled bleomycin as a marker of negatively charged liposomes to investigate parameters related to the structure and composition of the carrier which would favour its localization (as well as that of the entrapped agent) in malignant tissues. We found (Dapergolas et al., 1976; Gregoriadis et al., 1977b) that when small liposomes were used (about 80 nm average diameter) uptake of liposomal ^{111}In by tumours (e.g. Meth 'A', 6C3HED and Lewis lung carcinoma) implanted in a variety of mouse strains and by Novikoff hepatoma in Wistar rats was several-fold greater (to about 7% of the dose per gram mouse tumour tissue) than that obtained with large liposomes. Because of a parallel reduction in the uptake of the marker by the liver and spleen, it was reasoned that extended circulation of small liposomes in the blood enabled them to undergo transcapillary passage and reach tumour cells. Richardson et al. (1977) using liposomes tagged with another label have recently obtained similar results in rats implanted with Walker 256 carcinoma. Concentration of the liposomal marker ^{111}In in tumour tissues (Dapergolas et al., 1976; Gregoriadis et al., 1977b) has now been confirmed by the scanning of whole animals. Figure 6 shows clearly that 48 hours after injection of liposomal [111]In (by which time there is no measurable radioactivity in the blood) there is accumulation of ^{111}In in the tumour area. This is compatible with passage of liposomes through membranes into the tumour mass. There are, however, at least three alternative explanations for such findings: as small liposomes circulate in the blood for longer periods of time, drug may be released slowly to reach the extravascular space more effectively. In addition, liposomes may interact in some way with the capillary walls without actually crossing them. Again, small liposomes by virtue of their longer survival would be more efficient in doing so. Finally, the possibility exists that liposomes are transported by macrophages which are knwon to infiltrate tumours. Therefore, further work is needed to demonstrate the actual presence of liposomes within tumour cells or, at least, to show beyond reasonable doubt that after injection of doubly labelled liposomes, the ratio of the two labels in the cells is similar to that in the injected preparation. In such a

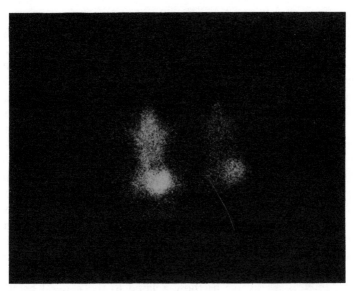

Figure 6 Scanning of tumour-bearing mice injected with free or liposome-entrapped ^{111}In-labelled bleomycin. Two Balb 'C' mice bearing Meth 'A' tumours in the thigh of the right leg were injected intravenously with ^{111}In-labelled bleomycin, free (right) or entrapped in small multilamellar liposomes composed of egg phosphatidylcholine, cholesterol and phosphatidic acid (molar ratio 7 : 5 : 1) (left). The mice were scanned 48 h after death and removal of all internal organs, using a Nuclear Chicago PhO/gamma IV H.P. gamma camera. The 247 keV peak of ^{111}In was selected with a 25% window and scintigrams with 2×10^5 counts were recorded on polaroid films. Radioactivity content per gram tumour tissue was 1.2 and 5.8% of the injected free and liposome-entrapped ^{111}In-labelled bleomycin respectively. Blood content of radioactivity in both mice (injected with equal amounts of ^{111}In) at the time of death was nil

case it would be essential to use markers that are retained quantitatively by the cells for 24–28 hours. By this time blood, which contaminates tumour tissue, should be practically free of circulating liposomes.

Preliminary work in Wistar rats bearing Novikoff hepatoma and injected with liposomes of reduced fluidity (egg phosphatidylcholine was replaced by dipalmitoyl phosphatidylcholine) or of positive charge showed no significant changes in the uptake of the marker by the tumour already observed with negatively charged egg phosphatidylcholine liposomes (Gregoriadis *et al.*, 1977b). In other experiments, however, after injection of mice bearing ADJ 3PC6 subcutaneous tumour with egg phosphatidylcholine liposomes, uptake of the entrapped *cis*-dichlorobiscyclopentylamine platinum (II) by the tumour was more than twice as much as that observed with dipalmitoyl phosphatidylcholine liposomes and fifteen fold greater than values obtained with the free drug (Deliconstantinos *et al*., 1977). Interestingly, the extent of liver participation in the uptake of the two liposomal drug preparations was reversed (Deliconstantinos *et al*., 1977).

Apparently localization of liposome-entrapped agents in the tumours of experimental animals led us to the testing of liposomal marker distribution in the tissues of cancer patients. The sonicated preparations used for injection (up to about 40 mg total lipid) were composed of dipalmitoyl phosphatidyl-choline or egg phosphatidylcholine, cholesterol and phosphatidic acid. They were given intra-arterially or intravenously and contained either ^{131}I-labelled human serum albumin (Gregoriadis *et al*., 1974b) or ^{111}In-labelled bleomycin (Segal *et al*., 1976). Assay of radioactivity in a variety of primary and secondary tumours revealed that a considerable proportion of the injected dose was taken up and is some cases uptake was superior to that seen in normal tissues harbouring the tumour. It is reasonable to assume that the extent of liposomal agent localization in tumours is influenced by blood supply, the capacity of tumour cells to endocytose and, perhaps, by the extent of macrophage accumulation in the malignant areas. Other parameters as diverse as those related to the general health of the patient (e.g. function of the reticuloendothelial system which would influence availability of liposomes in the periphery) and to the liposomal carrier itself (e.g. variations in size, composition, charge etc.) may also be important. Therefore, valid conclusions regarding the extent of liposome infiltration into the tumours of cancer patients cannot be drawn from these isolated studies. Recent attempts to visualize radioactivity in the tumours of cancer patients injected with ^{99m}Tc-containing liposomes have failed (Ryman *et al*., 1978). One of the explanations for tumour detection by scanning in animals (Figure 3 and Ryman *et al*., 1978) but not in man may be that the amount of radioactivity injected into patients, although sufficient for the imaging of the liver, is not nearly sufficient to allow similar imaging of small tumour tissues which are expected to concentrate the label to a lesser extent.

The mechanism by which liposomal cytotoxic agents act *in vivo* was studied in partially hepatectomized rats injected intravenously with liposomes containing actinomycin D in their lipid phase. It was found that inhibition of DNA directed RNA synthesis in the regenerating liver by the liposomal actinomycin D was as efficient as with similar amounts of the free drug. Because liposomal actinomycin D retains its association with the carrier in the blood (Gregoriadis, 1973), it was assumed that the drug entered hepatic cells by endocytosis. Indeed, subcellular fractionation of the liver at time intervals after treatment showed a gradual increase in the drug content of the lysosome-rich fraction which was paralleled by a similar increase in the nuclei-rich fraction. These results taken together with those from radioautographic studies in AKR-A mouse leukaemia cells exposed to a similar liposomal preparation of the drug (Gregoriadis and Neerunjun, 1975a) suggest that actinomycin D after its entrance into the lysosomes escapes to reach the cytoplasm and subsequently the nucleus where it exerts its effect. This lysosomotropic mechanism of drug action has also been suggested in the case of DNA-bound daunomycin which is taken up by endocytosis (de Duve *et al.*, 1974).

The proposition that liposomes may serve as suitable carriers of cytotoxic drugs in cancer chemotherapy (Gregoriadis, 1973) was soon tested in AKR mice inoculated intraperitoneally with AKR-A cells. Three to six days after inoculation, mice received repeatedly by the same route actinomycin D entrapped into the lipid phase of liposomes. Survival was increased from 9.7 days (buffer injected mice) to 16.1–18.5 days and it was greater than after treatment with similar doses of the free drug (Neerunjun and Gregoriadis, 1974; Gregoriadis and Neerunjun, 1975a). This extended survival was attributed to a reduced general toxicity resulting from the retention of the drug within the liposomal carrier in the peritoneal cavity or to an increased uptake of entrapped drug by the cells or both. Work with liposomal actinomycin D (entrapped in the aqueous phase) injected into CF1 mice gave similar results (Rahman *et al.*, 1974). Following these initial experiments on the chemotherapeutic efficacy of liposomal actinomycin D, other groups obtained comparable results in a variety of tumour-bearing animals. For instance, Mayhew *et al.* (1976), injected intraperitoneally DBA/2/HA male mice (1 day after their inoculation with L1210 cells) with liposome-entrapped 1-β-D-arabino-furanosylcytosine (ara-C) entrapped in small unilamellar liposomes. Mean survival was increased from 10.1 days (buffer injected mice) to 20.2 days with 10–20% of the animals surviving at 30 days. There was no increase in mean survival for mice treated with the free drug alone or with empty liposomes. The superior performance of the entrapped drug in inhibiting tumour growth was attributed to its increased uptake by cells (shown to occur *in vitro*) or to a slow release of the liposomal drug which would have allowed the cells to be exposed to cytotoxicity as they enter DNA synthesis, or both.

Kobayashi *et al.* (1975) who had already found a beneficial effect of liposomal ara-C in tumour-bearing mice did some further studies (Kobayashi *et al.*, 1977) in CD2F female mice inoculated intraperitoneally with L1210 cells. The animals were treated with various types of unsonicated liposomes containing ara-C and best results in terms of survival were obtained only when 1.6 g of the drug per kilogram body weight were given (60% survivors at 60 days with a mean survival of 27.4 days). Treatment of the mice by the subcutaneous or intravenous route also prolonged survival. The authors explained these results by assuming: (*a*) slow release of the drug from its carrier *in vivo* with most of the ara-C being protected from degradation by deoxycytidine deaminase; (*b*) extensive binding of the positively charged liposomes onto the negatively charged surface of the cells. The former assumption is supported by data from dialysis experiments (Kobayashi *et al.*, 1977). The latter is, however, rather weak since the positive charge on the surface of liposomes is expected to change *in vivo* into negative (Black and Gregoriadis, 1976).

While these results indicate that liposomal drugs can prolong the survival of mice with ascites tumours, the possibility exists that tumour cells which do not come in direct contact with liposomes (e.g. implanted tumours) may not be amenable to treatment. We tested this by using 6C3HED cells inoculated in C3H mice. 6C3HED cells depend for their growth on the exogenous supply of L-asparagine and in animal models administration of L-asparaginase is followed by low asparagine concentration in blood, rapid tumour regression, and complete cure. It is of interest that this form of treatment has met only with moderate success in the management of acute lymphocytic leukaemia (Capizzi *et al.*, 1970). In addition, long-term treatment is hampered by toxicity and by the development of anti-asparaginase antibodies which both inactivate the enzyme and provoke allergic reactions. C3H mice were inoculated into the interscapular area with 6C3HED cells and 7–9 days later were injected by various routes with Erwinia L-asparaginase, free or liposome-entrapped (Neerunjun and Gregoriadis, 1976). Results showed that in contrast to control mice which were injected with buffered saline and died in 17–34 days with grossly enlarged tumours, mice treated with free asparaginase (48 units) by the intravenous, intraperitoneal, intramuscular (hind leg) route and also by injecting into the tumour mass itself, were cured with their tumours being non-palpable within 1–2 days after treatment began. However, administration of 48 units of asparaginase entrapped in sonicated liposomes prolonged survival to only 27–40 days and complete tumour regression and cures were achieved only when 168 units of the enzyme were given by the intravenous (sonicated liposomes), by the intramuscular (unsonicated positive liposomes) route or by injecting directly into the tumour mass (unsonicated positive liposomes). With the last two injection schedules, results were probably due to the slow release of the enzyme from liposomes disrupted locally (Segal *et al.*, 1975). After injection of the tumour with sonicated liposomes which are known to diffuse rapidly from the injected area (Segal *et al.*, 1975) only 60% of the animals used were cured. Assay for asparaginase activity in the blood and tissues of intravenously injected tumour-bearing mice showed that, in contrast to the free enzyme, liposomal asparaginase was cleared from the circulation very rapidly and therefore long-term depletion of blood asparagine, believed to occur with the slowly disappearing free enzyme, could not account for the cures observed. However, the liver tissue (in which the bulk of asparagine is synthesized) contained much more of the administered enzyme than the liver of mice treated with free asparaginase and this may explain the mode of action of the liposomal enzyme. Interestingly, asparagine levels in the tumours 1, 3, and 24 hours after injection were lowest in mice receiving the entrapped enzyme (G. Gregoriadis, E. D. Neerunjun and H. E. Wade, unpublished data).

The reduced efficiency of liposomal asparaginase in curing 6C3HED tumour-bearing mice does not diminish its potential value in the therapy of acute lymphocytic leukaemia in man. Indeed, some of the toxic effects which prevent aggressive therapy with the free enzyme may be avoided or be less pronounced by the use of liposomal asparaginase. For instance, mice bearing tumours as above and preimmunized with asparaginase died of anaphylactic shock soon after intravenous injection with the free enzyme. Similar mice did not show signs of illness and were eventually cured after their treatment with the entrapped enzyme (Neerunjun and Gregoriadis, 1976), presumably because the lipid envelope of the carrier prevented its enzyme contents from interacting with anti-asparaginase antibodies in the blood.

Application of the liposomal system in animals bearing solid tumours is anticipated to be problematic since these, unlike ascites tumours in the peritoneal cavity, do not come into direct contact with liposomes circulating in the blood. Among the difficulties expected are interference by the liver and spleen and poor transport of liposomal drugs through the blood capillaries. As already mentioned these can be alleviated to some extent by using small liposomes which are known to circulate in the blood for longer periods of time. Although prolonged circulation of liposomes may help one way or another in localizing the carrier's contents in malignant tissues more efficiently, it may also lead to other undesirable events such as increased breakdown of the carrier in the circulation or its interaction with a variety of normal tissues. However, a compromise in terms of liposomal size and composition may enable liposomes to reach tumours more efficiently with the reticuloendothelial system serving as a sink for the excess. It is hoped that the fixed hepatic and splenic macrophages which are expected to take up much of the injected dose will be less vulnerable to cytotoxic drugs than other normal cells which are usually exposed to such drugs in conventional chemotherapy. With regard to targeting of liposomes through cytophilic ligands attached on the liposomal surface, this approach, although successful *in vitro*, is certain to meet with great difficulties *in vivo* (see later).

4.2.3. *Antimicrobial therapy*

The realization that liposomes are taken up avidly by the reticuloendothelial system prompted us to suggest their use in the treatment of certain parasitic diseases in which microbes reside within fixed macrophages (Gregoriadis, 1973). Thus, penicillin-containing liposomes were found to prolong the circulation of the drug in the blood and also alter its tissue distribution in that there was concentration of the drug in the fixed macrophages of the liver and spleen (Gregoriadis, 1973). In recent collaborative work with P. Bonventre, it was shown that dehydrostreptomycin which is unable to kill *Staphylococcus aureus* in the lysosomes of cultured macrophages, can do so when presented to the cells in the liposome form (Bonventre and Gregoriadis, 1978). It was assumed that the drug was delivered by the carrier into the cell lysosomes by endocytosis. In addition, this method of introducing the drug intracellularly may have diminished its inactivation in the lysosomal milieu (Tulken and Trouet, 1972).

The possibility of treating parasitic diseases with liposome-entrapped drugs has been greatly promoted recently by work performed in three different laboratories. Workers were able to apply the system in the treatment of visceral leishmaniasis in which the amastigote parasites reside chronically in vacuoles within the Kupffer cells of the liver causing visceral, mucocutaneous and cutaneous manifestations and, in the case of visceral disease, death. Antimonial and arsenical drugs used in the management of leishmaniasis are limited in effectiveness because of severe systemic toxicity.

Inoculation of C_{57}Black/Sn mice with *Leishmania donovani* and subsequent administration of liposome-entrapped sodium antimony gluconate reduced the number of parasites in the livers to a much greater extent (at best 200 times) than the free drug. Furthermore, doses of the entrapped drug which were ineffective when in the free form, cleared the livers completely and such improved action was concomitant to a more pronounced localization of the drug in the liver (Black *et al.*, 1977). New *et al.* (1978) obtained similar results in NMR1 mice inoculated intravenously with the same parasite and treated with liposomal antimonials. Furthermore, in golden hamsters injected by the cardiac route, liposomes improved the action of the antimonial drug by about 700 times with the death rate being virtually eliminated by a dose of 2.5 mg of the liposomal drug per kilogram body weight (Alving *et al.*, 1978). These workers found that a dose of 800 mg of the free drug per kilogram was required to reduce death rate with some of the mortality being probably associated with acute toxicity. Phosphatidylcholine liposomes with a positive charge were much less effective than similar liposomes bearing negative charge and, in general, negative liposomes composed of highly saturated long-chain phospholipids and cholesterol were more effective. This preliminary work on the potential of liposomes in the treatment of visceral leishmaniasis is most promising and toxicity studies in animals should establish whether the approach can be tested in patients.

Two other parasitic diseases which are possible candidates for treatment with liposomal drugs are trypanosomiasis and malaria. In both cases mass treatment is impractical because of the prolonged time required for therapy. In addition, drugs can be toxic and also ineffective often because of drug-resistance development. Again, it would be of interest to see whether liposomes given intravenously can help in speeding up therapy and in circumventing drug resistance, especially the type associated with changes in the permeability of cell membranes to drugs. In the case of trypanosomiasis, liposomes containing the appropriate drug should be capable of interacting with trypanosomes in intravascular, and to some extent extravascular, areas. Regarding malaria, liposomes may transport drugs to the liver and interfere with the parasite at its liver stage. In collaborative work with C. Vakirtzi-Lemonias we have found that the non-pathogenic insect trypanosome *Crithidia fasciculata* can take up *in vitro* considerable amounts of liposomes and their contents, mainly by endocytosis. With liposomes containing colchicine, such uptake was fifteen-fold greater than when the drug was presented to the cells in its free form (Vakirtzi-Lemonias and Gregoriadis, 1978). Work is needed to show whether pathogenic trypanosomes also interact with liposomes, especially in the presence of blood.

There are other bacterial, viral, and fungal infections of which treatment can be enhanced by the use of liposomes. These include brucellosis affecting livestock and humans, leprosy, trachoma, typhoid, and psittacosis as well as some viral infections associated with the herpes species. In brucellosis for instance, treatment requires daily oral administration of high doses of antibiotics over an extended period of time (e.g. 2 g daily for 28 days). Many antibiotics are not suitable for older patients or patients with renal disease and it may be that intravenously given liposomes will, by improving the uptake of the drug by phagocytic cells harbouring the micro-organisms, decrease both the course of treatment and the amount of drugs required.

4.2.4. Metal storage diseases

A major problem in treating metal storage diseases with chelating agents is poor penetration of the latter into cells. In many of these diseases metals accumulate intralysosomally. Because of their lysosomotropic action *in vivo* (Gregoriadis and Ryman, 1972a,b) liposomes qualify as a potential means of delivering metal chelators into the sites of storage. Indeed, Rahman and co-workers (this book) took advantage of this property of liposomes and showed that liposomal DTPA was capable of removing significant amounts of plutonium from the liver of mice loaded with the metal. The same group extended this approach to the elimination of mercury from the kidney and

c

Table 1 Fate of free and liposome-associated radiolabelled EDTA after injection into mice

Preparation	Time after injection (min)	Radioactivity (%)		
		Blood plasma	Liver	Spleen
A	15	4.3		
	30	1.5		
	60	0.3		
	210	0.0	0.1	0.0
B	15	46.6		
	30	37.6		
	60	28.6		
	210	11.0	4.8	1.2
C	20	20.0		
	38	17.9		
	120	14.6		
	270	9.5	41.6	4.6
D	15	62.5		
	37	53.2		
	120	38.0		
	282	24.2	17.0	4.3

T.O. mice were injected intravenously with ethylenediaminetetra ($2\text{-}^{14}C$) acetate (sodium salt) (labelled EDTA) free (A) or entrapped in liposomes composed of egg phosphatidylcholine, cholesterol and stearylamine (molar ratio 7:2:1) (B), with liposomes made of phosphatidyl-ethanolamine-labelled EDTA complex (C) and with the phosphatidylethanolamine-labelled EDTA complex incorporated into liposomes composed as in B (D). Animals were bled at time intervals and killed 210–282 min later. Radioactivity in blood plasma and tissues is expressed as % of the injected dose per ml of blood plasma or per whole organ. Each value is the mean from three mice. Liposomal entrapment for the labelled EDTA was 5.1%. Of the phosphatidyl-ethanolamine-labelled EDTA complex used 87.5 and 84.3% was incorporated in liposomes made in the absence or presence of other lipids respectively.

of colloidal gold through the faeces (Rahman and Rosenthal, 1973). In their more recent work, Rahman and co-workers used liposome-entrapped desferrioxamine which was localized in the liver and spleen more efficiently than the free drug (Guilmette *et al.*, 1978).

However, the actual amount of metal chelators which can be incorporated in liposomes is rather small and, in addition, a significant proportion of the entrapped material escapes from the carrier during its circulation in the blood. Obviously, this diminishes the transport efficiency of the carrier. In collaboration with R. Bulman we have recently investigated the possibility of both increasing entrapment of chelators in liposomes and also preventing their loss by diffusion through the lipid lamellae. ^{14}C-labelled EDTA-phosphatidylethanolamine was synthesized and used as such or in association with other lipids to prepare liposomes. Preliminary results in Table 1 show that most of the radioactive material used was incorporated in liposomes. After intravenous injection of either of the preparations, uptake of the label by the liver and spleen was much higher than when EDTA was given in its free form or after its entrapment in liposomes.

4.2.5. Adjuvant properties of liposomes in immunopotentiation

One of the reasons which prompted us to employ liposomes as enzyme carriers was the possibility of avoidance of immune reactions to the entrapped foreign enzyme. However, contrary to our expectations antibody titres after the injection of a liposomal protein were higher than when the protein was given as such. This finding was explored with A. C. Allison using as a model antigen diphtheria toxoid. It was hoped that this immunological property of liposomes could find application in animal and human vaccination programmes where there is a real need for an effective and safe adjuvant. Present adjuvants, although numerous, are by and large unacceptable because of their side effects and even those licensed for use in humans are far from ideal (World Health Organization, 1976). We found that antibody response in mice challenged by the intramuscular or intravenous route with diphtheria toxoid entrapped in liposomes composed of egg phosphatidylcholine, cholesterol, and dicetyl phosphate was much greater than when similar amounts of the free antigen were given (Allison and Gregoriadis, 1974). The presence of dicetyl phosphate in liposomes appeared to contribute to their adjuvant properties since its absence (Kotani *et al.*, 1977) or replacement by phosphatidic acid (Allison and Gregoriadis, 1974) reduced the adjuvant effect. In other studies, however, the immunogenicity of liposomal DNP-Cap-PE (N-2,4,dinitrophenyl-ε-aminocaproyl derivative of phosphatidylethanolamine), although influenced by the nature of phospholipids (e.g. saturation of acyl chains), did not depend on the presence of dicetyl phosphate, stearylamine or cholesterol in the liposomal structure (Dansey *et al.*, 1978).

We found, in addition, that when the adjuvants *Mycobacterium tuberculosis, Bordetella pertussis*, and saponin, were mixed with liposomal diphtheria toxoid prior to immunization, they acted synergistically and antibody response was even greater. In contrast to other adjuvants (e.g. Freund's adjuvant) no granulomas were formed at the sites of injection (Allison and Gregoriadis, 1976). A further advantage in the use of liposomes as an immunological adjuvant is the avoidance of hypersensitivity reactions to the entrapped antigen (Gregoriadis and Allison, 1974). Similar results were obtained with liposome-associated

Table 2 Antibody response to Port Chalmers influenza virus split products (haemagglutinin and neuraminidase)

Preparation	Antibody response ($\log_2$ IH titre)				
	Primary	Significance	Secondary	Significance	
A	0.0	A vs B, C, D, E; P < 0.05	8.8	A vs B, C, D, E; P < 0.05	
B	1.1		13.7		
C	2.3	C vs A, B, D, E; P < 0.05	24.1	C vs B, D, E; P < 0.001	
D	0.6		11.6		
E	0.6		12.1		

Guinea pigs were divided in groups of five and injected intramuscularly with 100 units of free antigen (A), liposome-entrapped (B), B mixed with 0.5 mg BCG (C), A mixed with BCG (D) and antigen adsorbed on alum (E). Animals were bled 2 weeks later, immunized again as above and bled after 2 weeks. Antigen mixed with tracer ^{125}I-labelled antigen was entrapped in liposomes composed of egg phosphatidylcholine, cholesterol, and dicetyl phosphate (7:2:1 molar ratio). After sonication for 45 s entrapped antigen was separated from the free antigen by molecular sieve chromatography (Gregoriadis, 1976c).

influenza virus neuraminidase and haemagglutinin injected intramuscularly into guinea pigs with and without other adjuvants (Table 2). In this respect, it is interesting that influenza virus subunits associate with liposomes to form virus-like structures named virosomes (Almeida *et al.*, 1975). In recent work from this laboratory it was shown that hepatitis B virus surface antigen (HB$_s$Ag) can be incorporated into large multilamellar liposomes composed of egg phosphatidylcholine and cholesterol with or without dicetyl phosphate or stearylamine. Some of the incorporated antigen was available on the liposomal surface since it was capable of interacting with anti-HB$_s$ antibodies (Manesis *et al.*, 1978). Furthermore, in immunization experiments with guinea pigs, antibody titres in animals injected subcutaneously with HB$_s$Ag incorporated in negatively charged liposomes were, at the end of 50 days, about 750 times greater than those obtained with similar amounts of the free antigen (Figure 7). Delayed hypersensitivity skin tests in these animals showed that immune response was cell-mediated as well (Manesis *et al.*, 1979).

The immunological adjuvant property of liposomes has now been confirmed in other laboratories using a variety of antigens ranging from albumin (Heath *et al.*, 1976; van Rooijen and van Nieuwmegen, 1977) to Semliki Forest virus spike glycoproteins (Morein *et al.*, 1978) and *Plasmodium falciparum* mature segmenters [which were mixed with liposomes and 6-*O*-stearoyl-*N*-acetyl muramyl-L-alanyl-D-isoglutamine (Siddiqui *et al.*, 1978)]. In the two latter cases immunization of Balb C mice and of owl monkeys with the respective preparations protected the animals after exposure to Semliki Forest virus and to *Plasmodium*

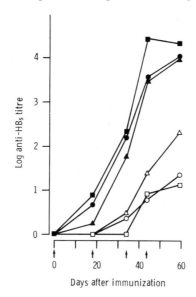

Days after immunization

Figure 7 Rise of anti-HB$_s$ titres in guinea pigs immunized with HB$_s$Ag. Outbred guinea pigs were treated (arrows) on day 0, 18, 34 and 44 with free HB$_s$Ag alone (○) or mixed with saponin (△) or *Bordetella pertussis* (□) and with liposomal HB$_s$Ag alone (●) or mixed with saponin (▲) or *B. pertussis* (■). Each does (0.6 ml) given subcutaneously in both hind limbs contained 1.4 μg free or liposomal (0.8 mg lipid) HB$_s$Ag and when appropriate, 1.2 × 10^{10} bacteria or 50 μg saponin. The animals were bled by cardiac puncture on day 18, 34, 44 and 59. Four animals died during sampling (from Manesis *et al.*, 1979)

falciparum. Immunopotentation via liposomes has also found application in tumour rejection (Huet and Ansel, 1977). These workers observed that after the incorporation into liposomes of a glycolipid extract from vesicular stomatitis virus grown on cell lines which contained the SV40 tumour-specific transplantation antigens, the preparation could induce tumour rejection or reduce its growth in hamsters challenged with such cells.

4.2.6. *Liposomes as carriers of orally given drugs*

There are many instances in medicine where administration of drugs by the oral route is advantageous not only for convenience but also because it is often preferable that drugs enter the periphery via the portal circulation. However, many drugs are either unabsorbable by the gut or are unstable in its environment. In our initial work, the possibility of employing liposomes for the oral administration of drugs was investigated with the polymer polyvinylpyrrolidone (PVP) serving as a model drug. PVP, when given orally, is totally unabsorbable and is excreted quantitatively in the faeces. In experiments in which rats were given intragastrically ^{125}I-labelled PVP entrapped in liposomes composed of egg phosphatidylcholine, cholesterol, and phosphatidic acid, there was only a small decrease of PVP excretion into the faeces and a slight (but significant) increase of PVP uptake by the liver and spleen (Dapergolas *et al.*, 1976).

The first report on the oral administration of liposomal insulin was a patent (Bayer, 1974) claiming that hypoglycaemic shock could be induced in mice treated intragastrically with an unknown amount of insulin entrapped in liposomes made of phosphatidylinositol. Our efforts to duplicate these results with similar liposomes failed and it was only possible to moderately reduce glucose levels in the blood of rats fed *ad libitum* (Dapergolas *et al.*, 1976). A similar reduction was obtained when insulin (35 units per rat) was substituted with glucose oxidase (Dapergolas *et al.*, 1976). However, there was no effect when phosphatidylinositol, as the lipid component of liposomes, was replaced with egg phosphatidylcholine, cholesterol, and phosphatidic acid. Promising results in terms of glucose reduction were obtained by other workers (Patel and Ryman, 1976) with even less insulin (5 units) entrapped in liposomes composed of egg phosphatidylcholine, cholesterol, and dicetyl phosphate.

Meanwhile it was reasoned that appropriate changes in the composition of insulin-containing liposomes could render liposomes more resistant to phospholipase and detergent attack in the gut thus allowing a more efficient transport of liposomal insulin into the periphery. The use of certain semi-synthetic phospholipids (which at the temperature of the body are more resistant to pancreatic phospholipases or to detergents) in preparing liposomes enabled us to reduce considerably blood glucose levels in diabetic (e.g. at 4 hours down to 37% of the levels before treatment using as little as 0.3 units of insulin per rat) and to some extent in normal rats. The effect was obvious as soon as 1 hour after intragastric administration and with some lipid compositions it was still measurable 24 hours later (Dapergolas and Gregoriadis, 1976 and 1977). Radioimmuno-assay of insulin in the blood of treated normal rats showed that the liposomal hormone was transported into the periphery in a form which could be measured fully only in the presence of Triton X-100 (Table 3). While these results suggest that part of the liposomal immunoreactive insulin was unavailable to its antibodies they do not necessarily prove that insulin is transferred in the blood within intact liposomes. It could be that a phospholipid–hormone complex is formed which can interact efficiently with anti-insulin antibodies only in the presence of detergent. Harding *et al.* (1978) introduced into the upper part of the small bowel of normal volunteers insulin entrapped in egg phosphatidylcholine-cholesterol liposomes. Although a 'small' rise in immunoreactive insulin was evident in serial blood samples, there was no significant decrease in blood glucose.

Table 3. Serum insulin in rats treated intragastrically with free or liposome-entrapped insulin

| | Insulin (μ units per ml serum $\pm$ S.E.) | | |
| | | After treatment | |
Experiment	Before treatment (pooled groups)	Free insulin	Liposomal insulin
1	73 ± 14 (10)	67 ± 7 (5) N.S.	290 ± 99 (5) $P < 0.05$
2	70 ± 21 (15)	48 ± 15 (5) N.S.	524 ± 284 (5) $P < 0.02$

Rats were given intragastrically 1.3 units of insulin, free or entrapped in liposomes composed of dipalmitoylphosphatidylcholine and cholesterol (molar ratio 7:2). Insulin in the liposomal preparation or in the blood of the animals 4 h after treatment was measured by a radioimmunoassay method in the presence of Triton X-100 to ensure availability of the hormone to its antibodies. In brief, to 0.1 ml of the appropriately diluted liposomal or serum sample, $10\,\mu l$ of 5% Triton X-100 was added (final concentration 0.5%) and the solution (0.11 ml) was then diluted with the RIA kit 'buffer' using 0.05 or 0.1 ml. RIA values were deduced from a standard curve (bovine or human insulin) made in the presence of Triton X-100 (10 μl of 5.0% Triton was added to each of the 0.1 ml insulin standards).

Numbers in parentheses denote animals used. Student's paired- t-test (modified from Dapergolas and Gregoriadis, 1976).

It is not known at present to what extent intragastrically given liposomal insulin survives in the gut and enters the periphery. Patel and Ryman (1977) administered liposome-entrapped ^{125}I-labelled insulin and found that by 15 minutes most of the radioactivity in the stomach was still associated with liposomes. There was no evidence to suggest that the hormonal activity was preserved to the same extent. Studies by Richards and Gardner (1978) have shown recently that the integrity of liposomes exposed *in vitro* at 37 °C to gut bile salts, sodium taurocholate and sodium glycocholate, is dependant on their phospholipid component. When liposomes were made of phospholipids with phase transition temperatures above 37 °C, integrity was retained to a greater degree. These findings are in agreement with our proposition (Dapergolas and Gregoriadis, 1976 and 1977) that the greater efficiency of orally given insulin incorporated in dipalmitoyl or distearoyl phosphatidylcholine is the result of more prolonged survival of such liposomes in the gut. The absorption of liposomal insulin by the gut has not as yet been studied systematically. In work with normal rats which received intragastrically insulin entrapped in dipalmitoyl phosphatidylcholine-cholesterol liposomes (Table 3), the total amount of immunoreactive insulin in the blood 4 hours after treatment was estimated as 0.25% of the total dose (1 unit) (Dapergolas and Gregoriadis, 1976). On the other hand, Harding *et al.* (1978) in the experiments discussed above estimated that about 1% of the immunoreactive insulin appeared in the blood of the volunteers 1 hour after treatment. However, to measure overall absorption of the liposomal hormone, the rate of its elimination from the circulation must first be determined.

The fashion by which liposomal insulin enters the periphery is still unknown. From data with liposomal ^{125}I-labelled PVP (Dapergolas et al., 1976) and radiolabelled tubocurarine (Dapergolas and Gregoriadis, 1977) it appears that most of the administered dose escapes into the faeces. It does, however, seem that liposomes contribute to the transport of agents which are normally unabsorbable into the blood and support for findings *in vivo* (Dapergolas and Gregoriadis, 1976; Harding et al., 1978) come from *in vitro* work which suggests that uptake of liposomal ^{125}I-labelled PVP by the intestinal epithelium cells is probably mediated by endocytosis and is greater than when free PVP is used (Bridges et al., 1978). In these experiments liposomes were made of dipalmitoyl phosphatidylcholine and dipalmitoyl phosphatidic acid and, as with *in vivo* work (Dapergolas and Gregoriadis, 1976), it may be that appropriate lipid composition and perhaps size of liposomes are prerequisites for enhanced absorption. It seems, however, that quantitative transport of insulin into the blood will require a more radical modification of the system. This is now being attempted in this laboratory by the use of liposoluble derivatives of insulin incorporated into liposomes.

4.2.7. Direction of liposomes to target sites

Numerous studies have established that unmodified liposomes present in the blood circulation show a preference for the cells of the reticuloendothelial system, mainly the Kupffer cells of the liver and the macrophages of the spleen. As already discussed, such uptake can be modified by adjusting liposomal size, surface charge, and composition. Obviously, with the treatment of diseases in which these tissues are involved, such preference can find good use. On the other hand, there are several instances in medicine in which uptake of liposomes by alternative targets is desired and therefore some versatility of the liposomal carrier in terms of tissue distribution is required. This would not necessarily imply complete avoidance of non-target areas, especially in cases where drugs can be tolerated by such areas. For instance, in the treatment of enzyme deficiencies with exogenous enzymes and of microbial diseases with certain antibiotics, participation of non-diseased cells is unlikely to be detrimental to their well-being. With cytotoxic drugs, however, selective uptake by target cells would be essential for successful targeting, unless drugs used can be either tolerated or inactivated by normal tissues.

In designing liposomes which can recognize target areas one should not only consider modification of variables pertaining to the carrier itself (e.g. size, surface charge, fluidity, surface groups) but also parameters related to the host and which are known to influence liposome–target interaction. The latter have been tentatively classified (Gregoriadis, 1978a) into two categories, namely parameters related either to the biological space travelled by the carrier (e.g. blood, various membrane barriers) or to the target itself (e.g. molecular weight, cell membrane composition and fluidity, receptors, endocytic capacity etc.). Examination of all such factors may help in rationalizing targeting and in designing the overall carrier unit. There are several instances which suggest that a simple modification of the liposomal carrier may be sufficient for its effective localization in areas in need of treatment. Caride and Zaret (1977), for instance, found thay by imposing a positive or negative charge on the surface of ^{99m}Tc-containing liposomes, there was a greater degree of radioactivity localization in infarcted myocardial regions of injected dogs. As already discussed, in treating diabetic rats intragastrically with liposomal insulin, the choice of phospholipids has helped in improving the biological effect of the hormone, apparently because of the extended survival of the carrier in the gut (Dapergolas and Gregoriadis, 1976 and 1977). A good example of modifying the non-target environment so as to improve localization of liposomal agents in areas in need of treatment is the concurrent administration of excess 'empty' large liposomes with smaller drug-carrying liposomes. Because large liposomes compete successfully for the liver (Gregoriadis and Neerunjun, 1974; Caride *et al.*, 1976) with small liposomes, the latter circulate in the blood for longer periods of time and can thus penetrate less accessible areas in the body. For instance, in experiments with tumour-bearing mice large liposomes, by virtue of their preferential uptake by the liver and spleen, allowed small liposomes to localize their drug content in tumour tissues (Gregoriadis *et al.*, 1977b).

It is expected that such modifications of the liposomal carrier or, when possible, of the biological environment will optimize drug action in a variety of situations. However, there may be instances where a more sophisticated approach in achieving selectivity will be needed. An obvious way to render liposomes specific for their target (e.g. cells) is to modify their surface so that a specific interaction between liposomes and target can occur. Towards this end we proposed (Gregoriadis, 1974a) coating of the liposomal surface with molecules possessing a specific affinity for the target. It was anticipated that such molecules would, by attaching themselves onto the relevant receptors on the target, mediate association of the liposomal moiety (and its active contents) with the target. This idea was tested (Gregoriadis, 1974a; Gregoriadis, 1975a; Gregoriadis and Neerunjun, 1975b; Gregoriadis *et al.*, 1977b) using antibodies raised against a variety of tumours and also desialylated fetuin which along with other desialylated glycoproteins (Gregoriadis, 1975b) exhibits a selective affinity for the hepatic parenchymal cells. Both antibodies and desialylated fetuin were associated with liposomes in a way that the Fab region of the former and terminal galactose molecules of the latter responsible for cell recognition became available on the liposomal surface. Initially (Gregoriadis, 1974a), this was achieved by cross-linking cytophilic proteins with portions of a protein which, although entrapped, was to some degree available on the liposomal surface. Subsequently we found (Gregoriadis and Neerunjun, 1975b; Gregoriadis, 1975a; Gregoriadis *et al.*, 1977b) that by following the classical procedure of solute entrapment, it was possible to incorporate into liposomes immunoglobulin molecules which in their liposomal form were still capable of interacting with their antigens. This property was abolished by papain (which splits immunoglobulins to the Fab and Fc fragments) implying that the antigen-recognizing Fab regions were available on the liposomal surface (Gregoriadis *et al.*, 1977b). The same seemed true for the liposomal fetuin since there was some release of *N*-acetyl-neuraminic acid upon treatment with neuraminidase (Gregoriadis and Neerunjun, 1975b).

Using these preparations (made to contain, in addition to the 'homing' proteins, an antitumour drug) we found that the receptor recognizing groups on the surface of liposomes were capable of mediating uptake of the liposomal moiety and its drug contents by the respective receptor-carrying targets (i.e. tumour cells *in vitro* and hepatic parenchymal cells *in vivo*). Our efforts to apply immunoglobulin-coated liposomes *in vivo* was, however, less successful as antibodies raised against a variety of mouse tumour cell antigens, also shared by the liver and spleen cells, were apparently 'targeting' liposomes to these cells as well (Gregoriadis *et al.*, 1977b). It therefore seems that unless antibodies are raised against purified tumour specific antigens (when these are available), immune sera must be absorbed with normal tissues prior to use.

Other approaches for targeting include coating liposomes with isologous aggregated immunoglobulins. These were found to mediate through their Fc regions association of horseradish peroxidase and hexosaminidase A (also entrapped in liposomes) with phagocytes from *Mustelus canis* and from a Tay–Sachs' disease patient respectively (Weissmann *et al.*, 1975; Cohen *et al.*, 1976). Juliano and Stamp (1976) incorporated into the liposome structure a sialoglycoprotein extracted from the membrane of erythrocytes on to which the protein could, in the presence of lectin, facilitate binding of the liposomal moiety. On the other hand, Surolia and Bachhawat (1977) used GM_1 ganglioside, which is believed to bind selectively to the hepatic parenchymal cells, as a homing device on the surface of liposomes. This glycolipid was found to mediate uptake of the contents of the associated liposomes by the target cells *in vivo*. Furthermore, in a recent report Magee *et al.* (1978) were able to apply *in vitro* the principle of antibody-mediated selective binding of liposomes to cells. They showed that liposomes containing anti-line 10 hepatocarcinoma cells immune RNA and coated with anti-lymphocyte antibodies could stimulate the cytotoxicity of lymphocytes specifically against the line 10 tumour cells. In addition, actinomycin-D-containing liposomes coated with antibodies raised against line 10 hepatocarcinoma cells, were highly cytotoxic to such cells. However, the work of Weinstein *et al.* (1978) suggests that in certain cases selective uptake of liposomes by cells may not be followed by interiorization of the carrier. In experiments with lymphocytes exposed to liposomes tailored to bind on to such cells selectively, no intracellular transfer of the liposomal contents could be detected.

5. COMMENTS ON THE TOXICITY OF LIPOSOMES

As with conventional drug therapy, gains achieved from the use of the liposomal drug carrier can be jeopardized by toxic effects. These can originate from liposomes themselves, from the active agent they contain or by synergistic action of the carrier and its contents. Because of the versatility of liposomes in possible medical uses toxicity must be seen as relative to a given situation. Obviously, acceptance of a liposomal preparation for clinical use will eventually depend on whether the overall effect is favourable to the patient.

The liposomal carrier can be toxic in various ways. To begin with, adverse reactions may occur simply as a result of certain structural features. For instance, liposomes above a certain size may block lung capillaries (Rahman *et al.*, 1974b) and a positively charged surface may 'bind out' circulating α_2-macroglobulin (Black and Gregoriadis, 1976), an event which would upset coagulation. However, our experience with a patient who was recently injected intravenously with about 100 mg lipid in the form of negatively charged lipsomes argues against such a decrease in α_2-macroglobulin levels for up to 3 days after treatment (Gregoriadis *et al.*, 1979). Another case of potential liposomal toxicity was observed by Chen and Keenan (1977) who found that egg phosphatidylcholine liposomes inhibit lymphocyte activation by attracting, and thus reducing levels of, cellular cholesterol.

Lipid components of liposomes may be toxic either directly or because of metabolic changes they induce. Thus, direct *in vivo* toxicity in the form of epileptic seizures or cerebral tissue necrosis has been observed (Adams *et al.*, 1977) after the intracerebral injection into mice of large amounts of liposomes containing dicetyl phosphate or stearylamine (250 to 500 mg lipid per kilogram body weight). However, it is very unlikely that a need for such treatment will ever arise in man. Furthermore, other workers found that long-term intraperitoneal treatment of mice with stearylamine-containing liposomes (150–300 mg/kg body weight) was not toxic (Kimelberg and Mayhew, 1978; Mayhew *et al.*, 1976). Early in our involvement with liposomes we established that the type of liposomes (egg lecithin, cholesterol, and phosphatidic acid in a molar ration of 7 : 2 : 1) we most frequently used were not toxic in rats. Animals received intravenously such liposomes for several months, the total amount of lipid given per rat being about 0.7 g, and histology of a large number of tissues showed no changes (C. D. V. Black and G. Gregoriadis, unpublished data). Nattermann Chemie in Germany (Gregoriadis, 1978a) have carried out recently systematic studies on liposomal toxicity. Rats and beagle dogs received intravenously on a daily basis sonicated soya phosphatidylcholine for several weeks and results on behavioural changes, urine biochemistry, and histology were negative. A variety of blood tests were also normal except that some transient increases in total fat, phospholipid, and free cholesterol were observed in rats receiving 1 g lipid per kilogram body weight.

6.   PERSPECTIVES

Only a few years have elapsed since the use of liposomes as membrane models was extended to that of a drug carrier and during this time liposomes became an important experimental tool. Their popularity in research is based on two attractive features of the system, namely similarity to natural membranes and versatility. Although the former is a characteristic shared by other drug carriers as well (e.g. erythrocytes, neutrophils, hepatocytes etc.; see Drug Carriers in Biology and Medicine, 1979), the latter is unique to liposomes. Owing to their (semisynthetic) nature, these can vary widely in size, surface characteristics, and composition and can be made to accommodate a remarkable array of pharmacologically active substances including antitumour and antimicrobial drugs, enzymes, hormones, and vaccines. Indeed, the long list of drugs which in one way or another have been associated with liposomes (Table 4), underlines the vast amount of work already carried out in search of potential uses. However, in spite of the many avenues which have been opened, knowledge on how liposomes interact with the biological environment is relatively poor. I am tempted to attribute this to the enthusiasm which prevailed in making new discoveries. As the dust is now settling and difficulties in exploiting such discoveries are mounting, more and more researchers are engaged with the intricate aspects of the interaction of liposomes with cells at the molecular level.

Regarding the liposomal carrier itself, it is perhaps correct to say that up to recently its use in terms of lipid composition, size, charge, etc. was almost random (see Table 4). However this is now being slowly replaced

Table 4 Substances incorporated into liposomes

Substance	Liposomal lipids	Reference
PROTEINS (ENZYMES, HORMONES ETC.)		
Lysodeictus lysozyme	7PC, 1CHOL, 2DCP 7PC, 1CHOL, 2SA	Sessa and Weissmann, 1970
Aspergillus niger amyloglucosidase	7PC, 2CHOL, 1DCP	Rat; Gregoriadis and Ryman (1972a), Fibroblast; Roerdink et al. (1976)
Yeast invertase	7PC, 2CHOL, 1PA	Man; Tyrrell et al. (1976a)
	7PC, 2CHOL, 1PA	Rat; Gregoriadis and Ryman (1972b)
		Macrophage, fibroblast; Gregoriadis and Buckland (1973)
	9PC, 3CHOL 9PC, 3CHOL, 1G 9PC, 3CHOL, 1 asialo G 9PC, 3CHOL, 1DCP 9PC, 3CHOL, 1PA	Rat; Surolia and Bachhawat (1977)
	7PC, 2CHOL, 1PA	Rat; Gregoriadis et al. (1974a)
Clostridium perfringens neuraminidase	7PC, 2CHOL, 1PA	
Dextranase	7PC, 2CHOL, 1PA	Rat; Colley and Ryman (1976)
Jack bean α-mannosidase	7PC, 2CHOL, 1PA	Rat; Patel and Ryman (1974)
Bacillus subtilis α-amylase	DPPC	Amoeba; Batzri and Korn (1975)
Horseradish peroxidase	7PC, 2CHOL, 1PA	Rat; Wisse et al. (1976)
	3SPH, 1.1CHOL, 1SA	HeLa cell; Magee et al. (1974)
	7PC, 1CHOL, 2DCP	Phagocyte; Weissmann et al. (1975)
	9PC, 1CHOL	Diploid human lymphoid cells; Weissmann et al. (1977)
	7PC, 2DCP, 1CHOL PC	Mouse; Morein et al. (1978)
Semliki Forest virus glycoproteins		
Influenza virus haemagglutinin and neuraminidase	9PC, 1DCP	Almeida et al. (1975)
Sendai virus spike proteins	4.1PC, 1CHOL	Mouse leukaemia cells; Uchida et al. (1979)
	7PC, 2CHOL, 1PA	Mouse; Neerunjun and Gregoriadis (1976)
Erwinia asparaginase	7PC, 2CHOL, 1SA	

Table 4 (Continued)

Substance	Liposomal lipids	Reference
Escherichia coli asparaginase	10PC, 2CHOL, 1DCP	Fishman and Citri (1975)
Glucose oxidase	PI	Rat; Dapergolas *et al.* (1976)
	7PC, 2CHOL, 1PA	
	7PC, 2CHOL, 1SA	
	PC, CHOL, SA	Solomon and Miller (1976)
	(various ratios)	
D-amino acid oxidase	PC	Naoi *et al.* (1977)
	PC, CHOL (various ratios)	
	1PC, 1PE	
	1PC, 1PS	
	1PC, 1DPPC	
	1PC, 1LPC	
	1PC, 0.2PA	
	1PC, 1DCP	
	1PC, 0.2SA	
	0.7PC, 0.2CHOL, 0.1SA	
	1PC, 1TL	
	1PC, 1TS	
L-amino acid oxidase	7DPPC, 2CHOL, 1PA	Fibroblast; de Brohun-Butler *et al.* (1978)
Urease	26PC, 6CHOL, 1DCP	Madeira (1977)
Catalase	7DPPC, 2CHOL, 1PA	Fibroblast; de Brohun-Butler *et al.* (1978)
Human glucocerebroside:β-	7PC, 2CHOL	Man; Belchetz *et al.* (1977), Braidman
glucosidase	7PC, 2CHOL, 1PA	and Gregoriadis (1977)
	7PC, 2CHOL, 2PA	
	7PC, 2CHOL, 4PA	
	7PC, 2CHOL, 1DCP	
	7PC, 2CHOL, 1SA	
Human hexosaminidase A	7PC, 1CHOL, 2DCP	Phagocyte; Cohen *et al.* (1976)
Feline β-galactosidase	7PC, 1CHOL, 2DCP	Feline fibroblasts; Reynolds *et al.* (1978)
Pseudomonas cytochrome oxidase	Crude soybean phospholipids	Saraste (1978)

Protein	Lipid composition	Reference
Cytochrome oxidase	1PE, 1PC, 0.15CL, 0.25LPC	Eytan et al. (1975)
$(Mg^{2+} + Ca^{2+})$-ATPase	DMPC	Kleeman and McConnell (1976)
	1DMPC, 1DPPC	
	9DMPC, 1CHOL	
	8DMPC, 2CHOL	
Bovine β-glucuronidase	7DPPC, 2CHOL, 1PA	Mouse; Steger and Desnick (1977)
	8DPPC, 2CHOL	
	6.5DPPC, 2CHOL, 0.5PA	
	7DPPC, 2CHOL, 1SA	
Creatinine phosphokinase	7PC, 1CHOL, 2SA	Davidenkova et al. (1977)
Bovine carbonic anhydrase	7DPPC, 2CHOL, 1PA	Mouse; Sengupta and Rous (1978)
Albumin	7PC, 2CHOL	Rat; Gregoriadis and Neerunjun (1974)
	7PC, 2CHOL, 1DCP	
	7PC, 2CHOL, 1PA	
	7PC, 2CHOL, 1G	
	7PC, 2CHOL, 1SA	
	7PC, 2CHOL, 1DCP	Gregoriadis et al. (1971)
	7PC, 2CHOL, 1PA	Rat; Segal et al. (1975)
	7PC, 2CHOL, 1SA	Rat; Gregoriadis (1973)
	7DPPC, 2CHOL, 1PA	Man; Gregoriadis et al. (1974b)
	9PC, 1DCP	Heath et al. (1976)
	6PC, 6CHOL, 2DCP	
	8PC, 2CHOL, 1DCP	
	PC	
	6PC, 3PE, 1DCP	
	9PC, 1DCP	
	9PC, 1PS	
	9PC, 1PA	
	9PC, 1SA	
	9SPH, 1DCP	

Table 4 (Continued)

Substance	Liposomal lipids	Reference
	7PC, 2CHOL, 1PA	Rabbit; van Rooijen and van Nieuwmegen (1977)
	7PC, 2CHOL, 1DCP	Parenchymal cells (rat liver); Hoekstra et al. (1978)
	7PC, 2CHOL	*Crithidia fasciculata*; Vakirtzi-Lemonias and
	7PC, 2CHOL, 1PA	Gregoriadis (1978)
	7PC, 2CHOL, 1SA	
Soya bean trypsin inhibitor	7PC, 1CHOL, 2DCP	Finkelstein et al. (1978)
α_1-antitrypsin	7PC, 1CHOL, 2DCP	Finkelstein et al. (1978)
α-chymotrypsin	7PC, 2CHOL, 1DPPE	Torchilin et al. (1978)
Halobacterium halobium	PC	Labelle and Racker (1977)
S_9 bacteriothodopsin	DMPC	
	DPPC	
	Heart plasmalogen	
	Crude soybean	
	phospholipid	
	Dihexadryl PC and dimyristoyl	
	PE with cholesterol at various	
	ratios	
Interferon	7PC, 1CHOL, 2SA	L$_{929}$ cell; La Bonnardiere (1977)
	7PC, 1CHOL, 2DCP	
Glycolipid extract from vesicular	1.3PC, 3SPH, 5.1CHOL	Hamster; Huet and Ansell (1977)
stomatitis virus		
Ferritin	7PC, 1CHOL, 2DCP	Macrophage; Wiktorowicz et al. (1977)
Diphtheria toxoid	7PC, 2CHOL, 1DCP	Mouse; Gregoriadis and Allison (1974)
	7PC, 2CHOL, 1PA	Allison and Gregoriadis (1974),
	7PC, 2CHOL, 1SA	Allison and Gregoriadis (1976)

Fragment A diphtheria toxin	4.1PC, 1CHOL	Mouse leukaemia cells; Uchida et al. (1979)
Fetuin, desialylated fetuin	7PC, 2CHOL, 1PA	Rat; Gregoriadis (1974a)
		Gregoriadis and Neerunjun (1975b)
Ricinus communis lectin	2DPPC, 1CHOL, 0.04–0.2G	Surolia et al. (1975)
Erythrocyte major sialoglycoprotein	2PC, 1CHOL	Erythrocyte; Juliano and Stamp (1976)
Thyroglobulin	7PC, 1CHOL, 2DCP	Thyroidal lysosome; Kawada et al. (1974), Kawada et al. (1976)
Insulin	PI	Rat; Dapergolas et al. (1976), Mouse; Bayer (1974)
	7PC, 2CHOL, 1PA	Rat; Dapergolas et al. (1976)
	7PC, 2CHOL, 1SA	
	10PC, 2CHOL, 1DCP	Rat; Patel and Ryman (1976)
	3PC, 9CHOL, 1DCP	Rat; Tanaka et al. (1975)
	7PC, 2CHOL	Rat; Dapergolas and Gregoriadis (1976)
	7DPPC, 2CHOL	
	7DPPC, 2CHOL, 1G	
	7PC, 2CHOL	Rat; Dapergolas and Gregoriadis (1977)
	7DOPC, 2CHOL	
	7DSPC, 2CHOL	
	7DPPC, 2CHOL	
	7DMPC, 2CHOL	
	7DLPC, 2CHOL	
	10PC, 2CHOL, 1DCP	Rat; Patel and Ryman (1977)
	10PC, 2CHOL	Man; Harding et al. (1978)
		Mouse; Dunnick et al. (1976a)
Thyrotropin	44DPPC, 4G	
	44DPPC, 33CHOL, 4G	
Cytochrome c	1PC, 1PE	Papahadjopoulos and Miller (1967)
Staphyloccoccal α-toxin	7PC, 1CHOL, 2DCP	Freer et al. (1968)
IgG immunoglobulin	7PC, 2CHOL, 1PA	HeLa cell, AKR-A cell, fibroblast; Gregoriadis and Neerunjun (1975b)
Anti-fibroblast, anti-HeLa cell, anti-AKR-A cell		
Anti-Meth 'A' cell, anti-6C3HED cell	7PC, 2CHOL, 1PA	Mouse Meth 'A' cell, 6C3HED cell; Gregoriadis et al. (1977b)

Table 4 (Continued)

Substance	Liposomal lipids	Reference
Anti-thyroglobulin	11PC, 3.7PE, 1G	Mouse; Dunnick et al. (1975)
	DPPC	
Anti-lymphocyte	44DPPC, 33CHOL	Mouse; Dunnick et al. (1976a)
Anti-coxsackie A-21 virus	2.6SPH, 0.9CHOL, 1SA	Lymphocyte; Magee et al. (1978)
Anti-α-glucosidase	2SPH, 1.5CHOL, 0.66DCP	ML cell; Magee and Miller (1972)
	4PC, 2CHOL, 1DCP	Rat, mouse; de Barsy et al. (1976)
	4PC, 2CHOL, 1SA	
Non-specific	7PC, 1CHOL, 2DCP	Weissmann et al. (1974)
Non-specific	7PC, 1CHOL, 2DCP	Phagocyte; Cohen et al. (1976)
IgM immunoglobulin	7PC, 1CHOL, 2DCP	Phagocyte; Cohen et al. (1976)
		Weissmann et al. (1976)
OTHER MACROMOLECULES		
Poly(I)	10SPH, 3.6CHOL, 1DCP	Mouse; Straub et al. (1974)
Poly(I) : Poly(C)	2.6SPH, 0.8CHOL	Mouse; Straub et al. (1974)
	2.6SPH, 0.8CHOL, 1SA	Mouse, lymphocytes; Magee et al. (1976)
	PS	Mouse, L_{929} cells, fibroblast; Mayhew et al. (1977)
rRNA	7PC, 2DCP, 1CHOL	Ostro et al. (1977)
mRNA, rRNA, tRNA	PS	L_{929} cells; Dimitriadis (1978a)
		Spleen lymphocytes; Dimitriadis (1978b)
mRNA	7PC, 2DCP, 1CHOL	Human epithelial carcinoma cells; Ostro (1978)
mRNA	PS and 7PC, 2CHOL, 1SA	Wreschner et al. (1978)
	(hybrid liposomes)	
Immune RNA	2.6SPH, 0.9CHOL, 1SA	Lymphocytes; Magee et al. (1978)
DNA from calf thymus	7PC, 2CHOL, 1PA	Rat; Gregoriadis et al. (1977a)
		Hoffman et al. (1978)

DNA from Ehrlich ascites cells, SV40 virus, λ phage	PC	Hoffman *et al.* (1978)
Metaphase chromosome	7PC, 2CHOL	Mouse-human somatic hybrid cell line (Ag/HRBC2; Mukherjee *et al.* (1978)
Polyuridilic acid	4DPPC, 1.5CHOL 4PC, 1.5CHOL, 1SA 4DPPC, 1.5CHOL, 1SA 4DPPC, 1.5CHOL, 1DCP 4DPPC, 1.5CHOL, 1PE 4PC, 1.5CHOL, 0.25SA	Kulpa and Tinghitella (1976)
Poly-1-phenylalanine Poly-1-leucine Poly-1-lysine Poly-1-alanine	11PC, 1G	Mouse; Dunnick *et al.* (1975)
Polyvinylpyrrolidone	7PC, 2CHOL, 1PA 7PC, 2CHOL, 1SA PI	Rat; Dapergolas *et al.* (1976)
Dextran	7.8DPPC, 1PA 7DPPC, 2CHOL, 1PA	Rat intestinal sac; Bridges *et al.* (1978) Fibroblast; de Brohun-Butler *et al.* (1978)
DRUGS		
Actinomycin D	7PC, 2CHOL, 1PA 7PC, 2CHOL, 1SA 7DPPC, 2CHOL, 1PA 7DPPC, 2CHOL, 1SA 7PC, 2CHOL, 1SA 7PC, 2CHOL, 1PA	Rat; Gregoriadis (1973) Rat; Segal *et al.* (1975) Mouse; Gregoriadis and Neerunjun (1975a), Neerunjun and Gregoriadis (1974)

Table 4 (Continued)

Substance	Liposomal lipids	Reference
	4PC, 7.7CHOL	Mouse; Rahman et al. (1974),
	1PC, 1CHOL	Rahman et al. (1975)
	9PC, 1PS, 10CHOL	DC-3F and DC-3F/ADX cell lines;
		Poste and Papahadjopoulos (1976b)
	PC	Rat; Juliano and Stamp (1978)
	5.3PC, 1.3CHOL	
	5.3PC, 1.5SA	
	5.3PC, 1.3CHOL, 1.5SA	
	5.3PC, 0.5PS	
	5.3PC, 1.3CHOL, 0.5PS	
	5.3PC, 2CHOL, 1.5SA	
5-fluorouracil	7PC, 2CHOL, 1PA	Rat; Gregoriadis et al. (1977a)
	7PC, 2CHOL, 1PA	Rat; Gregoriadis (1974b)
	7PC, 2CHOL, 1SA	
	7DPPC, 2CHOL, 1PA	
	7DPPC, 2CHOL, 1SA	
	4.8PC, 2.8CHOL, 1DCP	
Floxuridine	7PC, 2CHOL, 1DCP	Mouse; Simmons and Kramer (1977)
	7SPH, 2CHOL, 1DCP	Mouse; Simmons and Kramer (1977)
Methotrexate	5PC, 5CHOL, 1DCP	Rat; Colley and Ryman (1975)
	6PC, 2CHOL, 1DCP	Perfused rat liver, P815Y mastocytoma cells;
	4PC, 1CHOL, 1SA	Tyrrell et al. (1977)
	9PC, 2CHOL	
	9DPPC, 2CHOL	
	1PC, 0.52CHOL, 0.22SA	Monkey; Kimelberg et al. (1976),
	64.6PC, 45CHOL, 19.5SA	Kimelberg (1976)
		Mouse; Freise et al. (1977)
	5PC, 5CHOL, 1DCP	

Drug	Composition	Reference
Bleomycin (^{111}In-bleomycin)	7PC, 2CHOL, 1PA	Rat; Dapergolas et al. (1976), Gregoriadis and Neerunjun (1975b)
		HeLa cell, AKR-A cell, fibroblast; Gregoriadis and Neerunjun (1975)
	7PC, 2CHOL, 1PA	Rat, mouse; Gregoriadis et al. (1977b), Man; Segal et al. (1976)
1-β-D-arabinofuranosyl cytosine	7PC, 2CHOL, 1SA	
	7DPPC, 2CHOL, 1PA	
	2SPH, 1.5CHOL, 0.2SA	Mouse; Kobayashi et al. (1975)
	20SPH, 15CHOL, 2SA	Mouse, L$_{1210}$ cells; Kobayashi et al. (1977)
	20SPH, 15CHOL, 2DCP	
	20PC, 15CHOL, 2SA	
	20PC, 15CHOL, 2DCP	
	80PC, 120CHOL, 20PS	Mouse, L$_{1210}$ cells; Mayhew et al. (1976)
	PC	Rat; Juliano and Stamp (1978)
	5.3PC, 1.3CHOL	
	5.3PC, 1.5SA	
	5.3PC, 1.3CHOL, 1.5SA	
	5.3PC, 0.5PS	
	5.3PC, 1.3CHOL, 0.5PS	L$_{1210}$ cells; Mayhew et al. (1976)
1-β-D-arabinofuranosyl cytosine 5'-triphosphate	80PC, 120CHOL, 20PS	
	4PC, 3CHOL, 1SA	
Mechlorethamine	DPPC	Mitochondria; Rutman et al. (1977)
BCNU	DPPC	Ehrlich ascites tumour, L$_{1210}$ cells; Rutman et al. (1976)
Melphalan	7PC, 2CHOL, 1PA	Rat; Gregoriadis et al. (1977a)
Daunomycin	7PC, 2CHOL, 1PA	Rat; Gregoriadis et al. (1977a)
	5.3PC, 2CHOL, 1.5SA	Rat; Juliano and Stamp (1978)
Vinblastine	5.3PC, 2CHOL, 1.5SA	Rat; Juliano and Stamp (1978)
8-azaguanine	1.5DPPC, 1CHOL, 1SA	Mouse; Fendler and Romero (1976)
	0.47DPPC, 0.75CHOL, 1DCP	Kano and Gendler (1977), Tsuji et al. (1976)
6-mercaptopurine	0.47DPPC, 0.75CHOL, 1DCP	Kano and Fendler (1977)

Table 4 (Continued)

Substance	Liposomal lipids	Reference
cis-Dichlorobiscyclopentylamine platinum(II)	7PC, 2CHOL, 1PA	Mouse; Deliconstantinos *et al.* (1977)
Colchicine	7DPPC, 2CHOL, 1PA	
	2PC, 1CHOL	Rat; Juliano and Stamp (1975)
	7PC, 2CHOL, 1PA	*Crithidia fasciculata*; Vakirtzi-Lemonias and Gregoriadis (1978)
Penicillin G	7PC, 2CHOL, 1PA	Rat; Gregoriadis (1973)
	7PC, 2CHOL, 1SA	
	7DPPC, 2CHOL, 1PA	
	7DPPC, 2CHOL, 1SA	
Dehydrostreptomycin	7PC, 2CHOL, 1PA	Macrophage; Bonventre and Gregoriadis (1978)
Antimony potassium tartrate	PC	Mouse; New *et al.* (1978)
Sodium stibogluconate	PC	Mouse; New *et al.* (1978)
	7PC, 2CHOL, 1PA	Mouse; Black *et al.* (1977)
Sodium stibogluconate, Meglumine antimoniate	2DSPC, 1.5CHOL, 0.22SA	Hamster; Alving *et al.* (1978)
	2DMPC, 1.5CHOL, 0.44SA	
	2DMPC, 1.5CHOL, 0.88SA	
	2DMPC, 1.5CHOL, 0.22DCP	
	2SPH, 1.5CHOL, 0.22DCP	
	2SPH, 1.5CHOL, 0.22SA	
	2DSPC, 1.5CHOL, 0.22DCP	
	2DSPC, 1.5CHOL, 0.22SA	
Cyclic AMP	4PC, 3CHOL, 1SA	3T3 cell, SV3T3 cell; Papahadjopoulos *et al.* (1974a,b)
	4DPPC, 3CHOL, 1SA	
	9PC, 8CHOL, 1PS	

Thyroxine and triiodothyronine	PC	Hillier (1970)
	Lipid extract (rat liver)	Ahtee and Johnson (1974)
5-hydroxytryptamine and norepinephrine	2.4PE, 1CHOL 2.4PS, 1CHOL 2.4PA, 1CHOL	
Parethoxycaine derivatives	PC PS DPPC	Giotta et al. (1974)
Dibucaine	PC 4PC, 1DCP DPPC DPPC, DMPC DMPC	Singer (1973) Wilschut et al. (1976)
Tetracaine	PC 4PC, 1DCP 7PC, 2CHOL 7DPPC, 2CHOL 7DMPC, 2CHOL	Singer (1973) Rat; Dapergolas and Gregoriadis (1977)
Sodium salicylate	2.4PC, 1CHOL	Singer (1973)
Testosterone	7PC, 1CHOL, 2DCP	Sessa and Weissmann (1968)
17β-oestradiol	7PC, 1CHOL, 2DPC	Sessa and Weissmann (1968)
Cortisol palmitate	1DPPC, 1PA	Rabbit; Dingle et al. (1978)
Cortisol, cortisol octanoate, cortisol palmitate	DMPC, PA (various ratios) DPPC, PA (ditto) DSPC, PA (ditto)	Shaw et al. (1976)

Table 4 (Continued)

Substance	Liposomal lipids	Reference
VITAMINS AND DERIVATIVES		
Vitamin A	2DPPC, 1.5CHOL, 0.22DCP	Conrad et al. (1974)
Vitamin K	9.5PC, 0.5DCP	Martius et al. (1975)
Vitamin C, vitamin B_6 and lipoic acid	7DPPC, 2CHOL, 1PA	Fibroblast; de Brohun-Butler et al. (1978)
9-*cis*-Retinaldehyde, 11-*cis* retinaldehyde, 11-*cis*-retinol	DOPC	Frog retina cells; Yoshikami and Nöll (1978)
OTHER SMALL MOLECULES		
Histamine	PS	Abernethy et al. (1974)
Glutathione	PC	Rat; Malnöe et al. (1975)
Glutamate	7DPPC, 2CHOL, 1PA	Fibroblast; de Brohun-Butler et al. (1978)
	Rat brain lipid extract	Rat; Branca et al. (1976)
Pepstatin	2PC, 2CHOL, 1SA	Rat liver; Dean (1975)
Ergosterol	PC	L_{1210} cells; Schiffman and Klein (1977)
Inulin	PC	L_{1210} cells; Jansons et al. (1978)
	4PC, 3CHOL	
	4PC, 3CHOL, 1PS	
	4PC, 3CHOL, 1SA	
Forssman antigen	2DPPC, 1.5CHOL, 0.22DCP	Joseph et al. (1974)
6-Carboxyfluorescein	DOPC	Lymphocyte; Blumenthal et al. (1977)
		Weinstein et al. (1978)

Agent	Composition	Reference
Nitroblue tetrazolium	DPPL, DOPC	Frog retinal cells, lymphocyte; Weinstein et al. (1977)
	PS and 7PC, 2CHOL, 1SA (hybrid liposomes)	Wreschner and Gregoriadis (1978)
Sodium sulphite	7PC, 2CHOL, 1PA	Rat; Segal et al. (1974)
EDTA	7DPPC, 2CHOL, 1PA	Fibroblast; de Brohun-Butler et al. (1978)
	1.5PC, 1CHOL	Mouse; Rahman et al. (1973), Rahman et al. (1974), Rahman and Wright (1975)
	PC or DPPC	Mouse; Jonah et al. (1975)
	1PC, 2CHOL	
DTPA	3.5PC, 1.7CHOL, 1SA	Mouse; Rahman et al. (1973)
^{99m}Tc-DTPA	5.2PC, 3.8CHOL, 1PS	Mouse; Caride et al. (1976)
	1.5PC, 1CHOL	Dog; Caride and Zaret (1977)
	0.7PC, 1CHOL	
	5.2PC, 1CHOL	
	7PC, 1CHOL, 2DCP	
	8PC, 1CHOL, 1SA	
Desferrioxamine	7DMPC, 2CHOL, 1DCP	Mouse; Hinkle et al. (1978)
Cysteamine	3.6DPPC, 2.3CHOL, 1SA	Mouse; Guilmette et al. (1978)
Cysteamine, dithiothreitol, penicillamine, BAL, N-acetyl cysteine	7DPPC, 2CHOL, 1PA	Mouse, fibroblast; de Brohun-Butler et al. (1978)
	7DPPC, 2CHOL, 1PA	Fibroblast; de Brohun-Butler et al. (1978)
^{99m}TcO$_4$	PC	Mouse, rat; McDougall et al. (1974), McDougall et al. (1975)
	11PC, 1G	
	11PC, 8.2CHOL, 1G	
	11PC, 1G, 1.6PS	
	11PC, 1G, 1.7PE	

Table 4 (Continued)

Substance	Liposomal lipids	Reference
	44DPPC, 33CHOL, 4G 44PC, 33CHOL, 4G	Mouse blood cells, mouse spleen cells, human blood cells, human lymphocytes, mouse thymocytes, Maloney lymphoma cells, EMT-6 cells; Dunnick et al. (1976b)
$^{111}In^{3+}$	2DPPC 2DPPC, 1CHOL	Mouse; Hwang and Mauk (1977)
^{99m}Tc-Sn-oxine	6PC, 4CHOL, 0.3PS	Rat, mouse; Anghileri et al. (1976)
$^{22}Na^+$, $^{86}Rb^+$	4PC, 3CHOL, 1PS	Mouse; Kimelberg et al. (1975)
VIRUSES, PARTICLES		
Sindbis virus	Lipid extract (sheep red blood cells)	Mooney et al. (1975)
Sendai virus	4.4SPH, 12.2CHOL, 8.8PC	
Poliovirus, type I	1PE, 2PS, 6.4G PS	Haywood (1974) Ovary cells; Wilson et al. (1977)
Hepatitis B surface antigen(HB$_s$Ag)	7PC, 2CHOL 7PC, 2CHOL, 1DCP 7PC, 2CHOL, 1SA	Guinea pigs; Manesis et al. (1978) Manesis et al. (1979)
Plasmodium falciparum	1DPPC, 1CHOL	Monkey; Siddiqui et al. (1978)

Association of substances with liposomes was carried out either during the preparation of the liposomes or after mixture with preformed liposomes. Lipids (with molar ratios) are phosphatidylcholine (PC), cholesterol (CHOL), dicetylphosphate (DCP), stearylamine (SA), phosphatidic acid (PA), dipalmitoyl phosphatidylcholine (DPPC), dimyristoyl phosphatidylcholine (DMPC), distearoyl phosphatidylcholine (DSPC), dioleoyl phosphatidylcholine (DOPC), dilauroyl phosphatidylcholine (DLPC), sphingomyelin (SPH), phosphatidylinositol (PI), cardiolipin (CL), lysophosphatidylcholine (LPC), phosphatidylethanolamine (PE), phosphatidylserine (PS), gangliosides (G), trilinolein (TL), and tristearin (TS). For 'hybrid liposomes' see Wreschner and Gregoriadis (1978), and Figures 4 and 5.

by more rationalized and, in some instances, sophisticated fashions. It is also apparent that in certain situations specialized (homing) liposomes will be needed although advancements in this area will depend on our understanding cell surface behaviour and function. Regardless of the progress in these lines of research, applications in medicine will be enormously promoted if liposomes prove capable of crossing barriers to the extravascular space. Data from intraperitoneal injections indicate that liposomes can cross membranes but given the limitations in liposomal minimal size, it is obvious that not all membranes will be crossed by even the smallest liposomes. Undoubtedly there are difficulties to face and some of these may deflate even those who once listened to the sirens and have been unable to move away. However, I offer no apologies in repeating that, with many diseases affecting millions of individuals, drugs have not fulfilled original hopes that followed their discovery. Until drug specificity is achieved (and this may be practically impossible in the foreseeable future) drug carriers such as liposomes can and should play important roles in optimizing drug action.

Acknowledgments

I am grateful to the following individuals who have worked in this laboratory on the various aspects of liposomes as drug carriers: C. D. V. Black, Dr. Isobel P. Braidman, Rosemary Buckland, Jacqui Clarke, G. Dapergolas, Christine Davis, Pamela Davisson, Dr. G. Deliconstantinos, Dr. C. Kirby, Dr. E. K. Manesis, Dr. R. Moore, E. Diane Neerunjun, Susan Scott, Dr. A. W. Segal, Hishani Weereratne and Dr. D. H. Wreschner. I also thank Dr. A. C. Allison, Dr. P. Belchetz, Dr. P. Bonventre, Dr. R. A. Bulman, Sir Graham Bull, Dr. C. Cameron, J. C. W. Crawley, J. Dorling, Dr. R. R. Dourmashkin, Dr. A. S. Tavill, Dr. Catherine Vakirtzi-Lemonias and Dr. E. Wisse for collaboration and Mrs. Dorothy Seale for secretarial work. Part of the work was supported by the Wellcome Trust and by a N.I.H. National Cancer Institute Contract (NO. 1-CM-87171).

REFERENCES

Abernethy, D., Fitzgerald, T. J. and Walaszek, E. J. (1974). *Biochem. Biophys. Res. Comm.*, **59**, 535–541.

Adams, D. A., Joyce, G., Richardson, V. J., Ryman, B. E. and Wisniewski, H. M. (1977). *J. Neurol. Sci.*, **31**, 173–179.

Ahtee, L. and Johnson, S. M. (1974). *Acta Physiol. Scand.*, **20**, 94–106.

Allison, A. C. and Gregoriadis, G. (1974). *Nature*, **252**, 252

Allison, A. C. and Gregoriadis, G. (1976). In *Recent Results in Cancer Research* (eds. G. Mathé, I. Florentin and M.-C. Simmler) pp. 58–64, Springer Verlag, Heidelberg.

Almeida, J. D., Brand, C. M., Edwards, D. C. and Heath, T. D. (1975). *Lancet* **ii**, 899–901.

Alving, C. R., Steck, E. A. Champan, W. L. Jr., Waits, V. B., Hendricks, L. D., Swartz, G. M. Jr. and Hanson, W. L. (1978). *Proc. Nat. Acad. Sci. USA,* **75**, 2959–2963.

Anghileri, L. J., Firusian, N. and Bracksch, K. P. (1976). *J. Nucl. Biol. Med.,* **20**, 165–167.

Batzri, S. and Korn, E. D. (1975). *J. Cell Biol.,* **66**, 621–634.

Bayer Actiengesellschaft (1974). Institut National de la Propriété Industrielle, France. Demande de Brevet d'Invention, No. de Publication Fr. 2.221.122.

Belchetz, P. E., Braidman, I. P. Crawley, J. C. W. and Gregoriadis, G. (1977). *Lancet,* **2**, 116–117

Beutler, E., Dale, G.-L., Guinto, E. and Kuhl, W. (1977). *Proc. Nat. Acad. Sci. USA,* **74**, 4620–4623.

Black, C. D. V. and Gregoriadis, G. (1974). *Biochem. Soc. Trans.,* **2**, 869–871.

Black, C. D. V. and Gregoriadis, G. (1976). *Biochem. Soc. Trans.* **4**, 253–256.

Black, C. D. V., Watson, G. J. and Ward, R. J. (1977). *Trans. Roy. Soc. Trop. Med. Hyg.,* **71**, 550–552.

Blumenthal, R., Weinstein, J. N., Sharrow, S. O. and Henkart, P. (1977). *Proc. Nat. Acad. Sci. USA,* **74**, 5603–5607.

Bonventre, P. and Gregoriadis, G. (1978). *Antimicrobial Agents and Chemotherapy,* **13**, 1049–1051.

Brady, R. P. (1977). *Science,* **193**, 733–739.

Braidman, I. P. and Gregoriadis, G. (1977). *Biochem. J.,* **164**, 439–445.

Branca, D., Scutari, G. and Siliprandi, N. (1976). *Biochem. Pharmacol.,* **25**, 1773–1775.

Bridges, J. F., Millard, P. C. and Woodley, J. F. (1978). *Biochem. Biophys. Acta,* **544**, 448–451.

Bruni, A., Toffano, G., Leon, A. and Boarato, E. (1976). *Nature,* **260**, 331–333.

Capizzi, R. L., Bertino, J. R. and Handschumacher, R. E. (1970). *Ann. Rev. Med.,* **21**, 433–444.

Caride, V. J. and Zaret, B. L. (1977). *Science,* **198**, 735–737.

Caride, V. J., Taylor, W., Cramer, J. A. and Gottschalk, A. (1976). *J. Nucl. Med.,* **17**, 1067–1072.

Chen, S., S-H. and Keenan, R. M. (1977). *Biochem. Biophys. Res. Comm.,* **79**, 852–858.

Cohen, C. M., Weissmann, G., Hoffstein, S., Awasthi, Y. C. and Srivastava, S. K. (1976). *Biochemistry,* **15**, 452–460.

Colley, C. M. and Ryman, B. E. (1975). *Biochem. Soc. Trans.,* **3**, 157–159.

Colley, C. M. and Ryman, B. E. (1976). *Biochim. Biophys. Acta,* **451**, 417–425.

Conrad, D. H., Alving, C. R. and Wirtz, G. H. (1974). *Biochim, Biophys. Acta,* **332**, 36–46.

Dansey, G. F., Yasuda, T. and Kinsky, S. C. (1978). *J. Immunol.,* **120**, 1109–1113.

Dapergolas, G. and Gregoriadis, G. (1976). *Lancet,* **2**, 824–827.

Dapergolas, G. and Gregoriadis, G. (1977). *Biochem. Soc. Trans.,* **5**, 1383–1386.

Dapergolas, G., Neerunjun, E. D. and Gregoriadis, G. (1976). *FEBS Lett.,* **63**, 235–239.

Davidenkova, E. F., Rozenberg, O. A. and Shvarts, E. I. (1977). *Byulleten Eksperimental' noi Biologii Meditsiny,* **83**, 673–675.

Davis, C. and Gregoriadis, G. (1979). *Biochem. Soc. Trans.,* **7**, 680–682.

Dean, R. T. (1975). *Nature,* **257**, 414–416.

de Barsy, T., Devos, P. and Van Hoof, F. (1976). *Lab. Invest.,* **34**, 273–282.

de Brohun-Butler, J., Tietze, F., Pellefigue, F., Spielberg, S. P. and Schulman, J. D. (1978). *Pediat. Res.*, **12**, 46–51.
de Duve, C., de Barsy, T., Poole, B., Trouet, A., Tulkens, P. and Van Hoof, F. (1974). *Biochem. Pharmacol.*, **23**, 2495–2531.
Deliconstantinos, G., Gregoriadis, G., Abel, G., Jones, M. and Robertson, D. (1977). *Biochem. Soc. Trans.*, **5**, 1326–1328.
Desnick, R. J., Thorpe, S. R. and Fiddler, M. B. (1976). *Physiol. Rev.*, **56**, 57–99.
Dimitriadis, G. J. (1978a). *FEBS Letts.*, **86**, 289–293.
Dimitriadis, G. J. (1978b). *Nature*, **274**, 423–424.
Dingle, J. T. *et al.* (1978). *Nature*, **271**, 372–373.
Drug Carriers in Biology and Medicine, (1979) (ed. G. Gregoriadis) Academic Press, London, New York, San Francisco.
Dunnick, J. K., McDougall, I. R., Aragon, S., Goris, M. L. and Kriss, J. P. (1975). *J. Nucl. Med.*, **16**, 483–487.
Dunnick, J. K., Badger, R. S. Takeda, Y. and Kriss, J. P. (1976a). *J. Nucl. Med.*, **17**, 1073–1076.
Dunnick, J. K., Rooks, J. D., Aragon, S. and Kriss, J. P. (1976b). *Cancer Res.*, **36**, 2385–2389.
Eytan, G., Matheson, M. J. and Racker, E. (1975). *FEBS Lett.*, **57**, 121–125.
Fendler, J. H. and Romero, A. (1976). *Life Sci.*, **18**, 1453–1458.
Fendler, J. H. and Romero, A. (1977). *Life Sci.*, **20**, 1109–1120.
Finkelstein, M. C. and Weissmann, G. (1978). *J. Lipid. Research*, **19**, 289–303.
Finkelstein, M. C., Maniscalco, J. and Weissmann, G. (1978). *Anal. Biochem.*, **89**, 400–407.
Fishman, Y. and Citri, N. (1975). *FEBS Lett.*, **60**, 17–20.
Freer, J. H., Arbuthnott, J. P. and Bernheimer, A. W. (1968). *J. Bacteriol.*, **95**, 1153–1168.
Freise, J., Schäfer, G., Schmidt, F. W. and Magerstedt, P. (1977). *Z. Krebsforsch*, **90**, 187–195.
Giotta, G. J., Chen, D. S. and Wang, H. H. (1974). *Arch. Biochem. Biophys.*, **163**, 453–458.
Grant, C. W. M. and McConnell, H. M. (1973). *Proc. Nat. Acad. Sci. USA*, **70**, 1238–1240.
Gregoriadis, G. (1973). *FEBS Lett.*, **36**, 292–296.
Gregoriadis, G. (1974a). In *Enzyme Replacement Therapy in Lysosomal Storage Diseases* (eds. J. M. Tager, G. J. M. Hooghwinkel and W. Th. Daems), pp. 131–148, North Holland Publishing Co.
Gregoriadis, G. (1974b). *Biochem. Soc. Trans.*, **2**, 117–119.
Gregoriadis, G. (1975a). *Biochem. Soc. Trans.*, **3**, 613–618.
Gregoriadis, G. (1975b). In *Lysosomes in Biology and Pathology* (eds. J. T. Dingle and R. T. Dean), pp. 265–294, North Holland Publishing Co.
Gregoriadis, G. (1976a). *New Engl. J. Med.*, **295**, 704–710.
Gregoriadis, G. (1976b). *New Engl. J. Med.*, **295**, 765–770.
Gregoriadis, G. (1976c). *Meth. Enzymol.*, **44**, 218–227 and 698–709.
Gregoriadis, G. (1977). *Nature*, **265**, 407–411.
Gregoriadis, G. (1978a). *Ann. N.Y. Acad. Sci.*, **308**, 343–370.
Gregoriadis, G. (1978b). *Science*, **201**, 211–213.
Gregoriadis, G. (1978c). *Nature*, **275**, 695–696.
Gregoriadis, G. (1979). In: *Drug Carriers in Biology and Medicine* (ed. G. Gregoriadis), pp. 287–341, Academic Press, London, New York, San Francisco.
Gregoriadis, G. and Allison, A. C. (1974). *FEBS Lett.*, **45**, 71–74.
Gregoriadis, G. and Buckland, R. A. (1973). *Nature*, **244**, 170–172.

Gregoriadis, G. and Davis, C. (1979). *Biochem. Biophys. Res. Comm.* **89**, 1287–1293.
Gregoriadis, G. and Neerunjun, E. D. (1974). *Eur. J. Biochem.*, **47**, 179–185.
Gregoriadis, G. and Neerunjun, E. D. (1975a). *Res. Comm. Chem. Pathol. Pharmacol.*, **10**, 351–362.
Gregoriadis, G. and Neerunjun, E. D. (1975b). *Biochem. Biophys. Res. Comm.*, **65**, 537–544.
Gregoriadis, G. and Ryman, B. E. (1971). *Biochem. J.*, **124**, 58p.
Gregoriadis, G. and Ryman, B. E. (1972a). *Eur. J. Biochem.*, **25**, 485–491.
Gregoriadis, G. and Ryman, B. E. (1972b). *Biochem. J.*, **129**, 123–133.
Gregoriadis, G., Leatherwood, P. D. and Ryman, B. E. (1971). *FEBS Lett.*, **14**, 95–99.
Gregoriadis, G., Putman, D., Louis, L. and Neerunjun, D. (1974a). *Biochem. J.*, **140**, 323–330.
Gregoriadis, G., Swain, C. P., Willis, E. J. and Tavill, A. S. (1974b). *Lancet*, **1**, 1313–1316.
Gregoriadis, G., Davisson, P. J. and Scott, S. (1977a). *Biochem. Soc. Trans.*, **5**, 1323–1326.
Gregoriadis, G., Neerunjun, E. D. and Hunt, R. (1977b). *Life Sci.*, **21**, 357–369.
Gregoriadis, G., Siliprandi, N. and Turchetto, E. (1977c). *Life Sci.*, **20**, 1773–1786.
Gregoriadis, G., Neerunjun, E. D., Meade, T. W., Goolamali, S. K., Weereratne, H. and Bull, G. M. (1979). In *Enzyme Therapy in Genetic Diseases. Birth Defects: Original Article Series*. In press.
Guilmette, R. A., Cerny, E. A. and Rahman, Y. -E. (1978). *Life Sci.*, **22**, 313–320.
Harding, N., Keeson, C., Logue, F., McCuish, A., McKenzie, J., Patel, H. M., Ryman, B. E. and Scobie, J. (1978). *Biochem. Soc. Trans.*, **6**, 784–785.
Haywood, A. M. (1974). *J. Mol. Biol.*, **87**, 625–628.
Heath, T. D., Edwards, D. C. and Ryman, B. E. (1976). *Biochem. Soc. Trans.*, **4**, 129–133.
Hillier, A. P. (1970). *J. Physiol. (Lond.)*, **211**, 585–597.
Hinkle, G. H., Born, G. S., Kessler, W. V. and Shaw, S. M. (1978). *J. Pharm. Sci.*, **67**, 795–798.
Hoekstra, D., Tomasiti, R. and Scherphof, G. (1978). *Biochim. Biophys. Acta*, **542**, 456–469.
Hoffman, R. M., Margolis, L. B. and Bergelson, L. D. (1978). *FEBS Lett.*, **23**, 365–368.
Huet, C. and Ansel, S. (1977). *Int. J. Cancer*, **20**, 61–66.
Hwang, K. J. and Mauk, M. R. (1977). *Proc. Nat. Acad. Sci. USA*, **74**, 4991–4995.
Ihler, G. M. and Glew, R. (1977). In *Biomedical Applications of Immobilized Enzymes and Proteins* (ed. T. M. S. Chang), Vol. 1, pp. 219–226, Plenum Press, New York, London.
Inbar, M. and Shinitzky, M. (1974). *Proc. Nat. Acad. Sci. USA*, **71**, 2128–2130.
Jansons, V. K., Weis, P., Chen, T. -h, and Redwood, W. R. (1978). *Cancer Res.*, **38**, 531–535.
Jonah, M. M., Cerny, E. A. and Rahman, Y. -E. (1975). *Biochim. Biophys. Aca*, **401**, 336–348.
Joseph, K. C., Alving, C. R. and Wistar, R. (1974). *J. Immunol.*, **112**, 1949–1951.
Juliano, R. L. and Stamp, D. (1975). *Biochem. Biophys. Res. Comm.*, **63**, 651–658.
Juliano, R. L. and Stamp, D. (1976). *Nature*, **261**, 235–237.
Juliano, R. L. and Stamp, D. (1978). *Biochem. Pharmacol.*, **27**, 21–27.
Kano, K. and Fendler, J. H. (1977). *Life Sci.*, **20**, 1729–1734.
Kawada, V. J., Kuwae, T. and Kurata, M. (1974). *Life Sci.*, **13**, 613–620.
Kawada, V. J., Shindo, T. and Yoshimura, Y. (1976). *Endocrinology*, **98**, 1425–1429.

Kimelberg, H. K. (1976). *Biochem. Biophys. Acta*, **448**, 531–550.
Kimelberg, H. K. and Mayhew, E. (1978). In *Critical Reviews in Toxicology* (ed. L. Golberg), pp. 25–79, CRC-Press Inc.
Kimelberg, H. K., Mayhew, E. and Papahadjopoulos, D. (1975). *Life Sci.*, **17**, 715–724.
Kimelberg, H. K., Tracy, T. F., Biddlecome, S. M. and Bourke, R. S. (1976). *Cancer Res.*, **36**, 2949–2957.
Kimelberg, H. K., Tracy, T. F., Watson, R. E., King, D., Reiss, F. L. and Bourke, R. S. (1978). *Cancer Res.*, **38**, 706–712.
Kleeman, W. and McConnell, H. M. (1976). *Biochim. Biophys. Acta*, **419**, 206–222.
Kobayashi, T., Tsukagoshi, S. and Sakurai, Y. (1975). *Gann*, **66**, 719–720.
Kobayashi, T., Kataoka, T., Tsukagoshi, S. and Sakurai, Y. (1977). *Int. J. Cancer*, **20**, 581–587.
Kotani, S., Kinoshita, F., Morisaki, I., Shimono, T., Okunaga, T., Takada, H., Tsujimoto, M., Watanabe, Y. and Kato, K. (1977). *Biken. J.*, **20**, 95–103.
Kulpa, C. F. and Tinghitella, T. J. (1976). *Life Sci.*, **19**, 1879–1888.
Labelle, E. F. and Racker, E. (1977). *J. Memb. Biol.*, **31**, 301–315.
La Bonnardiere, C. (1977). *FEBS Lett.*, **77**, 191–196.
Leon, A., Benvegnu, D., Toffano, G., Orlando, P. and Massori, P. (1978). *J. Neurochem.*, **30**, 23–26.
McDougall, I. R., Dunnick, J. K., McNamee, M. G. and Kriss, J. P. (1974). *Proc. Nat. Acad. Sci. USA*, **71**, 3487–3491.
McDougall, I. R., Dunnick, J. K., Goris, M. L. and Kriss, J. P. (1975). *J. Nuc. Med.*, **16**, 488–491.
Madeira, V. M. C. (1977). *Biochim. Biophys. Acta*, **499**, 202–211.
Magee, W. E. and Miller, O. V. (1972). *Nature*, **235**, 339–341.
Magee, W. E., Goff, C. W., Schoknecht, J., Smith, M. D. and Cherian, K. (1974). *J. Cell Biol.*, **63**, 492–504.
Magee, W. E., Talcott, M. L., Straub, S. X. and Vriend, C. Y. (1976). *Biochim. Biophys. Acta*, **451**, 610–618.
Magee, W. E., Gronenberger, J. H. and Thor, D. E. (1979). *Cancer Res.*, **38**, 1173–1176.
Malnöe, A., Louis, A., Strolin Benedetti, Schneider, M., Smith, R. L., Kreber, L. and Lam, R. (1975). *Biochem. Soc. Trans.*, **3**, 730–732.
Manesis, E. K., Cameron, C. and Gregoriadis, G. (1978). *Biochim. Soc. Trans.*, **6**, 925–928.
Manesis, E. K., Cameron, C. and Gregoriadis, G. (1979). *FEBS Lett.* **102**, 107–111.
Martin, F. J. and McDonald, R. C. (1976). *J. Cell Biol.*, **70**, 515–526.
Martius, C., Ganser, R. and Viviano, A. (1975). *FEBS Lett.*, **59**, 13–14.
Masturzo, P., Gallamini, A., Murialdo, G., Nizzo, M. C. and Toffano, G. (1977). *New Engl. J. Med.*, **297**, 338–339.
Mayhew, E., Papahadjopoulos, D., Rustum, Y. M. and Dave, C. (1976). *Cancer Res.*, **96**, 4406–4411.
Mayhew, E., Papahadjopoulos, D., O'Malley, J., Carter, W. A. and Vail, W. J. (1977). *Molec. Pharmacol.*, **13**, 488–495.
Mooney, J. J., Dalrymple, J. M., Alving, C. R. and Russell, P. K. (1975). *J. Virol.*, **15**, 225–231.
Morein, B., Helenius, A., Simons, K., Peterson, R., Kääriäinen, L. and Schirrmacher, V. (1978). *Nature*, **276**, 715–718.
Mukherjee, A. B., Orloff, S., Butler, J. D., Triche, T., Lalley, P. and Schulman, J. D. (1978). *Proc. Nat. Acad. Sci.*, **75**, 1361–1365.

Naoi, M., Naoi, M., Shimizu, T., Malviya, A. H. and Yagi, K. (1977). *Biochim. Biophys. Acta*, **471**, 305–310.

Neerunjun, E. D. and Gregoriadis, G. (1974). *Biochem. Soc. Trans.*, **2**, 868–869.

Neerunjun, E. D. and Gregoriadis, G. (1976). *Biochem. Soc. Trans.*, **4**, 133–134.

New, R. R. C., Chance, M. L., Thomas, S. C. and Peters, W. (1978). *Nature*, **272**, 55–56.

Nizzo, M. C., Tegos, S., Gallamini, A., Toffano, G., Polleri, A. and Massarotti, M. (1978). *J. Neural Transmission*, **43**, 93–102.

Ostro, M. J., Giacomoni, D. and Dray, S. (1977). *Biochem. Biophys. Res. Comm.*, **76**, 836–842.

Ostro, M. J., Giacomoni, D., Lavelle, D., Paxton, W. and Dray, S. (1978). *Nature*, **274**, 921–923.

Pagano, R. E. and Huang, L. (1975). *J. Cell Biol.*, **67**, 49–60.

Papahadjopoulos, D. and Miller, N. (1967). *Biochim. Biophys. Acta*, **135**, 624–638.

Papahadjopoulos, D., Mayhew, E., Poste, G. and Smith, S. (1974a). *Nature*, **252**, 163–166.

Papahadjopoulos, D., Poste, G. and Mayhew, E. (1974b). *Biochim. Biophys. Acta*, **363**, 404–418.

Papahadjopoulos, D., Vail, W. J., Jacobson, K. and Poste, G. (1975). *Biochim. Biophys. Acta*, **394**, 483–491.

Patel, H. M. and Ryman, B. E. (1974). *Biochim. Soc. Trans.*, **2**, 1014–1017.

Patel, H. M. and Ryman, B. E. (1976). *FEBS Lett.*, **62**, 60–63.

Patel, H. M. and Ryman, B. E. (1977). *Biochem. Soc. Trans.*, **5**, 1739–1741.

Poste, G. and Papahadjopoulos, D. (1976a). *Proc. Nat. Acad. Sci., USA*, **73**, 1603–1607.

Poste, G. and Papahadjopoulos, D. (1976b), *Nature*, **261**, 699–701.

Rahaminoff, R., Meiri, H., Eralkar, S. D. and Barenholz, Y. (1978). *Proc. Nat. Acad. Sci. USA*, **75**, 5214–5216.

Rahman, Y. -E. and Rosenthal, M. W. (1973). *Radiat. Res.*, **55**, 516–517.

Rahman, Y. -E. and Wright, B. J. (1975). *J. Cell Biol.*, **65**, 112–122.

Rahman, Y. -E., Rosenthal, M. W. and Cerny, E. A. (1973). *Science*, **180**, 300–302.

Rahman, Y. -E., Cerny, E. A., Tollaksen, S. L., Wright, B. J., Lance, S. L. and Thomson, J. F. (1974a). *Proc. Soc. Exp. Biol. Med.*, **146**, 1173–1176.

Rahman, Y. -E., Rosenthal, M. W., Cerny, E. A. and Moretti, E. S. (1974b). *J. Lab. Clin. Med.*, **83**, 640–647.

Rahman, Y. -E., Kisieleski, W. E., Buess, E. M. and Cerny, E. A. (1975). *Eur. J. Cancer*, **11**, 883–889.

Reynolds, G. D., Baker, H. J. and Reynolds, R. H. (1978). *Nature*, **275**, 754–755.

Richards, M. H. and Gardner, C. R. (1978). *Biochim. Biophys. Acta*, **543**, 508–522.

Richardson, V. J., Jeyasingh, K., Jewkes, R. F., Ryman, B. E. and Tattersall, M. H. N. (1977). *Biochem. Soc. Trans.*, **5**, 290–291.

Roerdink, F. H., Van Renswoude, A. J. B. M., Wielinga, B. Y., Kroon, A. M. and Scherphof, G. L. (1976). *J. Mol. Med.*, **1**, 257–263.

Rutman, R. J., Ritter, C. A., Avadhani, N. G. and Hansel, J. (1976). *Cancer Treat. Rep.*, **60**, 617–618.

Rutman, R. J., Avadhani, N. G. and Ritter, C. (1977). *Biochem. Pharmacol.*, **26**, 85–88.

Ryman, B. E., Jewkes, R. F., Jeyasingh,, K., Osborne, M. P., Patel, H. M., Richardson, V. J., Tattersall, M. H. M. and Tyrrell, D. A. (1978). *Ann. N.Y. Acad. Sci.*, **308**, 281–307.

Saraste, M. (1978). *Biochim. Biophys. Acta*, **507**, 17–25.

Scherphof, G., Roerdink, F., Waite, M. and Parks, J. (1978). *Biochim. Biophys. Acta*, **542**, 296–307.

Schiffman, F. J. and Klein, I. (1977). *Nature*, **269**, 65–68.

Schwenk, R., Lee, W. Y. and Sehon, A. H. (1978). *J. Immunol.*, **120**, 1612–1615.

Segal, A. W., Wills, E. J., Richmond, J. E., Slavin, G., Black, C. D. V. and Gregoriadis, G. (1974). *Br. J. Exp. Pathol.*, **55**, 320–327.

Segal, A. W., Gregoriadis, G. and Black, C. D. V. (1975). *Clin. Sci. Mol. Med.*, **49**, 99–100.

Segal, A. W., Gregoriadis, G., Lavender, J. P., Tarin, D. and Peters, T. J. (1976). *Clin. Sci. Mol. Med.*, **51**, 421–425.

Sengupta, S. and Rous, S. (1978). *Biochem. Biophys. Res. Comm.*, **82**, 795–799.

Sessa, G. and Weissmann, G. (1968). *Biochim. Biophys. Acta*, **150**, 173–180.

Sessa, G. and Weissmann, G. (1970). *J. Biol. Chem.*, **245**, 3295–3301.

Shaw, I. H., Knight, C. G. and Dingle, J. T. (1976). *Biochem, J.*, **158**, 473–476.

Siddiqui, W. A., Taylor, O. W., Kan, S. -C., Kramer, K., Richmond-Cram, S. M., Kotani, S., Shina, T. and Kusumoto, S. (1978). *Science*, **201**, 1237–1239.

Singer, M. A. (1973). *Can. J. Physiol. Pharmacol.*, **51**, 785–789.

Solomon, B. and Miller, I. R. (1976). *Biochim. Biophys. Acta*, **455**, 332–342.

Steger, L. D. and Desnick, R. J. (1977). *Biochim. Biophys. Acta*, **464**, 530–546.

Straub, S. X., Garry, R. F. and Magee, W. E. (1974), *Infect. Immun.*, **10**, 783–792.

Surolia, A. and Bachhawat, B. K. (1977). *Biochim. Biophys. Acta*, **497**, 760–765.

Surolia, A., Bachhawat, B. K. and Podder, S. K. (1975). *Nature*, **257**, 802–804.

Tagesson, C., Stendahl, O. and Magnusson, K. -E. (1977). *Studia Biophysica*, **64**, 151–160.

Tanaka, T., Taneda, K., Kobayashi, H., Okumura, K., Muranishi, S. and Sezaki, H. (1975). *Chem. Pharm. Bull.*, **23**, 3069–3074.

Torchilin, V. P., Goldmacher, V. S. and Smirnov, V. N. (1978). *Biochem. Biophys. Res. Comm.*, **85**, 983–990.

Tsujii, K., Sunamoto, J. and Fendler, J. H. (1976). *Life Sci.*, **19**, 1743–1750.

Tulkens, P. and Trouet, A. (1972). *Arch. Int. Physiol. Biochim.*, **80**, 623–624.

Tyrrell, D. A., Ryman, B. E., Keeton, B. R. and Dubowitz, V. (1976a). *Br. Med. J.*, **2**, 88.

Tyrrell, D. A., Heath, T. D., Colley, C. M. and Ryman, B. E. (1976b). *Biochim. Biophys. Acta*, **457**, 259–302.

Tyrrell, D. A., Richardson, V. J. and Ryman, B. E. (1977). *Biochim. Biophys. Acta*, **497**, 469–480.

Uchida, T., Kim, J., Kamaizumi, M., Miyake, Y. and Okada, Y. (1979). *J. Cell Biol.*, **80**, 10–20.

Vakirtzi-Lemonias, C. and Gregoriadis, G. (1978). *Biochem. Soc. Trans.*, **6**, 1241–1244.

van Rooijen, N. and van Nieuwmegen, R. (1977). *Immunol. Comm.*, **6**, 489–498.

Weinstein, J. N., Yoshikani, S., Henkart, P., Blumenthal, R. and Hagins, W. A. (1977). *Science*, **195**, 489–492.

Weinstein, J. N., Blumenthal, R., Sparrow, S. O. and Henkart, P. A. (1978). *Biochim. Biophys. Acta*, **509**, 289–299.

Weissmann, G., Brand, A. and Franklin, E. C. (1974). *J. Clin. Invest.*, **53**, 536–543.

Weissmann, G., Bloomgarden, D., Kaplan, R., Cohen, C., Hoffstein, S., Collins, T., Gottlieb, A. and Nagle, D. (1975). *Proc. Nat. Acad. Sci. USA*, **72**, 88–92.

Weissmann, G., Collins, T., Evers, H. and Dunham, P. (1976). *Proc. Nat. Acad. Sci. USA*, **73**, 510–514.

Weissmann, G., Cohen, C. and Hoffstein, S. (1977). *Trans. Assoc. Am. Phys.*, **89**, 171–183.

Wiktorowicz, J. E., Baur, P. S. and Srivastava, S. K. (1977). *Cytobiologia*, **14**, 401–411.

Wilschut, J. C., Regts, J., Westenberg, H. and Scherphof, G. (1976). *Biochim. Biophys. Acta*, **433**, 20–31.

Wilson, T., Papahadjopoulos, D. and Taber, R. (1977). *Proc. Nat. Acad. Sci. USA*, **74**, 3471–3475.

Wisse, E., Gregoriadis, G. and Daems, W. Th. (1976). In *The Reticuloendothelial System in Health and Disease: Functions and Characteristics* (eds. S. M. Reichard, M. R. Escobar and H. Friedman), pp. 237–245, Plenum Publishing Corp., New York.

World Health Organization (1976). WHO Tech. Rep. Ser., No. 595.

Wreschner, D. H. and Gregoriadis, G. (1978). *Biochem. Soc. Trans.*, **6**, 922–925.

Wreschner, D. H., Gregoriadis, G., Gunner, D. B. and Dourmashkin, R. R. (1978). *Biochem. Soc. Trans.*, **6**, 930–933.

Yoshikami, S. and Nöll, G. N. (1978). *Science*, **200**, 1393–1395.

Zborowski, J., Roerdink, F. and Scherphof, G. (1977). *Biochim. Biophys. Acta*, **497**, 183–191.

Liposomes in Biological Systems
Edited by G. Gregoriadis and A. C. Allison
©1980, John Wiley & Sons, Ltd.

CHAPTER 3

Optimizing Drug Entrapment in Liposomes. Chemical and Biophysical Considerations

Janos H. Fendler

1.	**Introduction**	87
2.	**Interaction of molecules with liposomes**	89
3.	**Factors affecting drug entrapment in liposomes**	91
4.	**Enhancing drug entrapment in liposomes**	96
	References	98

1. INTRODUCTION

Liposomes are increasingly being utilized as drug carriers (Gregoriadis 1973a, 1973b, 1976; Tyrrell *et al.*, 1976; Fendler and Romero, 1977; Gregoriadis, this book). They are non-toxic and biodegradable. Reduced dosages, allergic and immunological reactions, increased cellular permeabilities and delayed drug eliminations represent some of the advantages of using liposomes as drug delivery agents. The desire to direct intact drugs selectively to given targets has prompted the explosive research in this area. A major disadvantage, at present, is the non-selective distribution of liposomes. They are predominantly taken up by the liver and spleen (McDougall *et al.*, 1974). The few attempts to divert drug carrying vehicles to other organs have fallen short of expectations (Tyrrell *et al.*, 1976). This is hardly surprising in view of the poor understanding of the processes involved. Indeed applications run far ahead of the theory. Information, even at the supramolecular level, on factors affecting drug entrapment and retainment in liposomes as well as that on their fate *in vivo* is meagre.

Liposomes are smectic mesophases with water interspaced between the phospholipid layers (Bangham, 1968; Papahadjopoulos and Kimelberg, 1973; Bangham *et al.*, 1974). Unlike micelles (Fendler and Fendler, 1975; Fendler, 1976), they are not dynamic. Once liposomes are formed, they do not dissociate into lipids constituting them. They are destroyed, however, if an excess of alcohol or detergent is added. Single compartment, multilamellar and macrovesicles (or giant liposomes) have been utilized, to date, as drug carriers. These vesicles have been prepared from a variety of synthetic and naturally occurring phospholipids and generally contain cholesterol, buffers, and electrolytes. Table 1 collects the lipids and additives most frequently used for the preparation of drug-carrying vehicles. Cholesterol provides a tighter packing of the hydrocarbon chains of the lipid. This in turn minimizes the leakage of drugs from the liposome. Hydrogen ion concentrations in the sequestered water are effectively maintained by buffers (*vide infra*). Addition of a long chain amine or phosphate provides a net positive or negative charge to the liposomes. The type of phospholipid, the amount of additives, and the method of preparation all have profound influence on the drug-carrying abilities of liposomes.

Attention in this chapter is focused on the optimization of drug entrapment. Interactions of simple molecules, drugs, and proteins with liposomes will be surveyed. Parameters affecting drug entrapment will also be considered. Attempts will be made to collect the available, but somewhat scattered, information. Emphasis will be placed on chemical and biophysical techniques which afford enhanced and selective entrapment.

Table 1 Constituents of Drug-Carrying Liposomes

Phospholipid[a]	Additives
Egg lecithin (EL)	Cholesterol
Brain Phosphatidylserine (BS)	Stearylamine
Sphingomyelin (SM)	Sodium dicetylphosphate
Phosphatidylserine (PS)	
Phosphatidylinositol (PI)	NaCl, KCl, RbCl
Phosphatidylic acid (PA)	
Asolectin (AS)	Na_2HPO_4, K_2HPO_4
Ovolecithin (OL)	NaH_2PO_4, KH_2PO_4
Dipalmitoyl-D,L-α-phosphatidylcholine (DPL)	Ca^{2+} – salt
Dimyristoyl-D,L-α-phosphatidylcholine (DML)	EDTA
Distearyl-D,L-α-phosphatidylcholine (DSL)	*N*-tris-(hydroxymethyl)-
Dioleoyl-D,L-α-phosphatidylcholine (DOL)	-methyl-2-aminoethene-
	sulphonic acid (TES)

[a]Abbreviations in parenthesis are used in Table 2.

2. INTERACTION OF MOLECULES WITH LIPOSOMES

Liposomes provide several sites of interactions and binding for guest molecules. Figure 1 schematically represents these sites. Highly polar and relatively small solutes are trapped in the aqueous compartments. Electrostatic interactions play an important part. Anionic liposomes attract cations, but repel anions. This point is illustrated by the interaction of trisodium 8-hydroxy-1,3,6-pyrene-trisulphonate pyranine, with charged dipalmitoyl-D,L-α-phosphatidylcholine liposomes (Kano and Fendler, 1978a). Using fluorescence polarization techniques, pyranine was shown to be well shielded in negatively charged liposome interiors from the phospholipid headgroups by a large number of water molecules. The microviscosity of the environment of this probe, 0.96 cP. corresponds, in fact, closely to that of water ($\eta_{H_2O}^{25} = 0.8904$ cP). Conversely, Pyranine is bound to the surface of cationic liposomes. Here, the microviscosity reported by the probe is greater than 20 cP.

Non-polar molecules are intercalated between the phospholipid bilayer. Amphipathic molecules are anchored into the vesicles by their hydrocarbon chains. The extent and the site of their binding depend on both electrostatic and hydrophobic interactions. Taking advantage of correlations between the fluorescence intensity, emission maxima, and solvent polarities, the effective environment of the dansyl moiety in dansyl

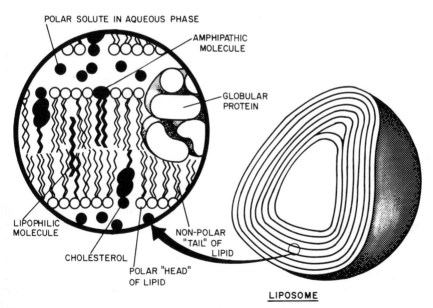

Figure 1 An oversimplified representation of the sites of interactions of polar, apolar, and amphipathic molecules, cholesterol and proteins with multicompartment liposomes

n-octadecyl amine, DSOA, in cationic liposomes was assessed to correspond to that in alcohol (Romero *et al.*, 1976). Interestingly, liposome-solubilized hexadecylpyridinium chloride did not quench the fluorescence of DSOA. Such quenching readily occurred in neat solvents. The probe and quencher are apparently at some distance from each other in the liposome. On the other hand, fluorescence of liposome-entrapped 1-anilino-8-naphthalene sulphonate, a relatively small molecule, was readily quenched both by pyridinium and hexadecylpyridinium chlorides. Clearly, the position of naphthylamine is markedly affected by the presence of a hydrophobic chain.

Macromolecules, particularly proteins often bind to the surface of liposomes (Tyrrell *et al.*, 1976). This is quite analogous to membrane–protein interactions. The predominant driving force is of electrostatic origin. Positively charged proteins are attracted to the surface of negatively charged liposomes and vice versa. In some cases, subsequent to initial electrostatic interactions, hydrophobic associations also come into play. Many proteins, particularly enzymes, have been reported to be in liposome interiors rather than at the outer surface. Such interactions are facilitated if the protein and the vesicle carry the same charge. Enzyme entrapment in liposome interiors, however, has not been unambiguously demonstrated.

A recent and significant development is the hydrogenation of the unsaturated carbon–carbon double bonds in both single and multicompartment intact liposomes (Chapman and Quinn, 1976). Hydrogenation was carried out by using Wilkinson's catalyst, chlorotris(triphenylphosphine) rhodium(I), R (PPh_3Cl). The catalyst partitioned into the phospholipid bilayer. The mobility of the latter ensures the required catalytic contact. Hydrogenation of liposomes will allow a selective modulation of the fluidity of the vesicles. This, of course, is significant in the optimization of drug entrapments in liposomes.

Effects of individual molecules are cumulative and often have pronounced consequences on liposome structures. These, in turn, influence the extent of drug entrapment and retainment. Addition of divalent metal ions promotes membrane aggregation and fusion. Formation of large spirally folded cochleate lipid cylinders, giant liposomes, has been observed in the presence of calcium ions (Papahadjopoulos *et al.*, 1976). Hydrophobic organic ions, on the other hand, inhibit liposome fusion and aggregation (Hauser *et al.*, 1975). Cyclic peptides, antibiotics, and crown ethers function as ionophores: they enhance the selective transport of small ions across lipid bilayers (Shamoo, 1975). Ionophoric properties of drugs should, therefore, be recognized in the utilization of liposomes as drug carriers. In general, the effect of drugs on liposomes should be carefully considered prior to their entrapment (Cater *et al.*, 1974). This is particularly important since the concentration of interacting drug is usually quite high. Maximum pharmacological effects are only to be expected if the amount of drug in a liposome is maximized.

Interaction of selective molecules with liposomes is given in Table 2.

3. FACTORS AFFECTING DRUG ENTRAPMENT IN LIPOSOMES

Extents of drug entrapment in liposomes are in the ranges of 2.2–8.4% for penicillin (Gregoriadis, 1973b), 2.3–11.6% for actinomycin D (Gregoriadis, 1973b), 18% for methoxythrexate (Colley and Ryman, 1975), 0.7–5.4% for 8-azaguanine (Fendler and Romero, 1976), 0.10–0.5% for 6-mercaptopurine (Tsujii *et al.*, 1976), up to 60% for bleomycin (Gregoriadis *et al.*, 1976; Dapergolas *et al.*, 1976), 5% for insulin (Dapergolas *et al.*, 1976), and 20% for cyclic-AMP (Papahadjopoulos *et al.*, 1974). Not all these values are unambiguous, however. Quantitative drug entrapments are best expressed in terms of the number of molecules entrapped in each vesicle and should be related to the volume of trapped water (Tyrrell *et al.*, 1976). Additionally, all pertinent details of liposome preparation and of drug encapsulation therein should be clearly stated.

The volume of the aqueous space within the liposome is one of the most important factors influencing drug entrapment. The larger this volume, the greater the amounts of polar drugs that can be encapsulated. More drugs can be entrapped in multilamellar than in single compartment liposomes (Gregoriadis, 1973a; Fendler and Romero, 1976). The interior volumes of vesicles can be increased by osmotic swelling. Binding of proteins also results in liposome enlargements (Sessa and Weissmann, 1970; Redwood *et al.*, 1975; Dufourq *et al.*, 1976). Alternatively, 'giant liposomes', having $0.13 \pm 0.06 \, \mu$m diameter, can be prepared by mixing sonicated liposomes with calcium ions (Papahadjopoulos *et al.*, 1976) or by the slow injection of ether solutions of the lipid into warm aqueous buffer (Deamer and Bangham, 1976). Although giant liposomes have been utilized as drug carriers (Mayhew *et al.*, 1977), there is only very limited information on their physical chemical properties. Nevertheless, they are potentially important since, in addition to their ability to entrap more drugs, they have different permeabilities than the smaller liposomes. This latter property can furnish some degree of target directing.

Solubilities of the drug in water or in a hydrocarbon solvent also effect the extent of entrapment. The higher the solubility of the drug in water, the greater the amount that can be entrapped in the aqueous compartments of liposomes. Similarly, the higher the solubility of the drug in a non-polar solvent, the greater the amount which can be sequestered in the hydrophobic regions of the liposome. The relatively meagre encapsulation of 6-mercaptopurine, a compound which is rather insoluble both in polar

Table 2 Interaction of Molecules with Liposomes

Molecule	Liposome[a]	Extent of Entrapment	Comment	Reference
EDTA	M EL° M EL$^+$, M EL$^-$, M DPL°, M DPL$^+$, M DPL$^-$	0.4–1.5 mg preparation	Order of entrapment: EL° > EL$^+$ > EI$^-$	Jonah et al., 1975
Cyclic-AMP	S EL$^+$	0.2 μmol of cyclic-AMP/μmol of EL		Papahadjopoulos et al., 1974
Alanyl glycine, alanylalanine	S DPL°		H-Bond formation involving AlaGly carbonyl and N$^+$(CH$_3$)$_3$ groups of DPL is inferred	Nicolav et al., 1974
Methotrexate	S EL$^+$, S EL$^-$, M EL$^+$, M EL$^-$	2–10%	Order of entrapment - M EI$^-$ > M EL$^+$ > S EL$^-$ > S EL$^+$	Kimelberg et al., 1976
6-Mercaptopurine	S DPL°	0.66–1.7 molecules of drug/liposome (depending on pH)		Tsujii et al., 1976
6-Mercaptopurine chloranil charge transfer complex	S DPL°	18–118 molecules of complex/liposome (depending on pH)	1 : 1 Charge transfer complex readily decomposes to donor and acceptor	Tsujii et al., 1976
6-Mercaptopurine 3,5-dinitrobenzoyl-n-butyl-amide charge transfer complex	S DPL°	0.29–3.2 molecules of complex/liposome (depending on pH)	1 : 1 Charge transfer complex readily decomposes to donor and acceptor	Tsujii et al., 1976

Compound	Code	Molecules/liposome	Remarks	Reference
6-Mercaptopurine 3,5-dinitrobenzoyl-phosphatidylethanol amine charge transfer complex	S DPL°	0.7–1.2 molecules of complex/liposome (depending on pH)	1 : 1 Charge transfer complex readily decomposes to donor and acceptor	Tsujii et al., 1976
6-Mercaptopurine vitamin B_{12} complex	S DPL°	79 molecules of complex/liposome	6-Mercaptopurine–vitamin B_{12} complex readily to parent molecules. Decomposition is slower in liposomes than in water	Kano and Fendler, 1977a
8-Azaguanine	S DPL°	2.8–3.2 molecules of drug/liposome (depending on pH)		Tsujii et al., 1976
8-Azaguanine chloranil charge transfer complex	S DPL°	6.6–21 molecules of complex/liposome (depending on pH)	1 : 1 Charge transfer complex readily decomposes to donor and acceptor	Tsujii et al., 1976
8-Azaguanine 3,5-dinitro-benzoly-n-butyl-amide charge transfer complex	S DPL°	3.0–3.6 molecules of complex/liposome	1 : 1 Charge transfer complex readily decomposes to donor and acceptor	Tsujii et al., 1976
8-Azaguanine vitamin B_{12} complex	S DPL°	49 molecules of complex/liposome	8-Azaguanine vitamin B_{12} complex decomposes in water promptly but it is stable for several days in liposomes	Kano and Fendler, 1977a
6-Carboxyfluorescein	S DOL°, S DPL°	200 mM stoichiometric probe	Probe does not fluoresce in liposomes due to self-quenching. If released, there is fluorescence. Can be used to localize liposome–cell fusions.	Weinstein et al., 1977
All-trans-1,6--diphenyl-1,3,5--hexatriene	S DML°		Nanosecond time dependent fluorescence polarization indicates that the range over which rotation of the probe can freely occur is restricted.	Chen et al., 1977

Table 2 (Continued)

Molecule	Liposome[a]	Extent of Entrapment	Comment	Reference
Halothene, trichloroethylene, diethyl ether	S EL°		Anaesthetics shift the phase transition of liposomes to lower temperature, increase the size of the melted lipids hence increase passive diffusion rates of various substances in membranes	Vanderkooi et al., 1977
Pentabarbitone, thiopentane, phenobarbitone	M DPL°, M DPL$^-$, M DPL$^+$		Phase transition temperature reduced	Lee, 1976
Vitamin K	S EL$^-$		Liposome-entrapped vitamin K reacts with vitamin K reductase. This reaction does not occur in water or in aqueous micellar solutions.	Martius et al., 1975
Tetracaine	S EL°	one vesicle: one tetracaine	Tetracaine added as solid to vesicles. Interaction at the liposome surface. Tetracaine replaces cations but does not transfer to inside	Yeagle et al., 1977
Penicillin and Actinomycin D	S DPL$^+$, S DPL$^-$, S EL$^+$, S EL$^-$	2.2–11.6%	Order of entrapment: DPL > EL	Gregoriadis, 1973b
Insulin	S EL$^-$	6–26% of initial insulin		Patel and Ryman, 1976
Double stranded RNA polyinosinic--polycytidylic acid	Giant liposome		Enhanced cellular uptake of liposome-entrapped RNA as compared to free RNA	Mayhew et al., 1977
Poly I : poly C and poly I	S DPL$^+$, S DPL$^-$ S SM	8.9%		Straub et al., 1974
Rhodopsin	M soya bean phospholipids		Light excitation of rhodopsin leads to the formation of a transmembrane channel	Darszon et al., 1977

Substance	Lipid	Value	Remarks	Reference
Bovine brain gangliosides	M DPL°	prepared as gangliosides: lipid = 0.05: 0.1 molar ratio	Gangliosides containing liposomes bind specifically to bovine thyrotropin	Aloj et al., 1977
Horseradish peroxidase	S SM Sphingomyelin	2.5–5%	Entrapment independent of added Mg^{2+} and pH (6–7)	Magee et al., 1974
Lysozyme	M EL°, M EL$^+$, M EL$^-$, M DPL°	~8%	Increasing incorporation of stearylamine (in M EL$^+$) increases the aqueous interspaces hence the entrapment	Sessa and Weissmann, 1970
Lysozyme, cytochrome c, ribonuclease, poly-L-lysine	S PS$^-$		Sodium permeability increases; proteins are bound to liposomes	Kimelberg and Papahadjopoulos, 1971
Cytochrome d-b$_5$	S EL°	One protein/one EL molecule	Hydrophilic moiety of cytochrome b$_5$ (cytochrome t-b$_5$) does not interact with liposomes. Cytochrome d-b$_5$ is anchored onto the liposome surface by the hydrocarbon tail. Diameter of the single compartment increases from 250 Å in the absence to 800 Å in the presence of the protein	Dufourcq et al., 1976
L-Asparaginase	M EL$^-$		12% of original enzyme activity remained in washed liposomes	Fishman and Citri, 1975
E. coli ^{3}[H] RNA	Giant liposome	5% of added RNA		Ostro et al., 1977
Dextranase	S EL°	15–20%		Colley and Ryman, 1976
Sialoglycoprotein of mammalian erythrocytes	S EL°		Size of liposomes increases in the presence of protein	Redwood et al., 1975
Noradrenalin and 5-Hydroxytryptamine	S EL°, S PI°, S PE°, S PS°		Accumulation of drugs on liposomes as a function of time, temperature, and chemical composition of vesicles was investigated	Ahtee and Johnson, 1974

[a]The symbols S and M refer to single compartment (sonicated) and multicompartment vesicles. Abbreviations for given lipids are in Table 1. The subscripts indicate neutral (°), positive ($^+$) and negatively ($^-$) charged vesicles.

and apolar solvents, in liposomes illustrates this point (Tsujii *et al.*, 1976). Changing the solubility of a drug by chemical modification is a relatively convenient way to ensure greater entrapment. The next section will provide some examples of this approach.

4. ENHANCING DRUG ENTRAPMENT IN LIPOSOMES

Enhanced aqueous solubility of drugs can be readily achieved by adjusting the pH of the solution to ionize available functional groups. It is quite possible to maintain pH gradients in excess of 2 units for a period of several hours or longer across liposomes. These gradients can be readily monitored by pyranine as a probe for measuring hydrogen ion concentrations in the aqueous interiors of anionic liposomes (Kano and Fendler, 1978a). Observing the excitation spectra at an emission wavelength of 510 nm, maxima of 400 and 450 nm are attributable to the un-ionized and ionized forms of pyranine. Intensity ratios of these maxima change 5,000-fold in the pH 4–8 region and remain unaffected by the presence of quenchers. Pyranine has three ionized sulphonate groups in this pH region and is, therefore, strongly repelled from the negatively charged head groups. The microviscosity reported by this probe in anionic liposomes, 0.96 cP (*vide supra*), is in accord with this solubilization site. Proton permeability across the lipid bilayer is dependent upon the buffer used to adjust the pH inside the liposome. Using borate or phosphate buffer, pH gradients can be maintained for longer than 24 hours. Proton permeability in the presence of sodium acetate buffer occurs, however, within minutes. These data provide means for the more effective entrapment of drugs. It should also be possible to preserve sensitive drugs in the carriers at pH values different from the surrounding *in vivo* media. Slow release of liposome-entrapped insulin is a conceivable application.

Formation of more soluble prodrugs is also a promising method for enhanced drug entrapment in liposomes. Incorporation of 8-azaguanine and 6-mercaptopurine increased dramatically by the addition of chloranil (Tsujii *et al.*, 1976; Table 2). Apparently, the chloranil–drug charge transfer complex is more soluble in the liposome than the drug. Subsequent to entrapment, the charge transfer complex readily decomposes to its parent donor and acceptor. Encapsulation of the charged transfer complexes 8-azaguanine and 6-mercaptopurine with 3,5-dinitrobenzoyl-phosphatidylethanolamine is only marginally greater than that of the parent purines (Table 2). A serious disadvantage of these methods is the toxicity of chloranil.

Enhanced entrapment of vitamin B_{12} complexes of purine antagonists presents several advantages. They are entrapped in increased amounts (Table 2). Rate constants for the interaction of these ligands (L) with vitamin B_{12} (B_{12}-Co-OH$_2$) have been determined in water as a function of pH (Kano and Fendler, 1978b). The complete reaction scheme is described by:

$$
\begin{array}{ccc}
\text{B}_{12}-\text{Co}-\text{OH} & & \\[4pt]
\quad Ko \big\updownarrow \text{H}^+ & \qquad K_1 & \\[6pt]
\text{B}_{12}-\text{Co}-\text{OH}_2^+ + \text{LH} \; \underset{k_{-1}}{\overset{k_1}{\rightleftharpoons}} \; \text{B}_{12}-\text{Co}-\text{LH}^+ + \text{H}_2\text{O} \\[6pt]
\quad K_1 \big\updownarrow \text{H}^+ \quad K_2 \qquad\qquad K_{II} \big\updownarrow \text{H}^+ \\[6pt]
\text{B}_{12}-\text{Co}-\text{OH}_2^+ + \text{L}^- \; \underset{k_{-2}}{\overset{k_2}{\rightleftharpoons}} \; \text{B}_{12}-\text{Co}-\text{L} + \text{H}_2\text{O} \\[6pt]
\quad Ko \big\updownarrow +\text{H}^+ \qquad\qquad K_{III} \big\updownarrow +\text{H}^+ \\[6pt]
\text{B}_{12}-\text{Co}-\text{OH} \qquad\qquad \text{B}_{12}-\text{Co}-\text{L}^-
\end{array}
$$

where k_1, k_2 are rate constants for complex formation with neutral and ionized purine antagonists, k_{-1} and k_{-2}, are corresponding constants for their decomposition and Ko, K_1, K_{II}, and K_{III} are dissociation constants for vitamin B_{12}, for the attacking ligand, and for the different protonated forms of the vitamin B_{12} complexes as defined by the above scheme. The kinetic data indicated the prompt formation of the 6-mercaptopurine ($k_1 = 40$ M^{-1} s^{-1}, $k_2 = 800$ M^{-1} s^{-1}) and 8-azaguanine ($k_1 = 62.0$ M^{-1} s^{-1}, $k_2 = 220$ M^{-1} s^{-1}) complexes of vitamin B_{12}. The 6-mercaptopurine complex decomposed considerably faster ($k_1 = 18.4$ s^{-1}, $k_{-2} = 1.4 \times 10^{-2}$ s^{-1}) than the 8-azaguanine complex ($k_{-1} = 2.0 \times 10^{-2}$ s^{-1}, $k_{-2} = 8.8 \times 10^{-2}$ s^{-1}). Very significantly, the decomposition of these complexes is considerably retarded if they are entrapped in negatively charged liposomes. At pH = 7 and 25 °C half-lives of the 6-mercaptopurine and 8-azaguanine complexes in water are 1 and 10 minutes, respectively. In liposomes, the half-life for the decomposition of the former is 50 minutes and liposome-entrapped vitamin B_{12}–8-azaguanine is stable for several days.

Vitamin B_{12} itself has many beneficial pharmacological effects. Methylcobalamine, the coenzyme of methionine synthetase has an important role in regulating folate metabolism. In the absence of this enzyme, 5-methyltetrahydrofolate accumulates with the resultant inhibition of cell replication. The *in vivo* inhibition of methionine synthetase can be affected by the use of the substrate or methylcobalamine analogues (Paranchych and Cooper, 1962; Finkler and Hall, 1967). The 6-mercaptopurine and 8-azaguanine complexes of vitamin B_{12} can serve as methylcobalamine analogues, and they provide, therefore, an additional target in cancer chemotherapy (Huennekens *et al.*, 1976). Additionally, enhanced incorporation and metabolism of vitamin B_{12} have been reported in tumour tissues (Blomquist *et al.*, 1969; Pakarskyte *et al.*, 1975a, 1975b). Entrapments of vitamin B_{12} complexes of 6-mercaptopurine and 8-azaguanine in liposomes have, therefore, several potential advantages. First, the amount of drug encapsulated is increased. Second, if the drugs are released from the liposomes as vitamin B_{12} complexes, they may recognize damaged tissues and act as substrate analogues for methylcobalamine thereby providing an additional chemotherapeutic target. Finally, if they are liberated from the liposomes subsequent to their decomposition, they will be free to act as purine antimetabolites and vitamin B_{12} (Kano and Fendler, 1977b).

An attempt has been made to survey drug entrapments in liposomes from chemical and biophysical vantage points. Although some progress has been made in this area, there are many unexplored aspects and, indeed, there are new and as yet unknown avenues of exploration. It is sincerely hoped that this chapter will stimulate new and significant research.

Acknowledgements

It is a pleasure to acknowledge the diligent and faithful work of my co-workers whose names appear in joint publications. Without their competent assistance, there would have been no material to write this survey. Thanks are due to the National Science Foundation and the Robert A. Welch Foundation for their financial support.

REFERENCES

Ahtee, L. and Johnson, S. M. (1974). *Acta Physiol. Scand.*, **90**, 94.
Aloj, S. M., Kohn, L. D., Lee, G. and Meldolesi, M. F. (1977). *Biochem. Biophys. Res. Commun.*, **74**, 1053.
Bangham, A. D. (1968). *Progress in Biophysics and Molecular Biology* (J. A. V. Gutler and D. Noble, eds.), **18**, p. 29, Pergamon Press, Oxford.
Bangham, A. D., Hill, M. W. and Miller, N. G. A. (1974). *Methods in Membrane Biology* (E. D. Korn, ed.), **11**, p. 38, Plenum Press, New York.
Blomquist, L., Flodh, H. and Ullberg, S. (1969). *Experientia*, **25**, 294.
Cater, B. R., Chapman, D., Hawes, S. M. and Saville, J. (1974). *Biochim. Biophys. Acta*, **363**, 54.
Chapman, D. and Quinn, P. J. (1976). *Proc. Nat. Acad. Sci.*, **73**, 3971.
Chen, L. A., Dale, R. E., Roth, S. and Brand, L. (1977). *J. Biol. Chem.*, **252**, 2163.
Colley, C. M. and Ryman, B. E. (1975). *Biochem. Soc. Transactions*, **3**, 157.
Colley, C. M. and Ryman, B. E. (1976). *Biochim. Biophys. Acta*, **451**, 417.
Dapergolas, G., Neerunjun, E. D. and Gregoriadis, G. (1976). *FEBS Lett.*, **63**, 235.
Darszon, A., Montal, M. and Zarko, J. (1971): *Biochem. Biophys. Res. Commun.*, **76**, 820.
Deamer, D. and Bangham, A. D. (1976). *Biochim. Biophys. Acta*, **443**, 629.

Dufourcq, J., Bernon, R. and Lussan, C. (1976). *Biochim. Biophys. Acta*, **433**, 252.

Fendler, J. H. (1976). *Accounts Chem. Res.,* **9**, 153.

Fendler, J. H. and Fendler, E. J. (1975). *Catalysis in Micellar and Macromolecular Systems*, Academic Press, New York.

Fendler, J. H. and Romero, A. (1976). *Life Sciences*, **18**, 1453.

Fendler, J. H. and Romero, A. (1977). *Life Sciences*, **20**, 1109.

Finkler, A. E. and Hall, C. A. (1967). *Arch. Biochem. Biophys.,* **120**, 79.

Fishman, Y. and Citri, N. (1975). *FEBS Lett.,* **60**, 17.

Gregoriadis, G. (1973a). *New Scientist*, **60**, 890.

Gregoriadis, G. (1973b). *FEBS Lett.,* **36**, 292.

Gregoriadis, G. (1976). *New England J. Med.,* **295**, 704.

Gregoriadis, G., Dapergolas, G. and Neerunjun, E. D. (1976). *Biochem. Soc. Transactions,* **4**, 256.

Hauser, H., Philips, M. C. and Barratt, M. D. (1975). *Biochim. Biophys. Acta,* **413**, 341–353.

Huennekens, F. M., Digirolamo, P. M., Fujii, K., Jacobsen, E. W. and Vitols, K. S. (1976). *Advances in Enzyme Regulations* (G. Weber, ed.), **14**, p. 187, Pergamon Press, Oxford.

Jonah, M. M., Cerny, E. A. and Rahman, Y. E. (1975). *Biochim. Biophys. Acta,* **401**, 336.

Kano, K. and Fendler, J. H. (1977a). *Life Sciences*, **20**, 1729.

Kano, K. and Fendler, J. H. (1977b). Unpublished results.

Kano, K. and Fendler, J. H. (1978a). *Biochim. Biophys. Acta,* **509**, 289–299.

Kano, K. and Fendler, J. H. (1978b). Unpublished results.

Kimelberg, H. K. and Papahadjopoulos, D. (1971). *J. Biol. Chem.,* **246**, 1142.

Kimelberg, H. K., Tracy, T. F., Jr., Biddlecome, S. M. and Bourke, R. S. (1976). *Cancer Res.,* **36**, 2949.

Lee, A. G. (1976). *Biochim. Biophys. Acta,* **455**, 102.

McDougall, I. R., Dunnick, J. K., McNamee, M. G. and Kriss, J. P. (1974). *Proc. Nat. Acad. Sci. USA,* **71**, 3487–3491.

Magee, W. E., Goff, C. W., Schoknecht, J., Smith, M. D. and Cherian, K. (1974). *J. Cell. Biol.,* **63**, 492.

Mayhew, E., Papahadjopoulos, D., O'Malley, J. A., Carter, W. A. and Vail, W. J. (1977). *Mol Pharmacol.,* **13**, 488.

Martius, C., Ganser, R. and Viviani, A. (1975). *FEBS Lett.,* **59**, 13.

Nicolav, C., Dreeskamp, H. and Schulte-Frohlinde, D. (1974). *FEBS Lett.,* **43**, 148.

Ostro, M. J., Giacomoni, D. and Dray, S. (1977). *Biochem. Biophys. Res. Commun.,* **76**, 836.

Pakarskyte, K., Kanopkaite, S., Brazenas, G., Zougte, V. and Aleksiene, A. (1974). Liet. TSR Mokslu Akad. Darb. Ser C.3., 187 (CA 82 93215e (1975a)).

Pakarskyte, K., Kanopkaite, S., Brazenas, G., Zougte, V. and Aleksiene, A. (1974). Liet. TST Mokslu Akad. Darb. Ser L.1., 201 (CA 82 80474p (1975b)).

Papahadjopoulos, D. and Kimelberg, K. K. (1973). *Prog. Surface Sci.,* **4**, 141.

Papahadjopoulos, D., Poste, G. and Mayhew, E. (1974). *Biochim. Biophys. Acta,* **363**, 404.

Papahadjopoulos, D., Vail, W. J., Pangborn, W. A. and Poste, G. (1976). *Biochim. Biophys. acta,* **448**, 265.

Paranchych, W. and Cooper, B. A. (1962). *Biochim. Biophys. acta,* **60**, 393.

Patel, H. M. and Ryman, B. E. (1976). *FEBS Lett.,* **62**, 60.

Redwood, W. R., Jansons, V. K. and Patel, B. C. (1975). *Biochim. Biophys. Acta,* **406**, 347.

Romero, A., Sunamoto, J. and Fendler, J. H. (1976). *Colloid and Interface Sci.,* **V,** 111.

Sessa, G. and Weissmann, G. (1970). *J. Biol. Chem.,* **245,** 3295.

Shamoo, A. E. (1975). *Carriers and Channels in Biological Systems,* Ann. N.Y. Acad. Sci., **264.**

Straub, S. X., Garry, R. F. and Magee, W. E. (1974). *Infect. Immunity,* **10,** 783.

Tsujii, K., Sunamoto, J. and Fendler, J. H. (1976). *Life Sciences,* **19,** 1743.

Tyrrell, D. A., Heath, T. D., Colley, C. M. and Ryman, B. E. (1976). *Biochim. Biophys. Acta,* **457,** 259.

Vanderkooi, J. M., Landesberg, R., Selick, H. and McDonald, G. G. (1977). *Biochim. Biophys. Acta,* **464,** 1.

Weinstein, J. N., Yoshikami, S., Henkart, P., Blumenthal, R. and Hagins, W. A. (1977). *Science,* **195,** 489.

Yeagle, P. L., Hutton, W. C. and Martin, R. B. (1977). *Biochim. Biophys. Acta,* **465,** 173.

Liposomes in Biological Systems
Edited by G. Gregoriadis and A. C. Allison
©1980, John Wiley & Sons, Ltd.

CHAPTER 4

The Interaction of Lipid Vesicles (Liposomes) with Cultured Cells and their use as Carriers for Drugs and Macromolecules

G. Poste

1. **Introduction**   102

2. **Mechanisms of vesicle–cell interactions** *in vitro*   103
    2.1. Endocytosis   111
    2.2. Exchange diffusion and/or transfer of membrane
          components between vesicles and cells   118
    2.3. Adsorption of vesicles to the cell surface and fusion with
          the plasma membrane   121
          2.3.1. Electron microscopy   122
          2.3.2. Subcellular localization of vesicle-derived
                  components by cell fractionation   127
          2.3.3. Ligand-induced redistribution and capping of
                  vesicle-derived components at the cell surface   128
          2.3.4. Measurement of the lateral mobility of vesicle-
                  derived components at the cell surface   129
          2.3.5. Vesicle-mediated transfer of novel proteins
                  and glycoproteins into the plasma membrane   130
          2.3.6. Elution of adsorbed vesicles   130
          2.3.7. Vesicle-induced cell fusion   131
          2.3.8. Release of vesicle-encapsulated materials into
                  the cytoplasm   133
          2.3.9. The molecular mechanism for fusion of lipid
                  vesicles with the plasma membrane   135

3. **Lipid vesicles as carriers for introducing biologically active
    materials into cells**   138

4. **Conclusions**   145

    References   148

1. INTRODUCTION

Studies of the plasma membrane have long emphasized its role as a barrier in separating the intra- and extracellular environments and the importance of this function in maintaining the stability of the intracellular milieu. Extracellular materials can enter cells by passive diffusion, by specific transport mechanisms or be taken up by endocytosis within invaginated segments of the plasma membrane which are internalized into the cytoplasm. Various combinations of these mechanisms are employed in different cell types to achieve some degree of selectivity in the uptake of extracellular materials and to exclude a wide range of materials that could perturb the intracellular environment. This selectivity, while vital to the cell, is often frustrating to the experimentalist who wishes to study the cellular response to a specific molecule or macromolecule, but finds that the cell either excludes the material completely or fails to incorporate it in sufficient amounts to affect cell function. There is thus a need for a carrier vehicle which can be used to introduce non-permeable biologically active materials into different compartments of the cell and bypass the mechanism(s) normally responsible for excluding such materials from the intracellular environment. As a result of work done in many laboratories over the last five years, there is a growing optimism that lipid vesicles (liposomes) may provide an efficient and versatile carrier system for introducing diverse biologically active materials into cells both *in vitro* and *in vivo*.

As discussed later in this chapter, and in several other chapters in this volume, lipid vesicles have emerged as a potentially powerful tool for enhancing the uptake of materials into cells both *in vivo* and *in vitro*, including materials which are not ordinarily taken up by cells. The goal in many of these initial studies of vesicle–cell interactions has been to demonstrate that materials encapsulated within vesicles can affect cell function and less attention has been given to the more basic question of how vesicles are incorporated into cells. It is clear, however, that effective use of lipid vesicles as carrier vehicles demands at least some basic appreciation of the mechanisms by which these structures interact with cells and knowledge of the intracellular distribution and eventual fate of various vesicle components. Insight into the mechanism(s) of vesicle uptake is also fundamental to the development of experimental methods whereby vesicles and their contents could be directed to specific regions of the cell. For example, fusion of a vesicle with the plasma membrane will result in release of the vesicle contents into the cytoplasm and incorporattion of the vesicle membrane into the plasma membrane (Figure 1). In contrast, uptake of intact vesicles via endocytosis offers a pathway for introducing vesicles and their contents into the lysosomal apparatus (Figure 1). Finally, the exchange and transfer of membrane components between vesicles adsorbed to the cell surface and the plasma membrane offers opportunities for modifying plasma membrane composition (Figure 1). The potential experimental applications of this type of 'targeting' of vesicle components to defined regions of the cell do not require emphasis.

In this chapter, we will review what is presently known concerning the interaction of lipid vesicles of differing size, surface charge, and lipid composition with cultured mammalian cells and the importance of vesicle membrane properties in determining the outcome of vesicle–cell interactions. The use of lipid vesicles as carriers to introduce drugs and macromolecules into cultured cells will also be discussed, emphasizing the value of this technology as an experimental tool in cell biology, cellular pharmacology, and virology.

2. MECHANISMS OF VESICLE–CELL INTERACTIONS *IN VITRO*

Most of the available information on the mechanisms involved in the interaction and uptake of lipid vesicles by cultured cells has come from experiments in which vesicles containing radiolabelled phospholipids in the vesicle membrane are incubated with cells under defined conditions and the amount of cell-associated radioactivity measured after various intervals. Other membrane markers such as fluorescent probes (Hock and Stöhr, 1977), electron spin probes (Grant and McConnell, 1973; Dunnick *et al.*, 1976), and antigens (Martin and MacDonald, 1976c) have been used in a few studies. Also, as discussed in more detail below, vesicles containing radiolabelled phospholipid lipid membrane marker and a different marker encapsulated within the vesicle lumen can be used to determine whether vesicles interact with cells as intact structures or if leakage of encapsulated material occurs during the interaction with cells. Encapsulated markers used for this purpose include radiolabelled compounds such as sucrose (Poste and Papahadjopoulos, 1976a; Bouma *et al.*, 1977), glucose (Batzri and Korn, 1975), inulin (Batzri and Korn, 1975; Huang and Pagano, 1975), cyclic nucleotides (Papahadjopoulos *et al.*, 1974a,c), bleomycin (Gregoriadis and Neerunjun, 1975), technetium (Dunnick *et al.*, 1976), and methotrexate (Tyrrell *et al.*, 1977), and markers which can be identified biochemically or cytochemically such as horseradish peroxidase (Magee *et al.*, 1974; Weissmann *et al.*, 1977), hexosaminidase (Cohen *et al.*, 1976), arsenazo III (Weissmann *et al.*, 1977) and 6-carboxyfluorescein (Szoka *et al.*, 1979).

The recovery of vesicle-derived lipids or other marker molecules in association with cells does not necessarily mean that vesicles have been incorporated into the cells. That at least some vesicles are incorporated is indicated by the many reports discussed later in this chapter and elsewhere

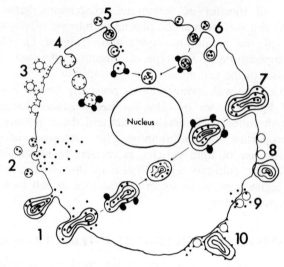

Figure 1 Schematic representation of the possible mechanisms by which small unilamellar (SUV) and multilamellar (MLV) vesicles could interact with cells cultured *in vitro*. SUVs and MLVs have not been drawn to scale with respect to each other or in relation to the cell and intracellular structures. Modified from Poste and Papahadjopoulos (1978).

1–5: Fusion of vesicles with the plasma membrane will result in the release of material(s) entrapped within vesicles (•) directly into the cytoplasm (1 and 2) and the assimilation of vesicle membrane components into the plasma membrane (3).

In the case of MLVs (1) fusion of the outermost lamella of the vesicle with the plasma membrane will result in the introduction of the bulk of the vesicle directly into the cytoplasm where it would probably undergo fusion with lysosomes (dark structures) followed by eventual breakdown of the vesicle by lysosomal enzymes and release of the vesicle contents. The ability of vesicle-encapsulated material to reach other regions of the cell will then depend on the permeability properties of the limiting membrane of the vacuole which is derived from both vesicle and lysosomal membranes.

Vesicle membrane components introduced into the plasma membrane via fusion (3) could either remain within the plasma membrane (and presumably be free to diffuse laterally within the plane of the membrane) or be internalized via endocytosis (4) and subsequently interact with lysosomes. Another possible pathway for vesicle uptake involving fusion is shown in (5) where the vesicle is initially internalized within an endocytic vacuole but this is immediately followed by fusion between the vesicle membrane and the membrane of the endocytic vacuole (i.e. before the interaction between the endocytic vacuole and lysosomes). If this fusion event is accompanied by enhanced membrane permeability similar to that reported in fusion of both natural and model membranes then vesicle contents (ᴗ) could well be released into the cytoplasm. A stable membrane-bound vacuole is formed after fusion and this would be expected to interact with lysosomes.

6–7: Endocytosis of unilamellar (6) and multilamellar vesicles (7) followed by fusion between endocytic vacuoles containing the internalized vesicles and lysosomes. The action of lysosomal lipases on the vesicle membrane(s) will probably result in vesicle breakdown and release of vesicle-encapsulated material. The resistance of in this volume showing that materials which are not normally taken up by cells in sufficient amounts to affect cell function can produce marked alterations in cellular metabolism and/or behaviour when added to cells encapsulated within vesicles. There is a growing recognition, however, that in many situations adsorption of vesicles to the cell surface without actual uptake by cells may represent a major fraction of the cell-associated vesicle population. Detailed knowledge of the true extent of intracellular incorporation of vesicle components is crucial for studies using lipid vesicles as carriers for drugs and other biologically active agents since accurate dose–response relationships cannot be defined until such information is available.

The interaction of lipid vesicles with cultured cells could involve the following non-exclusive mechanisms:

(1) fusion of vesicles with the plasma membrane (Figure 1, pathways 1–5);
(2) incorporation of intact vesicles by endocytosis (Figure 1, pathways 5–7);
(3) adsorption of vesicles or fragments of vesicle membrane to the cell surface without true incorporation of vesicle components (Figure 1, pathways 8 and 9);
(4) transfer or exchange of phospholipids (and proteins?) between the vesicle membrane and the plasma membrane (Figure 1, pathway 10); and
(5) any combination of the above mechanisms.

Some insight into which of the above mechanisms contribute to the total number of cell-associated vesicles in any given situation can be obtained by determining whether vesicles interact with cells as intact structures or whether vesicle membrane components associate with cells at a different rate to material(s) encapsulated inside the vesicle. This can be established using vesicles containing two different marker components—one associated with the vesicle membrane (usually radiolabelled phospholipid(s) or cholesterol) and the other, a water-soluble compound encapsulated within

---

released material to digestion by lysosomal enzymes and the permeability of the lysosomal membrane will determine whether material (or the digested product) will be able to diffuse out of the lysosome to reach other intracellular sites.

8: Adsorption of vesicles to the cell surface without true uptake of vesicle components by the cell.

9: Adsorption of vesicles to the cell surface with accompanying alterations in the permeability of vesicle and cellular membranes. Binding of vesicles to cell surface components could promote 'leakage' of vesicle-encapsulated material (•) which is incorporated into cells via passive diffusion as a result of a reciprocal vesicle-mediated increase in plasma membrane permeability.

10: Reciprocal transfer of components (▲) between adsorbed vesicles and the plasma membrane via exchange diffusion

the vesicle. Comparison of the ratio of the encapsulated and membrane labels recovered in association with cells with that in the original vesicle preparation will reveal whether the cell-associated vesicle population is composed of intact vesicles (i.e. no change in encapsulated · membrane label ratio) or whether preferential association of particular vesicle components has occurred (e.g. uptake of the membrane label without accompanying uptake of encapsulated label). Similarly, vesicles containing two or more membrane markers (e.g. radiolabelled phospholipids, cholesterol, glycolipids, proteins and glycoproteins) can be used to establish whether different membrane components become cell-associated at different rates.

Experiments of this kind using negatively and positively charged SUVs composed of phosphatidylcholine (PC) and cholesterol (Papahadjopoulos *et al.*, 1974a,c; Poste and Papahadjopoulos, 1976a) and neutral vesicles composed of egg phosphatidylcholine (Batzri and Korn, 1975) have shown that encapsulated and membrane labels associate with cells to a similar extent at 37 °C (ratio ≥ 0.95), indicating that the cell-associated vesicle population is comprised primarily of intact vesicles. Further experiments to identify the mechanisms involved in the interaction of these vesicles with cells would therefore logically focus on the respective contributions of vesicle adsorption, endocytosis, and fusion, and ignore mechanisms in which only limited or selective transfer of particular vesicle components would occur (e.g. exchange diffusion or transfer).

There is evidence from both model and natural membranes (reviews, Paphadjopoulos, 1978; Poste and Pasternak, 1978) that membrane fusion is accompanied by a significant increase in membrane permeability. It is not known at present whether fusion of vesicles with the cellular plasma membrane would produce such an increase in permeability and leakage of encapsulated materials from the vesicles. It is to be noted, however, that there have been various reports indicating that vesicle–cell interactions are accompanied by variable loss of vesicle-encapsulated materials (see below). This loss cannot be automatically attributed to fusion, since various other factors can promote leakage of encapsulated material from vesicles. For example, adsorption of vesicles to the cell surface could be accompanied by leakage of encapsulated materials. This, in turn, means that any endocytosis of 'leaky' adsorbed vesicles will also be recorded as being accompanied by loss of vesicle contents.

The extent of the loss of encapsulated materials from vesicles during their interaction with cells varies considerably (see below). In addition, leakage of encapsulated material is significantly greater in the presence of serum or high molecular weight proteins (Papahadjopoulos *et al.*, 1973b; Black and Gregoriadis, 1976; Tyrell *et al.*, 1977; Zborowski *et al.*, 1977). Binding of serum components to vesicles may also alter the mechanisms by which vesicles interact with cells *in vitro* (Weissmann *et al.*, 1975; Tyrrell *et al*., 1977). This problem not only hinders comparison of different *in vitro* studies done in the presence or absence of such materials, but also emphasizes the need for caution in concluding that the mechanisms involved in vesicle–cell interactions *in vitro* in serum-free chemically defined media or physiologic salt solutions are necessarily representative of events *in vivo*.

Loss of encapsulated material from vesicles during incubation with cells at 37 °C has been reported with both negatively and positively charged vesicles composed of phospholipids that are 'fluid' at 37 °C; (encapsulated : membrane label ratio typically falling within the range 0.8 to 0.95; Magee *et al*., 1974; Batzri and Korn, 1975; Gregoriadis and Neerunjun, 1975; Pagano and Huang, 1975; Poste and Papahadjopoulos, 1976a; Weissmann *et al*., 1977).

This partial loss of vesicle contents could result from several non-exclusive mechanisms:

(1) fusion of vesicles with the plasma membrane with partial loss of encapsulated label due to an increase in vesicle membrane permeability during fusion;
(2) an increase in the permeability of vesicles when adsorbed to the cell surface; and/or
(3) selective transfer of vesicle membrane components to the plasma membrane by exchange diffusion (without accompanying transfer of encapsulated label) simultaneous with some uptake of intact vesicles. This would result in an 'apparent' loss of vesicle contents. That significant exchange diffusion is not occurring at 37 °C with charged fluid vesicles is suggested by studies with vesicles containing two membrane-associated labels ([^{3}H]phospholipid; [^{14}C]cholesterol) in which both labels were found to associate with cells at the same rate (Papahadjopoulos *et al*., 1975a,c; Stendahl and Tagesson, 1977).

In addition to possible leakage of the vesicle contents during vesicle–plasma membrane fusion, it seems likely that mere adsorption of vesicles to the cell surface may increase leakage of encapsulated materials (see, for example, Szoka *et al*., 1979). As mentioned, binding of proteins to vesicles increases their permeability, and binding of vesicles to cell surface proteins (Bouma *et al*., 1977; Pagano and Takeichi, 1977) might thus promote permeability changes. The susceptibility of adsorbed vesicles to protein-mediated leakage may also be influenced by the 'fluidity' of the lipids in the vesicle membrane. Tyrrell *et al*. (1977) have reported that β-globulins induced significant leakage of material from 'fluid' vesicles but did not promote leakage from 'solid' vesicles. This greater susceptibility of fluid vesicles to protein-mediated leakage may account for the lack of leakage of encapsulated label from solid vesicles in the experiments discussed at the beginning of this section. Papahadjopoulos *et al.* (1973b) have reported that the presence of cholesterol in the vesicle membrane inhibits the increased permeability induced by various proteins.

Particularly extensive loss of vesicle-encapsulated material during incubation with cells at physiological temperatures has been reported for neutral vesicles composed of the synthetic lecithins dimyristoyl phosphatidylcholine (DMPC), and dipalmitoyl phosphatidylcholine (DPPC), in which only 10–40% of the encapsulated label becomes associated with cells (Batzri and Korn, 1975; Bouma *et al.*, 1977; but see Pagano and Huang, 1975 for dissenting data). Assuming that release of encapsulated label occurs uniformly in all vesicles, very few intact (non-leaky) vesicles can be present in the cell-associated population. Vesicles prepared from

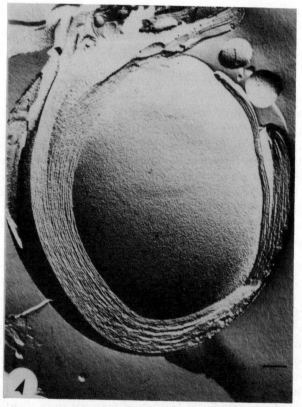

Figure 2 Freeze-fracture electron micrograph of dimyristoyl phosphatidylcholine (MLV) suspended by vortex shaking in 100 mM NaCl buffer at 37 °C and then equilibrated at 45 °C before freezing to low temperature. Bar = 0.25 μm. Reproduced with permission from Papahadjopoulos *et al.* (1979a)

these lipids are known to display an inherently greater permeability than SUVs prepared from natural (fluid) lecithins (Papahadjopoulos *et al.*, 1973b). In addition, structural disorder within the lipid bilayer of DMPC and DPPC vesicles at temperatures close to the phase transition (Wu and McConnell, 1973; Jacobson and Papahadjopoulos, 1975; Janik *et al.*, 1976) may facilitate binding and penetration of cell surface proteins into the bilayer which would further increase leakage from these vesicles.

The various patterns of transfer of membrane and encapsulated labels to cells seen with vesicles at 37 °C change significantly at lower temperatures. At 2 °C membrane label associates selectively with cells, with little or no transfer of encapsulated label (Batzri and Korn, 1975; Huang and Pagano,

Figure 3 Freeze-fracture electron micrograph of sonicated (SUVs) phosphatidyl-serine vesicles in 100 mM NaCl buffer, pH 7.4. Scale bar = 0.1 μm (1,000 Å). Reproduced with permission from Papahadjopoulos *et al.* (1975)

Liposomes in Biological Systems

1975). This, together with evidence showing that different vesicle membrane components become cell-associated at different rates at 2 °C (Huang and Pagano, 1975) suggests that exchange diffusion dominates vesicle–cell interactions at this temperature (also see p. 119).

Unless stated otherwise, the work reviewed in the following sections concerns the interaction between vesicles and cultured cell populations occurring in serum-free, chemically defined culture media or physiological salt solutions.

The following definitions will be used when referring to different classes of lipid vesicles. The term multilamellar vesicle (MLV) will be used to refer to large (0.5–10 μm diameter) liquid-crystalline structures containing multiple lamellae (bilayers) (Figure 2) which are formed when phospholipids are dispersed in aqueous solutions as described originally by

Figure 4 Freeze-fracture electron micrograph of sonicated phosphatidylserine after addition of CaCl$_2$ (10 mM) and EDTA (15 mM) showing large unilamellar vesicles (LUVs). Arrowhead shows direction of shadowing. Scale bar = 0.1 μm (1,000 Å). Reproduced with permission from Papahadjopoulos *et al*. (1975)

Bangham *et al.* (1965). The designation small unilamellar vesicle (SUV) will be used to refer to the small vesicles (Figure 3) formed by ultrasonication of MLVs (Papahadjopoulos and Miller, 1967; Huang, 1969). These structures are much smaller (250–1,000 Å diameter) and comprise a single internal aqueous space enclosed by a single lipid bilayer. A further class of unilamellar vesicles, referred to as large unilamellar vesicles (LUVs), will also be discussed in this article. These are produced by Ca^{2+}-induced fusion of sonicated SUVs (Papahadjopoulos *et al.*, 1975) to form large (0.2–2 μm diameter) vesicles with a single limiting membrane (Figure 4).

2.1. Endocytosis

Evidence that vesicles can be incorporated into cells by endocytosis has come from experiments showing that inhibitors of endocytosis reduce the cell-associated vesicle population, though the extent of the reduction varies depending on vesicle lipid composition. Poste and Papahadjopoulos (1976a) found that inhibition of endocytosis in BALB/c mouse 3T3 cells by treatment with inhibitors of cellular energy metabolism or cytochalasin B, produced a marked reduction (>90%) in the uptake of negatively charged SUVs and MLVs composed of phospholipids that were 'solid' at 37 °C (PS/DPPC/DSPC). The same treatments were less effective, however, in reducing the cell-associated vesicle population (>35% reduction) for vesicles of similar size and surface charge composed of 'fluid' phospholipids (PS/egg PC) indicating that these are taken up predominantly via a non-endocytic mechanism(s). Similar findings showing that endocytosis is not a major pathway in the interaction of charged 'fluid' vesicles with cells have been reported in studies with negatively charged fluid vesicles in which the charge is conferred by dicetylphosphate (DCP) (Weissmann *et al.*, 1975, 1977; Stendahl and Tagesson, 1977) and also with positively charged fluid vesicles (PC/Chol/Stearylamine) (Stendahl and Tagesson, 1977; Poste and Papahadjopoulos, unpublished observations).

The fact that SUVs and MLVs of identical lipid composition behave similarly with respect to their susceptibility to endocytosis (Poste and Papahadjopoulos, 1976a) suggests that the lipid composition of vesicles is more important than size in determining the outcome of vesicle–cell interactions.

Weissmann and his colleagues (Cohen *et al.*, 1976) have reported that the susceptibility of negatively charged fluid MLVs (PC/Chol/DCP) to endocytosis by polymorphonuclear lymphocytes (PMNs) can be increased to a limited degree by coating vesicles with heat-aggregated immunoglobulins (IgGs). Since aggregated IgGs form surface lattices in which the F_c regions of the molecules are directed both inward towards the outer lipid lamella of the vesicle and outward to the external aqueous medium, IgG-coated vesicles presumably act as ligands for the cell surface F_c receptor and provoke endocytosis by cross-linking receptor molecules. However, the value of this approach as a general method for promoting selective endocytic uptake of vesicles is limited by the lack of F_c receptors on most cells. For example, Tyrrell *et al.* (1977) found that coating of fluid charged SUVs with IgG did not enhance their endocytosis by human diploid fibroblasts and lymphocytes. Although the lack of enhancement in fibroblasts may be due to absence of F_c receptors, it is unlikely that this is the case for lymphocytes which are known to possess F_c receptors (see Seligmann *et al.*, 1975). Further studies are thus needed to determine whether IgG enhancement of endocytosis is simply a peculiarity of the PMN system or if it also occurs in other cells, and, if so, whether an F_c receptor is involved.

The question of whether vesicles will be endocytosed is not determined solely by the 'fluidity' of the vesicle membrane. Inhibition of endocytosis in *Acanthamoeba castellanii* (Batzri and Korn, 1975) and mouse 3T3 cells (Poste and Papahadjopoulos, 1976a) completely inhibited uptake of neutral egg phosphatidylcholine (PC) vesicles, even though this phospholipid is fluid at 37 °C. Inhibition of uptake of both neutral egg PC and negatively charged solid vesicles by inhibitors of endocytosis suggests that endocytosis is the dominant mechanism in the interaction of these vesicles with cells and that such vesicles show little or no tendency to fuse with the plasma membrane.

The apparent inability of these vesicles to fuse with the plasma membrane is consistent with other data indicating that neutral vesicles and charged solid vesicles display a poor fusion capacity. For example, they are highly resistant to fusion with other vesicles (Papahadjopoulos *et al.*, 1974b; Prestegard and Fellmeth, 1975; Martin amd MacDonald, 1976a; Miller and Racker, 1976; Papahadjopoulos *et al.*, 1976a,b). Neutral and solid charged vesicles are also unable to induce cell-to-cell fusion (Papahadjopoulos *et al.*, 1973a; Martin and MacDonald, 1976b; Poste and Papahadjopoulos, 1976b)—a process that is believed to require fusion of vesicles with the plasma membrane (see p. 131). It is also of interest to note that Haywood (1974) was unable to detect fusion of the lipid envelope of Sendai virus with neutral egg PC vesicles but fusion between these structures was readily observed when another phospholipid (phosphatidylethanolamine) was included in the vesicles. Similarly, inclusion of phosphatidylserine (PS) in neutral egg PC vesicles renders them susceptible to fusion with other vesicles (Papahadjopoulos *et al.*, 1974b, 1976b). In contrast to these negative observations on the fusion capacity of neutral vesicles, Pagano has suggested that neutral vesicles prepared from egg PC alone or from DPPC or DMPC can fuse with the plasma membrane of cultured cells and that fusion, rather than endocytosis, represents the major pathway for the uptake of these vesicles (Huang and Pagano, 1975; Pagano and Huang, 1975; Pagano and Takeichi, 1977). The apparent discrepancy between this proposal and the negative results discussed above deserves examination since an accurate definition of the fusion behaviour of egg PC vesicles is relevant to the interpretation of studies in which these vesicles are used as carrier vehicles for introducing materials into cells.

Pagano and Huang's conclusion that neutral lecithin vesicles can fuse with the plasma membrane was derived from data showing that treatment of cells with inhibitors of *either* respiration *or* glycolysis failed to reduce the cell-associated vesicle population. It is not clear, however, from Pagano and Huang's data whether the metabolic blockade was effective in inhibiting endocytosis since endocytic activity in the inhibitor-treated cells was not assayed. This point is by no means trivial since it has been noted in several studies that inhibition of glycolysis or respiration *alone* may be sufficient to impair endocytosis and that inhibition of both pathways of energy production is required to completely inhibit endocytosis (Oren *et al.*, 1963; Steinman *et al.*, 1974; Poste and Papahadjopoulos, 1976a; Silverstein *et al.*, 1976). Thus, Poste and Papahadjopoulos (1976a), like Pagano and Huang, found that uptake of egg PC vesicles was not impaired when cells were exposed to inhibitors of either respiration or glycolysis, but assay of [^{14}C]sucrose uptake (a specific test for endocytic activity) revealed that endocytosis was still occurring. However, when cells were incubated with a combination of inhibitors of respiration *and* glycolysis, endocytosis and vesicle uptake were both completely blocked. This suggests that neutral egg PC vesicles are incorporated exclusively by endocytosis, at least in 3T3 cells.

Another possible explanation for the conflicting results on the ability of neutral lecithin vesicles to fuse with cells concerns the 'purity' of the lipids in the vesicle membrane. For example, vesicles prepared from DMPC are highly resistant to fusion with other vesicles, but readily undergo fusion or lipid transfer when small amounts of negatively charged impurities such as myristic acid are present in the vesicle membrane (Kantor and Prestegard, 1975; Papahadjopoulos *et al.*, 1976a). Myristic acid (and also lysolecithin) can be produced during prolonged sonication of pure DMPC in a probe-type sonicator (even in the presence of nitrogen and adequate cooling), resulting in formation of vesicles with a negative ζ-potential (Hauser, 1971). Since Pagano and Huang (1975) used prolonged probe sonication (30 minutes at 41 °C) to produce their DMPC vesicles, it remains a real possibility that small amounts of negatively charged fatty acids were produced which would promote fusion of vesicles with cells at 37 °C.

Differences in the behaviour of various cell types could also contribute to the above discrepancies, and further studies are needed to evaluate this question.

Fusion of neutral vesicles with the plasma membrane has also been proposed by Weinstein *et al.* (1977). These investigators examined the uptake and intracellular localization of sonicated lecithin vesicles containing the fluorescent dye, 6-carboxyfluorescein (6-CF). When concentrated inside vesicles 6-CF is highly quenched, but when diluted by release within the cytoplasm (or by leakage from vesicles extracellularly) a marked increase in fluorescence occurs. Lymphocytes incubated at 37 °C with SUVs composed of dioleylphosphatidylcholine (DOL) or DPPC and containing 6-CF were found to exhibit a diffuse cytoplasmic fluorescence. Similar transfer of 6-CF from vesicles into the cytosol has been reported by Pagano and Takeichi (1977) in V79 hamster cells incubated at 37 °C with SUV composed of DPPC. Both these sets of observations were interpreted as evidence that vesicles had fused with the plasma membrane, with accompanying release of vesicle-encapsulated dye into the cytoplasm. However, as discussed below, the validity of this interpretation is by no means established. Even if vesicle–plasma membrane fusion were responsible, the question of whether these experiments provide examples of the ability of neutral vesicles to fuse remains equivocal. Interpretation of these data is obscured by the problem that 6-CF may bestow a negative surface charge on vesicles which would enhance their ability to fuse. Further experiments to determine the ζ-potential of vesicles of differing lipid composition containing encapsulated 6-CF are required to resolve this problem. In this respect it is of interest that Bouma *et al.* (1977) failed to detect transfer of encapsulated [^{14}C]sucrose from DPPC vesicles into erythrocytes even though large amounts of radiolabelled lipid were transferred to the cells. This suggests either vesicle–plasma membrane fusion is not occurring or, if it does not occur, the entire contents of the vesicle are lost. In view of this finding, future studies are clearly required to establish whether encapsulation of 6-CF modifies the fusion properties of neutral vesicles.

The more fundamental problem in the interpretation of data obtained with the 6-CF method concerns the validity of the assumption that transfer of dye into the cytoplasm is due to vesicle–plasma membrane fusion. This may well be so, but the data published to date do not satisfactorily exclude the possibility that transfer of vesicle-encapsulated 6-CF to cells might occur via leakage of dye from vesicles adsorbed to the cell surface followed by uptake into cells by passive diffusion as a result of alterations in plasma membrane permeability induced by vesicle adsorption (Figure 1, Pathway 9). Weinstein *et al.* (1977) stated that leakage of 6-CF from vesicles is very slow at 5 °C but the more important question of the extent of leakage at 37 °C *in the presence of cells* was not examined. More detailed data obtained by Szoka *et al.* (1979) have revealed that SUVs containing 6-CF become highly permeable when incubated with cells. These investigators found that leakage of 6-CF from vesicles ranged from 8–75% per hour at 37 °C depending on vesicle lipid composition (solid charged > fluid charged ≥ neutral fluid vesicles). The possibility must therefore be considered that release of 6-CF from vesicles adsorbed to cells can create high concentrations of dye in regions immediately adjacent to the plasma membrane which could result in a concentration driven transfer of 6-CF across the plasma membrane into the cytoplasm and thus mimic fusion. This process would be further augmented if the adsorption of vesicles to the cell surface were accompanied by reciprocal vesicle-mediated changes in plasma membrane permeability.

Szoka *et al.* (1979) also found that changes in pH not only affect the fluorescence quantum yield of 6-CF molecules but also influence the rate of efflux of dye from inside vesicles. At pH 6.5 the rate of efflux at 37 °C is ten times that at pH 7.4. Since the pH of the interface at the plasma membrane boundary may be lower than that of the bulk phase (Weiss, 1967) the existence of a pH gradient at the surface of the cell may further augment leakage of encapsulated dye from vesicles.

The observations of Szoka *et al.* (1979) suggest that the use of vesicle-encapsulated 6-CF as a tool for quantitating vesicle–cell interactions (by measuring cellular fluorescence) and for identifying specific pathways for vesicle uptake (fusion versus endocytosis) is complicated by substantial experimental and interpretational problems. First, the marked leakage of 6-CF from vesicles in the presence of cells dictates that 6-CF cannot be used as a marker for determining the number of vesicles associated with, and incorporated into cells. Indeed, experiments described by Szoka *et al.* (1979), in which cells were incubated with vesicles containing both [³H]DPPC as a membrane marker and 6-CF encapsulated in the vesicle lumen, revealed that the number of vesicles associated with the cells measured by lipid uptake was five to ten times that calculated using the 6-CF marker. Second, the effect of pH on leakage of 6-CF from vesicles complicates the analysis of experimental data since the pH at the inter-face zone, where vesicles interact with the plasma membrane, may not only differ from that of the bulk medium but is also difficult to measure. Third, there is considerable uncertainty as to whether the presence of 6-CF in the cytoplasm reflects vesicle–plasma membrane fusion or results from passive uptake of dye at regions of the plasma membrane exposed to local high concentrations of dye released from vesicles adsorbed to the plasma membrane. Also, the permeability of the plasma membrane itself may be altered by interaction with vesicles. Finally, the recently recognized effect of low pH in enhancing membrane permeability to 6-CF raises the possibility that vesicle-derived 6-CF could reach the cytosol by yet another route. For example, endocytosis of vesicles containing 6-CF would result in the release of dye within phagolysosomes and the low pH of the intraphagolysosomal environment might facilitate exit of 6-CF from these structures into the cytoplasm.

Consequently, until more definitive experiments are done to distinguish between these possibilities, results obtained with the 6-CF method will be difficult to interpret, and proposals concerning mechanics of vesicle–cell interactions derived using this method in isolation must be treated with caution.

Another discrepancy between different studies on vesicle–cell interactions concerns the behaviour of 'solid' vesicles at temperatures below the gel-to-liquid crystalline phase transition (Tc) of the vesicle lipid components. As mentioned earlier, Poste and Papahadjopoulos (1976a) found that uptake of solid negatively charged vesicles (PS/DSPC/DPPC) with a Tc of 43 °C was inhibited at low temperatures (0–4 °C) and also at 37 °C by metabolic inhibitors or cytochalasin B. From this, they concluded that such vesicles were endocytosed. However, studies with solid SUVs composed of DPPC (Batzri and Korn, 1975; Pagano and Takeichi, 1977) or DMPC (Pagano and Huang, 1975) failed to detect any significant reduction in the cell-associated vesicle population at low temperatures or in the presence of metabolic inhibitors. Indeed, at low temperatures uptake of DMPC vesicles is enhanced (Pagano and Takeichi, 1977). These findings were initially interpreted (Batzri and Korn, 1975) as indicating that solid vesicles could fuse with the plasma membrane, but subsequent studies by Pagano and Takeichi (1977) have shown that at temperatures below their Tc both DMPC and DPPC vesicles adsorb to the cell surface and are not apparently incorporated into the interior of the cell.

The difference in the behaviour of 'solid' vesicles prepared from a equimolar mixture of DPPC and DSPC (Tc, 32–47 °C) which apparently are incorporated into cells by endocytosis at 37 °C, and 'solid' DMPC (Tc, 14–27 °C) and DPPC (Tc, 29–40 °C) vesicles which do not appear to provoke endocytosis and merely adsorb to the cell surface at low temperatures, cannot be explained easily with the available data. As shown by Hauser and Barrett (1973), sonicated DMPC vesicles are relatively unstable, as indicated by their high cation diffusion rates and their tendency to aggregate into larger structures. In contrast, vesicles composed of longer chain saturated lecithins such as DPPC and DSPC are much more stable and are impermeable to cations (Papahadjopoulos *et al.*, 1973b). When appropriately annealed they do not fuse with other vesicles at temperatures below their Tc (Papahadjopoulos *et al.*, 1974c, 1976a; Lawaczek *et al.*, 1975).

The increased uptake of DMPC and DPPC vesicles at 2 °C compared with 37 °C seen by Pagano and Huang could well reflect the metastability and anomalous behaviour displayed by these vesicles at temperatures close to (or below) their Tc (Prestegard and Felmeth, 1975; Jacobson and Papahadjopoulos, 1975; Martin and MacDonald, 1976a; Suurkuusk *et al*., 1976). Although the incubation temperature of 2 °C is considerably lower than the Tc of non-sonicated DMPC and DPPC bilayers (Hinz and Sturtevant, 1972), it has been shown that sonication produces a dramatic lowering of the onset for the transition of pure dipalmitoyl phospholipids (Hinz and Sturtevant, 1972; Jacobson and Papahadjopoulos, 1975). Also, prolonged probe sonication can produce vesicles with a very ill-defined phase transition, which probably reflects extensive broadening of the endothermic peak (Hinz and Sturtevant, 1972). Consequently, the metastability of sonicated DMPC and DPPC vesicles suggests that they are not a suitable system for evaluating the behaviour of 'solid' vesicles.

Although the lack of effect of inhibitors of endocytosis on the interaction of certain types of vesicles with cells suggests that non-endocytic mechanisms must be operating, the possibility remains that vesicle uptake could still be occurring via a non-energy requiring endocytic process. For example, Martin and MacDonald (1976c) have suggested that vesicles might be able to enter cells via an energy-independent mechanism in which plasma membrane would invaginate around vesicles and be internalized as a result of surface tension effects. This possibility does not appear likely, however, since there is considerable circumstantial evidence that endocytosis is not driven by surface forces alone (see Mudd and Mudd, 1933 and review by Van Oss *et al*., 1975).

Micropinocytosis is not impaired by agents that inhibit phagocytosis and macropinocytosis, but it is considered unlikely that this mechanism participates in vesicle uptake. The small size of micropinocytic vesicles dictates that they are probably too small to accommodate SUVs and certainly could not internalize MLVs or LUVs. In addition, micropinocytic activity is not detectable in 3T3 cells under conditions where cell-associated vesicle (SUV) populations in excess of one million vesicles per cell are achieved (Poste and Papahadjopoulos, 1976a).

Observations on the effect of temperature on vesicle–cell interactions have also yielded information that complements the data from studies with inhibitors of endocytosis. With the exception of DMPC and DPPC vesicles (see below), the interaction of vesicles with cells is temperature-sensitive (Papahadjopoulos *et al*., 1974a; Batzri and Korn, 1975; Pagano and Huang, 1975; Poste and Papahadjopoulos, 1976a; Stendahl and Tagesson, 1977). However, the kinetics of vesicle–cell interactions at lower temperatures are influenced by the lipid composition of the vesicle. Poste and Papahadjopoulos (1976a) found that uptake of fluid negatively charged SUVs and MLVs (PS/PC) displayed a distinct transition at 16–18 °C (Figure 5) but a similar transition was not found with solid

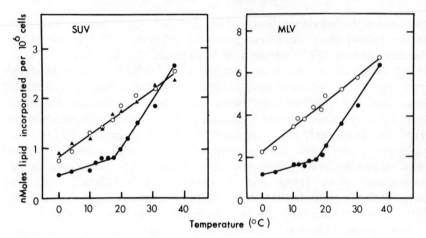

Temperature (°C)

Figure 5   The effect of temperature on the uptake of small unilamellar (SUVs) and multilamellar (MLVs) vesicles of differing lipid composition by BALB/C 3T3 cells. ● = PS/PC; ○ = PC/DSPC/DPPC; and ▲ = PC. Reproduced with permission from Poste and Papahadjopoulos, 1976a

vesicles of similar surface charge (PS/DPPC/DSPC) or with fluid neutral egg PC vesicles. Cellular processes requiring membrane fusion have been shown to display a similar transition at about 18 °C (Lagunoff and Wan, 1974) while endocytosis exhibits a simple linear temperature dependence (Steinman *et al.*, 1974). This prompted Poste and Papahadjopoulos (1976a) to propose that the data in Figure 5 be interpreted as supporting the conclusions reached in studies with inhibitors of endocytosis, namely, solid charged and fluid neutral vesicles are endocytosed while fluid charged vesicles interact with cells via non-endocytic mechanisms, including fusion of vesicles with the plasma membrane.

The interaction of sonicated DMPC and DPPC vesicles with cells exhibits a negative temperature coefficient (Pagano and Huang, 1975; Pagano and Takeichi, 1977). Since endocytosis and membrane fusion do not occur at low temperatures (0–4 °C), the increased cellular association of lipids from these vesicles at 2 °C must result from either adsorption of vesicles to the cell surface and/or exchange diffusion of lipids between vesicles and the plasma membrane. The role of these two mechanisms in vesicle–cell interactions at low temperatures and also at 37 °C will be considered in more detail in the following two sections.

2.2.   Exchange Diffusion and/or Transfer of Membrane Components Between Vesicles and Cells

Possible evidence for phospholipid exchange between vesicles and cells *in vitro* has been presented by Pagano and Huang (1975). They showed that incubation of V79 cells at 2 °C with lecithin–cholesterol SUVs containing [^{3}H]DOL and [^{14}C]cholesterol resulted in more rapid uptake of the lecithin radiolabel compared to cholesterol. This is, however, the reverse of the situation consistently found for phospholipid exchange reactions between microsomes, mitochondria, and vesicles in which cholesterol exchanges more rapidly than phospholipid (review, Wirtz, 1974; Kader, 1977).

Pagano and Huang (1975) also showed that incubation of V79 cells at 2 °C with sonicated DOL vesicles containing a membrane marker [^{14}C]DOL, and an encapsulated label, [^{3}H]inulin, resulted in significant association of phospholipid with the cells without accompanying transfer of [^{3}H]inulin. This finding was reasonably interpreted as indicating that phospholipid exchange between vesicles and the plasma membrane was occurring and that very few intact vesicles became associated with cells. However, in a more recent paper, Pagano and Takeichi (1977) proposed that incubation of V79 cells at 2 °C with DPPC vesicles containing encapsulated 6-CF resulted in adsorption of intact vesicles. It is possible, however, that DPPC vesicles containing 6-CF do not adsorb as intact structures and that extensive leakage of 6-CF from vesicles is occurring but the sensitivity of the fluorescence assay is too low to detect it. For example, up to 75% of the encapsulated 6-CF could leak from vesicles without causing detectable change in cell-associated fluorescence (Szoka *et al.*, 1979). In order to decide whether these vesicles are adsorbed intact or whether lipid transfer and exchange processes account for the cell-associated vesicle components, detailed information is needed on the extent of 6-CF leakage from vesicles at different temperatures and the reciprocal effect of vesicles on cellular permeability.

Exchange of phospholipids between vesicles and cell membranes may also be a consistent feature of vesicle–cell interactions at 37 °C but this has received little attention in the literature, presumably because of the difficulty of detecting it against the large background of cell-associated vesicle components derived from vesicle fusion, endocytosis, and/or vesicle adsorption. Optimal detection of exchange processes thus requires an experimental system in which fusion and endocytosis are eliminated and in which adsorbed vesicles can be eluted.

Transfer of phospholipids and cholesterol between vesicles and cells at 37 °C has been detected in human erythrocytes incubated with SUVs composed of egg PC (Grunze and Deuticke, 1974) and DPPC (Bouma *et al.*, 1977). Although the possibility of vesicle–plasma membrane fusion was not excluded in the former study, in the latter experiments the vesicles contained [^{14}C]sucrose but transfer of this marker to the cytosol was not detected.

Transfer of cell surface components to vesicles during vesicle–cell interactions must also be considered. Bouma *et al*. (1977) have shown that DPPC vesicles (SUVs) incubated with human erythrocytes for 1 hour at 37 °C acquire cellular sphinogomyelin, phosphatidylcholine and cholesterol Perhaps of greater interest, however, are recent observations showing that vesicles can acquire cellular proteins during incubation with cells *in vitro*.

Dunnick *et al*. (1976) reported that following incubation of ^{125}I-labelled spleen cells with SUV (DPPC/Chol/gangliosides or PC/Chol/gangliosides) approximately 10% of the ^{125}I-radiolabel was transferred to vesicles (the time period was not stated). In a more recent study, Bouma *et al*. (1977) have detected elution of ^{125}I-labelled proteins from erythrocytes after incubation with SUV composed of DPPC for 20 minutes at 37 °C. It is not clear, however, whether the eluted proteins were adsorbed onto intact vesicles or if they were associated with lipid material from the vesicles. Interestingly, no transfer of ^{125}I-labelled material was detected when erythrocytes were incubated with MLVs of similar composition. Polyacrylamide gel electrophoresis revealed that seven ^{125}I-labelled polypeptides were recovered in association with vesicles. Although one of these was identified as a membrane protein (acetylcholineesterase), the molecular weights of the remaining polypeptides did not correspond to any of the known major proteins of the erythrocyte membrane. The surface of cells cultured *in vitro* is known to be 'coated' with proteinaceous material derived from serum, and also by proteins released from cells, and it is possible that the iodinated material transferred to vesicles is derived from these sources.

Irrespective of the identity of the proteins, their transfer to vesicles can influence the subsequent interaction of the vesicles with cells. Thus, Dunnick *et al*. (1976) found that incubation of cells with vesicles that had been incubated previously with cells, and presumably acquired material from the cell surface (though this was not shown), resulted in a significantly lower cell-associated vesicle population than in cells exposed to freshly prepared vesicles.

Extraction of cellular proteins by incubation with vesicles, if widespread, offers a useful method for modifying cell surface composition. For example, Heustis (1977) has shown that transfer of surface proteins from human erythrocytes to DPPC or DMPC vesicles is accompanied by the onset of a selective defect in cell permeability with eventual osmotic cell lysis. The defective erythrocytes exhibit a massive sodium ion leak while maintaining normal impermeability to other cations, anions, and neutral small molecules. The sodium ion influx and haemolysis are inhibited by increasing pH and by tetrodotoxin and can be significantly reduced by incubating cells with vesicles carrying the extracted proteins.

2.3. Adsorption of Vesicles to the Cell Surface and Fusion with the Plasma Membrane

Evidence obtained using a variety of experimental techniques suggests that fluid vesicles carrying a net (electrostatic) surface charge may fuse with the plasma membrane of cultured cells. Although a broad framework of observations supporting this conclusion has been assembled, most of the evidence is circumstantial and definitive proof of vesicle–plasma membrane fusion has been difficult to obtain. Experimentally, the main difficulty in identifying vesicle–plasma membrane fusion has been the problem of defining whether vesicle-derived components associated with the cell surface have been incorporated into the plasma membrane as a result of vesicle fusion or are merely bound to the outer surface of the plasma membrane as adsorbed vesicles. Evidence is beginning to emerge which suggests that adsorbed vesicles may constitute a major fraction of the cell-associated vesicle population (Szoka *et al.*, 1979). Teleologically, this is perhaps not too surprising. For example, the cell-associated vesicle populations reported in the literature typically range from 1×10^5 to 3×10^6 vesicles (SUVs) per cell and assimilation of all, or even the majority, of these vesicles into the cell would be expected to pose considerable problems for the cell in terms of the uptake, storage, and degradation of such large amounts of lipid. This is well illustrated by considering the effect of fusion of vesicles with the plasma membrane. At typical vesicle input doses of 200 μmol phospholipid per 10^6 cells, the data in the literature indicate that only approximately 1% of the added vesicles become associated with cells. This is equivalent to 1 fmol of phospholipid per cell (4×10^5 SUV per cell). Using an acknowledged simplified analysis in which both vesicles and cells are treated as smooth spheres, then if fusion of vesicles with the plasma membrane were to account for the entire 1 fmol of phospholipid per cell this would mean that the surface area of a 10 μm diameter cell would increase by 60% (Szoka *et al.*, 1979). Even when the original cell surface area is assumed to be three times greater (to allow for microvilli, folds, surface projections, etc.), uptake of 1 fmol of vesicle lipid via fusion would still involve a 20% increase in cell surface area. These drastic changes might reasonably be expected to produce obvious, if not extreme, alterations in cellular morphology and surface properties and the development of intracellular lipid storage structures. However, such changes have not been reported so far, suggesting that either they do not occur (i.e. fusion and other incorporation processes are not occurring on a large scale) or that the cell can accommodate and compensate for, large changes in surface area and lipid content far better than current dogma predicts.

As outlined in the following sections, effective separation of fusion and adsorption is by no means a simple task and quantitative measurements of vesicle–plasma membrane fusion have still to be made. A number of experimental approaches have been used, either alone or in combination, in an effort to demonstrate fusion of vesicles with cells. These warrant critical review since certain of the methods utilized for this purpose do not satisfactorily distinguish between vesicle fusion and adsorption.

2.3.1. Electron microscopy

Attempts to directly observe fusion of vesicles with the plasma membrane using scanning electron microscopy (SEM) (Magee *et al.*, 1974; Pagano and Takeichi, 1977) or transmission electron microscopy (Magee *et al.*, 1974; Pagano *et al.*, 1974; Batzri and Korn, 1975; Pagano and Huang, 1975; Cohen *et al.*, 1976; Martin and MacDonald, 1976c; Weissmann *et al.*, 1977) have met with little success. Electron micrographs have been published by several authors showing small blebs on the surface of vesicle-treated cells which have been suggested to represent vesicles in the process of fusion with the plasma membrane (Magee *et al.*, 1974; Pagano *et al.*, 1974; Martin and MacDonald, 1976c). It is an equally real possibility, however, that these structures are artefactual evaginations of the plasma membrane induced by vesicle treatment and/or fixation for electron microscopy (see Hasty and Hay, 1978). Pure lipid vesicles do not fix and stain well, making detailed analysis of the structural relationship between vesicles and the plasma membrane very difficult. In the case of SUVs, this problem is further complicated by their very small size. The resolution of electron micrographs published to date is insufficient to permit reliable conclusions to be made regarding the fusion behaviour of vesicles.

The first attempt to localize vesicle-derived components in cultured cells by electron microscopy was made by Magee *et al.* (1974). These investigators used electron histochemical methods to follow the adsorption and uptake of cationic MLVs (sphingomyelin/Chol/stearylamine) containing horseradish peroxidase (HRP) by HeLa cells. Staining of vesicle-treated cells by the diaminobenzidine procedure revealed substantial amounts of peroxidase-positive material associated with the cell surface, often in the form of large aggregates. However, the important question of whether this material was situated on the outer membrane surface in the form of adsorbed vesicles or was associated with the inner face of the plasma membrane as a consequence of vesicle fusion could not be resolved. Numerous membrane-bound structures containing peroxidase-positive material were also identified in the cytoplasm of these cells suggesting that endocytosis of vesicles was also occurring. This would be consistent with the data discussed earlier on the effect of inhibitors of endocytosis on the uptake of positively charged fluid vesicles which indicated that endocytosis accounted for 30–40% of the total cell-associated vesicle population (Stendahl and Tagesson, 1977; Poste and Papahadjopoulos, 1978).

Similar ultrastructural cytochemical methods were used by Weissmann *et al.* (1977) to follow the interaction of HRP-containing negatively charged fluid MLVs (DCP/PC/Chol) with human diploid fibroblasts and lymphocytes. In contrast to the observations of Magee *et al.* (1974), accumulation of peroxidase-positive material at the cell surface was not seen, but significant intracellular accumulation of peroxidase-containing structures was detected. Weissmann and co-workers considered that these cytoplasmic structures were not surrounded by any obvious cellular membranes and had thus not been incorporated by endocytosis. They proposed that uptake had instead occurred via fusion between the outermost lamella of the MLV and the plasma membrane, with resulting introduction of the remaining portion of the MLV (minus the outer bilayer) into the cytosol (Figure 1, Pathway1). Additional support for this conclusion was provided by the finding that inhibition of endocytosis did not prevent accumulation of peroxidase-positive multilamellar profiles in the cytoplasm. Although this lends support to their conclusion that vesicle incorporation occurred via a non-endocytic mechanism, the electron microscopic evidence presented by Weissmann *et al.* does not provide definitive proof for vesicle–plasma membrane fusion. A major problem in any ultrastructural study of uptake of exogenous material into cells is to accurately define the interaction of the incorporated material with the vacuolar apparatus of the cell. For example, endocytosed material will be surrounded by a membrane derived from the original endocytic vacuole and the lysosomes that fuse with the endocytic vacuole. In practice, however, reliable identification of the origin of membranes found in association with incorporated material can be a problem, particularly when the incorporated material is itself membranous, as in the case of MLVs.

Despite the confident statement by Weissmann *et al.* (1977) that the peroxidase-positive MLV profiles seen in the cytoplasm were not surrounded by cell membranes, this is certainly not clear from their published electron micrographs. While free peroxidase-positive material is clearly absent from the cytoplasm, it is not possible in any of the micrographs to conclude whether the outer membrane separating the peroxidase-positive multilamellar profiles from the cytoplasm is of vesicle or cellular origin. The presence of peroxidase-positive staining on the inside of the outermost membrane does not establish that the membrane was part of the original vesicle. For example, endocytic capture of a MLV followed by digestion of the outer vesicle membrane(s) by lysosomal lipases would release peroxidase which would then bind to the inner face of the phagolysosome membrane creating profiles similar to those seen by Weissmann *et al*. Even if endocytosis is ignored, it is possible that after initial fusion between the outer bilayer of the MLV and the plasma membrane, the remaining portion of the vesicle introduced into the cytoplasm interacts directly with lysosomes (Figure 1, Pathway 1). This would mean that the events just discussed for endocytosed vesicles would occur and again produce multilamellar profiles with peroxidase-positive reaction on the inner face of the outer membrane (which would be derived in part from the MLV and in part from lysosomes which fuse with the MLV). We thus consider that further experiments are needed to clarify the ultrastructural interaction of MLVs with cells.

An experiment that might be particularly instructive would be to examine the uptake of MLV containing an ultrastructural marker (e.g. ferritin) confined to the outer surface of the outermost bilayer of the vesicle. If, as proposed by Poste and Papahadjopoulos (1976b) and Weissman *et al*. (1977), the outer bilayer of fluid charged MLV can fuse with the plasma membrane, then the marker should not be found in association with cytoplasmic multilamellar profiles. Even if compensatory endocytosis (Figure 1, Pathway 4 and also see p. 128) were to occur following initial fusion of the vesicles with the plasma membrane, the internalized marker would then be associated with unilamellar structures. Conversely, if the vesicles were endocytosed the marker would be recovered in the cytoplasm associated with multilamellar structures.

The best evidence for fusion of vesicles with the plasma membrane obtained using transmission electron microscopy has been presented by Martin and MacDonald (1976c). These investigators incubated erythrocytes with a mixed population of positively charged (stearylamine/PC/lysolecithin) SUVs and MLVs and showed that a lipid hapten (2,4-dinitrophenyl-amino-caproyl phosphatidylethanolamine) present in the vesicle membrane could be detected in association with the erythrocyte plasma membrane using ferritin-conjugated antibodies to the hapten. Although the presence of vesicle-derived antigens on the outer face of the plasma membrane does not prove that fusion has occurred (also see comments below on ligand-induced redistribution of vesicle-derived antigens), Martin and MacDonald also showed that the

---

Figure 6 Electron microscope autoradiograph of mixed population of L1210 cells incubated for 5 minutes at 37 °C with [^{3}H]DPPC-labelled phosphatidylserine/egg phosphatidylcholine (1 : 9) small unilamellar vesicles and non-vesicle treated glutaraldehyde fixed avian erythrocytes showing redistribution and transfer of the [^{3}H]DPPC label from L1210 cells to erythrocytes during tissue processing.
The L1210 cells were fixed with glutaraldehyde for 1 hour after treatment with vesicles and then mixed with similarly fixed by non-vesicle treated erythrocytes for subsequent processing as a cell mixture. Reproduced with permission from Poste *et al*. (1978)

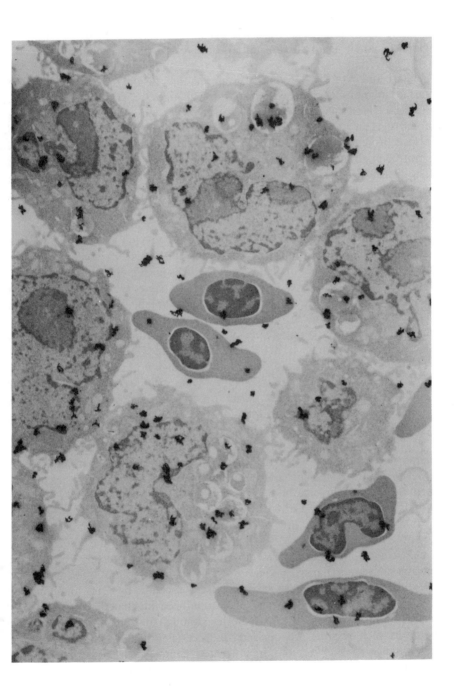

contents of SUVs (sucrose) and the internal lamellae of MLVs were present in the cytoplasm of antigen-positive erythrocytes. This provides compelling evidence, albeit again circumstantial, that vesicle–plasma membrane fusion had occurred.

Batzri and Korn (1975) have proposed that fusion of vesicles with the plasma membrane can be detected by changes in surface morphology. Vesicle–plasma membrane fusion is proposed as increasing the surface area of the plasma membrane leading to a marked increase in the number of surface projections and an increasingly pleomorphic surface. This criterion is not compelling, however, particularly in view of the pleomorphic nature of the surface of many cells and that alterations similar to those described by Batzri and Korn can also result from minor differences in incubation conditions, from differences in the age, density, and proliferative activity of cells, and from the fixation procedures used for electron microscopy.

Huang and Pagano (1975) have attempted to characterize the uptake and intracellular localization of sonicated DOL vesicles containing trace amounts of [^{3}H]DSPC by hamster V79 cells using electron microscopic autoradiography. However, a later study by Poste *et al*. (1978) has shown that this method is unreliable because the radiolabelled lipid is extracted and can be redistributed by the solvents used in processing specimens for electron microscopy creating spurious labelling patterns. This problem was identified by mixing L1210 cells which had been incubated with [^{3}H]DPPC-labelled vesicles and then fixed with glutaraldehyde with similarly fixed cells of a different type (avian erythrocytes) which had not been incubated with vesicles. After processing of the cells for electron microscopy as a mixed pellet, radiolabelled grains were now found in both cell types indicating that intercellular transfer had occurred (Figure 6).

The best ultrastructural evidence for fusion of vesicles with the plasma membranes has come from freeze-fracture studies of vesicle-treated cells. Freeze-fracture reveals changes in the internal structure of the plasma membrane and this method does not therefore encounter the problem found with SEM and TEM of defining whether material is in or on the membrane. Freeze-fracture observations of erythrocytes incubated with negatively charged fluid MLVs (PS/PC) have revealed the formation of areas within the plasma membrane that are completely devoid of intramembranous particles (Figure 7) (Papahadjopoulos *et al*., 1974c). Identical changes have also been reported recently by Orci and Perrelet (1978) in the plasma membrane of spermatozoa incubated with negatively charged fluid MLVs (DCP/PC/Chol). Although definitive proof that the lipids in such regions are derived from vesicles has yet to be obtained, the absence of such regions in untreated control cells, and their similar size to MLVs, strongly suggest that they represent sites at which vesicles have fused with the plasma membrane. However, in common with

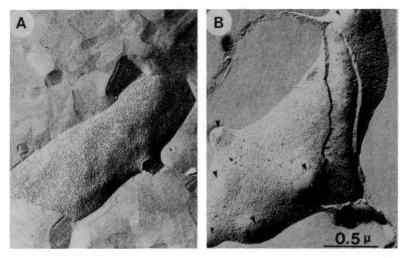

Figure 7 Freeze-fracture electron micrograph of human erythrocyte ghost (A) and ghost after incubation with multilamellar lipid vesicles 10% phosphatidylcholine; (1.3 nmol of lipid per 1×10^6 cells) for 30 minutes at 37 °C (B) showing cell surface 'patches' devoid of intramembranous particles (arrows). The dimensions and surface topography of these patches are similar to those of vesicles, suggesting that they may represent points at which vesicles have fused with the cell surface. Similar patches are not found on the untreated control ghosts. Arrowheads indicate direction of shadowing. Reproduced with permission from Papahadjopoulos *et al*. (1974c)

all electron microscopic methods, vesicle–plasma membrane fusion cannot be easily quantitated using this technique.

2.3.2. *Subcellular Localization of Vesicle-Derived Components by Cell Fractionation*

Increasingly effective methods for cell and tissue fractionation have been developed over the last decade and accurate localization of many of the constituent molecules of the cell is now possible. This technology has proved less successful, however, in localizing exogenous materials incorporated into cells. The reason for this is twofold. First, incorporation of exogenous material is a dynamic process and the intracellular distribution of incorporated materials may change between initial uptake and the time of cell fractionation. Second, for materials introduced into the cytosol, non-specific adsorption to various organelles may hinder identification of the true localization. Existing reviews on the use of cell fractionation methods have largely ignored these problems and confined their comments to methods of analysis for well-defined cell components whose structure, composition, and distribution are stable.

Recovery of vesicle-derived phospholipids in association with both the plasma membrane and intracellular fractions of vesicle-treated cells has been mentioned (Pagano *et al.*, 1974; Papahadjopoulos *et al.*, 1974c; Huang and Pagano, 1975; Stendahl and Tagesson, 1977) but detailed data on the kinetics of localization of vesicle components in different subcellular fractions using rigorously purified preparations have yet to be published.

The recovery of vesicle membrane components in purified plasma membrane fractions (Stendahl and Tagesson, 1977) does not prove that vesicle–plasma fusion has occurred since adsorbed vesicles could remain bound to the plasma membrane during purification.

Even if the adsorbed vesicle fraction could be identified, fractionation methods may still be unable to quantitate vesicle–plasma membrane fusion. For example, following fusion of vesicles with the plasma membrane it is by no means certain that the vesicle membrane components will remain within the plasma membrane. Fusion of vesicles with the plasma membrane would be expected to increase the surface area of the cell and the cell may act to limit such increases by removing excess membrane by 'compensatory endocytosis' (Figure 1, Pathway 4). This proposal is not unreasonable in view of the many examples of compensatory endocytosis seen in exocytic secretory cells where fusion of large numbers of secretory granules with the plasma membranes is accompanied by removal of plasma membrane by endocytosis (review, Holtzmann *et al.*, 1977). If similar compensatory endocytosis were triggered by fusion of vesicles with the plasma membrane, the newly introduced vesicle membrane components would be internalized and, assuming that the endocytic vacuoles interact with lysosomes, the vesicle components would then be recovered in the lysosomal fraction with the obvious danger of misinterpretation as evidence that the vesicles had been endocytosed.

2.3.3. *Ligand-Induced Redistribution and Capping of Vesicle-Derived Components at the Cell Surface*

Vesicle components associated with the cell surface can bind multivalent ligands (antibodies, lectins, etc.) and undergo aggregation and redistribution to form large patches of caps in analogous fashion to natural plasma membrane receptors (Schroitt and Pagano, 1978). However, this does not prove that the vesicle components have been incorporated into the plasma membrane. There are at least two mechanisms by which vesicle-derived ligand receptors situated on, rather than in, the plasma membrane could be induced to cap.

First, cross-linking and aggregation of adsorbed vesicles by an appropriate ligand would probably induce parallel aggregation and redistribution of the plasma membrane components to which the vesicles are adsorbed. The latter may be a sufficient stimulus to induce capping of the plasma membrane receptors which then carry the adsorbed vesicles with them. In this sense, by aggregating underlying plasma membrane components, the adsorbed vesicle–ligand complexes would act directly as a ligand and thus function in the same fashion as a single ligand directed specifically to the same plasma membrane component(s).

Second, adsorbed vesicles which have been cross-linked by ligands could also undergo passive redistribution on the cell surface to form patches of cross-linked vesicle–ligand complexes. These, in turn, could coalesce to form a large single cap simply as a passive event in which patches are swept backward over the cell surface due to cell locomotion.

The question of whether ligand-induced capping of vesicle components is an active process requiring contraction of intracellular microfilaments or merely involves passive redistribution of cross-linked material on the cell surface can best be answered by examining the ability of micro-filament-disruptive drugs such as cytochalasin B or local anaesthetics to prevent capping. Although instructive from the standpoint of defining whether microfilaments are involved, inhibition of capping by cytoskeletal-disruptive drugs cannot be used as proof that the vesicle's components have been incorporated into the plasma membrane and become 'linked' to cytoskeletal elements in the cytoplasm. As mentioned above, binding of ligands to adsorbed vesicles could indirectly induce capping by aggregating the plasma membrane components to which the vesicles are adsorbed. In this situation, inhibition of capping of vesicle components by cytoskeletal-disruptive drugs might merely reflect drug effects on cytoskeletal-mediated redistribution of plasma membrane components and not involve any direct action on vesicle components.

2.3.4. Measurement of the Lateral Mobility of Vesicle-Derived Components at the Cell Surface

It might reasonably be expected that vesicle membrane components introduced into the plasma membrane via fusion would be able to diffuse within the membrane, whereas adsorbed vesicles would display little or no lateral mobility or even exhibit 'hopping' movements between adjacent surface sites.

Szoka *et al.* (unpublished) have attempted to study this question using photobleaching techniques to monitor the lateral diffusion of fluorescent labelled vesicle membrane components associated with the cell surface. Measurements of fluorescence recovery after photobleaching (FRAP) (for method see Jacobson and Papahadjopoulos, 1976) in cells treated with

SUV (PS/PC) containing the fluorescent lipid analogue, 3,3-dioctadecyloxa-carbocyanine (diO-C_{18}) or N-4-nitrobenz-2-oxa-1,3-diazole phospha-tidylethanolamine, failed to reveal any significant recovery of fluorescence in bleached regions of the cell surface. This indicates that at least 90% of the cell-associated vesicles were merely adsorbed. Evidence for vesicle fusion was not detected, though up to 10% of the total cell-associated vesicles could have fused and not be detected by this method. In addition, fusion of vesicles could be occurring in the absence of significant fluorescence recovery if fusion were confined to non-contiguous plasma membrane domains that were small in relation to the large size of the bleaching laser beam (1.5 μm diameter).

2.3.5. Vesicle-Mediated Transfer of Novel Proteins and Glycoproteins into the Plasma Membrane

Definitive proof of the ability of vesicles to fuse with the plasma membrane would be provided by showing that purified hydrophobic membrane proteins or glycoproteins incorporated into vesicle membranes could be transferred to the plasma membrane of cells and express their functional activity in the recipient cells (for the specific purpose of demonstrating vesicle–plasma membrane fusion it would be useful if the functional activity of the introduced protein were to involve alteration(s) in intracellular properties since this would provide strong evidence for the true intramembranous location of the protein). Despite the obvious and fascinating opportunities that this approach offers as an experimental tool for altering plasma membrane composition, successful vesicle-mediated transfer of an integral membrane protein into a different cell type has yet to be reported.

2.3.6. Elution of Adsorbed Vesicles

The problem of defining what proportion of vesicles associated with the cell surface may have fused can also be approached indirectly by quantitating the adsorbed vesicle population. This can be done by attempting to elute adsorbed vesicles by enzymic modification of the cell periphery or simple reversible dissociation induced by changes in pH, temperature, ionic strength, etc. *Complete* elution of the adsorbed vesicle population is obviously needed if this approach is to be useful. Different treatments may vary significantly in their efficiency and it is therefore essential that several procedures be evaluated to ensure that maximum elution is obtained.

Few experiments have been done to characterize the optimal conditions needed for elution of vesicles and the available information is thus incomplete. Pagano and Takeichi (1977) have reported recently that trypsinization of hamster V79 induced elution of sonicated DPPC vesicles but the susceptiibility of vesicles to elution was influenced by the temperature at which vesicles were incubated with cells. After incubation at 2 °C, up to 85% of the cell-associated vesicles could be removed by trypsin compared with less than 20% elution from cells incubated with vesicles at 37 °C. The significance of the onset of resistance to elution by proteases at higher temperatures is not clear. Trypsinization does not, however, alter vesicle binding. Magee *et al.* (1974) reported that incubation of HeLa cells with 0.25% trypsin or 0.1 M EDTA for 10 minutes at 37 °C failed to decrease the binding of cationic MLVs (sphingomyelin/Chol/stearylamine). Similarly, unpublished work by the present authors using negatively charged solid (PS/DSPC/DPPC) or fluid (PS/PC) SUVs and MLVs and sonicated egg PC vesicles indicates that trypsinization of 3T3 cells does not alter vesicle binding. We have also found that pretreatment of 3T3 cells with neuraminidase, hyaluronidase, and RNAase does not alter vesicle binding to 3T3 cells indicating that surface components susceptible to these enzymes are not involved in vesicle binding.

2.3.7. Vesicle-Induced Cell Fusion

The first indication that lipid vesicles might fuse with the plasma membrane came from observations made in 1973 showing that fluid negatively charged SUVs could induce cell fusion to form polykaryocytes (Papahadjopoulos *et al.*, 1973a; and see Poste and Papahadjopoulos, 1976b for a detailed review of this subject). By analogy with cell fusion induced by lipid-enveloped viruses which requires fusion of virus particles with the plasma membrane (review, Poste and Pasternak, 1978), it was suggested (Papahadjopoulos *et al.*, 1973a) that vesicle-induced cell fusion might involve a similar sequence of events involving fusion of vesicles with the plasma membrane. Although this proposal is conceptually attractive, direct experimental evidence to support this analogy is lacking. Formal proof that vesicle-induced cell fusion is similar to viral fusion will require that vesicles be shown to be capable of acting as 'fusion bridges' between cells by fusing simultaneously with the plasma membrane of adjacent cells and/or that cell fusion be shown to occur at sites on the plasma membrane which have been modified by fusion with vesicles.

Vesicles of different lipid composition vary markedly in their ability to induce cell fusion. Fluid negatively charged SUVs induce significant cell

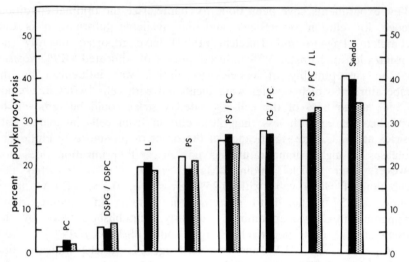

Figure 8   Fusion of mouse 3T3 (☐), mouse 1929 (■), and hamster BHK21 (▨) cells by lipid vesicles, inactivated Sendai virus, and lysolecithin. Monolayer cell cultures were treated with vesicles of the indicated composition (10^4 vesicles per cell) for 2 hours at 37 °C, or with 2,000 HAU of β-propiolactone-inactivated Sendai virus for 1 hour at 37 °C. For fusion of cells by lysolecithin similar numbers of cells were incubated as a loose pellet with 200 μg of lysolecithin per milliliter for 5 minutes at 37 °C. The extent of cell fusion, expressed as the percentage of polykaryocytosis, was determined 24 hours after the various treatments. PC, egg yolk phosphatidylcholine vesicles; PS, phosphatidylserine vesicles; PS/PC 10% phosphatidylserine in phosphatidylcholine vesicles; PG/PC, 10% phosphatidylglycerol in phosphatidylcholine vesicles; PS/PC, 10% phosphatidylserine in phosphatidylcholine vesicles; PG/DSPG, 10% distearoylphosphatidylglycerol in distearoyl phosphatidylcholine vesicles; PS/PC/LL: 10% phosphatidylserine in phosphatidylcholine vesicles containing 3% lysolecithin; LL, free lysolecithin; and Sendai, β-propiolactone-inactivated Sendai virus

fusion (Figure 8), but similarly charged vesicles composed of solid phospholipids and neutral vesicles are devoid of fusion activity (Martin and MacDonald, 1976b; Poste and Papahadjopoulos, 1976b). These findings again emphasize the apparent importance of surface charge and membrane 'fluidity' in determining the fusion capacity of vesicles. The inability of neutral vesicles and solid negatively charged vesicles to induce cell fusion is reminiscent of the work discussed earlier in which vesicles with these properties were unable to fuse with other vesicles and were incorporated into cells by endocytosis with no evidence for a major involvement of non-endocytic mechanisms such as fusion with the plasma membrane. Fluid negatively charged vesicles, on the other hand, induce extensive cell fusion.

Martin and MacDonald (1976b) have reported that positively charged fluid SUVs can induce cell fusion but, in contrast to negatively charged vesicles, this property was not expressed by vesicles composed of diacyl phospholipids and inclusion of lysolecithin in the vesicle membrane was required for successful cell fusion. However, electron microscopic evidence presented by the same authors indicates that positively charged vesicles without lysolecithin can fuse with the plasma membrane. A possible explanation for the differing ability of positively and negatively charged vesicles to induce cell fusion will be given on p. 138.

2.3.8. *Release of Vesicle-Encapsulated Materials into the Cytoplasm*

Fusion of vesicles with the plasma membrane should be accompanied by release of at least some of the vesicle contents into the cytoplasm (Figure 1). Detection of vesicle-encapsulated marker molecules free within the cytoplasm thus offers an alternative strategy for identifying vesicle–plasma membrane fusion. This approach is illustrated by the work of Weinstein *et al.* (1977), discussed earlier, in which changes in the self-quenching of the dye, 6-CF, were used to demonstrate the presence of vesicle contents within the cytoplasm. This is presently the only study in which evidence for cytoplasmic localization of vesicle contents has been presented. Many studies have shown that vesicle-encapsulated materials can be introduced. into cells and induce alterations in cell function (reviews, Poste *et al.*, 1976; Tyrrell *et al.*, 1976) but in none of these reports has the exact intracellular location of the introduced material been defined. Although it seems likely that the ability of vesicle-encapsulated cytotoxic drugs (Poste and Papahadjopoulos, 1976c; Papahadjopoulos *et al.*, 1976c; Mayhew *et al.*, 1977), polynucleotides (Mayhew *et al.*, 1976), and viral nucleic acids (Wilson *et al.*, 1977) to alter cell function requires that they are released into the cytoplasm, formal proof has not been presented. The belief that such materials are present in the cytoplasm is based entirely on indirect evidence from work showing that lysosomes are impermeable to material with a molecular weight > 300 (see below), making it unlikely that the above components could diffuse out of lysosomes if the vesicles had been endocytosed.

Even though recovery of vesicle-encapsulated materials free within the cytosol suggests that vesicle–plasma membrane fusion has occurred, the possibility that additional mechanisms are responsible, or are occurring in parallel with vesicle fusion, cannot presently be discounted. Theoretically, vesicle-encapsulated materials could be introduced into the cytoplasm by at least three pathways other than vesicle–plasma membrane fusion, and these must be excluded before final conclusions concerning vesicle fusion are made.

The first possibility, discussed on pp. 108 and 115, is that adsorption of vesicles to the plasma membrane alters the permeability of both vesicles and cells allowing leakage of encapsulated material from vesicles and its uptake into cells by passive diffusion (Figure 1, Pathway 9). The importance of this mechanism would obviously depend on the extent of the permeability alterations in both systems. As mentioned earlier, more information is still required to answer this potentially important question.

A second possibility is that vesicles are endocytosed but vesicle contents released into the phagolysosome by breakdown of the vesicle membrane(s) by lysosomal lipases are able to resist digestion by lysosomal enzymes and diffuse out of the phagolysosome into the cytosol. The resistance of specific compounds to digestion by lysosomal hydrolases can be analysed in cell-free systems and this approach could be used to examine the likelihood of particular vesicle-encapsulated materials surviving assault by lysosomal enzymes. The more difficult problem is to identify and quantitate transfer of endocytosed material from lysosomes to the cytosol. Studies with non-metabolizable hydrophilic molecules (mol. wt. range 200 to 2×10^6) have shown that material with a molecular weight of above 300 cannot easily leave the lysosome and is retained for long periods of time (Ehrenreich and Cohn, 1969; Schulman and Bradley, 1970; Goldman, 1976).

It is known, however, that several classes of viruses (and also isolated infective viral nucleic acids) can be endocytosed yet successfully initiate virus replication. This must presumably require transfer of the viral genome out of the vacuolar apparatus into the cytoplasm. Also, it is not clear whether virus is actually exposed to lysosomal hydrolases, though for reovirus infection it has been shown that lysosomal proteases are responsible for removal of the viral capsid (Silverstein, 1975) and the uncoated nucleic acid must somehow be able to escape from the lysosome. Thus in our present state of knowledge it would be premature to conclude that high molecular weight (>300) materials encapsulated in endocytosed vesicles cannot reach the cytosol.

Finally, the possibility must be considered that vesicles might be internalized by a process similar to endocytosis (i.e. the vesicle is internalized by a segment of plasma membrane) but then fusion takes place immediately between the vesicle and the endocytic vacuole with release of vesicle contents into the cytosol (Figure 1, Pathway 5). In this scheme, fusion between the vesicle and the endocytic vacuole would occur before fusion with lysosomes or, alternatively, fusion with lysosomes need not even occur. This scheme, while theoretical, warrants consideration in the light of recent findings which suggest that not all endocytic vacuoles are committed to fuse with lysosomes. For example, during infection of cells with pox viruses, release of the DNA-containing viral core into the cytoplasm is achieved by fusion between the outer lipoprotein coat of the virus and the surrounding membrane of the endocytic vacuole (Silverstein *et al.*, 1976). The surface properties of the virus are important in this process since treatment of virus with heat or antibodies prevents its escape from the endocytic vacuole and results in sequestration within phagolysosomes where it is destroyed (Silverstein *et al.*, 1976). Further evidence that plasma membrane internalized as endocytic vacuoles need not interact with lysosomes has been presented by Tulkens *et al.* (1977). By following the behaviour of fluorescein-labelled rabbit anti-rat antibodies bound to rat cell surface antigens these investigators demonstrated that plasma membrane plus bound antibodies was internalized via endocytosis but the antigen–antibody complexes were not incorporated into phagolysosomes and were instead returned to the cell surface. However, when anti-rabbit antibodies were added (together with the rabbit anti-rat antibodies) the triple-layer antigen–antibody complexes were endocytosed but were now digested in lysosomes. These fascinating observations suggest that the degree of cross-linking of surface components in the membrane of an endocytic vacuole may determine whether it interacts with lysosomes.

Evidence indicating that endocytic vacuoles need not necessarily fuse with lysosomes has also been obtained in recent studies of plasma membrane turnover in cultured cells. Several groups of investigators have shown that the plasma membrane in cultured cells may be continually internalized by endocytosis but only a small fraction of the internalized vacuoles fuse with lysosomes and the majority are rapidly recycled back to the cell surface where they are presumed to fuse with the plasma membrane (reviews, Silverstein *et al.*, 1976; Edelson and Cohn, 1978). Although the functional significance of this phenomenon is unknown, its occurrence in a variety of cell types emphasizes that it is no longer valid to assume that endocytic vacuoles will inevitably fuse with lysosomes.

2.3.9. *The Molecular Mechanism for Fusion of Lipid Vesicles with the Plasma Membrane*

Collectively, the observations reviewed in the preceding sections provide a broad framework of evidence which indicates that fluid-charged vesicles may fuse with the plasma membrane of cultured cells, though this phenomenon has yet to be quantitated. The molecular mechanism(s) underlying vesicle–plasma membrane fusion is presently unknown.

Pagano and Huang (1975) have proposed a model for fusion of vesicles with the plasma membrane based on the interaction and incorporation (so called 'snapping') of oil droplets into the plasma membrane of living cells

(Chambers and Kopac, 1937). Pagano and Huang propose that uptake of vesicles by fusion with the plasma membrane involves the formation of an 'intermediate' structure in which the vesicle is incorporated entirely within the lipid bilayer of the plasma membrane in an analogous fashion to the formation of oil droplet lenses within bilayers (Henn and Thompson, 1968). Although we find this model interesting, we believe that several features of this scheme are not consistent with thermodynamic considerations and that the analogy with the 'snapping' of oil droplets into cells is not appropriate. The driving force for the interaction of an oil droplet with a lipid bilayer is the large difference in surface energy of the two systems due to the comparatively high surface energy of oil droplets in water (Davis and Rideal, 1961; Thompson and Henn, 1970). However, phospholipid bilayers have very low surface energies (Thompson and Henn, 1970) and the difference in surface energy between a sonicated phospholipid vesicle and a planar lipid bilayer in the plasma membrane should not be expected *a priori* to provide a sufficient driving force to perturb the stability of the two membranes and lead to fusion. Indeed, published data are available showing that sonicated neutral vesicles do not fuse with relatively flat large multilamellar vesicles (Papahadjopoulos *et al.*, 1974b, 1976a) and are also incapable of fusing with each other even at temperatures above their Tc (Kantor and Prestegard, 1975; Lawaczek *et al.*, 1975; Papahadjopoulos *et al.*, 1976a). Finally, the 'intermediate' proposed by Pagano and Huang would seem to be thermodynamically unfavourable because of the very high contact angles required at the points of bifurcation between the plasma membrane and the vesicle. An intermediate of this type would be much more feasible for an oil droplet within a lipid bilayer where much smaller contact angles can be achieved (Haydon and Taylor, 1968). Furthermore, rupture of the proposed intermediate would be much more likely to occur at the bifurcation region and not in the middle of the relatively stable bilayer as proposed by Pagano and Huang.

Even if an intermediate structure were possible, the structure envisaged by Pagano and Huang could not possibly represent the first stage since it would require multiple points of attachment of the vesicle within the membrane. An alternative, and thermodynamically more reasonable form of initial interaction between a vesicle and the plasma membrane would simply involve a single attachment point similar to that seen in fusion between natural membranes (Apostolov and Almeida, 1972; Pinto da Silva *et al.*, 1977). Subsequent rupture of the membranes at this single attachment point of high energy would then result in true membrane fusion with material trapped within the internal aqueous space of the vesicle being introduced into the cytoplasm. This alternative model would not preclude 'leaky' fusion during which low molecular weight materials within the vesicles and intracellular materials might diffuse back out into the external medium (see Poste and Allison, 1973; Poste and Pasternak, 1978). It is also possible that the single point attachment is followed by an intermediate such as that proposed by Pagano and Huang and also by Pinto da Silva *et al.* (1977) in which mixing of only the two outer monolayers results in partial fusion. As outlined above we consider this as an unstable structure which would rupture most probably at a point of bifurcation to produce complete fusion of the two membranes.

We have recently put forward a unitary hypothesis for membrane fusion in which fusion is considered to result from Ca^{2+}-induced lateral phase separation of membrane lipids to form crystalline domains of acidic phospholipids within a mixed lipid membrane, with fusion occurring between closely apposed membranes at the boundaries of these domains (see Papahadjopoulos, 1978; Papahadjopoulos *et al.*, 1979a). The domain boundaries represent structurally unstable points of high free energy and thus offer focal points for mixing of molecules between two membranes. The details of this proposed mechanism for membrane fusion, which is based on detailed observations of events in fusion of model membranes of defined composition, have been reviewed elsewhere (Papahadjopoulos, 1978; Papahadjopoulos *et al.*, 1979a).

The scheme mentioned above also offers a possible mechanism for events in cell-to-cell fusion induced by lipid vesicles. Recent freeze-fracture electron microscopic studies of cell fusion induced by lipid-enveloped viruses have shown that prior to fusion the intramembranous particles seen in fracture faces of the plasma membrane become aggregated, creating membrane regions devoid of particles. Fusion occurs by apposition of these particle-free areas on adjacent membranes (review Bächi *et al.*, 1977; Poste and Pasternak, 1978). It has been proposed that the redistribution of intramembraneous particles requires participation of membrane-associated cytoplasmic microfilaments. Drugs such as cytochalasin B and local anaesthetics that impair microfilament function inhibit both particle aggregation and cell fusion (Poste and Pasternak, 1978). These agents do not, however, block fusion of virus particles with the plasma membrane. This finding suggests that cell-to-cell fusion occurs after virus-to-cell fusion has been completed. Fusion of virus particles with the plasma membrane is accompanied by a marked increased in plasma membrane permeability (review Poste and Pasternak, 1978). Papahadjopoulos *et al.* (1979a) have suggested that increased entry of Ca^{2+} into the cell might be responsible for promoting the structural changes in the plasma membrane needed for cell-to-cell fusion. They propose that entry of Ca^{2+} induces contraction of actomyosin-containing microfilaments which, in turn, causes redistribution of intramembranous particles and creates particle free areas in the bilayer which serve as sites of fusion.

We consider that a comparable sequence of events may also be involved in cell-to-cell fusion induced by lipid vesicles and that the phase separation model can be used to explain cell fusion induced by both lipid-enveloped viruses and lipid vesicles. In this scheme, the Ca^{2+}-induced phase separation of acidic phospholipids into crystalline domains required for initial fusion of vesicles (or virus) with the plasma membrane, would also initiate the further series of structural rearrangements in the plasma membrane needed for cell-to-cell fusion to take place.

According to the same scheme (Papahadjopoulos et al., 1979a) fusion of positively charged vesicles with the plasma membrane would not increase the acidic phospholipid content of the outer monolayer in the plasma membrane and thus formation of extensive domains of acidic phospholipid will not occur. This, in turn, would dictate that the permeability of the plasma membrane would not be altered sufficiently to enable Ca^{2+} to enter the cell and achieve the intracellular concentration needed to induce microfilament-mediated redistribution of membrane proteins, thus frustrating fusion between cells. However, inclusion of lysolecithin (LL) within positively charged vesicles enables them to induce cell fusion (Martin and MacDonald, 1976b). In this situation, initial fusion of vesicles with the plasma membrane would introduce LL directly into the lipid bilayer of the plasma membrane. As discussed in detail elsewhere (Papahadjopoulos et al., 1979a), we consider that once within the bilayer, LL can promote structural rearrangements which result in trans-bilayer redistribution of phospholipids and accumulation of acid phospholipids such as phosphatidylserine in the external monolayer of the plasma membrane. Once sufficient amounts of phosphatidylserine have accumulated, Ca^{2+}-induced phase separation of phosphatidylserine into crystalline domains will occur with onset of increased membrane permeability to Ca^{2+} which, in turn, will initiate the sequence of cytoskeletal-assisted changes in membrane architecture needed for cell-to-cell fusion. We consider that the reason neutral vesicles containing LL fail to induce cell fusion (Martin and MacDonald, 1976b) is because these vesicles are unable to fuse with the cellular plasma membrane and LL is therefore unable to gain access to the lipid bilayer of the plasma membrane

3. LIPID VESICLES AS CARRIERS FOR INTRODUCING BIOLOGICALLY ACTIVE MATERIALS INTO CELLS

The use of lipid vesicles as carrier vehicles for introducing biologically active materials into cells *in vitro* and *in vivo* is an exciting and rapidly expanding area of current research in biology and medicine.

The utility of any carrier system is determined by: (1) lack of cytotoxicity; (2) biodegradability; (3) lack of immunogenicity (unless designed specifically to carry antigens); (4) the efficiency with which molecules and macromolecules are incorporated into the carrier under conditions that do not alter and/or inactivate the incorporated material(s); (5) the ability to protect carrier-associated material(s) from alteration and/or breakdown by exposure to the extracellular environment; and (6) the efficiency with which carrier-associated material(s) are transferred to cells.

Lipid vesicles merit favourable review with respect to each of these criteria. The versatility of the methodology for producing vesicles has probably been the major factor to the successful use of these structures as carrier vehicles. The ability to produce vesicles of widely differing size and surface properties enables a wide range of materials to be incorporated into vesicles, either within the vesicle membrane or encapsulated within the internal aqueous space(s) of the vesicle. This flexibility in vesicle design, together with the efficient transfer of vesicle-associated materials to cells, dictates that vesicles provide a carrier whose versatility cannot be matched by other recently advocated carrier systems such as lipid micelles (Fendler, 1976), polymer or macromolecular-bound materials (De Duve, 1974; Yolles *et al.*, 1975; Wise *et al.*, 1976), synthetic microcapsules (Chang, 1971) or cell fusion microinjection techniques (Furusawa *et al.*, 1974; Loyter *et al.*, 1975; Uchida *et al.*, 1977).

Lipid vesicles have been used successfully as carriers both *in vivo* and *in vitro* and several chapters in this volume attest to the diverse and fascinating applications of this technology over the past five years. We will confine our remarks, however, to *in vitro* studies in which lipid vesicles have been used as carriers to introduce materials into cultured cells as an investigative tool in cell biology, pharmacology, and virology.

The first demonstration that vesicles could be used as carrier vehicles to introduce biologically active materials into cells *in vitro* was made by Magee and Miller in 1972, who showed that treatment of cultured ML cells with MLVs containing IgG with a high neutralizing titre to Coxsackie virus A-21 protected cells against subsequent infection by this virus. The IgG-containing vesicles were 3,000–10,000 times more effective in protecting cells than an equivalent titre of free antibody. Since direct incubation of IgG-containing vesicles with isolated virions also resulted in significant virus neutralization, it would appear that the IgG was associated with the surface of the vesicle rather than trapped inside. Although Magee and Miller did not formally localize the distribution of vesicles within treated cells, the observed inhibition to virus penetration clearly suggests that effective amounts of virus-neutralizing IgG remained at the cell surface. Since the IgG could not be removed from the cell surface by extensive washing (in contrast to free IgG), it is tempting to speculate that the vesicles had in fact fused with the cellular plasma membrane thus incorporating IgG directly into the cell surface. In view of our earlier comments (this chapter, Section 2) on the importance of surface charge in enabling vesicles to fuse with cells, it is of interest that Magee and Miller found it necessary to add a charged amphiphile (stearylamine) to vesicles in order to achieve significant association of IgG with the cell surface.

Evidence that vesicles might also be useful for introducing material into the intracellular environment was next obtained by Gregoriadis and Buckland (1973). They showed that MLVs could serve as carriers to introduce invertase into invertase-deficient mouse macrophages and human fibroblasts (MRC-5) cultured *in vitro*. Cells were first prelabelled with [^{14}C]sucrose. This sugar is not normally metabolized because of the invertase deficiency and instead accumulates within lysosomes. Successful vesicle-mediated transfer of invertase into these cells was demonstrated by the fact that the treated cells acquired the ability to hydrolyse [^{14}C]sucrose to [^{14}C]fructose. This study did not, however, include a control experiment to test whether simple addition of free invertase to the culture medium might also result in uptake of the enzyme. This is by no means an extreme possibility. Several studies using fibroblast cultures derived from patients with specific lysosomal enzyme deficiencies have shown that addition of the appropriate deficient enzyme to the culture medium will result in its incorporation into lysosomes in a functional state with accompanying temporary remission of the deficient phenotype (review, Brady, 1975). However, a recent report by Weissmann *et al.* (1975) has shown that the uptake of horseradish peroxidase trapped inside MLVs by dogfish phagocytes is up to 100 times greater than in cells exposed to the free enzyme.

The feasibility of using SUVs, as opposed to MLVs, as carriers to enhance the incorporation of non-permeable materials into cultured cells was demonstrated by Papahadjopoulos *et al.* (1974a,c). They showed that incorporation of fluid charged SUVs containing entrapped cyclic AMP (cAMP) by mouse 3T3 cells and virally transformed 3T3 cells (SV3T3) resulted in significant inhibition of cell growth at concentrations where free cAMP or dibutyryl cAMP together with theophylline had little or no effect on cell proliferation. This work also demonstrated the potential importance of vesicle composition in determining whether material entrapped within the vesicle can be released intracellularly in an active form. The marked inhibition of cell growth produced by vesicle-derived cAMP obtained using fluid charged vesicles as carriers was not found when cAMP was entrapped within solid charged vesicles, even though cells incorporated similar amounts of both types of vesicle.

Papahadjopoulos *et al.* (1974a,c) proposed that the differing cellular responses to cAMP delivered via solid and fluid vesicles were due to the fact that solid and fluid vesicles were incorporated into cells by different mechanisms, with resulting differences in the intracellular site(s) at which cAMP was eventually released. They proposed that fluid charged vesicles were able to fuse with the cellular plasma membrane and thus release the entrapped cAMP directly into the cytoplasm. In contrast, it was proposed that solid charged vesicles were unable to fuse with the plasma membrane and were incorporated by endocytosis with release of the entrapped cAMP into the lysosomal apparatus. The lack of effect of cAMP on cell growth when introduced into lysosomes was suggested as resulting from failure of cAMP to be released from the lysosome in an active form at sufficient concentrations. The limited permeability of the lysosomal membrane (this chapter, p. 134) and the likelihood of inactivation of cAMP lysosomal phosphodiesterases (Tappel, 1969) would both favour this situation.

Several laboratories have directed their attention to the possibility of using lipid vesicles as carriers for the spectrum of cytotoxic drugs currently used in treating neoplastic disease. Exposure of cultured tumour cell populations to SUVs containing actinomycin D (Poste and Papahadjopoulos, 1976c; Papahadjopoulos *et al.*, 1976c) or cytosine arabinoside (Mayhew *et al.*, 1976) enhances drug uptake by cells and significantly reduces the amount of drug required to kill the cells. These findings have been paralleled by *in vivo* studies in which SUVs and MLVs containing similar antimetabolites have been shown to significantly prolong the life of tumour-bearing animals (Neerunjun and Gregoriadis, 1974; Rahman *et al.*, 1974; Kobayashi *et al.*, 1975; Mayhew *et al.*, 1976). These findings, together with a detailed analysis of the advantages and limitations of vesicle-encapsulated antimetabolites as a possible modality in cancer therapy, are discussed in several chapters elsewhere in this volume.

Recent *in vitro* studies from the present authors' laboratories also indicate that encapsulation of antitumour drugs within vesicles may provide a possible method for overcoming drug resistance in tumour cell populations. The emergence of drug-resistant tumour cell variants is a well-documented problem in clinical cancer chemotherapy and the development of a procedure whereby drug-resistant cells could be rendered susceptible to killing by chemotherapeutic agents would have obvious benefit.

Resistance of tumour cells to such drugs as actinomycin D, methotrexate, nitrogen mustard, daunomycin, and the vinca alkaloids is considered to be due to changes in plasma membrane permeability that result in reduced drug uptake by resistant cells compared with their sensitive counterparts (Kessel, 1974). Support for this hypothesis has been based largely on demonstrated differences in drug uptake by sensitive and resistant cells (see Kessel, 1974) and on the finding that enhancement of drug uptake by detergent-induced modification of membrane permeability results in increased killing of tumour cells (Yamada and Iwanami, 1962; Riehm and Biedler, 1972). The latter method suffers, however, from the shortcoming that detergent treatment *per se* causes significant cyto-toxicity and thus complicates interpretation of cellular response to the drug. The use of drug-containing vesicles to enhance drug uptake into low permeability drug-resistant variants offers a potential solution to this problem (Poste and Papahadjopoulos, 1976c; Papahadjopoulos *et al.*, 1976c). Vesicle-mediated introduction of drugs directly into tumour cells not only produces significant enhancement of drug uptake, but is also devoid of complicating side effects on cell viability.

Poste and Papahadjopoulos (1976c) and Papahadjopoulos *et al.* (1976c) used SUVs as a carrier vehicle to enhance the uptake of actinomycin D (AD) into an AD-resistant hamster cell line (DC3F-ADX), which is resistant as a result of a decreased capacity to transport AD across the plasma membrane. This cell line is able to grow in media supplemented with concentrations of AD (10 μg/ml) that are highly toxic for the sensitive parent cell line (DC3F). Incubation of resistant DC3F-ADX cells with AD-containing fluid-charged SUVs produced a five fold increase in cell-associated drug uptake over that achieved by exposure to identical concentrations of free drug and was accompanied by significant inhibition of cellular RNA synthesis and cell growth at drug concentrations that had little or no effect when added as free drug to the culture medium.

In many situations, however, tumour cell resistance to cytotoxic drugs is not mediated by alterations in plasma membrane properties. A large category of drug-resistant phenotypes are recognized in which the drug is incorporated into the cell but as a result of alterations in the cellular metabolic machinery the drug is not 'converted' to an active cytotoxic form. This is illustrated by cellular resistance to cytotoxic nucleotides. Because of the relatively low permeability of cells to nucleotides these agents are usually administered in the form of nucleosides which freely enter the cell and which are subsequently phosphorylated to form the toxic nucleotide. If, however, a cell lacks one or more of the kinases responsible for sequential phosphorylation of the nucleoside it will not form the toxic nucleotide and will thus be resistant to drug-induced killing. Theoretically, by introducing the already phosphorylated nucleotide into such cells it should be possible to overcome the drug-resistant phenotype.

The first step in demonstrating the practical feasibility of this approach has been made recently by Mayhew *et al.* (1976). These investigators showed that 1-β-D-arabinofuranosylcytosine-5-triphosphate (ara-CTP) encapsulated in SUVs was a significantly more efficient inhibitor of L1210 leukaemia cell growth *in vitro* (ID_{50} 2×10^{-8}M) than free ara-CTP ($ID_{50} > 10^{-7}$M). It was not established in this study, however, whether the greater biological activity of the vesicle-encapsulated drug resulted from enhanced uptake, protection against inactivation by degradative enzymes, or both. Further studies to answer this question are in progress and to evaluate the equally important question of whether vesicle-mediated introduction of ara-CTP into ara-C-resistant cells can render them susceptible to killing by this drug (this latter experiment of course assumes that the ara-C resistant phenotype is determined by the absence of a phosphokinase).

Both MLVs and SUVs were developed originally as model systems for the lipid bilayer of natural membranes (see Chapter 1). Their successful adoption as carriers without further modification has meant that little attention has been given to the development of new classes of vesicles whose properties might be better suited for carrier functions.

This problem is highlighted by the limited ability of conventional MLVs and SUVs to serve as carriers for macromolecules or complex intact structures such as intact micro-organisms or cell organelles. Although the *total* internal aqueous space of MLVs is relatively large, the individual compartments between each lipid lamella are too small to accommodate large macromolecules (Figure 2). The single internal aqueous space of sonicated SUVs is also too small (Figure 3) and this problem is also shared by SUVs produced by the ethanol injection method (Batzri and Korn, 1973). Unilamellar vesicles produced by ultrasonication suffer from the additional drawback that sonication is damaging to a variety of biologically active macromolecules. Unilamellar vesicles prepared by dialysis or gel filtration of detergent-containing lipid solutions (Kagawa, 1972; Razin, 1972) are in general larger than those produced by sonication but their capacity to encapsulate macromolecules has not been determined. Deamer and Bangham (1976) have recently described an ether injection method that produces unilamellar vesicles of intermediate size with a large internal aqueous volume. This method appears, however, to require a large total volume for vesicle formation which may well limit the efficiency of encapsulation. Furthermore, the high temperature (60 °C) requried for formation of these vesicles prevents their use with thermolabile materials.

We have recently described a new class of large unilamellar vesicles (LUVs) which are produced by Ca^{2+}-induced fusion of sonicated phosphatidylserine SUVs (Figure 4) (Papahadjopoulos *et al.*, 1975). These structures have so far proved to be efficient vehicles for encapsulating macromolecules and transferring them to cultured cells. Under proper conditions of preparation, LUVs entrap a high percentage of the total aqueous volume, permitting materials to be encapsulated efficiently without exposure to detergents, denaturing agents or sonication. The initial cochleate structures which are formed by fusion of SUVs can be lyophilized and/or frozen at -20 °C under nitrogen for long-term storage (J. Klarnet and D. Papahadjopoulos, unpublished observations) and subsequently converted to LUVs when required. Measurements of the percentage capture by LUVs of large materials such as ferritin (mol. wt. 0.6–0.9×10^6 daltons), synthetic polynucleotides (mol. wt. 2×10^5 daltons), intact polio virus (mol. wt. 8×10^6 daltons), and high molecular weight dextran (mol. wt. 4×10^7 daltons) is comparable (8–12%) to that obtained with small molecules such as sucrose (Mayhew et al., 1976; Wilson et al., 1977; Papahadjopoulos et al., 1979b). This suggests that these materials are passively entrapped by simple enclosure of a portion of the aqueous phase by vesicle membrane rather than by specific association or filtration effects. The LUVs formed by final chelation of Ca^{2+} by EDTA are quite stable and impermeable and, as discussed below, are capable of transferring their content into cells. The construction of LUVs from PS (or an equimolar mixture of PS and cholesterol) means that under physiologic conditions the LUV membrane is negatively charged and may thus be capable of fusing with the plasma membrane and delivering the vesicle contents directly into the cytoplasm. LUVs behave similarly to negatively charged fluid SUVs and MLVs in that endocytosis is apparently not a major pathway in vesicle uptake by cells (Poste and Papahadjopoulos, unpublished observations). However, no information is available on the kinetics of LUV–cell interactions and the role of adsorption, fusion, phospholipid exchange or other transfer mechanisms in the interaction of these vesicles with cells.

LUVs produced by fusion of sonicated SUVs have been used to introduce large macromolecules into cells. Mayhew et al. (1977) showed that encapsulation of $rI_n \cdot rC_n$ within LUVs produced a five- to tenfold increase in uptake by mouse L929 and human neonatal foreskin fibroblasts over that seen with free $rI_n \cdot rC_n$. Vesicle-mediated stimulation of polynucleotide uptake was also accompanied by a five- to tenfold increase in interferon production and protection against virus challenge. Measurements of the uptake of LUV-encapsulated $[^{14}C]rI_n \cdot [^3H]rC_n$ revealed that the two homopolymers associated with cells at similar rates. This contrasts with the behaviour of the free polynucleotide, in which the $[^{14}C]rI_n$ strand associates preferentially with cells. Previous studies had suggested that induction of interferon by polynucleotides was mediated extracellularly by binding to cell surface receptors and that rC_n was more susceptible than rI_n to enzymic degradation at the cell surface (see Carter et al., 1976). Although the results with vesicle-encapsulated polynucleotides do not disprove a physiologic role for surface receptors, they indicate that $rI_n \cdot rC_n$ introduced directly into the cell is also capable of inducing interferon production and that selective digestion of rC_n is not required for 'activation' of the metabolic pathways responsible for producing interferon. As Mayhew et al. acknowledge, their results do not provide any direct information on the cellular sites that bind vesicle-derived polynucleotides and further studies are needed to clarify this point.

The feasibility of using LUVs as carriers for micro-organisms has been demonstrated recently by Wilson *et al.* (1977). These investigators successfully encapsulated intact poliovirus virions in LUVs and showed that vesicle-encapsulated virus was able to initiate infection in both permissive and non-permissive cell types. The latter clearly suggests that virus is introduced directly into the cytoplasm by vesicle–plasma membrane fusion or some other mechanism that allows free cytoplasmic delivery. More recently, the same investigators have been able to successfully infect cells using isolated poliovirus RNA encapsulated within LUVs (Papahadjopoulos *et al.*, 1979b).

These experiments indicate that LUVs may offer a valuable carrier system for introducing nucleic acids and other biologically active macromolecules into cells. The very large lumen of LUVs also appears to be suitable for the encapsulation of micro-organisms, and also perhaps cell organelles, opening the way for the use of LUVs as carriers for organelle transfer to achieve defined changes in cell structure and composition.

4. CONCLUSIONS

The interaction of lipid vesicles with cultured cells is a complex phenomenon. In addition to adsorption of vesicles to the cell surface, there is evidence that vesicle components are incorporated into cells by endocytosis of intact vesicles, by fusion of vesicles with the plasma membrane, and also by selective and reciprocal exchange of phospholipids and proteins between the vesicle membrane and the plasma membrane. None of these mechanisms is mutually exclusive and in most examples of vesicle–cell interactions several mechanisms appear to be operating simultaneously. The combination of mechanisms operating in any given situation appears to be determined by the properties of the vesicle membrane, the cell type, and also by environmental factors such as temperatures and the presence or absence of serum. Identification of the combination of mechanisms involved in vesicle–cell interactions, and their respective contribution to the total cell-associated vesicle population, has proved to be a formidable problem. Although information has been obtained on the mechanisms involved, little quantitative data have been obtained and this represents an obvious area for future research. The role of endocytosis in vesicle uptake by cells can be identified using metabolic inhibitors and other agents which impair endocytosis. Opportunities for the reciprocal transfer of phospholipids and other membrane components between vesicles and cells via exchange diffusion can be examined at temperatures (0–4 °C) where endocytosis and membrane fusion are inhibited, though it is still necessary to exclude the possibility that vesicle components recovered in association with cells are not merely in the form of vesicles adsorbed to the cell surface. Our knowledge of the adsorption of vesicles to the cell surface is incomplete and further studies are required to identify the range of cell surface components which can serve as 'receptors' for vesicle attachment. With this knowledge, adsorbed vesicles could be eluted from the cell surface which, in turn, would enable the true extent of vesicle uptake by cells to be distinguished from the non-incorporated population of adsorbed vesicles. Considerable evidence has been accumulated which indicates that vesicles with certain properties can fuse with the plasma membrane. Much of this evidence is circumstantial, however, and definitive proof has been difficult to obtain because of the experimental probelm of defining whether vesicle membrane components associated with the cell surface are present within the plasma membrane as a result of vesicle fusion or are merely bound to the plasma membrane as adsorbed vesicles.

Vesicle surface charge and the physical state of phospholipids within the vesicle membrane are of major importance in determining vesicle–cell interactions. The outcome of vesicle–cell interactions is similiar for both small sonicated unilamellar vesicles and large multilamellar vesicles of identical composition, indicating that vesicle size and structure are less important in determining the route of vesicle uptake, though these parameters will, of course, influence the number of vesicles incorporated into cells and thus, in turn, the amount of vesicle-derived lipid or other components that accumulate within cells. Fusion of vesicles with the plasma membrane appears to be confined to charged vesicles composed of phospholipids which are fluid at 37 °C. Even so, fusion is probably not the dominant mechanism in the interaction of these vesicles with cells. Endocytosis occurs in parallel with fusion and accounts for 20–30% of the total cell-associated vesicle population. Evidence is emerging which suggests that adsorbed besicles may constitute the major fraction of the cell-associated vesicle population. The 'fluidity' of phospholipids in the vesicle membrane is important in determining the fusion susceptibility of charged vesicles since 'solid' vesicles with similar surface charge properties do not fuse with cells. However, a 'fluid' membrane is not the only requirement for fusion. Surface charge is also important. No convincing evidence has been obtained to show that neutral vesicles can fuse with the plasma membrane, including neutral vesicles composed of lipids which are fluid at 37 °C. The inability of neutral fluid vesicles and solid charged vesicles to fuse is consistent with a large body of evidence from studies in cell-free systems showing that such vesicles are highly resistant to fusion.

Neutral vesicles composed of egg PC are incorporated into cells by endocytosis but neutral vesicles composed of the synthetic phospholipids, DMPC and DPPC, are not endocytosed and apparently remain adsorbed to the cell surface where reciprocal exchange of phospholipids and proteins between the vesicle membrane and the plasma membrane can occur. 'Solid' vesicles also vary in their susceptibility to endocytosis. The evidence indicates that charged solid vesicles prepared from a mixture of PS and the saturated lecithins DSPC and DPPC are endocytosed but neutral solid vesicles composed of DMPC or DPPC alone appear to bind to the cell surface, and their ability to provoke endocytosis remains to be clarified.

These observations suggest that vesicle lipid composition is of major importance in determining the pattern of vesicle–cell interactions. By manipulating the lipid composition of vesicles it may be possible to frustrate certain mechanisms of vesicle–cell interactions and selectively favour others.

Lipid vesicles offer a new and potentially powerful technique for achieving cellular uptake of materials that would not ordinarily be taken up by cells or would be incorporated at insufficient concentrations to affect cellular function. The availability of a well established technology for the production and characterization of different types of vesicle provides a firm foundation for the further development of studies on the interaction of vesicles with cells *in vitro* and *in vivo*. Vesicles can be constructed to meet a diversity of experimental requirements by altering such characteristics as surface charge, permeability to ions, and the physical state of the lipids. Vesicles can also be prepared over a wide size range (250 Å to 10 μm diameter) and homogenous subpopulations of differing size isolated by density gradient centrifugation and gel-filtration techniques. This size range enables materials of widely differing molecular weight to be incorporated into vesicles, either in association with the vesicle membrane or trapped within the internal aqueous space(s) of the vesicle.

Lipid vesicles have now been used successfully as carriers for introducing a wide range of biologically active molecules and macromolecules into cultured cells in recent work on several important questions in cell biology, virology, and cellular pharmacology. The flexibility in vesicle design, together with the efficient transfer of vesicle-associated materials, dictate that vesicles provide a carrier whose versatility cannot be matched by other recently advocated carriers such as polymer- or macromolecular-bound materials, synthetic microcapsules, lysosomotrophic agents or cell fusion microinjection techniques. Progress in the use of lipid vesicles as carriers has been rapid and we are optimistic that these structures will find increasing use as a valuable experimental tool in many areas of research in biology and medicine.

Acknowledgements

We are indebted to Dr. W. J. Vail for providing the freeze-fracture electron micrographs shown in Figures 2,3,4,7, and Dr. C. Porter for the micrographs shown in Figure 6.

The work described here was partly supported by grants: GM-18921, CA-18527 (D.P.) and CA-18260 (G.P.) from the National Institutes of Health.

REFERENCES

Apostolov, K. and Almeida, J. (1972). *J. Gen. Virol.,* **15**, 227–234.
Bächi, T., Deas, J. E. and Howe, C. (1977). In *Virus Infection and the Cell Surface.* (G. Poste and G. L. Nicoloson, eds.), *Cell Surface Reviews,* Vol. 2, pp. 83–127. Elsevier/North Holland, Amsterdam.
Bangham, A. D., Standish, M. M. and Watkins, J. C. (1965). *J. Mol. Biol.,* **13**, 238–252.
Batzri, S. and Korn, E. D. (1973). *Biochim. Biophys. Acta,* **298**, 1015–1019.
Batzri, S. and Korn, E. D. (1975). *J. Cell Biol.,* **66**, 621–634.
Black, C. D. V. and Gregoriadis, G. (1976). *Biochem. Soc. Trans.,* **4**, 253–256.
Bouma, S. R., Drislane, F. W. and Huestis, W. H. (1977). *J. Biol. Chem.,* **252**, 6759–6763.
Brady, R. O. (1975). *Ann. Int. Med.,* **82**, 257–261.
Carter, W. A. and DeClercq, E. (1974). *Science,* **186**, 1172–1178.
Carter, W. A., O'Malley, J., Beeson, M., Cunnington, P., Kelvin, A., Vere-Hodge, T. and Ts'O, P. O. P. (1976). *Mol. Pharmacol.,* **12**, 400–453.
Chambers, R. and Kopac, M. J. (1937). *J. Cell Comp. Physiol.,* **9**, 331–345.
Chang, T. M. S. (1971). *Nature,* **229**, 117–118.
Cohen, C. M., Weissmann, G., Hoffstein, S., Awasthi, Y. C. and Srivastava, S. K. (1976). *Biochemistry* **15**, 452–460.
Davies, J. T. and Rideal, E. K. (1961). *Interfacial Phenomena.* Academic Press, New York.
Deamer, D. and Bangham, A. D. (1976). *Biochim. Biophys. Acta,* **443**, 629–634.
De Duve, C. (1974). *Biochem. Pharmacol.,* **23**, 2495–2531.
Dunnick, J. K., Kaliman, R. F. and Kriss, J. P. (1976). *Biochem. Biophys. Res. Commun.,* **73**, 619–624.
Edelson, P. and Cohn, Z. A. (1978). In *Membrane Fusion* (G. Poste and G. L. Nicolson, eds.), *Cell Surface Reviews.* Vol. **5**, pp. 388–410. North-Holland, Amsterdam.
Ehrenreich, B. A. and Cohn, Z. A. (1969). *J. Exp. Med.,* **129**, 227–240.
Fendler, J. H. (1976). *Accounts. Chem. Res.,* **9**, 153–161.
Furusawa, M., Nishimura, T., Yamaizumi, M. and Okada, Y. (1974). *Nature,* **249**, 449–450.
Goldman, R. (1976). In *Lysosomes in Biology and Pathology* (J. T. Dingle and R. T. Dean, eds.), Vol. **5**, pp. 309–336. North-Holland, Amsterdam.
Grant, C. W. M. and McConnell, H. M. (1973). *Proc. Nat. Acad. Sci. USA,* **12**, 3662–3667.
Gregoriadis, G. and Buckland, R. A. (1973). *Nature,* **244**, 170–172.
Gregoriadis, G. and Neerunjun, E. D. (1975). *Biochem. Biophys. Res. Comm.,* **65**, 537–544.

Grunze, M. and Deuticke, B. (1974). *Biochim. Biophys. Acta*, **356**, 125–130.
Hasty, N. and Hay, E. (1978). *J. Cell Biol.*, **78**, 756–768.
Hauser, H. O. (1971). *Biochem. Biophys. Res. Commun.*, **45**, 1049–1055.
Hauser, H. O. and Barratt, M. D. (1973). *Biochem. Biophys. Res. Commun.*, **53**, 399–405.
Haydon, D. A. and Taylor, J. R. (1968). *Nature* **217**, 739–740.
Haywood, A. M. (1974). *J. Mol. Biol.*, **87**, 625–628.
Henn, F. A. and Thompson, T. E. (1968). *J. Mol. Biol.*, **31**, 227–235.
Heustis, W. H. (1977). *J. Biol. Chem.*, **252**, 6764–6768.
Hinz, J. J. and Sturtevant, J. M. (1972). *J. Biol. Chem.*, **247**, 6071–6075.
Hock, D. and Stöhr, M. (1977). *Histochemistry*, **52**, 97–103.
Holtzman, E., Schacher, S., Evans, J. and Teichberg, S. (1977) In *The Synthesis, Assembly and Turnover of Cell Surface Components* (G. Poste and G. L. Nicolson, eds.) *Cell Surface Reviews*, Vol. 4, pp. 165–246. North Holland, Amsterdam.
Huang, C. H. (1969). *Biochemistry*, **8**, 344–352.
Huang, L. and Pagano, R. E. (1975). *J. Cell Biol.*, **67**, 38–48.
Jacobson, K. and Papahadjopoulos, D. (1975). *Biochemistry*, **14**, 152–161.
Janiak, M. J., Small, D. M. and Shipley, G. G. (1976). *Biochemistry*, **15**, 4575–4580.
Kader, J. C. (1977). In *Dynamic Aspects of Cell Surface Organization* (G. Poste and G. L. Nicolson, eds.), *Cell Surface Reviews*, Vol. 3, pp. 127–204. Elsevier/North Holland, Amsterdam.
Kagawa, Y. (1972). *Biochim. Biophys. Acta*, **265**, 297–338.
Kantor, H. K. and Prestegard, J. (1975). *Biochemistry*, **14**, 1790–1794.
Kessel, D. and Wedinsky, I. (1968). *Biochim. Pharmacol.*, **17**, 161–164.
Kobayashi, T., Tsukagoshi, S. and Sakurai, Y. (1975). *Gann.*, **66**, 719–720.
Lagunoff, D. and Wan, H. (1974). *J. Cell Biol.*, **61**, 809–811.
Lawaczek, R., Kainosho, M., Girardet, J-L. and Chan, S. I. (1975). *Nature (Lond.)*, **256**, 584–586.
Le Neveu, N., Rand, P. and Parsegian, A. (1976). *Nature (Lond)*, **259**, 601–603.
Loyter, A., Zakai, N. and Kulka, R. G. (1975). *J. Cell Biol.*, **66**, 292–304.
Magee, W. E., Goff, C. W., Schoknecht, J., Smith, M. D. and Cherian, K. (1974). *J. Cell Biol.*, **63**, 492–504.
Martin, F. J. and MacDonald, R. C. (1976a). *Biochemistry*, **15**, 321–327.
Martin, F. J. and MacDonald, R. C. (1976b). *J. Cell Biol.*, **70**, 506–514.
Martin, F. J. and MacDonald, R. C. (1976c). *J. Cell Biol.*, **70**, 515–526.
Mayhew, E., Papahadjopoulos, D., Rustum, Y. M. and Dave, C. (1976). *Cancer Res.*, **36**, 4406–4411.
Mayhew, E., Papahadjopoulos, D., O'Malley, J. A., Carter, W. A. and Vail, W. J. (1977). *Mol. Pharmacol.*, **13**, 488–495.
Miller, C. and Racker, E. (1976). *J. Memb. Biol.*, **26**, 319–333.
Mudd, E. B. H. and Mudd, S. (1933). *J. Gen. Physiol.*, **16**, 265–636.
Neerunjun, D. E. and Gregoriadis, G. (1974). *Biochem. Soc. Trans.*, **2**, 868–869.
Orci, L. and Perrelet, A. (1978). In *Membrane Fusion* (G. Poste and G. L. Nicolson, eds.) *Cell Surface Reviews*, Vol. 5, pp. 630–657. North-Holland, Amsterdam.
Oren, R., Farnham, A. E., Saito, J., Milofsky, E. and Karnovsky, M. L. (1963). *J. Cell Biol.*, **17**, 487–501.
Pagano, R. E. and Huang, L. (1975). *J. Cell Biol.*, **67**, 49–60.
Pagano, R. E. and Takeichi, M. (1977). *J. Cell Biol.*, **74**, 531–546.
Pagano, R. E., Huang, L. and Wey, C. (1974). *Nature*, **252**, 166–167.

F

Papahadjopoulos, D. (1978). In *Membrane Fusion* (G. Poste and G. L. Nicolson, eds.) *Cell Surface Reviews*, Vol. 5, pp. 766–791. North-Holland, Amsterdam.
Papahadjopoulos, D. and Miller, N. (1967). *Biochim. Biophys. Acta*, 135, 624–638.
Papahadjopoulos, D., Poste, G. and Schaeffer, B. E. (1973a). *Biochim. Biophys. Acta*, 323, 23–42.
Papahadjopoulos, D., Nir, S. and Ohki, S. (1973b). *Biochim. Biophys. Acta*, 266, 561–583.
Papahadjopoulos, D., Poste, G. and Mayhew, E. (1974a). *Biochim. Biophys. Acta*, 363, 404–418.
Papahadjopoulos, D., Poste, G., Schaeffer, B. E. and Vail, W. J. (1974b). *Biochim. Biophys. Acta*, 352, 10–28.
Papahadjopoulos, D., Mayhew, E., Poste, G., Smith, S. and Vail, W. J. (1974c). *Nature* 252, 163–166.
Papahadjopoulos, D., Vail, W. J., Jacobson, K. and Poste, G. (1975). *Biochim. Biophys. Acta*, 394, 483–491.
Papahadjopoulos, D., Hui, S., Vail, W. J. and Poste, G. (1976a). *Biochim. Biophys. Acta*, 448, 245–264.
Papahadjopoulos, D., Vail, W. J., Pangborn, W. and Poste, G. (1976b). *Biochim. Biophys. Acta*, 448, 265–283.
Papahadjopoulos, D., Poste, G., Vail, W. J. and Biedler, J. L. (1976c). *Cancer Res.*, 36, 2988–2994.
Papahadjopoulos, D., Poste, G. and Vail, W. J. (1979a). In *Methods in Membrane Biology* (E. Korn, ed.), 10, 1–121. Plenum Press.
Papahadjopoulos, D., Mayhew, E., Taber, R. and Wilson, T. (1979b). In *Protein Turnover and Lysosomal Function* (H. Segal and D. Doyle, eds.), pp. 543–560. Academic Press.
Pinto da Silva, P. and Nogueira, M. L. (1977). *J. Cell Biol.*, 73, 161–181.
Poste, G. and Allison, A. C. (1973). *Biochim. Biophys. Acta*, 300, 421–465.
Poste, G. and Nicolson, G. L. (1976). *Biochim. Biophys. Acta*, 426, 148–155.
Poste, G. and Papahadjopoulos, D. (1976a). *Proc. Nat. Acad. Sci. USA*, 73, 1603–1607.
Poste, G. and Papahadjopoulos, D. (1976b). In *Methods in Cell Biology* (D. M. Prescott, ed.), Vol. 14, pp. 23–32, Academic Press, New York.
Poste, G. and Papahadjopoulos, D. (1976c). *Nature (Lond.)*, 261, 699–701.
Poste, G. and Papahadjopoulos, D. (1978). *Ann. N.Y. Acad. Sci.*, 308, 164–184.
Poste, G. and Pasternak, C. A. (1978). In *Membrane Fusion* (G. Poste and G. L. Nicoloson, eds.), *Cell Surface Reviews*, Vol. 5, pp. 305–365 Elsevier/North Holland, Amsterdam.
Poste, G., Papahadjopoulos, G. and Nicolson, G. L. (1975). *Proc. Nat. Acad. Sci. USA*, 72 4430–4434.
Poste, G., Papahadjopoulos, D. and Vail, W. J. (1976). In *Methods in Cell Biology* (D. M. Prescott, ed.), Vol. 14, pp. 33–71, Academic Press, New York.
Poste, G., Porter, C. W. and Papahadjopoulos, D. (1978). *Biochim. Biophys. Acta*, 510, 256–263.
Prestegard, J. H. and Fellmeth, B. (1975). *Biochemistry*, 14, 1790–1794.
Rahman, Y. E. Cerny, E. H., Tolaksen, S. L., Wright, B. J., Rauce, S. L. and Thomson, J. F. (1974). *Proc. Soc. Exp. Biol. Med.*, 146, 1173–1176.
Razin, S. (1972). *Biochim. Biophys. Acta*, 265, 241–296.
Riehm, H. and Biedler, J. M. (1972). *Cancer Res.*, 32, 1195–1200.
Schulman, J. D. and Bradley, K. H. (1970). *J. Exp. Med.*, 132, 1090–1102.
Schroitt, A. J. and Pagano, R. E. (1968) *Proc. Nat. Acad. Sci. USA*, 75, 5529–5533.
Silverstein, S. C. (1975). In *Mononuclear Phagocytes in Immunity, Infection and Pathology* (R. Van Furth, ed.), pp. 557–573, Blackwell, Oxford.

Silverstein, S. C., Christman, J. K. and Acs, G. (1976). *Ann. Rev. Biochem.*, **45**, 375–408.

Steinman, R. M., Silver, J. M. and Cohn, Z. A. (1974). *J. Cell Biol.*, **63**, 949–969.

Stendahl, O. and Tagesson, CHR. (1977). *Exp. Cell Res.*, **108**, 167–174.

Suurkuusk, J., Lentz, B. R., Berenholtz, Y., Biltonen, R. L. and Thompson, T. E. (1976). *Biochemistry*, **15**, 1393–1401.

Szoka, F., Jacobson, K. and Papahadjopoulos, D. (1979). *Biochim. Biophys. Acta.*, **551**, 295–303.

Tappel, E. L. (1969). In *Lysosomes in Biology and Pathology* (J. T. Dingle and H. B. Fell, eds.), Vol. **2**, pp. 207–242. North-Holland, Amsterdam.

Thompson, T. E. and Henn, F. A. (1970). In *Membranes of Mitochondria and Chloroplasts*. (E. Racker, ed.), pp. 1–52, Van Nostrand, New York.

Trinkaus, J. P. (1976). In *The Cell Surface in Animal Embryogenesis* (G. Poste and G. L. Nicolson, eds.), *Cell Surface Reviews*, Vol. **1**, pp. 225–329, Elsevier/North Holland, Amsterdam.

Tulkens, P., Schneider, Y. J. and Trovet, A. (1977). In *Intracellular Protein Catabolism*. (V. Turk and N. Marks, eds.), pp. 73–84. Plenum Press, New York.

Tyrrell, D. A., Heath, T. D., Colley, C. M. and Ryman, B. E. (1976). *Biochim. Biophys. Acta*, **457**, 259–302.

Tyrrell, D. A., Richardson, V. J. and Ryman, B. E. (1977). *Biochim. Biophys. Acta*, **497**, 469–480.

Uchida, T., Yamaizumi, M. and Okada, Y. (1977). *Nature*, **266**, 839–840.

Van Oss, C. J., Gillman, C. F. and Neumann, A. W. (1975). *Phagocytic Engulfment and Cell Adhesiveness as Cellular Surface Phenomena*. Dekker, New York.

Weinstein, J. N., Henkart, P., Blumenthal, R. and Hagins, W. A. (1977). *Science*, **195**, 489–492.

Weiss, L. (1967). *The Cell Periphery, Metastasis and Other Contact Phenomena*, North Holland, Amsterdam.

Weissmann, G., Bloomgarden, D., Kaplan, R., Hoffstein, S., Collins, T., Gotlieb, A. and Nagle, D. (1975). *Proc. Nat. Acad. Sci. USA*, **72**, 88–92.

Weissmann, G., Cohen, C. and Hoffstein, S. (1977). *Biochim. Biophys. Acta*, **498**, 375–385.

Wilson, T., Papahadjopoulos, D. and Taber, R. (1977). *Proc. Nat. Acad. Aci. USA*, **74**, 3471–3475.

Wirtz, K. W. A. (1974). *Biochim. Biophys. Acta*, **344**, 95–117.

Wise, D. L., McCormick, G. J., Willett, G. P. and Anderson, L. C. (1976). *Life Sci.*, **19**, 867–974.

Wu, S. H. W. and McConnell, H. M. (1973). *Biochem. Biophys. Res. Commun.*, **55**, 484–491.

Yamada, T. and Iwanami, Y. (1962). *Gann.*, **52**, 225–233.

Yolles, S., Leafe, T. D. and Meyer, F. J. (1975). *J. Pharm. Sci*, **64**, 115–116.

Zborowski, J., Roerdink, F. and Scherphof, G. (1977). *Biochim. Biophys. Acta*, **497**, 183–191.

Liposomes in Biological Systems
Edited by A. C. Allison and G. Gregoriadis
©1980, John Wiley & Sons, Ltd

CHAPTER 5

Uptake of Enzyme-bearing Liposomes by cells *in vivo* and *in vitro*

Gerald Weissmann and Morris Finkelstein

1.	Introduction	153
2.	Enzyme entrapment within liposomes	155
3.	Enzyme delivery *in vitro* by means of liposomes	160
4.	Interaction of enzyme-laden liposomes with cells *in vitro*: Attempts at targeting	163
5.	Liposome-mediated enzyme delivery *in vivo*	165
	5.1. *In vivo* liposomal 'latency'	165
	5.2. *In vivo* fate of liposomes	166
	5.3. Morphologic analysis of liposomal distribution	170
	5.4. Clinical trials in man	171
	5.5. Potential hazards involved in the use of liposomes	172
6.	Summary	173
	References	174

1. INTRODUCTION

Human genetic diseases due to the absence or malfunction of cytoplasmic enzymes can be divided into two main clusters. When the enzyme which is missing (or abnormal) is localized in the 'vacuolar

Aided by grants (AM–11949, HL–19072, GM–23211, HL–19721) from the National Institutes of Health, The National Foundation–March of Dimes, the National Science Foundation (76–05621), the Whitehall Foundation, The Arthritis Foundation and 78–13221.

apparatus', uncleaved substrates regularly accumulate in the lysosomes of affected tissue. Diseases of this sort include Tay–Sachs disease, Gaucher's disease, peroxidase deficiency, and various mucopolysaccharidoses. However, when activity is missing (or abnormal) from non-membrane-bounded portions of the cytosol, the resultant accumulation of substrates exerts more diffuse effects, such as in adenosine deaminase deficiency and the Lesch–Nyhan syndrome.

Because lysosomal storage diseases result from genetic deficiencies of specific acid hydrolases in lysosomes, their reversal has been attempted by means of direct infusions of the missing enzyme. Since the affected system, the lysosomal apparatus of cells, normally endocytoses extracellular macromolecules and particles, attempts have been made to effect degradation of the GM_2-ganglioside (which accumulates in Tay–Sachs disease) by direct infusion of purified hexosaminidase (Johnson *et al.*, 1973). Unfortunately, the injected enzyme is rapidly cleared from the circulation, the bulk of enzyme becoming localized to the liver rather than to the most involved sites such as the central nervous system. Qualitatively similar results follow administration of purified glucocerebrosidase and ceramide-trihexosidase (Brady *et al.*, 1973; Brady *et al.*, 1974). Direct infusion of enzymes leads to four chief problems:

(1) failure by this means to direct the enzyme to the appropriate tissues in which substrate accumulates;
(2) the potential antigenicity of the enzyme;
(3) the introduction of enzymes directly into the circulation where they may pre-emptively interact with their substrates or other proteins; and
(4) inability of free enzyme to cross the blood–brain barrier.

Genetic disorders of lysosomes, and accounts of their attempted correction by means of enzyme replacement therapy, have recently been described *in extenso* (Hirschhorn and Weissmann, 1977; Desnick *et al.*, 1976).

To protect the enzyme against biodegradation after infusion and to minimize the risk of a systemic immunological reaction, enzymes have been entrapped by various techniques prior to infusion. Catalase, entrapped in synthetic, collodion-membrane microcapsules, has been used for enzyme replacement in catalase-deficient mice (Chang and Poznansky, 1968; Chang, 1973); microencapsulated L-asparaginase, injected intraperitoneally, has also been used successfully to suppress an implanted L-asparagine-dependent lymphosarcoma in C3HHeJ mice (Chang, 1973). The use of synthetic microcapsules in enzyme therapy is limited by their inability to be targeted to intracellular sites. A proposal for the usage of enzymes (asparaginase) entrapped in polyacrylamide gel particles of sizes suitable for either intravenous or intraperitoneal injection (less than 6 μm)

(Updike *et al.*, 1973), suffers from the inability of recipient animals to degrade the polyacrylamide matrix, thereby causing a long-term accumulation of the gel by cells of the reticuloendothelial system. The successful entrapment of β-glucosidase and β-galactosidase within erythrocyte ghosts has led to the proposal that enzyme-loaded erythrocytes be used in the treatment of lysosomal storage diseases, since such altered erythrocytes would probably be phagocytized by cells of the reticuloendothelial system (Ihler *et al.*, 1973).

Liposomes have also been employed as vectors for enzyme replacement therapy, due to their capacity to both trap enzymes and to facilitate their delivery to cells *in vitro* and *in vivo*. The formation of such artificial lipid structures was first described by Bangham and co-workers (1965). By 1968 (Sessa and Weissmann, 1968) we had coined the term 'liposome' to describe these structures which in their response to steroids, lytic proteins, and antibiotics, closely resembled natural biomembranes. Yet it was not until 1970 (Sessa and Weissmann, 1970) that it became possible to encapsulate an enzyme (lysozyme), rather than low molecular weight molecules such as ions, glucose, and dyes, in the aqueous interstices between the multilamellar lipid bilayers of liposomes. This observation cleared the way for using liposomes as vectors for enzymes or other macromolecules. By now, a large number of enzymes have been shown capable of being sequestered in liposomes (Table 1).

2. ENZYME ENTRAPMENT WITHIN LIPOSOMES

In our laboratory, liposomes are prepared in the following fashion (Bangham *et al.*, 1965; Bangham, 1968; Weissmann *et al.*, 1975; Cohen *et al.*, 1976; Weissmann *et al.*, 1976). Purified lipids are dissolved in chloroform and dried *in vacuo*, leaving a lipid film on the wall of the flask. Next, an aqueous solution of enzyme and/or other solutes that we wish to entrap, is added. After brief mechanical shaking (vortex for 10 minutes), the lipid dispersion is allowed to equilibrate for 2 hours. The resulting liposomes have been characterized as consisting of a series of concentric bilayers which alternate with aqueous compartments, and are heterogeneous in size, ranging from 0.05–$1.00\,\mu m$ in diameter (Papahadjopoulos and Miller, 1967; Papahadjopoulos and Watkins, 1967). If unilamellar liposomes are required, the dispersion is briefly treated (20 minutes) with ultrasonic vibration in a bath-type sonicator; the resulting unilamellar liposomes are more homogeneous in size (0.05–$0.10\,\mu m$ diameter) (Papahadjopoulos and Miller, 1967; Papahadjopoulos and Watkins, 1967). For work with enzymes, multilamellar liposomes are preferred rather than unilamellar liposomes because of their greater entrapment capacity (hand-shaken multilamellar liposomes contain $1.8 \pm 0.6\,\mu l/\mu mol$ lipid whereas sonicated

Table 1 Enzymes incorporated into Liposomes

Enzyme (source)	Lipid composition				References
Lysozyme (egg white)	PC 7	: DCP 2 :	Chol 1		Sessa and Weissmann, 1970
	PC 7	: SA 2 :	Chol 1		
Hexosaminidase A (human)	PC 7	: DCP 2 :	Chol 1		Cohen *et al.*, 1976
Amyloglucosidase (*Aspergillus niger*)	PC 7	: DCP 1 :	Chol 2		Gregoriadis and Ryman, 19 Tyrrell *et al.*, 1976
Peroxidase (horseradish)	PC 7	: DCP 2 :	Chol 1		Weissmann *et al.*, 1975
	SPH 3	: SA 1 :	Chol 1.1		Magee *et al.*, 1974
	PC 7	: PA 1 :	Chol 2		Wisse and Gregoriadis, 197
β-D-Fructofuranosidase (yeast)	PC 7	: PA 1 :	Chol 2		Gregoriadis and Ryman, 19 Gregoriadis and Buckland, 1973; Gregoriadis and Neerunjun, 1974
Dextranase	PC 7	: PA 1 :	Chol 2		Colley and Ryman, 1974, 1
α-Mannosidase (jack-bean)	PC 7	: PA 1 :	Chol 2		Patel and Ryman, 1974
Hexokinase (yeast)	PC 2	: DCP 0.2 :	Chol 1.5		Kataoka *et al.*, 1973
	SPH 2	: DCP 0.2 :	Chol 1.5		Kataoka *et al.*, 1973
Glucose-6-phosphate dehydrogenase (yeast)	PC 2	: DCP 0.2 :	Chol 1.5		Kataoka *et al.*, 1973
	SPH 2	: DCP 0.2 :	Chol 1.5		Kataoka *et al.*, 1973
β-Galactosidase (*E. coli*)	PC 2	: DCP 0.2 :	Chol 1.5		Kataoka *et al.*, 1973
	SPH 2	: DCP 0.2 :	Chol 1.5		Kataoka *et al.*, 1973
Glucocerebrosidase (human)	PC 7	: PA 1 :	Chol 2		Braidman and Gregoriadis, 1977
β-Glucuronidase (bovine)	DPPC 7	: SA 1 :	Chol 2		Steger and Desnick, 1977
	DPPC 7	: PA 1 :	Chol 2		Steger and Desnick, 1977
Neuraminidase (*Clostridium perfringens*)	PC 7	: PA 1 :	Chol 2		Gregoriadis *et al.*, 1974a
Neuraminidase (Influenza virus)	PC 9	: DCP 1			Almeida *et al.*, 1975
Asparaginase (*Erwinia*)	PC 7	: PA 1 :	Chol 2		Neerunjun and Gregoriadis, 1976
	PC 7	: SA 1 :	Chol 2		
Asparaginase (*E. coli*)	PC 10	: DCP 1 :	Chol 2		Fishman and Citri, 1975
Glucose oxidase (*Aspergillus niger*)	PI				Dapergolas *et al.*, 1976
	PC 7	: PA 1 :	Chol 2		Dapergolas *et al.*, 1976
	PC 7	: SA 1 :	Chol 2		Dapergolas *et al.*, 1976
Cytochrome oxidase	PE 1	: PC 1 :	CL 0.15 :	LL 0.25	Eytan *et al.*, 1975
Cytochrome *c* (horse heart)	PC 1	: PE 1			Papahadjopoulos and Miller, 1967
(Na$^+$ + KA$^+$)-ATPase (*S. fecalis*)					Redwood and Patel, 1974

Abbreviations Used in Table 1

Phosphatidylcholine	(PC)	Dipalmitoyl phosphatidylcholine	(DPPC)
Dicetylphosphate	(DCP)	Phosphatidylinositol	(PI)
Cholesterol	(Chol)	Phosphatidylethanolamine	(PE)
Stearylamine	(SA)	Cardiolipin	(CL)
Sphingomyelin	(SPH)	Lysolecithin	(LL)
Phosphatidic acid	(PA)		

unilamellar liposomes contain 0.8 ± 0.3 μl/μmol lipid (Deamer and Bangham, 1976), and because labile enzymes may be denatured, even by brief sonication.

Deamer and Bangham (1976) have recently described a preparative procedure for large unilamellar liposomes (LUVs), based on the 'solvent evaporation' method of Papahadjopoulos and Watkins (1967); liposomes formed when ether solutions of lipids are injected into warm aqueous solutions trap 14 ± 6 μl/μmol lipid. Experiments recently performed in our laboratory show that although small molecules (CrO_4^{2-}, glucose) can be more efficiently trapped by LUVs than by multilamellar vesicles (MLVs), some proteins (e.g. soya bean trypsin inhibitor) interfere with their own capture by the LUVs (Schieren *et al.*, 1978).

We have suggested that entrapment of any enzyme or solute in the aqueous spaces between the lipid lamellae of MLV liposomes should be tested according to the following criteria: (1) resolution of the liposome-associated enzyme from the free enzyme by exclusion chromatography; (2)

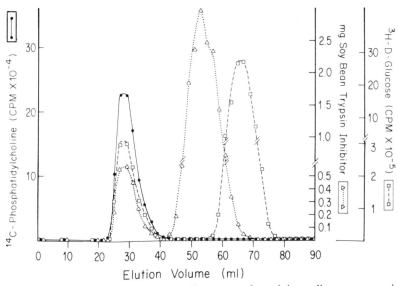

Figure 1 Illustration of chromatographic means of resolving a liposome-associated protein from untrapped species. Separation of liposomes, soya bean trypsin inhibitor, and ^{3}H-labelled D-glucose on a Sephadex G-200 (1.6×40 cm) column Liposomes, prepared with lecithin, dicetyl phosphate, and cholesterol in a molar ratio of $7:2:1$ (15 μmol of lipid/ml), were swollen in Dulbecco's PBS without Ca^{2+} and Mg^{2+}, pH 7.4, containing 10.0 mM ^{3}H-D-glucose (3.303 pmol D-glucose/CPM) and 4.0 mg SBTI/ml. Liposomes were radiolabelled with ^{14}C-phosphatidylcholine: 2.0 μCi, at a specific activity of 50 μCi/μmol, contributed 0.04 μmol ^{14}C-PC to the 90 μmol lipid preparation (52.91 pmol total lipid/CPM)

latency of the liposome-entrapped enzyme; and (3) correlation of increments in trapping with increments in the net surface charge adjacent lamellae:
operationally as the molar percentage of charged species of lipid.

After formation of liposomes in their aqueous milieu, they are resolved
from the untrapped enzyme and other solutes by gel filtration. The liposomes, being too large to enter the gel, typically elute immediately after
the void volume, while the untrapped enzyme and solutes are retained by
the gel and elute later in the bed volume. The quantity of enzyme associated with the lipid peak may be determined. In our experience, 6.9% of
hexosaminidase A (Cohen *et al.*, 1976), 15.1% of lysozyme (Sessa and
Weissmann, 1970), and 5.8% of horseradish peroxidase (Weissmann *et al.*,
1975) became entrapped by anionic liposomes. Moreover, the co-entrap-
ment of glucose and/or CrO_4^{2-} in the enzyme-laden liposomes further indicates the integrity of the aqueous compartments (Figure 1).

Latency of the trapped enzyme may be judged by the inaccessibility of
the substrate to the liposome-associated enzyme, if substrate is incapable of
diffusing across the lipid bilayers. Trapped enzymes hydrolyse impermeant
substrates only after structural integrity of the liposomes is disrupted by
Triton X-100 (a non-ionic detergent), amphotericin B, or nystatin (Sessa

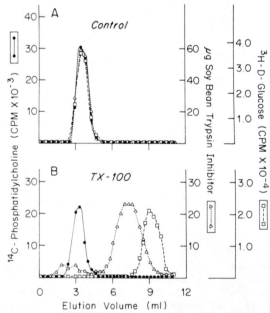

Figure 2 Illustration of 'latency' of a liposome-entrapped protein. Aliquots
(900 μl) of the liposome peak (Figure 1) were incubated without (A) or with (B)
Triton X-100 (0.2% v/v). They were rechromatographed on a Sephadex G-200
(0.9 × 15 cm) column and eluted with PBS in 0.5 ml fractions

and Weissmann, 1970). In contrast, free enzyme, as well as liposome-associated enzyme bound either electrostatically or hydrophobically to the exterior of the outermost lipid lamellae, will catalyse hydrolysis of substrate in the absence of detergent or polyenes. Rechromatography of the pooled peak liposome fractions should demonstrate retention of the trapped enzyme and any other aqueous compartment markers (glucose, CrO_4^{2-}) within the lipid peak, whereas rechromatography of disrupted liposomes should demonstrate that the majority of the previously entrapped enzyme and aqueous compartment markers now elute independently of the lipid materials (Figure 2).

The formation of MLV liposomes depends upon the capacity of the phospholipids to swell and form hydrated liquid crystals, consisting of a series of concentric bilayers which alternate with aqueous compartments. The volume of these compartments, within which enzymes may be entrapped, is determined by the net charge of the lipids and the ionic strength of the swelling solution (Bangham, 1968; Papahadjopoulos and Miller, 1967). We have observed that as the net anionic surface charge on the lamellae is increased by increasing the molar percentage of dicetyl phosphate from 5 to 10 to 20, capture of enzyme is also increased; like-sign repulsion of adjacent lipid layers increases the volume of the aqueous compartments (V_{H_2O}). Demonstration of increments in the entrapment within anionic liposomes of horseradish peroxidase (pI = 7.2), and hexosaminidase A (pI = 5.4), both of which are slightly anionic at pH 7.4 (swelling solution), and of the cationic enzyme lysozyme (pI = 11.0) within cationic liposomes, strongly suggests that these enzymes are free in the aqueous compartments; they are probably not entrapped as the result of non-specific, electrostatic interactions (Sessa and Weissmann, 1970; Weissmann *et al.*,

Table 2 Incremental entrapment of soya bean trypsin inhibitor (2 mg/ml) and D-glucose (10 mM) by Multilamellar (MLV) Liposomes with varying surface charge

Lipid Composition	Entrapment*	
PC : DCP : Chol	SBTI	D-Glucose
	μg/μmol lipid (n)	nmol/μmol lipid (n)
70 : 20 : 10	18.7 ± 3.4 (5)	88.1 ± 12.0 (3)
80 : 10 : 10	12.5 ± 0.7 (3)	51.2 ± 1.6 (3)
85 : 05 : 10	8.9 ± 2.6 (3)	29.7 ± 1.2 (3)

*Entrapment values were determined by association with the liposome peak of Sepharose 2B and Sephadex G-200 chromatographs using 1.6 × 40 cm columns, ± S.D. PC = phosphatidyl choline, DCP = dicetyl phosphate, chol = cholesterol. DCP used to impart negative surface charge. D-Glucose used as measure of aqueous compartments (V_{H_2O} of MLV liposomes.

1975; Cohen *et al.*, 1976). Indeed, this criterion renders MLV experiments more capable of interpretation than similar experiments with LUVs, since the V_{H_2O} of the latter cannot be varied in this fashion (Table 2).

3. ENZYME DELIVERY *IN VITRO* BY MEANS OF LIPOSOMES

Two general mechanisms have been described whereby liposomes are taken up by cells (Weissmann *et al.*, 1975; Cohen *et al.*, 1976; Batzri and Korn, 1975; Poste and Papahadjopoulos, 1976; Mattenberger-Kreber *et al.*, 1976; Papahadjopoulos *et al.*, 1974; Pagano and Huang, 1975; Grant and McConnell, 1973; Martin and McDonald, 1976; Pagano *et al.*, 1974; Huang and Pagano, 1975; Weissmann *et al.*, 1977). In the first, uni- or multilamellar liposomes enter by endocytosis and become sequestered in lysosomal apparatus of the cell (Weissmann *et al.*, 1975; Cohen *et al.*, 1976; Batzri and Korn, 1975; Poste and Papahadjopoulos, 1976; Mattenberger-Kreber *et al.*, 1976). In the second, unilamellar liposomes appear to fuse with the plasma membranes of the target cell, and to introduce their contents directly into the cytosol (Poste and Papahadjopoulos, 1976; Papahadjopoulos *et al.*, 1974; Pagano and Huang, 1975). Such liposomes are 'leaky'; indeed loss of solutes from the liposome has been demonstrated during this process of fusion (Grant and McConnell, 1973). Furthermore, when MLV liposomes fuse with the plasmalemma of target cells, the liposome minus its outermost bilayer comes to reside in the cytoplasm (Batzri and Korn, 1975; Martin and McDonald, 1976; Weissmann *et al.*, 1977). The intracytoplasmic liposome (now with $n - 1$ bilayers) may undergo gradual degradation *in situ*; alternatively, it may fuse with other membrane-bound organelles, such as lysosomes. No evidence in favour of either pathway has been adduced.

The kinetics of liposome uptake via phagocytosis by mouse peritoneal macrophages was recently evaluated by Mattenberger-Kreber and co-workers (1976). Saturable uptake of sonicated phosphatidylcholine liposomes, containing tracer amounts of either [^{14}C]- or [^{3}H]cholesterol, was demonstrated. Maximal uptake was attained within 30 minutes. Ultrastructural autoradiography demonstrated that within 10 minutes, liposomes became sequestered within numerous peripheral cytoplasmic vacuoles. Morphologically intact liposomes, as well as liposomal debris, were evident in these vacuoles for up to 2 hours after incubation.

When liposomes were exposed to cells which do not ordinarily engage in phagocytosis (e.g. Chinese hamster lung cells), both unilamellar and multilamellar liposomes exchanged membrane lipids and trapped solutes with cells, via vesicle–cell fusion and vesicle–cell lipid exchange (Pagano and Huang, 1975; Pagano *et al.*, 1974; Huang and Pagano, 1975). At 37 °C, the vesicle–cell fusion was held to predominate, whereas at 2 °C, or when recipient cells were depleted of energy stores, lipid exchange between vesicles and cells became significant. Direct fusion was inferred by the association with target cells of both the aqueous compartment, containing [^{3}H]inulin, and the phospholipid component, labelled with [^{14}C]phosphatidylcholine, in proportion to the content of these markers within liposomes. Under conditions which favoured lipid exchange, the phospholipid marker became cell-associated whereas the aqueous compartment marker did not. Pagano and Huang (1975) determined that the kinetics of uptake for unilamellar liposomes was independent of the net surface charge of the liposome. Phagocytosis, as a mode of uptake was excluded on the basis of electron microscopy: EM autoradiography demonstrated distribution of liposomal lipid ^{14}C throughout the cell, rather than within lysosomes.

Poste and Papahadjopoulos (1976), using 3T3 mouse fibroblasts, observed uptake both by vesicle–cell fusion and endocytosis. Negatively charged liposomes, in a 'fluid' state, favoured uptake by vesicle–cell fusion while neutral fluid liposomes and negative 'solid' liposomes favoured uptake via endocytosis. Uptake of solid vesicles was reduced by 80–90% by incubation with deoxyglucose (glycolysis inhibitor) plus sodium azide (respiration inhibitor). Uptake of 'fluid' negative vesicles, under similar conditions, was reduced by only 30–40%. Pretreatment of cells with either cytochalasin B, an inhibitor of phagocytosis, or prefixation with glutaraldehyde, reduced the uptake of negative 'fluid' vesicles by 20–32% as compared to 79–85% for 'solid' vesicles. MLV liposomes and small unilamellar liposomes (SUVs) displayed identical behaviour.

In contrast to Poste and Papahadjopoulos' claim that liposomes gain entry into fibroblasts either by fusion or by endocytosis, depending entirely upon the physical state (charge and fluidity) of the liposomal bilayers, Pagano and Huang (1975) did not observe endocytosis of liposomes; furthermore, the magnitude of uptake by vesicle–cell fusion was not influenced by the charge of the liposomes.

Batzri and Korn (1975), employing the phagocytic soil amoeba *Acanthamoeba castellani*, presented evidence that it is the phospholipid composition of the liposome which determines whether uptake is to proceed chiefly by fusion or by phagocytosis. At 28 °C, egg lecithin liposomes and dimyristoyl lecithin liposomes were predominantly taken up by phagocytosis, whereas there was fusion of dipalmitoyl lecithin and distearoyl liposomes with the plasma membrane. Phagocytic uptake was inhibitable either by incubation at 4 °C or by treatment with dinitrophenol. Positively charged, egg lecithin liposomes were more avidly taken up than neutral, or negatively charged liposomes; positively charged dipalmitoyl lecithin vesicles were taken up to only a slightly greater extent than were neutral, or negatively charged DPPC liposomes. The uptake by *Acanthamoeba castellani* of unilamellar DPPC liposomes, presumably by fusion, resulted in the loss of 60% of the aqueous contents (D-[^{3}H]glucose) of the vesicles (Batzri and Korn, 1975). In agreement, Grant and McConnell (1973) also observed a 96% loss of entrapped solute upon fusion of unilamellar DPPC liposomes with the mycoplasma *Acholeplasma laidlawii.*

Experiments performed in our laboratory (Weissmann *et al.*, 1977) in which cultured human lymphoid cells and human fibroblasts were incubated in the presence of multilamellar, anionic liposomes, L(PC 69:DCP 20 : Chol 10 : LL 1) [HRP], demonstrated that phagocytosis was probably not a significant factor in MLV uptake. Although it was possible that some cells, capable of phagocytosis, may have contaminated the lymphoid cell lines, non-cytoxic amounts of cytochalasin B, an inhibitor of phagocytosis, did not appreciably diminish uptake. The liposomes were essentially intact (94%) during incubation; entry of peroxidase into the cells could therefore not be explained by its leak from the liposomes and subsequent endocytosis by cells. Free enzyme was not taken up (less than 0.01% of presented load). As judged by ultrastructural analysis, liposomes bearing enzyme did not simply adhere to the cultured cells, a problem when cationic liposomes encounter the anionic surfaces of natural membranes (Magee *et al.*, 1974; Martin and McDonald, 1976). Finally, ultrastructural evidence was provided of the intracytoplasmic localization of liposomes still bearing cytochemically identifiable enzyme, a demonstration that had previously eluded other investigators (Batzri and Korn, 1975; Poste and Papahadjopoulos, 1976; Pagano and Huang, 1975). In two of the three cell lines studied, preincorporation of lysolecithin (a 'fusogen') into the liposomal membranes was required in order to obtain significant levels of uptake; exogenous lysolecithin was ineffective.

Liposomes may also simply adsorb to the surfaces of cells consequent to electrostatic attraction (Magee *et al.*, 1974). Magee and co-workers (1974) have demonstrated that cationic liposomes, L(SPH 3 : SA 1 : Chol 1.1) adhere to cultured HeLa cells with great avidity. Maximal adherence of cationic liposomes containing horseradish peroxidase was observed within 30 minutes and exceeded by at least 300-fold that of free enzyme. Adherence was not inhibitable by incubation at 0 °C; this observation strongly suggested adsorption. Ultrastructural and cytochemical examination of cells exposed to cationic liposomes demonstrated the association of single liposomes, as well as aggregates, with the cell surface, in close proximity to pseudopodia. Positive staining for peroxidase was also observed in sections of the outer surface of the cell membrane and pseudopodia. Membrane-bound cytoplasmic inclusions (phagocytic vacuoles) containing peroxidase-positive particulate material, presumably liposomal, were also seen. The authors suggested that positive liposomes initially interact with negative cells via adsorption, and are subsequently internalized by fusion and endocytosis. It seems likely that some of these, if not the majority, had become ruptured prior to incorporation by the cell.

4. INTERACTION OF ENZYME-LADEN LIPOSOMES WITH CELLS *IN VITRO:* ATTEMPTS AT TARGETING

Unfortunately, when liposomes are infused into animals they wind up trapped primarily in the liver, and to a lesser extent in the spleen, regardless of route of introduction (Gregoriadis and Ryman, 1972a,b; Patel and Ryman, 1974; Steger and Desnick, 1977; Gregoriadis *et al.*, 1974a; McDougall *et al.*, 1974; Dunnick *et al.*, 1975; Gregoriadis and Ryman, 1971; Juliano and Stamp, 1975; Jonah *et al.*, 1975; Caride *et al.*, 1976; Magee *et al.*, 1976). If, however, liposomes are ever to be used successfully in the delivery of enzymes to discrete organs or tissues, methods must be devised to bypass the accumulation of liposomes at unwanted sites and to 'target' their delivery. The type (fusion v. endocytosis) and magnitude of cellular uptake of liposomes, *in vitro*, is determined by three physical parameters of the liposome: (1) phospholipid composition (fluidity); (2) charge; and (3) size. Perhaps these parameters may be so altered as to favour accumulation of liposomes by a particular organ. However, the most direct approach to targeting would be offered by means of surface ligands which would provide the required recognition signals for receptors at the cell surface.

We have observed that liposomes coated with aggregated IgG (AggIgG) provide a far better endocytic stimulus than do uncoated liposomes. Aggregated, rather than native immunoglobulins, preferentially coat, and partially insert into liposomes. Over 98% of the aggregated human IgG became associated with L(PC 70 : DCP 20 : Chol 10) both by electrostatic and hydrophobic association, when AggIgG was presented at a concentration of 10 μg/μmol phospholipid (Weissmann *et al.*, 1974). Since aggregated immunoglobulins form lattices in which the key Fc regions are disposed towards the interior of the outermost lamellae of liposomes and also towards the surrounding medium, it would be expected that these would act as ligands for the Fc receptors of the polymorphonuclear leucocytes (PMN) and consequently provoke endocytosis (Cohen *et al.*, 1976). In fact, hexosaminidase A was more actively taken up when presented to Tay–Sachs phagocytes as AggIgG.L [Hex A, glucose] that when presented in liposomes coated with native IgG or in uncoated liposomes (Cohen *et al.*, 1976). Similarly, the uptake of AggIgM.L [HRP, glucose] by dogfish phagocytes exceeded that of free enzyme by 120-fold, native IgM-coated liposomes by 60-fold, and uncoated liposomes by 50-fold (Weissman *et al.*, 1975). Immunoglobulin-coated liposomes presumably enter phagocytes as a result of an internalization of the cell membrane which contains the aggregated immunoglobulin-Fc receptor complex (Cohen *et al.*, 1976).

Gregoriadis and Neerunjun (1975) have described experiments in which homing of liposomes was accomplished by cell-directed antibodies; uptake

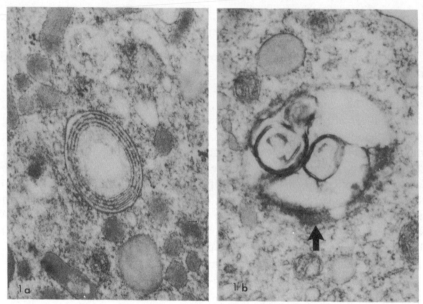

Figure 3 Portions of human peripheral blood polymorphonuclear leucocytes from a patient with Tay–Sachs disease which have been exposed to aggIgG-coated multilamellar (MLV) liposomes containing hexosaminidase A. Magnification for both 50,000 ×. (a) A liposome-containing vacuole which does not appear to have fused with lysosomes to form a secondary vacuole. (b) This configuration was more commonly seen. In this figure two multilamellar liposomes are present within what is clearly a phagocytic vacuole. The dark amorphous material within the vacuole (arrow) represents lysosomal contents which entered the vacuole by fusion

of liposomes was enhanced several fold (3–25-fold) when HeLa cells, AKR-A mouse leukaemia cells, or human fibroblasts were presented with liposomes associated with IgG immunoglobulins raised against the particular cell strain. The association of liposomes with cells during the incubation was monitored by use of radiolabelled markers: ^{125}I-labelled IgG, ^{111}In labelled bleomycin, and cholesteryl [1-^{14}C]palmitate. The proportions of the cell-associated radiolabels remained quite similar to their proportions in the liposomes, suggesting the integrity of the liposomes. By subcellular fractionation, 79.5% of the entrapped bleomycin was recovered in the lysosome-rich particulate fraction, and 20.5% in the membrane fraction.

Juliano and Stamp (1976) report the incorporation of the major sialoglycoprotein of human erythrocyte membranes into liposomal membranes; this glycoprotein displays activity as a receptor for the lectins wheat germ agglutinin (WGA) and phytohaemagglutinin (PHA), but not for concanavalin A. The glycoprotein was considered likely to have been displayed on the outer surface of the liposome since it was released from the liposome by treatment with trypsin under conditions which failed to release [³H]sucrose entrapped within the aqueous compartment. After 4 hours of incubation, sialoglycoprotein liposomes displayed five-fold more agglutination with erythrocytes in the presence of WGA than in the absence of lectin. Post-treatment of the WGA-induced cell–liposome aggregates with the haptene sugar N-acetylglucosamine, at concentrations capable of preventing the formation of the aggregates, failed to reverse the aggregation; this observation was taken to indicate cellular internalization (by fusion) of the liposomes. Electron microscopic evidence supporting this conclusion was not presented.

5. LIPOSOME-MEDIATED ENZYME DELIVERY *IN VIVO*

5.1.   *In vivo* liposomal 'latency'

Kimelberg and co-workers (1975), examined the fate of liposomes containing $^{22}Na^+$ and $^{86}Rb^+$ in mice, and found that the distribution of trapped isotopes followed more closely the plasma and tissue distribution of free markers than of a lipid marker. Their suspicion that the entrapped species leaked from the liposomes and were accumulated by the tissues independently of liposomes was confirmed by their demonstration that *in vitro* incubation of liposomes in 30% mouse serum released 44% of the entrapped $^{22}Na^+$ within 2 hours. Gregoriadis (1973) has also demonstrated that the time course of plasma clearance of liposome-entrapped penicillin followed more closely that of free penicillin than that of liposomes, and also suggested that the drug was lost by accelerated diffusion through the liposomal membranes. Arakawa and co-workers (1975) found that the rate of clearance of drugs from intramuscular sites following injections of drug-loaded liposomes was inversely proportional to the cholesterol content of the liposomes. *In vitro* studies of diffusion revealed that serum accelerated the leak of [¹⁴C]cefazolin; by increasing the cholesterol content of the vesicles, leakage rates were reduced. Recently, Krupp *et al.* (1976) presented evidence that unilamellar liposomes comprised of egg lecithin and cholesteryl oleate change in density and size within 5 minutes of injection into rats or incubation in plasma and suggested that lipids of the vesicles had become associated with high density lipoproteins of plasma.

Furthermore, it is not unlikely that liposomes activate the complement pathway *in vivo*, since polymeric anions or cations can activate the alternative pathway. The ability of complement to mediate the lysis of liposomes has been well documented (Kataoka *et al.*, 1973; Lachman *et al.*, 1970; Hesketh *et al.*, 1971); the membrane lesions resulting from complement-mediated damage are large enough to permit loss of enzymes as large as β-galactosidase (mol. wt. 518,000) (Kataoka *et al.*, 1973).

5.2. *In vivo* fate of liposomes

McDougall *et al*. (1974, 1975) and Dunnick *et al*. (1975, 1976b) have conducted thorough analyses of the *in vivo* distribution of liposomes, as a function of their phospholipid composition, size, their interaction with antibodies and proteins, and their route of administration. Liposomes sonicated for 5 minutes (900 Å diameter) (Dunnick *et al*., 1975), L(PC 11 : gangliosides 1), entrapping the radioactive ion pertechnetate, $^{99m}TcO_4-$, and/or the spin label tempocholine chloride, were administered intravenously to mice (McDougall *et al*., 1974). Within 30 minutes, 90% of the entrapped radioactivity had been cleared from the circulation. Examination of electron paramagnetic resonance (EPR) spectra for blood specimens indicated that liposomes remaining in circulation were, for the most part, intact. Autopsy of mice as soon as 5 minutes after injection revealed accumulation of 25% of the injected radioactivity in liver, 2% in spleen, 2% in kidney, 2% in lung, and 2% in stomach. Accumulation of liposomes by the liver was doubled, and accumulation in the stomach reduced, by either increasing the duration of sonication of the liposomes, L(PC 11 : gangliosides 1), or incorporating cholesterol into the liposomes, L(PC 11 : gangliosides 1 : Chol 8.2). The similarity of the *in vivo* effects of prolonged sonication of liposomes and addition of cholesterol to liposomes suggested to the authors that both manipulations caused the liposomes to be less 'leaky'. Efflux studies by a dialysis method conducted *in vitro* confirmed this interpretation. When charged phospholipids (phosphatidic acid, phosphatidylethanolamine, phosphatidylserine) were incorporated into the standard liposomes, their *in vivo* distribution was not significantly altered.

Next, the effect was evaluated of the route of administration on the *in vivo* fate of liposomes, L(PC 11: gangliosides 1) $[^{99m}TcO_4^-]$, sonicated for 60 minutes (500 Å diameter) (Dunnick *et al*., 1975). The organ and tissue distribution was qualitatively similar following either intravenous, intraperitoneal, or subcutaneous injection. Quantitatively, however, intraperitoneal injections (as compared to i.v.) resulted in an eightfold reduction in liposomal trapping by liver and spleen, and subcutaneous injection results in a 21-fold reduction in uptake by liver and a 50-fold reduction in uptake by spleen. Recovery of liposomal isotope was reduced by approximately twofold in the lung by intraperitoneal or subcutaneous injections. Gregoriadis' group (Dapergolas *et al*., 1976) has reported that intragastric administration to rats of $[^{125}I]$polyvinylpyrrolidone-loaded liposomes resulted in the recovery of 98% of the marker in the faeces; only 0.12% of the injected load was recovered in the liver, regardless of liposome charge. These results imply that intraperitoneal and subcutaneous routes of administration may serve to bypass the rapid sequestration of liposomes in liver and spleen.

Finally, Dunnick and co-workers (1975, 1976b), examined the ability of various macromolecules (polyamino acids, immunoglobulins, human thyrotropin, human antihyroglobulin) to act as surface ligands and to direct the *in vivo* distribution of unilamellar liposomes, L(PC 11 : gangliosides 1) [^{99m}TcO$_4^-$]. The accumulation of liposomes in liver and spleen following intravenous infusion was increased threefold for poly-L-phenylalanine vesicles and twofold for poly-L-tyrosine vesicles (Dunnick *et al.*, 1975). Liposomes coated with IgG also displayed a twofold increase in hepatic and splenic accumulation, as well as a two- to threefold increase in lung accumulation, following i.v. injection (Dunnick *et al.*, 1975). Liposomes containing gangliosides were shown to bind human antithyroglobulin and human thyrotropin two-to fivefold more efficiently than liposomes lacking gangliosides (Dunnick *et al.*, 1976b). The binding of bovine thyrotropin also displays a requirement for gangliosides (Aloj *et al.*, 1977). The tissue distribution following i.v. administration of [^{125}I]antithyroglobulin IgG.L(DPPC 11 : gangliosides 1 : Chol 8.2) is similar to that for uncoated liposomes; cholesterol is required to stabilize the antibody–liposome interaction, *in vivo*.

The *in vivo* fate of liposomes, L(PC 7 : DCP 1 : Chol 2), containing either ^{131}I-labelled albumin or [^{3}H]amyloglucosidase in their aqueous compartments, and [^{3}H]cholesterol in their lipid bilayers, was determined (Gregoriadis and Ryman, 1971, 1972a). Approximately 70% of the liposomal markers are cleared from circulation within 15 minutes of intravenous injection and are concomitantly accumulated by the liver (56%) and spleen (12%); subcellular fractionation of liver reveals that approximately half of the enzyme marker is in the mitochondrial/lysosomal fraction. Gregoriadis and Ryman (1971, 1972a) have demonstrated that the ratio of [^{3}H]cholesterol (lipid phase marker) to ^{131}I-labelled albumin (aqueous compartment marker) is constant for liposomes circulating in the blood for as long as 250 minutes. Their conclusion that liposomes remain intact during circulation may perhaps not extend to liposomes which have trapped other proteins or markers, since the apparent 'latency' of L[^{131}I-labelled albumin] may reflect the inability of albumin to dissociate from damaged liposomes. Albumin has been shown to engage in hydrophobic and electrostatic interactions with liposomal bilayers (Sweet and Zull, 1970).

Clearance of liposomes from the plasma following an intravenous injection of neutral, L(PC 7 : Chol 2), or negatively charged liposomes, L(PC 7 : PA 1 : Chol 2) and L(PC 7 : DCP 1 : Chol 2), is characterized by a prominent rapid phase whereas clearance of positive liposomes, L(PC 7 : SA 1 : Chol 2), does not; the slow phase is similar regardless of the charge of the liposome (Gregoriadis and Neerunjun, 1974). Furthermore, the rate of hepatic accumulation is proportional to the rate of plasma clearance (Gregoriadis and Neerunjun, 1974). The rapid phase could be reduced for negative liposomes (3.4 mg lipid) by simultaneously injecting a large dose of either negative or positive liposomes (13.2 mg lipid) and could be eliminated for positive liposomes, by the same technique, suggesting that the rapid phase represents a common mechanism of tissue accumulation for liposomes regardless of charge (Gregoriadis and Ryman, 1972a; Gregoriadis and Neerunjun, 1974; Gregoriadis and Ryman, 1971). Juliano and Stamp (1975), Kimelberg (1976) and Jonah *et al*. (1975) have confirmed the biphasic kinetics of liposome elimination from the plasma and the preferential clearance of negative liposomes as compared to positive ones. Caride and co-workers (1976) have since demonstrated that the hepatic accumulation of neutral liposomes, L(PC 3 : Chol 3.8) [^{99m}Tc–Sn–diethylene triamine pentaacetic acid], could be reduced significantly by injecting mice with unlabelled liposomes 30 minutes prior to injections with labelled liposomes; in contrast to Gregoriadis' (Gregoriadis and Neerunjun, 1974) results, they also observed increases in uptake by spleen and lung of twofold and fourfold, respectively.

The charge of liposomes also influences their rate of accumulation by organs other than the liver. Splenic uptake of large negative liposomes, containing either [^{14}C]EDTA (Jonah *et al*., 1975) or [^{14}C]poly(I) : poly(C), (Magee *et al*., 1976), is approximately twofold greater than for positive liposomes. Uptake by brain and lung tissue displays a two- to fourfold preference for positive, as compared to negative liposomes containing [^{14}C]EDTA (Jonah *et al*., 1975). In contrast, Kimelberg (1976), using *Macaca* monkeys as recipients for small sonicated liposomes containing [^{3}H]methotrexate, has observed a preference by brain, spleen, and bone marrow for positive liposomes and by lung for negative liposomes. Presumably lisosomal size as well as charge contribute to the determination of *in vivo* fate.

The size of liposomes has been shown to affect their kinetics of clearance from the bloodstream. Juliano and Stamp (1975) and also Kimelberg (1976) report that small unilamellar liposomes, produced by prolonged sonication, were cleared less rapidly ($t\frac{1}{2} = 200$ minutes) than large multilamellar liposomes ($t\frac{1}{2} = 22$ minutes), following intravenous infusion, Furthermore, small sonicated liposomes are recovered in the plasma at approximately five-fold higher levels than unsonicated liposomes following intraperitoneal injection and at approximately ten-fold higher levels following intramuscular injection (Dapergolas *et al*., 1976). These results suggest that large liposomes are limited in their ability to penetrate vascular membranes and to pass through small capillaries.

Next, Gregoriadis and Ryman (1972b) confirmed the *in vivo* distribution pattern of radioactive liposome markers (^{131}I-labelled albumin, [^{3}H]amyloglucosidase, [^{3}H]cholesterol), (Gregoriadis and Ryman, (1972a,

1971) by using a high specific activity enzyme, β-fructofuranosidase (invertase), entrapped within liposomes, L(PC 7 : PA 1 : Chol 2). Within one hour of i.v. infusion, half of the enzyme activity, said to be latent, was cleared from circulation. After 6 hours 45% of the injected enzyme was in the liver and 10% in the spleen; after 48 hours 25% still remained in the liver, and after 100 hours 5% remained. Subcellular fractionation of liver again revealed that nearly half of the intracellular invertase was present in the mitochondrial/lysosomal fraction. These early findings have since been confirmed with demonstrations of a similar fate of intravenously infused α-mannosidase-loaded liposomes (Patel and Ryman, 1974) and neuraminidase-loaded liposomes (Gregoriadis *et al.*, 1974a); liposomes accumulate in the liver and spleen, localized intracellularly mostly to the lysosome-rich fraction and express their entrapped enzyme's catalytic activity *in situ* for several days.

More recently, Steger and Desnick (1977) examined the *in vivo* tissue and subcellular fate of β-glucuronidase entrapped in sonicated liposomes, following intravenous infusion into mice. Enzyme entrapped in either negative, L(DPPC 7 : PA 1 : Chol 2), or positive, L(DPPC 7 : SA 1 : Chol 2), liposomes was rapidly cleared from circulation and accumulated in the liver. Approximately 50–80% of the injected entrapped enzyme was in the liver after 1 hour and was stable for 48 hours, thereafter diminishing gradually over 8 to 11 days. Renal accumulation and retention of enzyme appeared enhanced when the enzyme was packaged in negative, rather than positive, liposomes.

The fate of [^{3}H]cholesterol-labelled liposomes was strongly dependent upon the enzyme entrapped, presumably within bilayers (Steger and Desnick, 1977). Enzyme-loaded liposomes display a more rapid hepatic accumulation, of a greater magnitude, and are retained in the liver for approximately ninefold longer than buffer-loaded liposomes (3 days v. 8 hours). This result suggested to the authors that the entrapped β-glucuronidase, although shown to be latent by the established criteria, must be partially exposed on the liposome surface, thus providing a surface ligand causing increased affinity for uptake by hepatic cells.

Yet even more revealing were the results of Steger and Desnick's (1977) examination of the hepatic intracellular localization of the administered bovine β-glucuronidase. Following administration of enzyme-loaded negative liposomes, 70% of the exogenous enzyme appeared in the lysosomal/mitochondrial fraction at times ranging from 1–144 hours post-injection. In contrast, the use of positive liposomes for enzyme delivery results in the appearance of only 50% of the exogenous enzyme in the lysosome-rich fraction at 1 hour post-injection, and 20–30% from 1–4 days post-injection. In addition, four endogenous lysosomal enzymes were shown to undergo a concurrent translocation from the lysosomal fraction to the soluble fraction, 1–3 days following administration of positive liposomes; by 5 days, the intracellular distribution of lysosomal hydrolases appeared to return to normal. The authors suggest that the lysosomal membranes may have been destabilized by the positively charged stearylamine in the liposomal bilayers, resulting in the release of lysosomal contents into the cytoplasm.

The ability of invertase to express its catalytic function intracellularly was demonstrated previously, *in vitro* (Gregoriadis and Buckland, 1973). Cultured mouse peritoneal macrophages and Chinese hamster fibroblasts, both lacking endogenous invertase activity, were loaded with sucrose for 24 hours, resulting in a model lysosomal storage disease. Incubation of cells with invertase-containing liposomes resulted in the hydrolysis of stored sucrose to glucose and fructose and the subsequent disappearance of sucrose-laden cytoplasmic vacuoles.

Colley and Ryman (1974, 1976) created an *in vivo* model storage disease by injecting [^{3}H]dextran (mol. wt. 80,000) into rats, in order to further prove the therapeutic usefulness of liposomes in enzyme replacement therapy. While hepatically-accumulated dextran was stable for up to 6 days, administration of liposome-entrapped dextranase or untrapped dextranase caused a precipitous 70% reduction within 2 days. Unfortunately, the latency of dextranase-containing liposomes in the blood has not been evaluated; the possibility exists that within moments of injection, dextranase is released from liposomes and is independently taken up by the liver. In order to substantiate their claim, the authors must demonstrate that lipid phase markers, aqueous compartment markers, and dextranase are accumulated by the liver in the same proportions as exist in intact liposomes.

5.3 Morphologic analysis of liposomal distribution

The hepatic uptake of liposomes appears to be mediated initially by Kupffer cells, and secondarily by the parenchymal cells. De Barsy and co-workers (1975, 1976) have demonstrated by ultrastructural analysis that 1 hour after intravenous administration to newborn rats of liposomes, L(PC 4 : SA 1 : Chol 2), containing fluorescein-conjugated antibodies to lysosomal acid β-glucosidase, liposomes were free in the lumen of sinusoidal spaces and within the phagocytic vacuoles of macrophages and Kupffer cells. Only after 7½ hours could liposomes be identified within parenchymal cells, at which time the Kupffer cells were grossly vacuolated and bordered on necrosis. In another investigation (Segal *et al.*, 1974), electron microscopic examination of liver 2 hours after i.v. injection of liposomes, L(PC 7 : PA 1 : Chol 2), containing nitroblue tetrazolium revealed internalization of liposomes within the phagocytic vacuoles of Kupffer cells; no evidence was obtained for uptake by parenchymal hepatocytes. Wisse and Gregoriadis (1975) similarly suggested that the initial uptake of horseradish-peroxidase-loaded liposomes from 3 to 30 minutes post i.v. infusion was by Kupffer cells; uptake by parenchymal cells was first observed between 30–60 minutes, and was most evident at 3 hours; liposomes were still present at 24 hours. In still another electron microscopic study of the liver, Rahman and Wright (1975) observed endocytic uptake of EDTA-loaded liposomes within minutes of infusion into mice, by the Kupffer cells and parenchymal hepatocytes; no evidence for liposome–cell fusion was obtained. Phagocytic vacuoles containing liposomes increased in size and number within the cytoplasm of both cell types for several hours; no attempt was made to quantitate the relative uptake by Kupffer cells and hepatocytes. These ultrastructural findings (Wisse and Gregoriadis, 1975; De Barsy *et al.*, 1975, 1976; Segal *et al.*, 1974; Rahman and Wright, 1975) are further substantiated by cellular fractionation of the liver into populations of Kupffer cells and hepatocytes; 70% of the hepatic accumulation of liposome-entrapped [^{14}C]inulin, 15 minutes after i.v. injection of liposomes, L(PC 3 : DCP 1 : Chol 9), was recovered in the Kupffer cell-rich fraction (Tanaka *et al.*, 1975). Tanaka and co-workers calculate that Kupffer cells accumulate five-fold more [^{14}C]inulin, entrapped in liposomes, than parenchymal cells, on a per gram basis, assuming that Kupffer cells comprise 30% of the liver mass.

An early claim by Gregoriadis and Ryman (1972a) that 3 minutes after injection albumin-containing liposomes are present in parenchymal cells and 'probably' in Kupffer cells has been challenged by the investigations cited above. Gregoriadis has more recently suggested (Segal *et al.*, 1974) that his earlier observations, based on autoradiographic visualization of [^{3}H]cholesterol-labelled liposomes, may have been biased by [^{3}H]cholesterol exchange between liposome and hepatocyte membranes. It appears not unlikely that Gregoriadis' early results (Gregoriadis and Ryman, 1972a) may reflect the effects of macromolecular surface ligands. The albumin-loaded liposomes may, to some extent, have had portions of the albumin molecules exposed on the outer liposome surface, therby influencing *in vivo* tissue and cellular localization.

5.4. Clinical trials in man

In the first of two studies (Gregoriadis *et al.*, 1974b) in which liposomes were administered to human subjects, Gregoriadis and his colleagues investigated the fate of sonicated liposomes, L(DPPC 7 : PA 1 : Chol 2) [^{131}I-labelled albumin], in three patients with metastatic cancer. Patients received a single dose of either 37 or 7.5 mg lipid by intra-arterial or intravenous injection, respectively. The early time course, followed using the hybrid-scanner technique, demonstrated a close correlation between hepatic accumulation and the rapid clearance of liposomal radioactivity from circulation; greater than 80% of the injected load was cleared within 6 hours. Tissue specimens, examined for accumulation of radioactivity, were obtained at surgery 3 hours after injection from one patient, and from the second patient at autopsy, 5 days after injection. Comparison of accumulation by tumour tissue and 'normal' tissue from the same organs revealed enhancement of uptake by tumour tissue: liver tumour tissue had 20–30% more accumulation than normal liver tissue, kidney tumour tissue had 50-fold more accumulation than normal kidney tissue, and tumour tissue from spleen and colon had twofold more accumulation than their normal counterparts. The authors suggest that the enhanced uptake by tumour tissue may reflect either increased vascularization of the diseased tissue or the increased endocytic capacity of tumour cells. Finally, ultrastructural analysis of liver, 3 hours post i.v. injection, indicated uptake of liposomes by approximately one-third of the parenchymal cells; uptake by Kupffer cells was 'extremely uncommon'.

Recently, Tyrrell's group (Tyrrell *et al.*, 1976) used liposomes, L(PC 7 : PA 1 : Chol 2), containing amyloglucosidase in an attempt to treat a patient with type II glycogenosis (Pompe's disease). The absence of lysosomal β-glucosidase leads to the accumulation of its substrate, glycogen, which in turn is reflected in clinical symptoms of muscular hypotonia, weakness, and finally death. Liposome-entrapped enzyme was intravenously injected each day for a week (total dose was 170 mg lipid and 3 mg enzyme); the patient died on the eighth day. The investigators note that the enlarged liver significantly decreased in size during therapy. At autopsy, although the liver glycogen level was half of that expected (on the basis of data accumulated for other children with Pompe's disease), glycogen storage by other tissues appeared to be unaltered by the enzyme replacement therapy. Trace amounts of administered β-glucosidase could be detected only in liver and spleen. The therapeutic usefulness of liposomes in the treatment of Pompe's disease is limited, as the authors point out, unless a technique is devised for the targeting of liposomes to muscle tissue.

5.5. Potential hazards involved in the use of liposomes

While liposomes are generally innocuous, substantial reason for concern has arisen regarding their use in enzyme replacement therapy. The two potential hazards inherent in their use in animals are the toxicity of the lipid constituents and the immunogenicity of the lipids and the entrapped proteins. Gregoriadis (1976) warns of the toxicity of charged amphiphiles; intracerebral injections of liposomes into mice resulted in epileptic seizures and cerebral tissue necrosis when liposomes contained either stearylamine or dicetyl phosphate. Injection of high doses of dicetylphosphate-containing liposomes into newborn mice resulted in death within 90 minutes; autopsy revealed petechiae and cardiac exudates (De Barsy *et al.*, 1976). In addition, intravenous administration of sonicated phos-phatidylserine liposomes to mice causes significant elevation of the free glucose levels in the blood and the brain tissue, probably triggered by catecholamine release by the adrenal glands (Bruni *et al.*, 1976). Recently, Steger and Desnick (1977) have demonstrated that administration of posi-tively charged liposomes containing stearylamine, L(DPPC 7 : SA 1 : Chol 2), to mice resulted in disruption of lysosomal integrity in the liver whereas negatively charged liposomes, L(DPPC 7 : PA 1 : Chol 2), did not.

The toxicity of phosphatidylserine and stearylamine has also been demonstrated *in vitro*. Dunnick *et al.* (1976a) report that cultured tumour cells exposed to liposomes consisting of phosphatidylcholine, cholesterol, and gangliosides continued to proliferate normally whereas cells exposed to liposomes containing either phosphatidylserine or stearylamine became non-proliferative. These charged lipids are presumably incorporated into the cell membrane (via liposome–cell lipid exchange and liposome–cell fusion) and thereby exert adverse effects, by altering essential membrane functions, such as transport of nutrients. Similarly, Magee and co-workers (1974) have observed that stearylamine-containing liposomes, L(SPH 3 : SA 1 : Chol 1), when incubated with cultured HeLa cells at high doses, caused toxic effects; cells detached from the substratum, displaying severe bulging and cell membrane deformation.

In addition to the potentially adverse physiological consequences imposed by foreign lipids, there also exist immunological hazards. Enzymes entrapped within liposomes, although latent with respect to their catalytic activity, may have non-catalytic portions exposed on the outer surface of the liposome; this is strongly implied by the demonstration that β-glucuronidase-loaded liposomes display a totally different kinetics of hepatic accumulation and retention than buffer-loaded liposomes (Steger and Desnick, 1977); presumptive exposed protein moieties act to direct the *in vivo* fate of the liposome. Proteins and other antigens entrapped in lipo-somes may be more immunoreactive and elicit the production of more antibody than the same dose of free protein or antigen (Almeida *et al.*, 1975; Allison and Gregoriadis, 1974; Uemura *et al.*, 1975).

6. SUMMARY

The experiments detailed above, performed in many laboratories, make it clear that problems of engineering render selective delivery of enzymes to target tissues difficult at present. Whereas liver, spleen, and (unfortunately) lung can be reached by means of the i.v. or i.p. routes, pathways to other organs have not been found. Moreover, short- and long-range toxicities have not been properly evaluated, and, in fact, the stability of liposomes, in circulation (or carrier leucocytes, *in* which, or *on* which, they may be carried about), has recently been questioned. Indeed, in 1978, liposomal encapsulation appears to be practical as a means of introducing enzymes into cells *in vitro*, but not *in vivo*. Techniques for permitting us to judge the fate and distribution of these vectors in animals or humans are as yet poorly discriminatory, as compared to similar techniques in the dish.

The studies described above may be summarized as follows:

(1)   Liposomes may be formed so as to encapsulate enzymatically active proteins, or other macromolecules.

(2)   The enzymes which have been trapped include many which are missing in lysosomal storage diseases.

(3)   *In vitro* and *in vivo*, administration of enzymes by means of liposomes increases uptake by lysosomes of cells relative to the uptake of free enzyme.

(4)   Targeting of liposomes containing enzyme to specific tissues is, at present, only minimally successful.

(5)   Uptake by one or another tissue depends both upon the route of administration of liposomes (e.g. intravenous v. intraperitoneal) and upon the composition of the liposomes (charge, size, content).

(6)   Association of liposomes with cells may be enhanced by coating the liposomes with ligands recognizable by surface receptors.

(7)   Problems of safety, toxicity, long-range effects, and doubts as to the exact subcellular localization of liposomes and their cargo are not yet resolved. This area of investigation is young, appears promising, but much work is required with experimental animals before it can be extended into the clinic.

REFERENCES

Allison, A. C. and Gregoriadis, G. (1974). Liposomes as immunological adjuvants, *Nature*, **252**, 252.

Almeida, J. D., Brand, C. M., Edwards, D. C. and Heath, T. D. (1975). Formation of virosomes from influenza subunits and liposomes *Lancet*, **2**, 899–901.

Aloj, S.M., Kohn, L.D., Lee, G. and Meldolesi, M. F. (1977). The binding of thyrotropin to liposomes containing gangliosides *Biochem. Biophys. Res. Commun.* **74**, 1053–1059.

Arakawa, E., Imai, Y., Kobayashi, H., Okumura, K. and Sezaki, H. (1975). Application of drug-containing liposomes to the duration of intramuscular absorption of water-soluble drugs in rats *Chem. Pharm. Bull.*, **23**, 2218–2222.

Bangham, A. D. (1968). Membrane models with phospholipids, *Progr. Biophys. Mol. Biol.*, **18**, 29–95.

Bangham, A. D., Standish, M. M. and Weissmann, G. (1965). The action of steroids and streptolysin S on the permeability of phospholipid structures to cations, *J. Mol. Biol.*, **13**, 253–259.

Batzri, S. and Korn, E. D. (1975). Interaction of phospholipid vesicles with cells; endocytosis and fusion as alternate mechanisms for the uptake of lipid-soluble and water-soluble molecules, *J. Cell Biol.*, **66**, 621–634.

Brady, R. O., Tallman, J. F., Johnson, W. G., Gal, A. E., Leahy, W. R., Quirk, J. M. and DeKaban, A. S. (1973). Replacement therapy for inherited enzyme deficiency. Use of purified ceramidetrihexosidase in Fabry's disease, *N. Engl. J. Med.*, **289**, 9–14.

Brady, R. O., Pentchev, P., Gal, A., Hibbert, S. and DeKaban, A. (1974). Replacement therapy for inherited enzyme deficiency. Use of purified glucocerebrosidase in Gaucher's disease, *N. Engl. J. Med.*, **291**, 989–993.

Braidman, I. and Gregoriadis, G. (1977). Rapid partial purification of placental glucocerebroside: β-glucosidase and its entrapment in liposomes, *Biochem. J.*, **164**, 439–445.

Bruni, A., Toffano, G., Leon, A. and Boarato, E. (1976). Pharmacological effects of phosphatidylserine liposomes, *Nature*, **260**, 331–333.

Caride, V. J., Taylor, W., Cramer, J. A. and Gottschalk, A. (1976). Evaluation of liposome-entrapped radioactive tracers as scanning agents, Part 1: Organ distribution of liposome ^{99m}Tc-DTPA in mice, *J. Nucl. Med.*, **17**, 1067–1072.

Chang, T. M. S. (1973). Immobilization of enzymes, adsorbents, or both within semipermeable microcapsules (artificial cells) for clinical and experimental treatment of metabolite-related disorders, in *Enzyme Therapy in Genetic Diseases*, Vol. **9**, pp. 66–76 (D. Bergsma, ed.), Baltimore, Md, William and Wilkins.

Chang, T. M. S. and Poznansky, M. J. (1968). Semipermeable microcapsules containing catalase for enzyme replacement in acatalasaemic mice, *Nature*, **218**, 243–245.

Cohen, C. M., Weissmann, G., Hoffstein, S., Awasthi, Y. and Srivastava, S. K. (1976). Introduction of purified hexosaminidase A into Tay–Sachs leucocytes by means of immunoglobulin-coated liposomes *Biochemistry*, **15**, 452–460.

Colley, C. M. and Ryman, B. E. (1974). A model for lysosomal storage disease and a possible method of therapy *Biochem. Soc. Trans.*, **2**, 871–872.

Colley, C. M. and Ryman, B. E. (1976). The use of a liposomally entrapped enzyme in the treatment of an artificial storage condition *Biochim. Biophys. Acta*, **451**, 417–425.

Dapergolas, G., Neerunjun, E. D. and Gregoriadis, G. (1976). Penetration of target areas in the rat by liposome-associated bleomycin, glucose oxidase, and insulin, *FEBS Lett.*, **63**, 235–239.

Deamer, D. and Bangham, A. D. (1976). Large volume liposomes by an ether vaporization method *Biochim. Biophys. Acta*, **443**, 629–634.

DeBarsy, T., Devos, P. and Van Hoof, F. (1975). The cellular distribution of liposomes in the liver of newborn rats *Biochem. Soc. Trans.*, **3**, 159–160.

DeBarsy, T., Devos, P. and Van Hoof, F. (1976). A morphologic and biochemical study of the fate of antibody-bearing liposomes, *Lab. Invest.*, **34**, 273–282.

Desnick, R. J., Thorpe, S. R. and Fiddler, M. B. (1976). Toward enzyme therapy for lysosomal storage diseases *Physiol. Rev.*, **56**, 57–99.

Dunnick, J. K., McDougall, I. R., Aragon, S., Goris, M. L. and Kriss, J. P. (1975). Vesicle interactions with polyamino acids and antibody: *in vitro* and *in vivo* studies *J. Nucl. Med.*, **16**, 483–487.

Dunnick, J. K., Kallman, R. F. and Kriss, J. P. (1976a). Lipid vesicle interaction with EMT–6 tumor cells and effect on subsequent cell growth, *Biochem. Biophys. Res. Commun.*, **73**, 619–624.

Dunnick, J. K., Badger, R. S., Takeda, Y. and Kriss, J. P. (1976b). Vesicle interactions with antibody and peptide hormone: role of vesicle composition, *J. Nucl. Med.*, **17**, 1073–1076.

Eytan, G., Matheson, M. J. and Racker, E. (1975). Incorporation of biologically active proteins into liposomes *FEBS Lett.*, **57**, 121–125.

Fishman, Y. and Citri, N. (1975). L-asparaginase entrapped in liposomes: preparation and properties *FEBS Lett.*, **60**, 17–20.

Grant, C. W. M. and McConnell, H. M. (1973). Fusion of phospholipid vesicles with viable *Acholeplasma laidlawii*, *Proc. Nat. Acad. Sci.*, **70**, 1238–1240.

Gregoriadis, G. (1973). Drug entrapment in liposomes, *FEBS Lett.*, **36**, 292–296.

Gregoriadis, G. (1976). The carrier potential of liposomes in biology and medicine, *N. Engl. J. Med.*, **295**, 704–710 and 765–770.

Gregoriadis, G. and Buckland, R. A. (1973). Enzyme-containing liposomes alleviate a model for storage diseases *Nature*, **244**, 170–172.

Gregoriadis, G. and Neerunjun, D. E. (1974). Control of the rate of hepatic uptake and catabolism of liposome-entrapped proteins injected into rats: possible therapeutic applications *Eur. J. Biochem.*, **47**, 179–185.

Gregoriadis, G. and Neerunjun, E. D. (1975). Homing of liposomes to target cells, *Biochem. Biophys. Res. Commun.*, **65**, 537–544.

Gregoriadis, G. and Ryman, B. E. (1971). Liposomes as carriers of enzymes or drugs: a new approach to the treatment of storage diseases *Biochem. J.*, **124**, 58p.

Gregoriadis, G. and Ryman, B. E. (1972a). Fate of protein-containing liposomes injected into rats. An approach to the treatment of storage diseases, *Eur. J. Biochem.*, **24**, 485–491.

Gregoriadis, G. and Ryman, B. E. (1972b). Lysosomal localization of β-fructofuranosidase-containing liposomes injected into rats *Biochem. J.*, **129**, 123–133.

Gregoriadis, G., Leathwood, P. D. and Ryman, B. E. (1971). Enzyme entrapment in liposomes *FEBS Lett.*, **14**, 1495–99.

Gregoriadis, G., Putnam, D., Louis, L. and Neerunjun, D. (1974a). Comparative effect and fate of non-entrapped and liposome-entrapped neuraminidase injected into rats *Biochem. J.*, **140**, 323–330.

Gregoriadis, G., Swain, C. P., Wills, E. J. and Tavill, A. S. (1974b). Drug-carrier potential of liposomes in cancer chemotherapy, *Lancet*, **1**, 1313–1316.

Hesketh, T. R., Dourmashkin, R. R., Payne, S. N., Humphrey, J. H. and Lachmann, P. J. (1971). Lesions due to complement in lipid membranes *Nature*, **233**, 620–623.

Hirschhorn, R. and Weissmann, G. (1977). Genetic disorders of lysosomes, *Progress in Medical Genetics*, **1**, 49–101.

Huang, L. and Pagano, R. E. (1975). Interaction of phospholipid vesicles with cultured mammalian cells. I. Characteristics of uptake *J. Cell Biol.*, **67**, 38–48.

Ihler, G. M., Glew, R. H., Schnure, F. W. (1973). Enzyme loading of erythrocytes, *Proc. Nat. Acad. Sci.*, **70**, 2663–2666.

Johnson, W. G., Desnick, R. J., Long, D. M., Sharp, H. L., Krivit, W., Brady, B. and Brady, R. O. (1973). Intravenous injection of purified hexosaminidase A into a pateint with Tay–Sachs disease, in *Enzyme Theraphy in Genetic Diseases*, Vol. **9**, pp. 120–124, (D. Bergsma, ed.), Baltimore, Md., William and Wilkins.

Jonah, M. M., Cerny, E. A. and Rahman, Y.-E. (1975). Tissue distribution of EDTA encapsulated within liposomes of varying surface properties *Biochim. Biophys. Acta*, **401**, 336–348.

Juliano, R. L. and Stamp, D. (1975). The effect of particle size and charge on the clearance rates of liposomes and liposome encapsulated drugs *Biochem. Biophys. Res. Commun.*, **63**, 651–658.

Juliano, R. L. and Stamp, D. (1976). Lectin-mediated attachment of glycoprotein-bearing liposomes to cells *Nature*, **261**, 235–238.

Kataoka, T., Williamson, J. R. and Kinsky, S. C. (1973). Release of macromolecular markers (enzymes) from liposomes treated with antibody and complement. An attempt at correlation with electron microscopic observations *Biochim. Biophys. Acta*, **298**, 158–179.

Kimelberg, H. K. (1976) Differential distribution of liposome-entrapped [^{3}H]methotrexate and labelled lipids after intravenous injection in a primate *Biochim. Biophys. Acta*, **448**, 531–550.

Kimelberg, H. K., Mayhew, E. and Papahadjopoulos, D. (1975). Distribution of liposome-entrapped cations in tumor-bearing mice *Life Sci.*, **17**, 715–723.

Krupp, L., Chobanian, A. V. and Brecher, P. I. (1976). The *in vivo* tramsformation of phospholipid vesicles to a particle resembling HDL in the rat *Biochem. Biophys. Res. Commun.*, **72**, 1251–1258.

Lachman, P. J., Munn, E. A. and Weissmann, G. (1970). Complement-mediated lysis of liposomes produced by the reactive lysis procedure *Immunology*, **19**, 938–986.

Magee, W. E., Goff, C. W., Schoknecht, J., Smith, M. D. and Cherian, K. (1974). The interaction of cationic liposomes containing entrapped horseradish peroxidase with cells in culture *J. Cell Biol.*, **63**, 492–504.

Magee, W. E., Talcott, M. L., Straub, S. X. and Vriend, C. Y. (1976). A comparison of negatively and positively charged liposomes containing entrapped polyinosinic polycytidylic acid for interferon induction in mice *Biochim. Biophys. Acta*, **451**, 610–618.

Martin, F. J. and McDonald, R. C. (1976). Lipid vesicle–cell interactions. III. Introduction of a new antigenic determinant into erythrocyte membranes *J. Cell Biol.*, **70**, 414–426.

Mattenberger-Kreber, L., Auderset, G., Schneider, M., Louis-Broillet, A., Benedetti, M. S. and Malnoe, A. (1976). Phagocytosis of liposomes by mouse peritoneal macrophages *Experientia*, **32**, 1522–1524.

McDougall, I. R., Dunnick, J. K., McNamee, M. G. and Kriss, J. P. (1974). Distribution and fate of synthetic lipid vesicles in the mouse. A combined radionuclide and spin label study *Proc. Nat. Acad. Sci.*, **71**, 3487–3491.

McDougall, I. R., Dunnick, J. K., Goris, M. L. and Kriss, J. P. (1975). *In vivo* distribution of vesicles loaded with radiopharmaceuticals: a study of different routes of administration *J. Nucl. Med.*, **16**, 488–491.

Neerunjun, E. D. and Gregoriadis, G. (1976) Tumour regression with liposome-entrapped asparaginase: some immunological advantages *Biochem. Soc. Trans.*, **4**, 133–134.

Pagano, R. E. and Huang, L. (1975). Interaction of phospholipid vesicles with cultured mammalian cells. II. Studies of mechanism *J. Cell Biol.*, **67**, 49–60.

Pagano, R. E., Huang, L. and Wey, C. (1974). Interaction of phospholipid vesicles with cultured mammalian cells *Nature*, **252**, 166–167.

Papahadjopoulos, D. and Miller, N. (1967) Phospholipid model membranes. I. Structural characteristics of hydrated liquid crystals *Biochim. Biophys. Acta* **135**, 624–638.

Papahadjopoulos, D. and Watkins, J. C. (1967). Phospholipid model membranes. II. Permeability properties of hydrated liquid crystals *Biochim. Biophys. Acta* **135**, 639–652.

Papahadjopoulos, D., Mayhew, E., Poste, G., Smith, S. and Vail, W. J. (1974). Incorporation of lipid vesicles by mammalian cells provides a potential method for modifying cell behaviour *Nature* **252**, 163–165.

Patel, H. M. and Ryman, B. E. (1974). α-Mannosidase in zinc-deficient rats: possibility of liposomal therapy in mannosidosis *Biochem. Soc. Trans.*, **2**, 1014–1017.

Poste, G. and Papahadjopoulos, D. (1976). Lipid vesicles as carriers introducing materials into cultured cells: influence of vesicle lipid composition on mechanism(s) of vesicle incorporation into cells *Proc. Nat. Acad. Sci.*, **73**, 1603–1607.

Rahman, Y.–E. and Wright, B. J. (1975). Liposomes containing chelating agents: cellular penetration and a possible mechanism of metal removal *J. Cell Biol.*, **65**, 112–122.

Redwood, W. R. and Patel, B. C. (1974). Binding of a solubilized membrane ATPase to phospholipid bilayers. *Biochim. Biophys. Acta*, **363**, 70–85.

Schieren, S., Rudolph, S., Finkelstein, M., Coleman, P. and Weissmann, G. (1978). Comparison of large unilamellar vesicles prepared by a petroleum ether vaporization method with multilamellar vesicles: ESR, diffusion, and entrapment analyses, *Biochim. Biophys. Acta* **542**, 137–153.

Segal, A. W., Wills, E. J., Richmond, J. E., Slavin, G., Black, C. D. V. and Gregoriadis, G. (1974). Morphological observations on the cellular and subcellular destination of intravenously administered liposomes *Br. J. Exp. Path.*, **55**, 320–327.

Sessa, G. and Weissmann, G. (1968). Phospholipid spherules (liposomes) as a model for biological membranes. *J. Lipid Res.* **9**, 310–318.

Sessa, G. and Weissmann, G. (1970) Incorporation of lysozyme into liposomes. A model for structure-linked latency *J. Biol. Chem.*, **245**, 3295–3301.

Steger, L. D. and Desnick, R. J. (1977). Enzyme therapy. VI. Comparative *in vivo* fates and effects on lysosomal integrity of enzyme entrapped in negatively and positively charged liposomes *Biochim. Biophys. Acta*, **464**, 530–546.

Sweet, C. and Zull, J. E. (1970). The binding of serum albumin to phospholipid liposomes *Biochim. Biophys. Acta*, **218**, 253–262.

Tanaka, T., Taneda, K., Kobayashi, H., Okumura, K., Muranishi, S. and Sezaki, H. (1975). Application of liposomes to the pharmaceutical modification of the distribution characteristics of drugs in the rat *Chem. Pharm. Bull.*, **23**, 3069–3074.

Tyrrell, D. A., Ryman, B. E. E., Keeton, B. R. and Dubowitz, V. (1976). Use of liposomes in treating type II glycogenosis *Br. Med. J.*, **2**, 88.

Uemura, K. I., Claflin, J. L., Davie, J. M. and Kinsky, S. C. (1975). Immune response to liposomal model membranes: restricted IgM and IgG anti-dinitrophenyl antibodies produced in guinea pigs *J. Immunol.*, **114**, 958–961.

Updike, S., Prieve, C. and Magnuson, J. (1973). Immobilization in hypoallergenic gel, a method of protecting enzymes from proteolysis and antibody complexing, in *Enzyme Therapy in Genetic Diseases*, Vol. **9**, pp. 77–80 (D. Bergsma, ed.), Baltimore, Md., William and Wilkins.

Weissmann, G., Brand, A. and Franklin, E. C. (1974). Interaction of immunoglobulins with liposomes *J. Clin. Invest.*, **53**, 536–543.

Weissmann, G., Bloomgarden, D., Kaplan, R., Cohen, C., Hoffstein, S., Collins, T., Gottlieb, A. and Nagle, D. (1975). A general method for the introduction of enzymes, by means of immunoglobulin-coated liposomes, into lysosomes of deficient cells *Proc. Nat. Acad. Sci.*, **72**, 88–92.

Weissmann, G., Collins, T., Evers, A. and Dunham, P. (1976). Membrane perturbation: studies employing a calcium-sensitive dye, arsenazo III, in liposomes *Proc. Nat. Acad. Sci.*, **73**, 510–514.

Weissmann, G., Cohen, C. and Hoffstein, S. (1977). Introduction of enzymes, by means of liposomes, into non-phagocytic human cells *in vitro Biochim. Biophys. Acta*, **498**, 375–385.

Wisse, E. and Gregoriadis, G. (1975). The uptake of liposomes by the rat liver RES *J. Reticuloendothelial Soc.*, **18**, 10a.

Liposomes in Biological Systems
Edited by G. Gregoriadis and A. C. Allison
©1980, John Wiley & Sons, Ltd.

CHAPTER 6

Stability of Liposomes in presence of Blood Constituents: Consequences for uptake of Liposomal Lipid and Entrapped Compounds by Rat liver cells

Gerrit Scherphof, Frits Roerdink, Dick Hoekstra,
Józef Zborowski, and Eddie Wisse

1. Introduction   179

2. Clearance of liposomal [^{14}C]lecithin from the blood after
    intravenous injection   184

3. The role of the liver in the uptake of liposomal lecithins   184

4. The fate of liposome-entrapped proteins after intravenous
    injection   187

5. Release of liposome-entrapped compounds during
    incubation with plasma or plasma constituents   193

6. The fate of HDL-bound lecithin   199

7. Uptake of liposomes and entrapped albumin by isolated
    hepatocytes in maintenance culture   201

8. Concluding remarks   205

    References   207

1. INTRODUCTION

Since Gregoriadis and Ryman (1971) first suggested the use of liposomes as intravenous carriers of enzymes numerous reports have appeared which describe the application of these lipid vehicles to introduce various substances into a wide variety of cells (see Tyrrell *et al.*, 1976; Gregoriadis, 1976a,b for review articles). Among the compounds which have been entrapped in liposomes with the purpose of effecting their uptake by animal tissues after intravenous injection are enzymes (Gregoriadis and Ryman, 1972a,b; Wisse *et al.*, 1976; Colley and Ryman 1974; Dapergolas *et al.*, 1976), other proteins (Dapergolas *et al.*, 1976; Gregoriadis and Neerunjun, 1974; Heath *et al.*, 1976; Gregoriadis and Neerunjun, 1975; Surolia and Bachhawat, 1977), drugs (Colley and Ryman, 1975; Gregoriadis, 1973; Black and Gregoriadis, 1974; Kimelberg, 1976a), and various other low molecular weight molecules (Rahman and Wright, 1975; McDougall *et al.*, 1974; Kimelberg *et al.*, 1975).

Several investigators have emphasized the significance of lasting liposomal stability in the circulation. However, only in a few cases was the influence of blood or blood constituents on liposomal integrity investigated in detail. In most other studies only indirect evidence was presented of either a high degree of liposomal stability or, alternatively, of substantial release of liposome-entrapped substances. A number of different factors can be envisaged to influence liposomal integrity after introduction in the circulation or, for that matter, following addition to cell cultures in complex media. Among these factors are: lipolytic or other lipid-metabolizing activities in plasma as well as at cell surfaces, exchange or net transfer of liposomal lipid to plasma constituents or cellular membranes, interaction with plasma proteins, imperfect fusion of liposomes with cells involving partial release of entrapped material [fusion leakage, Kimelberg, 1976a], and release of lysosomal lipolytic enzymes during liposome-induced endocytosis. Hardly any of these possibilities has been explored seriously. Yet it is of crucial importance that we know how the capacity of liposomes to retain entrapped substances can be influenced when they are exposed to complex biological conditions. A brief survey is presented of literature describing observations on influences of blood or blood constituents on liposomal integrity.

A limited influence of albumin on the release of methotrexate from liposomes was found by Kimelberg (1976b). We reported, on the other hand, considerable release of sucrose and inulin from liposomes during incubation with albumin solutions (Zborowski *et al.*, 1977). Other plasma proteins also, were recently reported to interact with liposomes. Black and Gregoriadis (1976) found that the α-macroglobulins tightly associate with liposomes while Tyrell *et al.* (1977) provided evidence for a similar interaction between liposomes and β-globulins. In addition, they showed the β-globulins to increase the leakage of methotrexate from liposomes.

Gregoriadis (1973) observed a considerable discrepancy between clearance from the circulation of liposome-entrapped benzyl penicillin and clearance of the liposomal carrier suggesting untimely release of at least part of the enclosed drug. Previously, however, Gregoriadis and Ryman (1972b) could not detect any free β-fructofuranosidase activity in plasma after intravenous injection of enzyme-containing liposomes, indicating satisfactory retention of the enzyme by the liposomes. Also in favour of long-lived liposomal integrity in the bloodstream is the observation by Gregoriadis *et al*. (1974) that liposome-entrapped neuraminidase failed to decrease plasma-associated N-acetylneuraminic acid after intravenous injection, whereas free neuraminidase reduced the bound N-acetylneuraminic acid content in plasma up to 80%·

Results obtained by Kimelberg *et al*. (1975) on the uptake of liposome-entrapped cations by several tissues of the mouse clearly indicated that a substantial proportion of the ions must be released from the liposomes due to the action of one or more serum factors.

The tissue distribution of radiolabelled technetate captured in liposomes, as reported by McDougall *et al*. (1974) is also highly suggestive of partial release of the entrapped ion because morphological barriers should prevent the ingestion of even the smallest liposomes (vesicles) by the cells of such tissues as heart, muscle, and stomach. A similar conclusion can be drawn from the work of Jonah *et al*. (1975) describing tissue distribution of EDTA captured within liposomes of varying composition. Arakawa *et al*. (1975) provided direct evidence of enhanced drug release from liposomes during *in vitro* incubation with serum. The vast majority of studies on blood clearance and tissue distribution of liposomes have been concerned with the substances entrapped in the liposomes rather than with the lipid wrapping material itself. Although we wish to emphasize that concurrent clearance of liposome and entrapped material does not provide conclusive evidence of uptake of intact liposomes containing the entrapped compound it is obvious that such integral uptake requires the lipid and the encapsulated substance to be cleared simultaneously and identically. It is important, therefore, that the rate and mechanism of clearing of the liposomal lipid be investigated separately from that of liposomal contents.

Occasionally, clearance and tissue distribution studies included the fate of liposome-incorporated cholesterol (Gregoriadis and Ryman, 1972a; Kimelberg, 1976a; Gregoriadis and Ryman, 1972b; Steger and Desnick, 1977) and in a single case (Juliano and Stamp, 1975) the phospholipid moiety of the liposome was taken into consideration. The high efficiencies with which cholesterol was found to exchange between cell surfaces and plasma constituents (Nelson, 1972; Cooper, 1970) and phospholipids between various classes of lipoproteins (Gurd, 1960) should caution against an impetuous interpretation of cellular uptake of liposomal constituents. Morphological studies on the fate of the lipids of injected liposomes (Rahman and Wright, 1975; de Barsy *et al*., 1976; Segal *et al*., 1974) or liposomes added to cell cultures (Cohen *et al*., 1976; Huang and Pagano,

G

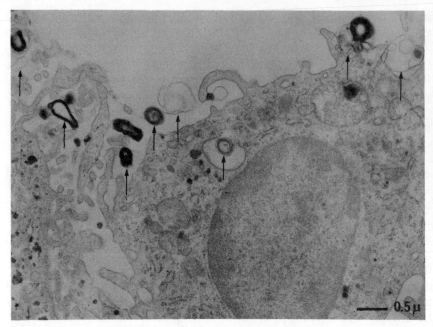

Figure 1 Kupffer cell of a control rat, not injected with liposomes. Due to unknown factors glutaraldehyde fixation, as used here, may cause the formation of artefacts in the form of liposome-like myelin figures (arrows), located both intra- and extracellularly, × 18,000

1975; Batzri and Korn, 1975) should be considered with great scepticism as myelin-like structures closely resembling liposomes are easily produced as artefacts during fixation of cells or tissues with glutaraldehyde. Figure 1, showing a Kupffer cell of a control liver not injected with liposomes and fixed with glutaraldehyde, provides a striking example of such artefacts.

Direct evidence of liposomes being internalized by any type of tissue after intravenous injection is, therefore, scarce, although numerous indications suggest that it may happen. All tissue distribution studies (Gregoriadis and Ryman, 1972a; Kimelberg, 1976a; McDougall *et al.*, 1974; Kimelberg *et al.*, 1975; Jonah *et al.*, 1975; Steger and Desnick, 1977; Segal *et al.*, 1974; Kimelberg *et al.*, 1976; Gregoriadis and Allison, 1974; Rahman *et al.*, 1975; Caridè *et al.*, 1976) have demonstrated that the liver is the main target of injected liposomes in man, monkey, rat, as well as mouse. Not only because of its size but also per gram of tissue the liver usually takes up the highest proportion of liposome-entrapped materials. The question of course arises as to what is the relative involvement in the total uptake of various cell types which make up the organ. From a therapeutical point of view it would be of importance to know if the parenchymal cells contribute to any extent in the uptake process or if, alternatively, the non-parenchymal cells (i.e. Kupffer and endothelial cells) are exclusively responsible for the uptake of liposome-associated material by the liver. Gregoriadis and Ryman (1972a) were the first to report on this subject. They found by means of autoradiography that both Kupffer and parenchymal cells were involved in the uptake of [³H]cholesterol-labelled liposomes. In a later study by Gregoriadis and co-workers nitro-blue tetrazolium trapped in liposomes was found exclusively in the phago-cytic vacuoles of the macrophages lining the sinusoids in bone marrow, spleen, and liver, i.e. in the Kupffer cells as far as the liver is concerned (Segal *et al.*, 1974). In a later study involving electron microscopical cytochemical localization of liposome-entrapped horseradish peroxidase (Wisse *et al.*, 1976) the initially claimed involvement of the parenchymal cells (Gregoriadis and Ryman, 1972a) was re-established.

From the above survey of the literature it is clear that the stability of liposomes in the blood circulation as well as the cellular distribution of liposome-associated material after uptake by the liver constitute an area of considerable controversy in which further investigations are needed. Our work has been mainly concerned with aspects of the use of liposomes as intravenous carriers. We will present evidence that lecithin-made liposomes are susceptible to deleterious attacks from several plasma constituents resulting in release of entrapped substances of diverging molecular weights such as sucrose, inulin and albumin. Both albumin and high density lipo-proteins in physiological concentrations are shown to take up and bind suf-ficient proportions of liposomal lecithins to cause severe damage to the liposomal integrity. In plasma most of the lecithin lost by the liposomes is transferred to the high density lipoprotein fraction and only very little to the albumin. Another high molecular weight compound, presumably low density lipoprotein, also binds small proportions of the lecithin released by the liposomes. Although liposomal lecithin is recovered in substantial amounts in the parenchymal cells of the liver following intravenous injec-tion, the hepatocytes apparently do not internalize the liposomes as such. This was demonstrated by the lack of appearance of liposome-entrapped horseradish peroxidase in the parenchymal cells as shown by electron micro-scopy. Possibly, the liposomal lecithin enters the hepatocytes after it has been transferred to high density lipoproteins.

Experiments with maintenance cultures of hepatocytes show that these cells do possess the capacity to take up liposomes as such. This suggests that liposomes which manage to pass in intact form the endothelial lining with its 0.1μm fenestrations (Wisse, 1970) may be considered suitable car-riers to introduce entrapped substances into the hepatocytes.

We believe it to be very important that the stability of liposomes in the bloodstream be investigated more systematically than has been done to date. Too often indirect evidence has been used to conclude that liposomes retain their integrity under biological conditions. Also, it would be important to know why some investigators find satisfactory trapping capacities for certain compounds whereas others observe severe leakage under similar conditions. Different results in this respect found by the same investigators on different trapped compounds also ask for further explanation.

We hope that our work in this area may stimulate others to take part in this aspect of liposome research as we feel that the promising initiative taken by Gregoriadis and Ryman (1971) cannot lead to useful application before some of the questions raised in this chapter have been answered satisfactorily.

2. CLEARANCE OF LIPOSOMAL [^{14}C]LECITHIN FROM THE BLOOD AFTER INTRAVENOUS INJECTION

In agreement with the findings of several others the clearance of liposomal lecithin from the circulation has a biphasic character (Figure 2). A rapid initial phase leading to 75% disappearance from the blood in the first 5 minutes for large unsonicated liposomes and about 50% elimination for the smaller sonicated ones is followed by a considerably slower rate of clearance after 15 minutes for both types of liposomes. In contrast to other investigators (Gregoriadis and Neerunjun 1974; Juliano and Stamp, 1975), however, we did not observe a preferential removal of negatively charged liposomes from the blood. Rather, the lecithin in negatively charged liposomes remained in circulation significantly longer than that of neutral or positively charged ones, which was most obvious for the slower phase of the clearance curves. Several possible explanations may be given: firstly, (*cf*. Gregoriadis and Neerunjun, 1974) we studied a different parameter, i.e. phospholipid rather than cholesterol or trapped material, and secondly (*c.f.* Juliano and Stamp, 1975), we studied the fate of multilamellar liposomes rather than of unilamellar vesicles. At the end of Section 6 (this chapter) we will return to this subject when discussing the transfer of liposomal lecithins to blood constituents and its consequences for the elimination of lecithin from the circulation.

3. THE ROLE OF THE LIVER IN THE UPTAKE OF LIPOSOMAL LECITHINS

As several investigators reported before, the liver takes up most of the injected liposomal material (Table 1). For unsonicated liposomes 1 hour after intravenous injection of neutral or positively charged ones, labelled with [^{14}C]lecithin, almost three-quarters of the radioactivity, was recovered

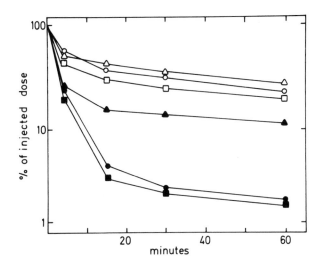

Figure 2 Effect of particle size and surface charge of liposomes on clearance of liposomal lecithin from the blood. Neutral liposomes were prepared from [^{14}C–Me]egg lecithin, labelled according to the method of Stoffel (1975), and cholesterol (molar ratio 7 : 1). Positive and negative liposomes were prepared from [^{14}C]egg lecithin, cholesterol, and stearylamine or dicetylphosphate, respectively (molar ratio 7 : 1 : 2). Sonicated liposomes (30 seconds 70 W with a Branson Sonifier^R) were fractionated on Sepharose-4B. Void-volume fractions were used for injection. One ml of sonicated or unsonicated liposomes, containing 2.5 μmol of lecithin (1.1–1.8 × 10^6 dpm) were injected intravenously into starved male rats. At the times indicated 50 μl of blood were drawn from the tail and assayed for radioactivity after discoloration with H$_2$O$_2$. Blood volume was calculated from body weight according to Wang (1959). Each point in the figure represents the average of five experiments. Open symbols, sonicated liposomes; filled symbols, unsonicated liposomes; squares, neutral; circles, positively charged; triangles, negatively charged

in the liver. Of the negatively charged ones only one-half was found in the liver at that time, in line with the somewhat slower rate of clearance of these particles from the bloodstream (Figure 2). With the sonicated preparations no significant differences were found between charged or neutral liposomes (Table 1), irrespective of the surface charge of the particles.

Table 1 shows that 80–85% of the radioactivity taken up by the liver is recovered as chloroform-soluble material. Taking into consideration the way the lecithin was labelled (in the polar head group) the label can only be lecithin or lysolecithin. Degradation to water-soluble products was apparently limited. In all cases we analysed the chloroform-soluble radioactivity, more than 80% was recovered as lecithin. This moderate degree of hydrolysis of the internalized phospholipid may either indicate limited sus-

Table 1   Effect of particle size and surface charge on the uptake and degradation of intravenously administered liposomes by the liver

Liposomes sonicated	charge	Uptake by whole liver (% of injected dose ± S.D.)	% Soluble in water	% Soluble in chloroform
−	neutral	68.2 ± 0.7	8	92
−	negative	48.7 ± 1.2	12	88
−	positive	74.6 ± 5.8	5	95
+	neutral	41.4 ± 3.7	21	79
+	negative	38.7 ± 1.5	8	92
+	positive	46.1 ± 2.9	15	85

Briefly sonicated void-volume liposomes from Sepharose-4B, or unsonicated liposomes, consisting of [^{14}C]lecithin and cholesterol (molar ratio 7 : 2) or of [^{14}C]lecithin, cholesterol, and stearylamine or dicetylphosphate (molar ratio 7 : 2 : 1) were injected intravenously into starved male rats (2.5 μmol of lecithin; 1.1–1.8 × 10^6 dpm). One hour after injection the liver was briefly perfused under anaesthesia with 0.9% NaCl/5 mM Tris, pH 7.2. The liver was homogenized and extracted according to the method of Bligh and Dyer (1959). Homogenate, chloroform, and aqueous methanol layer were separately assayed for radioactivity.

ceptibility of the lecithin towards lysosomal phospholipases (Waite *et al.*, 1969) or a substantial contribution by fusion with the plasma membrane causing the phospholipid to be hydrolysed more slowly. Alternatively, the label may also enter the liver cells by a mechanism other than endocytosis or fusion, e.g. mediated by the plasma (lipo)proteins as will be discussed in Sections 5 and 6 of this chapter.

Relatively little attention has been paid so far to the cellular distribution of internalized liposomal material within the liver. Foreign particular material is rapidly eliminated from the circulation by the macrophages of the liver, i.e. the Kupffer cells. It was to be expected therefore that intravenously administered liposomes would also be phagocytized by the Kupffer cells rather than taken up by the parenchymal cells of the liver. Particularly for the larger type liposomes (> 0.1 μm) uptake by the hepatocytes would seem unlikely as they are expected to be barred from the parenchyma by the lining of endothelial cells. The latter possess open fenestrations with an average diameter of about 0.1 μm (Wisse, 1970) and may thus function as a filter only allowing particles smaller than 0.1 μm to have access to the hepatocytes. Recently, a filtering function of the fenestrations was demonstrated for chylomicrons in neonatal livers (Naito and Wisse, unpublished results).

Much to our surprise we found (Table 2) that irrespective of the size of the liposomes the constituent lecithin was recovered for up to 50% in the parenchymal cells isolated from the liver of rats killed 10 minutes to 1 hour after intravenous injections of liposomes. It seemed highly unlikely

Table 2   Uptake of liposomal lecithin by liver parenchymal cells after intravenous injection of neutral liposomes

Expt. no	Time after injection (min)	Sonicated	Uptake by whole liver (% of injected dose)	Uptake by parenchymal cells (% of injected dose)
1	10	–	56	17
2	10	–	42	18
1	60	–	61	44
2	60	–	62	51
1	60	+	52	33
2	60	+	56	34
3	60	+	53	26

Sonicated or unsonicated liposomes consisting of [^{14}C]lecithin and cholesterol (7 : 2) were injected intravenously into starved rats (1.0 μmol of lecithin, 1.4×10^5 dpm). 10 or 60 minutes after injection the liver was perfused with collagenase (Geelen and Gibson, 1976) to obtain parenchymal cells. Recovery of parenchymal cells was calculated as in the legend to Figure 4.

that unsonicated liposomes with a diameter of more than 1 μm, as estimated by electron microscopy, would be taken up by the parenchymal cells if it is assumed that the endothelial fenestrations represent an impermeable barrier for particles of that size.

4.   THE FATE OF LIPOSOME-ENTRAPPED PROTEINS AFTER INTRAVENOUS INJECTION

The unexpected involvement of the hepatocytes in the uptake of liposomal lecithin by the liver led us to investigate the clearance and cellular distribution in the liver of a liposome-entrapped substance. Irrespective of the mechanism of uptake of liposomes by a cell, i.e. either by endocytosis or fusion, it is obvious that as long as the liposome remains intact prior to the uptake process, its contents should be recovered from the cell to the same extent as its lipid envelope.

Figure 3 shows a comparison of the rates of clearance from the blood of liposomal [^{14}C]lecithin and free and liposome-entrapped [^{125}I]albumin. It is clear that there is a discrepancy between the elimination rates of liposomal lecithin and liposome-captured albumin. The lipid is removed significantly faster than the entrapped protein, suggesting at least a partial disconnection of liposome and contents.

This conclusion is in line with the relatively low uptake by the liver of liposome-entrapped albumin (Figure 4) as compared with that of liposomal lecithin (Table 1). Less than 20% of the injected liposome-bound

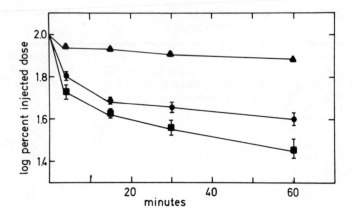

Figure 3 Clearance of free and liposome-entrapped [^{125}I]albumin from the blood, compared with clearance of liposomal [^{14}C]lecithin. Starved, male rats were injected intravenously with free [^{125}I]albumin, prepared from bovine serum albumin according to Bocci (1969) (100 μg; 1.10^5 dpm) or with liposome-entrapped [^{125}I]albumin (25 μg; 1.4 × 10^5 dpm) or with [^{14}C]lecithin-containing liposomes alone (1.1 × 10^6 dpm; 2.5 μmol). Composition of liposomes, egg lecithin: cholesterol: dicetylphosphate (7 : 1 : 2). See for further details legend to Figure 2. Each point is the average of three to five experiments, the vertical bars representing the standard deviations. Triangles, free albumin; circles, liposome-entrapped albumin; squares, liposomal lecithin

[^{125}I]albumin was found, maximally, in the whole liver, most of it as TCA-precipitable material, whereas at comparable times about half of the injected lecithin was recovered in this organ. A similarly low magnitude of uptake of liposome-entrapped albumin was found by Gregoriadis and Ryman (1972a). The regression of the percentage of uptake by the liver (from approximately 15% after 15 minutes to 5% after 60 minutes; Figure 4) was also reported by these authors. The most likely explanation would be that the iodinated albumin is degraded relatively rapidly once inside the lysosomal system and that low molecular weight products are subsequently released by the liver and taken up by other tissues or excreted. Figure 4 also shows that, in contrast to liposomal lecithin, there is only a few per cent uptake of entrapped albumin by parenchymal cells of the liver.

Morphological observations on the localization within the liver of intravenously injected, liposome-entrapped horseradish peroxidase are in good agreement with the biochemical results on the cellular distribution of entrapped albumin. Light microscopy in Figure 5 shows the distribution in the liver of the reaction product of horseradish peroxidase activity 1 hour after intravenous administration of 23 μg of peroxidase packaged in 1.5 mg briefly sonicated liposomes consisting of lecithin, cholesterol, and

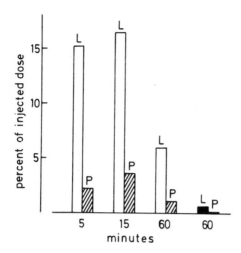

Figure 4 Uptake by whole liver and parenchymal cells of free and liposome-entrapped [^{125}I]albumin. Free or liposome-entrapped [^{125}I]albumin was injected in amounts and under conditions as in Figure 2. Each bar represents the mean of three experiments. Parenchymal cells were isolated essentially according to Berry and Friend (1969). Recovery of hepatocytes was calculated as *dry weight isolated cells/0.9 × dry weight whole cells × 100%* using the figure of 90% for the fraction of total liver mass accounted for by parenchymal cells, according to Weibel *et al.* (1969). L designates whole liver; P designates parenchymal cells. The filled bars represent uptake of free albumin. The open and hatched bars represent the uptake of liposome-entrapped albumin

dicetylphosphate (7 : 1 : 2). The exogenous enzyme activity is conspicuously concentrated in the sinusoidal cells while no significant activity can be detected in the parenchymal cells. Also 3 hours after injection of peroxidase-containing liposomes no significant peroxidase activity could be demonstrated in the hepatocytes (Figure 6). These observations seem contradictory to those reported by Wisse *et al.* (1976). These authors observed significant peroxidase activity in the parenchymal cells 3 hours after injection of the entrapped enzyme. We have reason to believe that the latency of the enzyme activity in these preparations was considerably less than 100%. Since, in addition, much higher amounts of enzyme were used to entrap (500 or 1,000 μg in 450 or 900 μg of lipid v. 100–150 μg in 3–5 mg of lipid injected in our 3-hour experiments), the amount of free peroxidase brought into circulation must have been considerable even before any plasma-induced enzyme release had occurred. In our experiments latency at the time of injection was better than 90% and, in addition, much lower concentrations of enzyme were used. Intravenously administered free peroxidase is partially recovered in the hepatocytes, provided that sufficiently high enzyme concentrations are injected (Wisse *et al.*,

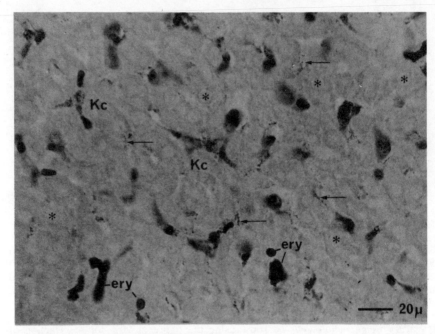

Figure 5 Bright-field light micrograph of rat liver 1 hour after intravenous injection of peroxidase-containing liposomes. A 20 μm Vibratome-section of 40 seconds perfusion-fixed liver was incubated for the demonstration of peroxidase activity. Reaction product can be observed in Kupffer (stellate) cells (Kc) and in the endothelial lining of the sinusoids (arrows). The nuclei of parenchymal cells show up as lighter discs (asterisks). Unstained section. ery = erythrocytes. $\times$ 465

1976). It would seem possible, therefore, that the appearance of peroxidase activity in the parenchymal cells, as observed by Wisse *et al.* (1976) after injection of, supposedly, liposome-entrapped enzyme is due to uptake by the parenchymal cells of no-longer entrapped enzyme. By electron microscopy it becomes clear that both Kupffer cells and endothelial cells are involved in the uptake of entrapped peroxidase. The distribution between these two cell types has been elucidated thoroughly by Wisse (1972). Figure 6 shows a low-magnification electron micrograph of the liver of a rat 3 hours after intravenous administration of 100 μg of horseradish peroxidase entrapped in 3.0 mg of liposomes with the same composition as in the experiment of Figure 5. No exogenous enzyme activity is found over the hepatocytes. At higher magnifications (Figure 7) it is clear that the peroxidase reaction products in both endothelial (7A) and Kupffer (7B) cells are confined to phagosomes and lysosomes. The cells shown in Figure 7 are from a liver fixed 1 hour after injection of 31 μg peroxidase entrapped in 5 mg of liposomes. No liposomal structures can be recognized in any of the

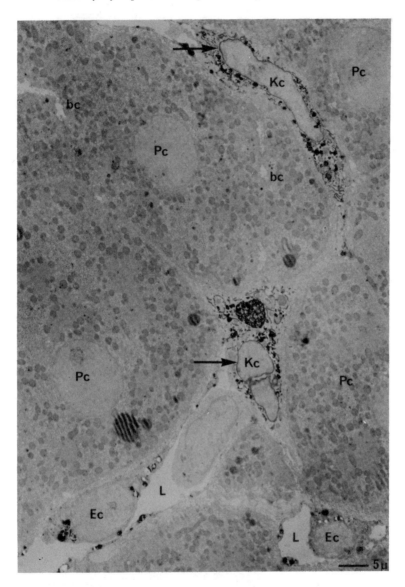

Figure 6 Low magnification electron micrograph of liver 3 hours after injection of peroxidase-containing liposomes. Exogenous peroxidase activity is shown in endothelial (Ec) and Kupffer cells (Kc), 3 hours after injection of 100 μg horseradish peroxidase entrapped in liposomes. Parenchymal cells (Pc) are devoid of peroxidatic activity. Kupffer cells also show specific staining for endogenous peroxidase activity in endoplasmic reticulum and nuclear envelop (arrows). L =lumen of the sinusoid; bc = bile canaliculus, × 1700

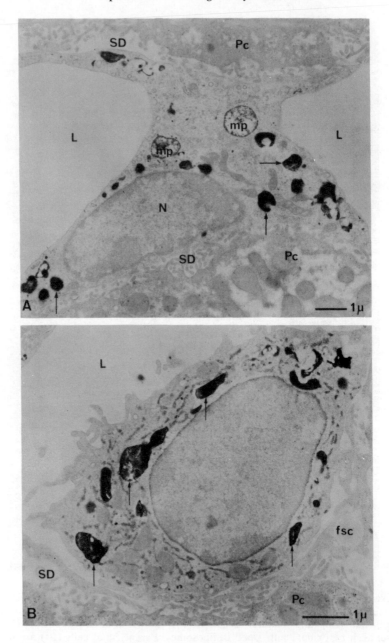

Figure 7 Endothelial and Kupffer cell 1 hour after injection of 30 μg liposome-entrapped horseradish peroxidase. A. Endothelial cell, devoid of endogenous peroxidatic activity showing reaction product in macropinocytic vesicles (mp) and more homogeneous dense bodies (arrows). L = lumen of the sinusoid, SD = space of Disse, Pc = parenchymal cell, N = nucleus of the endothelial cell, × 8,800. B.

preparations. However, this should not be taken as evidence that the peroxidase does not enter the cell entrapped in liposomes. It has become apparent in our studies that the regular tissue fixation and staining procedures (glutaraldehyde followed by osmium tetroxide and staining with lead hydroxide) are inadequate to visualize the liposomal structures, particularly if they are prepared from the moderately unsaturated egg lecithin. Methods to visualize liposomes and entrapped material simultaneously, and thus subsequent uptake by the cell, are currently under investigation. As pointed out in the introduction we believe that the observation of liposome-like structures within cells without additional evidence of their liposomal character should be interpreted with great restraint on account of the possibility of artefacts such as glutaraldehyde-induced myelin figures.

The discrepancies between the fate of the envelope material of the liposome and the entrapped protein described above, in addition to the high lecithin uptake by the parenchymal cells, are highly suggestive of a process in which the liposomes are affected by blood components in such a way that they lose their ability to firmly retain entrapped substances and become structurally modified allowing the liposomal lecithin to be taken up by the hepatocytes.

5. RELEASE OF LIPOSOME-ENTRAPPED COMPOUNDS DURING INCUBATION WITH PLASMA OR PLASMA CONSTITUENTS

Direct evidence of the inability of lecithin liposomes to retain entrapped substances was reported by us recently (Zborowski *et al.*, 1977). Both sucrose and inulin were found to leak from liposomes when incubated with whole blood or plasma at 37 °C (Figure 8). Also compounds with high molecular weight, such as [^{125}I]albumin, were readily released from liposomes when incubated for 30 minutes or shorter with plasma (Figure 9). It is conceivable that the liposomal membrane becomes slightly modified by the incorporation of plasma proteins (Kimelberg, 1976b) causing an increase in permeability but leaving the gross morphology of the liposome unchanged. It would seem that under those conditions increased rates of leakage would be limited to relatively low molecular weight compounds (Sweet and Zull, 1969; Kimelberg and Papahadjopoulos, 1971). The release of high molecular weight substances such as albumin suggests,

---

Kupffer cell from the same liver. Both endogenous and exogenous peroxidatic activity can be seen. Horseradish peroxidase reaction product is present in dense bodies (arrows) and the nuclear envelop and endoplasmic reticulum show peroxidase staining which can be used as a specific staining for Kupffer cells. L = lumen of the sinusoid, SD = space of Disse, fsc = process of fat-storing cell, Pc = parenchymal cell, × 12,700

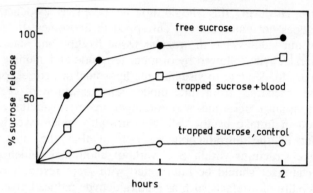

Figure 8 Leakage of [^{14}C]sucrose from liposomes in presence of rat blood. [^{14}C]sucrose was encapsulated in liposomes consisting of egg lecithin and phosphatidic acid (molar ratio 96 : 4). Liposomes were not sonicated and non-entrapped sucrose was removed by dialysis. Release of [^{14}C]sucrose at 37 °C was measured by dialysis as described before (Zborowski *et al.*, 1977). Filled circles, release of free non-entrapped sucrose; open circles, release of liposome-entrapped sucrose (control); squares, release of liposome-entrapped sucrose in presence of blood

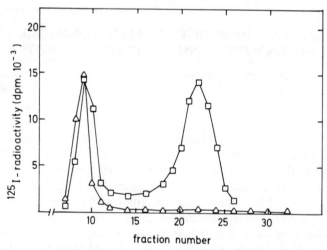

Figure 9 Release of [^{125}I]albumin from liposomes induced by incubation with rat plasma. Liposomes consisting of lecithin, cholesterol, and dicetylphosphate (7 : 2 : 1) and containing [^{125}I]albumin (12 μg equal to 72,000 cpm per μmol phospholipid) were prepared via gel filtration on Sepharose-4B. 2.5 μmol (P-lipid) in 1.0 ml NaCl/Tris were incubated with 1.0 ml rat plasma for 30 minutes at 37 °C. After incubation the mixture was rechromatographed on Sepharose-4B to separate released albumin from liposomes and 4-ml fractions were assayed for radioactivity. △——△ control liposomes without incubation. □——□ liposomes incubated with plasma

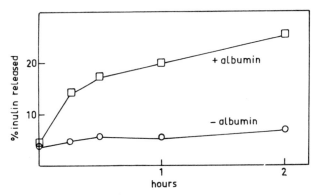

Figure 10   Release of [³H]inulin from liposomes in the presence of serum albumin. Liposomes consisting of lecithin and containing [³H]inulin were incubated at 37 °C in the presence or absence of bovine serum albumin (30 mg/ml). At the times indicated samples were taken and centrifuged in Amicon CF50 filter cones. The per cent of total radioactivity recovered in the filtrate is plotted against time. Circles, without albumin. Squares, in the presence of albumin

however, that more than superficial damage is done to the liposome. This consideration led us to search for a mechanism which might bring about rigorous stripping of bilayer lipid from the liposomes virtually causing the particle to fall apart.

The first plasma constituent we investigated for such properties was albumin (Zborowski *et al.*, 1977). We found that bovine serum albumin at physiological concentrations was able to bring about leakage of sucrose and inulin from liposomes of the same order of magnitude as that caused by whole blood or plasma (Figure 10). Kimelberg (1976a) found less than 1% per hour release of methotrexate from positively charged liposomes in the presence of high albumin concentrations. It should be understood, however, that electrostatic interaction between the negatively charged drug and the positively charged liposome may obscure considerable permeability increases of the liposomal membranes due to a drug–lipid association not based on entrapment.

When liposomes containing radioactive lecithin were incubated with bovine serum albumin, we observed that transfer of lecithin to the albumin had taken place as demonstrated by the separation of liposomes and albumin on Sepharose columns (Figure 11). Up to one molecule of lecithin could be transferred per molecule of albumin and this transfer was shown to be reversible. The lecithin–albumin complex thus formed might be of the type obtained by Jonas by means of incubation of albumin with Celite-adsorbed lecithin (Jonas, 1975; Jonas, 1976). When similar experiments were done with plasma rather than albumin solutions we found, upon gel filtration of the incubation mixture, that the bulk of the radioactivity

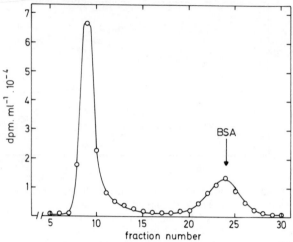

Figure 11 Formation of a complex between lecithin and albumin. Sonicated liposomes prepared from radioactive lecithin (2.8 μmol; 1.2×10^6 dpm) and isolated from the void-volume fractions of a Sepharose-4B column were incubated at 37 °C with bovine serum albumin (30 mg/ml). After 2 hours the incubation mixture was applied on the same Sepharose column as was used for preparation of the liposomes and eluted with NaCl/Tris. Fractions of 3.0 ml were collected. The arrow indicates the volume in which the authentic bovine serum albumin elutes from the column

released by the liposomes was not associated with the albumin but rather with a compound of higher molecular weight (Figure 12). This component was shown to float in a KBr solution of density 1.23 and to cochromatograph on Ultrogel AcA 34 with a sample of authentic monkey high density lipoproteins (HDL). Immunoelectrophoresis unequivocally demonstrated the main lecithin-binding component to be the high density lipoprotein (Figure 13). Some binding of lecithin to another plasma component, presumably low density lipoprotein, was also shown to occur (fraction nos. 17–20). Radioactivity recovered in the albumin fractions (nos. 34–39) invariably appeared to consist of free fatty acid released from the [^{14}C]linoleic-acid-labelled lecithin as a result of either spontaneous or phospholipase–A–induced (Paysant *et al.*, 1969) hydrolysis.

Incubation of the pure HDL with liposomes showed that not only is phospholipid transferred from liposomes to HDL but that protein is transferred from the lipoprotein to the liposomes as well. This suggests that the lecithin which can still be recovered from the void volume of the Sepharose column after incubation with plasma does not by necessity represent the original liposomal population. The incorporation of some lipoprotein polypeptides must at least have altered the surface characteristics of the liposomes which may cause permeability changes and affect the uptake of

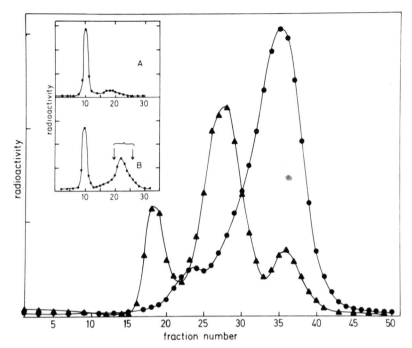

Figure 12 Gelfiltration of an incubation mixture of liposomes and plasma. Liposomes were prepared from [^{14}C–Me]lecithin, sonicated briefly and chromatographed on Bio–Gel A-15m (inset A). Peak fraction 10 (0.1 μmol) was incubated for 30 minutes at 37 °C with an equal volume of freshly isolated rat plasma. After rapid cooling the mixture was rechromatographed on the Bio–Gel column and fractions were again assayed for radioactivity (inset B). Fractions 19–26 were pooled and concentrated by ultrafiltration and chromatographed on Ultrogel AcA 34. Radioactivity (▲–▲) and A_{280nm} (•–•) were assayed in the fractions obtained. Authentic HDL elutes in fractions 25–30 and bovine serum albumin in fractions 34–38

such particles by cells. Alternatively, the incorporation of protein material may lead to even more drastic alterations in the liposomal structure. Tall and Small (1977) recently described the formation of discoid structures from liposomes in the presence of high density lipoproteins. Although the detailed architecture of these protein-lipid discs remains unknown it would seem unlikely that such structures are capable of trapping water-soluble components. We observed that radioactive lecithin and radioactive albumin remain associated with the void volume to similar extents following incubation of albumin-containing liposomes with plasma (compare Figures 9 and 12B). One would think, therefore, that also after incubation with plasma the bulk of the void-volume-associated lecithin still constitutes grossly intact liposomal structures.

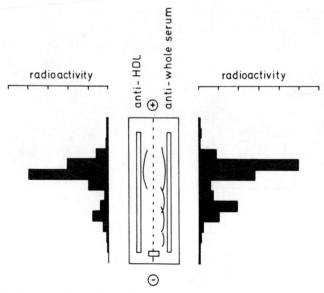

Figure 13 Immunoelectrophoresis of an incubation mixture of liposomes and plasma. Extensively sonicated liposomes (0.2 μmol) prepared from 2−[^{14}C]linoleoyl-lecithin (1.6×10^4 cpm/nmol) in 1.0 ml NaCl/Tris, were incubated with 1.0 ml monkey plasma. After 30 minutes at 37 °C the bulk of the mixture was chromatographed on Ultrogel AcA 34, revealing that only 15% liposomes were remaining. Samples of 20 μl were used for electrophoresis in 1% agarose on microscope slides. After electrophoresis rabbit antiserum was added against whole monkey serum (right-hand trough) or against human HDL (left-hand trough). Precipitation lines were allowed to form and left and right part of the gel were cut into small pieces which were assayed for radioactivity. The distribution of radioactivity along the direction of electrophoresis is presented for both halves of the gel

Table 3 Lack of reversibility of lecithin transfer from liposomes to high-density lipoproteins

Expt. no.	Lecithin added (μmol)	Lecithin transferred (μmol)	Specific radioactivity of liposomes (dpm/nmol P)	
			before incubation	after incubation
1	0.60	0.37	1580	1635
2	1.5	0.62	1169	1119

Liposomes consisting of [^{14}C]egg lecithin were sonicated for 3 minutes until an almost clear suspension was obtained. Two ml of such liposomes (0.6 or 1.5 μmol in two different experiments) were incubated for 30 minutes at 37 °C with an equal volume of rat plasma. After rapid cooling the mixture was subjected to gel filtration on Ultrogel AcA34. Remaining liposomes or vesicles were recovered in the void volume and specific radioactivity of the peak void-volume fraction was determined. The amount of lecithin transferred to HDL was measured from the radioactivity peak eluting from the column with the HDL (compare Figure 12)

The transfer of phospholipid from liposomes to HDL appears to be a one-way process. In other words, transfer of radioactive lecithin is not the result of an exchange process between the liposomal and the HDL-associated lecithin. This is indicated by our observation that the specific radioactivity of the lecithin which is recovered in the void volume of the Sepharose column after incubation with plasma remains constant (Table 3).

Our results show that plasma has the capacity to degrade liposomes extensively, mainly as a result of massive transfer of the liposomal lecithin to the plasma high density lipoproteins, causing the release of low as well as high molecular weight liposome-entrapped substances.

We have not yet obtained direct evidence that the phenomena described here also occur *in vivo* after intravenous injection of liposomes. We believe, however, that our experiments leave little doubt that several of the inconsistencies described in the literature concerning blood clearance and cellular uptake of liposome-entrapped compounds find their origin in limited stability of liposomes in circulating blood.

The experiments described in these sections also emphasize that lecithin is probably of as little use as a marker of liposomes in the circulation as cholesterol which is subject to rapid exchange with cholesterol pools of lipoproteins and cell membranes.

6   THE FATE OF HDL-BOUND LECITHIN

The question, of course, arises what will happen to the liposomal lecithin once it has become associated with the HDL. The appearance of radioactive lecithin from liposomes in the parenchymal cells of the liver (Table 2) suggests that the uptake mechanism possibly involves the HDL particle. Uptake of the intact liposome can be excluded on the basis of the virtual lack of uptake by the parenchymal cells of liposome-entrapped albumin (Figure 4) or horseradish peroxidase (Figures 5 and 6). The HDL particles (mol. wt. $1.75–3.6 \times 10^5$ and diameter 75–200 Å) (Eisenberg and Levy, 1975) have a sufficiently small size to enter the space of Disse through the fenestrated endothelium (Wisse, 1970) thus allowing the injected lecithin relatively easy access to the hepatocytes. We are currently investigating the mechanism of lecithin uptake by the liver from [^{14}C]lecithin–HDL complexes both *in vivo* and in perfused liver.

In view of the relatively long half-life of ^{125}I–labelled HDL in the circulation (Roheim *et al.*, 1971) we favour at present an uptake mechanism in which, following interaction of the HDL particle with the plasma membrane of the hepatocyte, only the lecithin or a portion of it is transferred to the cell. In this case uptake is presumably achieved not by means of endocytosis but rather by a fusion-like mechanism in which the lecithin becomes part of the plasma membrane. Our observation that the lecithin taken up by the liver *in vivo* is recovered mostly in intact form, i.e. not

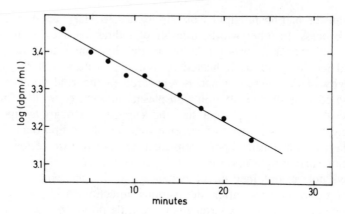

Figure 14 Clearance of HDL-associated [14C]lecithin from a liver perfusate. 14C-labelled HDL was prepared by incubating [14C]lecithin liposomes with rat plasma and subsequent chromatography on Ultrogel AcA 34. The radioactive HDL was added to 100 ml Hank's balanced salt solution containing 1 g of glucose per litre which was used to perfuse the liver of a rat in closed system. The oxygenated perfusate was recirculated for 30 minutes at 37 °C and at the times indicated 1.0-ml samples of perfusate were assayed for radioactivity

hydrolysed, (see Section 3, this chapter) is in agreement with this view because a considerable proportion of the injected lecithin is taken up by the parenchymal cells and would thus negatively influence the overall proportion of water-soluble product formed in the whole liver (Table 1).

Direct evidence of the uptake of HDL-associated lecithin by the liver was found when we perfused a rat liver with a balanced salt solution containing the HDL–[14C]lecithin complex obtained by incubation of liposomes with plasma followed by gel filtration on Bio-Gel and Ultrogel columns. Figure. 14 shows the clearance of [14C]lecithin radioactivity from the perfusate. A half-life of 25 minutes can be calculated for the radioactivity in the perfusate. Nearly all radioactivity recovered from the liver after the perfusion was made up by lecithin, in agreement with the line of thought presented in the previous paragraphs. Consequently, if there is any contribution of the Kupffer cells in the uptake process it will presumably be moderate and the uptake by any cell type will probably not involve endocytosis but rather a direct transfer of phospholipid to the cell membrane.

We are currently continuing our search for a method to construct liposomes with a lipid composition adequate to resist attacks from blood constituents, with dimensions suitable to overcome the barrier of fenestrated endothelial cells and yet large enough to contain sizeable amounts of trapped material. With respect to the lipid composition a host of possibilities seems to be at hand, such as varying surface charge, phospholipid classes, and additions such as cholesterol or glycolipids. The relatively low rate of clearance we found for negatively charged liposomes (Figure 2) and the relatively low proportion of lecithin recovered in the hepatocytes from negative liposomes (Table 1) could be suggestive of a limited attack of the lipoproteins on liposomes with negative surface charge. The compromise between 'small enough' and 'large enough' can probably be found in the modification by Kremer *et al.* (1977) of the method of Batzri and Korn (1973). With this method of injecting ethanol solutions of lipids in a large volume of buffer single-bilayer vesicles of controlled diameter can be prepared depending on rate of injection and lipid concentration.

An important question to be answered is, obviously, whether a hepatocyte, once a liposome gets access to it, will be capable of taking up the liposome. In the following section some preliminary results will be presented, suggesting that the liver parenchymal cell is, indeed, able to do so.

7. UPTAKE OF LIPOSOMES AND ENTRAPPED ALBUMIN BY ISOLATED HEPATOCYTES IN MAINTENANCE CULTURE

Several investigations during the past few years have dealt with the uptake of liposomes and liposome-associated substances by isolated cells. Among the cell types used are mouse 3T3 and SV 3T3 cells (Papahadjopoulos *et al.*, 1974a,b; Poste and Papahadjopoulos, 1976), HeLa cells (Magee *et al.*, 1974; Gregoriadis and Neerunjun, 1975; Gregoriadis, 1975), macrophages (Gregoriadis and Buckland, 1973), leucocytes (Weissmann *et al.*, 1975), fibroblasts (Gregoriadis and Neerunjun, 1975; Gregoriadis, 1975; Weissmann *et al.*, 1975; Cohen *et al.*, 1976; Roerdink *et al.*, 1976), hamster V79 cells (Huang and Pagano, 1975), and amoebae (Batzri and Korn, 1975). No attempt was made thus far to introduce liposomes or entrapped substances into isolated liver cells. In view of the considerations outlined in the preceding section we thought it relevant to investigate the capacity of liver parenchymal cells to take up liposomes.

Hepatocytes were isolated according to the method of Berry and Friend (1969) and brought into maintenance culture following the procedure described by Geelen and Gibson (1976). The cells were incubated with multilamellar liposomes or unilamellar vesicles composed of [^{14}C]lecithin, cholesterol, and either dicetylphosphate or stearylamine (molar ratio 7 : 2 : 1) to confer negative or positive charge. Figure 15 shows that the cells take up radioactivity from all four types of liposomes with a clear preference for unilamellar vesicles as compared to the multilamellar liposomes. For both vesicles and liposomes a negative charge seems to be preferred although the difference is small.

The proportion of phospholipid taken up may seem low (maximally even less than 1% of the amount added to the cells) but a simple calculation

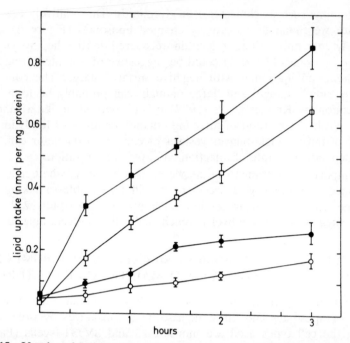

Figure 15 Uptake of lecithin from liposomes and unilamellar vesicles by isolated hepatocytes in maintenance culture. Hepatocytes, isolated by collagenase perfusion of rat livers, as described by Berry and Friend (1969) were suspected in Hams F–12 culture medium supplemented with 15% foetal calf serum and buffered with 14.5 mM bicarbonate and 12.5 mM MES and TES. Conditions for plating and culturing were as described by Geelen and Gibson (1976). After 4 hours when complete adhesion of the cells to the bottom of the culture dish was achieved the medium was removed and the cells were washed three times with 0.9% NaCl at 37 °C. Liposomes were prepared from [^{14}C]egg lecithin, cholesterol, and dicetylphosphate or stearylamine in a molar ratio 7 : 2 : 1. After sonication liposomes were fractionated on Sepharose-4B in a void-volume fraction containing multilamellar liposomes and a fraction containing unilamellar vesicles. 0.5 μmol of liposomes were fractionated on Sepharose-4B in a void-volume fraction containing ($1.3–1.5 \times 10^6$ cells). For each time four to seven dishes were used. At the time indicated the medium containing the liposomes was removed and the cells were washed four times with 0.9% NaCl. Then the cells were detached from the dish and used for protein and radioactivity assays. Filled symbols, negatively charged particles; open symbols, positively charged particles; circles, multilamellar liposomes; squares, unilamellar vesicles

based upon the presence of 2,700 phospholipid molecules in a single-bilayer vesicle (Papahadjopoulos and Kimelberg, 1973) tells us that, per cell, several hundreds of thousands of vesicles are taken up in 3 hours. This is the same order of magnitude as found by others with other types of cells (Martin and McDonald, 1974; Papahadjopoulos *et al.*, 1975).

From results such as those presented in Figure 15 it is impossible to conclude whether the liposomes are actually internalized by the cells, either by endocytosis or fusion, or remain associated with the cells on the outer surface of the plasma membranes. Such association without internalization may withstand the extensive washing procedures applied. Solid evidence of actual uptake can be provided by morphological examination, by studying the effects of liposome-entrapped compounds interfering with intracellular metabolism or by demonstrating metabolic conversion of an entrapped compound. The problems encountered with the morphological visualization of liposomal structures have been discussed in previous sections. Obviously, when studying the intracellular activity or conversion of a liposome-encaptured compound it should be unequivocally established that the observed effect is absent in case the compound is added in free, uncaptured form, which is not always simple.

We have attempted to show that at least some of the cell-associated liposomes become internalized by demonstrating that entrapped [^{125}I]albumin is partly hydrolysed after it becomes associated with the cell (Table 4). After a 3–hour incubation of parenchymal cells with liposomes or vesicles containing [^{125}I]albumin, approximately 10% of the ^{125}I-radioactivity associated with the cells was recovered as TCA-soluble material, i.e. as low molecular weight degradation products of the albumin. No significant uptake of radioactivity was observed when the cells were incubated with non-entrapped [^{125}I]albumin. When attempting to relate the 10% TCA-soluble material with the proportion of cell-associated liposomes actually being internalized it should be realized that this is a minimal figure. Part of the degraded, TCA-soluble, material may have been released by the cells during the incubation. Because the proportion of added liposome-entrapped albumin taken up is very low it is impossible to assess in a reliable way any increase in the TCA-soluble material in the incubation medium outside the cell. As little as 1% TCA-soluble material in the original albumin preparation would be sufficient to obscure any additional release of TCA-soluble products from the cells. Various approaches are currently being followed in our laboratory to substantiate these observations and to establish the mechanisms of uptake of the liposomes by hepatocytes as well as other cell types. In addition to the mechanism of endocytosis which is suggested by the partial degradation of internalized albumin there may be significant contribution by a fusion process which would release the albumin in the cytoplasm. Such a mechanism might also contribute to the figure of TCA-soluble radioactivity in Table 4 being only 10%.

Influence of serum factors such as described in previous sections and by others (Tyrrell *et al.*, 1977) was also observed with the system of parenchymal cells in maintenance culture. The experiments described in Figure

Table 4 Uptake of liposome-entrapped [^{125}I]albumin by parenchymal cells in maintenance culture

Albumin added	Radioactivity (cpm)		fraction
	TCA-precipitable	TCA-soluble	TCA-soluble (%)
Trapped in liposomes	2387	310	8.1
Trapped in vesicles	1659	255	13.3
Non-entrapped	70	59	—

^{125}I-labelled bovine serum albumin was entrapped in sonicated multilamellar liposomes or unilamellar vesicles consisting of egg lecithin, cholesterol, and dicetylphosphate ($7:2:1$) (28.4 and 5.2 μg albumin/μmol lecithin, respectively). After complete adhesion of the cells (see legend to Figure 15 for further details) albumin-containing liposomes (0.3 μmol/10^6 cells) or vesicles (0.1 μmol/10^6 cell) were added to the cells in culture medium containing 15% foetal calf serum. An equivalent amount of free [^{125}I]albumin was added to a control plate. Four hours after addition of the liposomes or albumin the medium was removed and the cells were washed five times with ice-cold 0.9% NaCl. The cells were scraped from the plates and homogenized by sonication. Proteins were precipitated with trichloroacetic acid (TCA, 7.5% final concentration). The precipitates were washed with 7.5% TCA. Supernatants and precipitates were assayed for radioactivity.

15 were all done in the presence of 15% foetal calf serum, i.e. in the regular culture medium for the cells. When the serum was omitted considerably higher rates of uptake of [^{14}C]lecithin from liposomes was observed (Figure 16). This was found for positively as well as negatively charged liposomes or vesicles. We can only speculate so far as to what causes this large

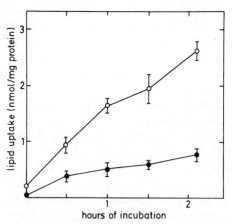

Figure 16 Serum effect on uptake of unilamellar vesicles by hepatocytes in maintenance culture. Hepatocytes were isolated and cultured as described in the legend to Figure 15. Negatively charged unilamellar vesicles were prepared from lecithin, cholesterol, and dicetylphosphate ($7:2:1$). The vesicles were added either in complete culture medium (●) or in medium without foetal calf serum (○). Each point is the average of four to six measurements (i.e. dishes) with the vertical bars representing the standard error of the mean

increase in lecithin uptake. In view of our results on lecithin transfer to HDL in the presence of plasma it is tempting to speculate that in the presence of serum the liposomes donate their lecithin to the HDL. Presumably, the resulting radioactive HDL particle is relatively slowly taken up by the hepatocytes as compared to the rapid uptake of the larger liposomes by Kupffer and endothelial cells. This would mean that the uptake found in the absence of serum would more accurately represent the capacity of the parenchymal cells to take up liposomes than the rates found in the presence of serum. Alternatively, the additional uptake found in the absence of serum may merely represent liposomes associated with the outside of the cell. The presence of serum would then, supposedly, prevent such adhesion, presumably by means of electrostatic effects of serum proteins (Tyrrell *et al.*, 1977). It remains to be established which of the two possibilities mentioned reflects the actual situation.

8. CONCLUDING REMARKS

Experimental evidence obtained by us during the last two years and compiled in this chapter demonstrated that liposomes containing lecithins are not as stable in the bloodstream as suggested by several investigators when using such lipid spherules as intravenous carriers of drugs or other compounds. Liposomes readily lose entrapped substances such as sucrose, inulin or albumin when exposed to blood plasma. Our results strongly suggest that such loss is caused by disintegration of the liposomal structure as a result of massive one-way transfer of lecithins from liposomes to plasma high density lipoproteins

Liposomal lecithin, when injected intravenously, is cleared from the circulation in much the same way as found by others for liposome-entrapped substances, i.e. a very rapid initial phase followed by a much slower second phase. Such lecithin as well as entrapped material is recovered for the greater part in the liver. Our electron microscopical observations on liposome-entrapped horseradish peroxidase suggest that the rapid initial uptake by the liver has to be ascribed to endocytic activity of both Kupffer and endothelial cells of the liver. Presumably, these cells rapidly phagocytize a considerable proportion of the injected enzyme-containing liposomes, reflecting the rapid initial rate of clearance, before the destructive action of the lipoproteins on the liposomes has been completed. On the other hand, it seems that this phagocytic activity does not proceed rapidly enough to prevent substantial transfer of lecithin to high-density lipoproteins with a concomitant destruction of the liposomes and release of the entrapped peroxidase. After it has been released, the enzyme is also taken up by Kupffer and endothelial cells as is demonstrated by the uptake pattern of injected non-entrapped, enzyme. Other entrapped compounds may, obviously, display a different behaviour after being released from the liposomes and follow a different pattern of tissue and cell-type distribution. As opposed to the peroxidase activity, approximately half of the liposomal lecithin recovered in the liver is found in the hepatocytes. We are tempted to speculate that most of the lecithin uptake by the hepatocytes is mediated by the high density lipoproteins and that the slow second phase of clearance from the blood primarily reflects this uptake. This is in line with the observation that the appearance of lecithin label in the hepatocytes is clearly lagging behind that in whole liver. The high density lipoproteins are sufficiently small to have access to the parenchymal cells through the open fenestrations in the endothelial lining of the sinusoids and can thus carry the lecithin within reach of the hepatocytes. Presumably, the endothelial fenestrations function as a filter to keep the much larger liposomes away from the hepatocytes.

Experiments with cultured hepatocytes suggest that these cells do possess the ability to take up liposomes as well as entrapped compounds. Thus, liposome-entrapped compounds may be expected to enter parenchymal cells after intravenous injection, provided that the liposomes can withstand the action of the plasma lipoproteins and, simultaneously, are small enough to pass the lining of endothelial cells.

Better resistance to the destructive action of lipoproteins may be found by variation of the lipid composition of the liposome. Recent developments in liposome research may provide a method to prepare liposomes of sufficiently small diameter to allow passage through the endothelial fenestrations and yet large enough to allow reasonable trapping efficiency.

Our work emphasizes the importance of a thorough study of factors in blood as well as in culture media influencing liposomal integrity or permeability of liposomal membranes to the benefit of all the work on applications of liposomes in biological systems.

ACKNOWLEDGEMENTS

Part of these investigations were carried out under the auspices of the Netherlands Foundation for Medical Research (FUNGO) with financial support from the Netherlands Organization for the Advancement of Pure Research (ZWO).

We thank Dr. Moseley Waite and Dr. Lawrence Rudel from the Bowman Gray School of Medicine in Winston-Salem, N.C., in whose laboratories some of the experiments described in this chapter were carried out, for stimulating discussions and for their kind hospitality.

We also gratefully acknowledge the cooperation in various aspects of our investigations of Dr. John Parks, Henriette Morselt, Bert Dontje, Hans van der Meulen, and Ron Tomasini. The assistance of Karin van Wijk in the preparation of the manuscript is also thankfully acknowledged.

REFERENCES

Arakawa, E., Imai, Y., Kabayashi, H., Okumura, K. and Sezaki, H. (1975). *Chem. Pharm. Bull.*, **23**, 2218–2222.

Batzri, S. and Korn, E. D. (1973). *Biochim. Biophys. Acta*, **298**, 1015–1019.

Batzri, S. and Korn, E. D. (1975). *J. Cell Biol.*, **66**, 621–634.

Berry, M. N. and Friend, D. S. (1969). *J. Cell Biol.*, **43**, 506–520.

Black, C. D. V. and Gregoriadis, G. (1974). *Biochem. Soc. Trans.*, **2**, 869–871.

Black, C. D. V. and Gregoriadis, G. (1976). *Biochem. Soc. Trans.*, **4**, 253–256.

Bligh, E. G. and Dyer, W. J. (1959). *Can. J. Biochem. Physiol.*, **37**, 911–917.

Bocci, V. (1969). *Ital. J. Biochem.*, **18**, 346–375.

Buckland, R. A. and Gregoriadis, G. (1973). *Biochem. Soc. Trans.*, **1**, 733–734.

Caride, V. J., Taylor, W., Cramer, J. A. and Gottschalk, A. (1976). *J. Nuclear Med.*, **17**, 1067–1072.

Cohen, C. M., Weissmann, G., Hoffstein, S., Awasthi, Y. C. and Srivastava, S. K. (1976). *Biochemistry*, **15**, 452–460.

Colley, C. M. and Ryman, B. E. (1974). *Biochem. Soc. Trans.*, **2**, 871–872.

Colley, C. M. and Ryman, B. E. (1975). *Biochem. Soc. Trans.*, **3**, 157–159.

Cooper, R. A. (1970). *Semin. Hematol.*, **7**, 296–322.

Dapergolas, G., Neerunjun, E. D. and Gregoriadis, G. (1976). *FEBS Lett.*, **63**, 235–239.

De Barsy, T., Devos, P. and Van Hoof, F. (1976). *Lab. Invest.*, **34**, 273–282.

Eisenberg, S. and Levy, R. I. (1975). In *Advances in Lipid Research*, Vol. **13**, (R. Paoletti, and D. Kritchevsky, eds.), pp. 1–89, Academic, Press, New York.

Geelen, M. J. H. and Gibson, D. M. (1976). In *Use of Isolated Liver Cells and Kidney Tubules in Metabolic Studies* (J. M. Tager, H. D. Söling and J. R. Williamson, eds.), North-Holland Publishing Company, Amsterdam.

Gregoriadis, G. (1973). *FEBS Lett.*, **36**, 292–296.

Gregoriadis, G. (1975). *Biochem. Soc. Trans.*, **3**, 613–618.

Gregoriadis, G. (1976a). *New Eng. J. Med.*, **295**, 704–710.

Gregoriadis, G. (1976b). *New Eng. J. Med.*, **296**, 765–770.

Gregoriadis, G. and Allison, A. C. (1974). *FEBS Lett.*, **45**, 71–74.

Gregoriadis, G. and Buckland, R. A. (1973). *Nature*, **244**, 170–172.

Gregoriadis, G. and Neerunjun, E. D. (1974). *Eur. J. Biochem.*, **47**, 179–185.

Gregoriadis, G. and Neerunjun, E. D. (1975). *Biochem. Biophys. Res. Commun.*, **65**, 537–544.

Gregoriadis, G. and Ryman, B. E. (1971). *Biochem. J.*, **124**, 58.

Gregoriadis, G. and Ryman, B. E. (1972a). *Eur. J. Biochem.*, **24**, 485–491.

Gregoriadis, G. and Ryman, B. E. (1972b). *Biochem. J.*, **129**, 123–133.

Gregoriadis, G., Putman, D., Louis, L. and Neerunjun, D. (1974). *Biochem. J.*, **140**, 223–230.

Gurd, F. R. N. (1960). In *Lipid Chemistry*, pp. 260–325 (D. J. Hanahan, ed.), John Wiley, New York.

Heath, T. D., Edwards, D. C. and Ryman, B. E. (1976). *Biochem. Soc. Trans.*, **4**, 129–133.

Huang, L. and Pagano, R. E. (1975). *J. Cell Biol.*, **67**, 38–48.

Jonah, M. M., Cerny, E. A. and Rahman, Y.-E. (1975). *Biochim. Biophys. Acta*, **401**, 336–348.

Jonas, A. (1976). *Biochim. Biophys. Acta*, **427**, 325–336.

Jonas, A. (1975). *Biochem. Biophys. Res. Commun.*, **64**, 1003–1008.

Juliano, R. L. and Stamp, D. (1975). *Biochem. Biophys. Res. Commun.*, **63**, 651–658.

Kimelberg, H. K. (1976a). *Biochim. Biophys. Acta,* **448**, 531–550.

Kimelberg, H. K. (1976b). *Molec. Cell Biochem.,* **10**, 171–190.

Kimelberg, H. K. and Papahadjopoulos, D. (1971). *Biochim. Biophys. Acta,* **233**, 805–809.

Kimelberg, H. K., Mayhew, E. and Paphadjopoulos, D. (1975). *Life Sci.,* **17**, 715–724.

Kimelberg, H. K., Tracey, T. F., Biddlecome, S. M. and Bourke, R. S. (1976). *Cancer Res.,* **36**, 2949–2957.

Kremer, J. M. H., Van den Esker, M. W. J., Pethmamanoharan, C. and Wiersema, P. H. (1977). *Biochemistry,* **16**, 3932–3935.

Magee, W. E., Goff, C. W., Schoknecht, J., Smith, M. D. and Cherian, K. (1974). *J. Cell Biol.,* **63**, 492–504.

Martin, F. and MacDonald, R. (1974). *Nature,* **252**, 161–163.

McDougall, I. R., Dunnick, J. K., McNamee, M. G. and Kriss, J. P. (1974). *Proc. Nat. Acad. Sci. USA,* **71**, 3487–3491.

Nelson, G. L. (1972). In *Blood Lipids and Lipoproteins: Quantitation, Composition and Metabolism,* (G. L. Nelson, ed.), pp. 317–386, J. Wiley & Sons Ltd., New York.

Papahadjopoulos, D. and Kimelberg, H. K. (1973). In *Progress in Surface Science,* Vol. **4**, part 2, p. 163. (S. G. Davidson, ed.), Pergamon Press, New York.

Papahadjopoulos, D., Poste, G. and Mayhew, E. (1974a). *Biochim. Biophys. Acta,* **363**, 404–418.

Papahadjopoulos, D., Mayhew, E., Poste, G., Smith, S. and Vail, W. J. (1974b). *Nature,* **252**, 163–166.

Papahadjopoulos, D., Poste, G. and Mayhew, E. (1975). *Biochem. Soc. Trans.,* **3**, 606–608.

Paysant, M., Bitran, M., Etienne, J. and Polonovski, J. (1969). *Bull. Soc. Chim. Biol.,* **51**, 863–873.

Poste, G. and Papahadjopoulos, D. (1976). *Proc. Nat. Acad. Sci. USA,* **73**, 1603–1607.

Rahman, Y.-E. and Wright, B. J. (1975). *J. Cell Biol.,* **65**, 112–122.

Rahman, Y.-E., Kisielseski, W. E. Buess, E. M. and Cerny, E. A. (1975). *Europ. J. Cancer,* **11**, 883–889.

Roerdink, F. H., Van Renswoude, A. J. B. M., Wielinga, B. Y., Kroon, A. M. and Scherphof, G. L. (1976). *J. Mol. Med.,* **1**, 257–263.

Roheim, P. S., Rachmilewitz, D., Stein, O. and Stein, Y. (1971). *Biochim. Biophys. Acta,* **248**, 315–329.

Segal, A. W., Wills, E. J., Richmond, J. E., Slavin, G., Black, C. D. V. and Gregoriadis, G. (1974). *Brit. J. Exp. Pathol.,* **55**, 320–327.

Steger, L. B. and Desnick, R. J. (1977). *Biochim. Biophys. Acta,* **464**, 530–546.

Stoffel, W. (1975). In *Methods in Enzymology Vol. XXXV,* pp. 533–541, (S. P. Colowick and N. O. Kaplan, eds.), Academic Press, New York.

Surolia, A. and Bachhawat, B. K. (1977). *Biochim. Biophys. Acta,* **497**, 760–765.

Sweet, C. and Zull, J. E. (1969). *Biochim. Biophys. Acta,* **173**, 94–103.

Tall, A. R. and Small, D. M. (1977). *Nature,* **265**, 163–164.

Tyrrell, D. A., Heath, T. D., Colley, C. M. and Ryman, B. E. (1976). *Biochim. Biophys. Acta,* **457**, 295–302.

Tyrrell, D. A., Richardson, V. J. and Ryman, B. E. (1977). *Biochim. Biophys. Acta,* **497**, 469–480.

Waite, M., Scherphof, G. L., Boshouwers, F. M. G. and Van Deenen, L. L. M. (1969). *J. Lipid Res.,* **10**, 411–420.

Wang, L. (1959). *Amer. J. Physiol.,* **196**, 188–192.

Weibel, E. R., Stäubli, W., Gnägi, H. R. and Hess, R. A. (1969). *J. Cell Biol.*, **42**, 68–91.

Weissmann, G., Bloomgarden, D., Kaplan, R., Cohen, C., Hoffstein, S., Collins, T., Gotlieb, A. and Nagle, D. (1975). *Proc. Nat. Acad. Sci. USA,* **72**, 88–92.

Wisse, E. (1970). *J. Ultrastruc. Res.,* **31**, 125–150.

Wisse, E. (1972). *J. Ultrastruc. Res.,* **38**, 528–562.

Wisse, E., Gregoriadis, G. and Daems, W. Th. (1976). In *The Reticuloendothelial System in Health and Disease: Functions and Characteristics* (S. M. Reichard, M. R. Escobar and H. Friedman, eds.), pp. 237–245, Plenum Publishing Corporation, New York.

Zborowski, J., Roerdink, F. and Scherphof, G. (1977). *Biochim. Biophys. Acta,* **497**, 183–191.

Liposomes in Biological Systems
Edited by G. Gregoriadis and A.C. Allison
©1980, John Wiley & Sons, Ltd.

CHAPTER 7

Effect of Antibodies Administered in Liposomes*

Thierry de BARSY† and François VAN HOOF

1. **Introduction**   211

2. **Liposomes bearing antibodies directed against a purified lysosomal enzyme**   212

3. **Liposomes coated with heat aggregated gamma globulins**   216

4. **Liposomes bearing antiviral antibodies**   217

    References   217

1. INTRODUCTION

Sessa and Weissmann (1968) called liposomes lipidic spherules composed of concentric bilayers (Bangham *et al.*, 1965; Bangham, 1968), in which different substances can be entrapped. This vector can be used for the introduction of drugs either directly into the cytosol of cells by fusion of the spherules with the plasma membrane, or into the lysosomal system by the mechanism of endocytosis (see Chapter 4). The advantage of the liposomes is to avoid immunological complications or interaction with blood components, and to direct material more specifically towards some types of cells. Moreover, in some instances, liposomes can induce fusion between cells or between intracellular organelles such as phagosomes and

*Original investigations reported in this work were supported by the Belgian Fonds de la Recherche Scientifique Médicale, and by the U.S. Public Health Service (Grant AM9235).
†Thierry de Barsy is Chercheur Qualifié of the Fonds National de la Recherche Scientifique.

lysosomes. The present chapter is devoted to the use of liposomes associated with antibodies. We will first comment on attempts to block the activity of a lysosomal enzyme by means of specific antibodies entrapped within liposomes. Experiments performed with liposomes covered by heat-aggregated immunoglobulins or bearing antiviral antibodies are then reported.

2. LIPOSOMES BEARING ANTIBODIES DIRECTED AGAINST A PURIFIED LYSOSOMAL ENZYME

In order to inhibit the acid α-glucosidase present in the lysosomes, antibodies directed against the purified human placental enzyme were prepared (de Barsy *et al.*, 1972) and entrapped into liposomes (de Barsy *et al.*, 1974, 1976; de Barsy, 1976). Liposomes were made of lecithin, cholesterol, and dicetyl phosphate, or lecithin, cholesterol, and

Table 1 Effect of intravenous administration to newborn rats of γ-globulins entrapped within liposomes. (Reproduced from de Barsy *et al.*, 1976, © 1976 US Canadian Division of the International Academy of Pathology)

Drug administration

Vol (ml)	Gamma globulins (mg) non-specific	specific	Interval before death	Gamma globulins present in the liver (mg)	Acid α-glucosidase measured on glycogen	maltose (milliunits per liver)
A						
0.4	0.6	—	48 minutes	0.20	72	35
0.4	0.6	—	90 minutes	0.22	67.5	36
0.4	—	0.8	50 minutes	0.21	33	32.5
0.4	—	0.8	45 minutes	0.17	57	37
B						
0.1	5.7	—	$7\frac{1}{2}$ hours	2.7	45	34.5
0.1	5.7	—	$7\frac{1}{2}$ hours	4.5	46	35.5
0.1	—	3.5	$7\frac{1}{2}$ hours	1.3	22	22.5
0.1	—	3.5	$7\frac{1}{2}$ hours	2.0	21	27

Liposomes are composed of lecithin, cholesterol, dicetylphosphate (molar ratio 4 : 2 : 1 (A); or of lecithin, cholesterol, stearylamine, with the same molar ratio (B). Gamma globulins were purified on DEAE–Sephadex A-50 (A), or by affinity chromatography (B). One mg of specific antibodies inhibits approximately 0.1 μunit of enzyme, when the activity is measured on glycogen. The effect of antibodies is much less pronounced if the enzymic activity is appreciated by hydrolysis of micromolecular substrate. (See Barsy *et al.*, 1972) stearylamine in a molar ratio of $4:2:1$. The entrapment of fluorescein-labelled antibodies was greatly influenced by the composition of the liposomes. If stearylamine was used instead of dicetyl phosphate in the preparation of the spherules, the amount of γ-globulins associated with the spherules was about 20 times higher. This difference can be explained, at least in part, by an electrostatic adsorption of the protein on the surface of the liposomes (Kataoka *et al.*, 1973). The intravenous administration of the negatively charged liposomes (made of lecithin, cholesterol, and dicetyl phosphate) to newborn rats was badly tolerated (Table 1). All animals died within $1\frac{1}{2}$ hours. The charge of the liposomes, the volume injected and/or the total amount of lipids may play a role in this dramatic effect. Positively charged liposomes containing a higher amount of proteins have been injected in a smaller volume. This preparation was well tolerated. Approximatively half of the total injected quantity of fluorescent γ-globulins was recovered in the liver (Table 1) and evidence for the intralysosomal localization of the spherules has been provided by ultrastructural analysis of the liver. Lipidic spherules were present both in reticuloendothelial and parenchymal cells but the timing of the uptake was different according to the type of cell. One hour after the injection the lipidic spherules were observed only in the sinusoidal spaces, in the

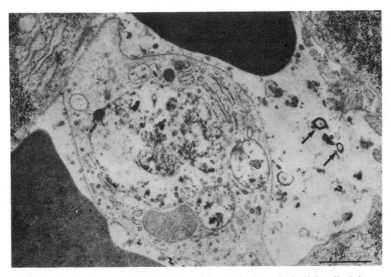

Figure 1   Liver of a newborn rat. Aspect of a reticuloendothelial cell, 1 hour after intravenous injection of liposomes made of lecithin, cholesterol and stearylamine in a molar ratio of $4:2:1$. The lipidic spherules contained specific antibodies directed against rat liver acid α-glucosidase. Vacuoles, bounded by a unit membrane, contain some osmiophilic material, which has the aspect of lipid debris. Free liposomes (arrows) are present in the sinusoidal space (RBC: red blood cell)

H

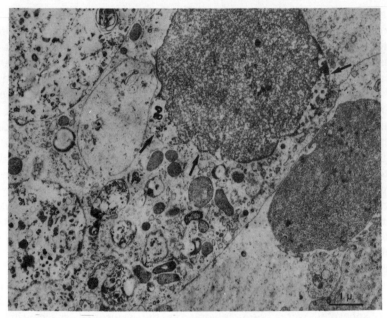

Figure 2 Same conditions as Figure 1. One of the digestive vacuoles (arrow) contains liposomes together with a partially digested cell, probably a reticulocyte

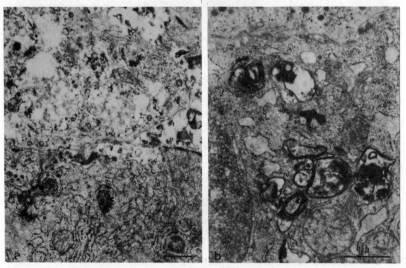

Figure 3 Liver of a newborn rat, $7\frac{1}{2}$ hours after administration of liposomes. The reticuloendothelaial cell (a), present at the upper part of the figure, is still swollen by huge vacuoles, containing fine granular material and lipidic debris. The general morphology of the hepatocytes is well preserved, but multilamellar lipidic material is easily recognizable in intracellular digestive vacuoles (b)

macrophages, and in the Kupffer cells, (Figures 1 and 2). In these cells, the liposomes were present within vacuoles delimited by a single membrane. Some of the spherules were partially disrupted and dispersed between large clear spaces. The parenchymal cells remained intact.

The morphological aspect of the liver $7\frac{1}{2}$ hours after the injection was entirely different (Figures 3 and 4). The reticuloendothelial cells were

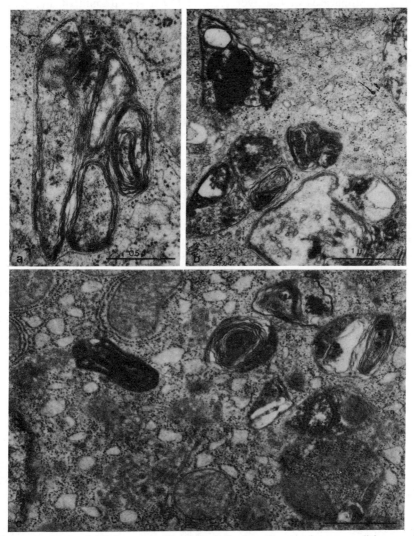

Figure 4 (a, b, c) Higher magnification of the hepatocytes (same conditions as in Figure 3). The lamellar structures considered as liposomes are present in digestive vacuoles with other cellular components as glycogen, mitochondria, and endoplasmic reticulum

distended by huge vacuoles, while in the hepatocytes, the lysosomal apparatus was only slightly enlarged by the presence of almost intact liposomes. Glycogen, mitochondria, and other cytoplasmic components were recognizable in these vacuoles together with liposomes that had preserved their regular multilamellar aspect. Dense bodies without lamellar structure were scarce. Despite the fact that liposomes were present in the lysosomal apparatus of the liver cells, and that the amount of antibodies, measured by their fluorescent labelling, was theoretically sufficient to inhibit completely the acid α-glucosidase activity, only 50% of the inhibition was measured in liver homogenates (Table 1). Accordingly, the glycogen content of the liver was not significantly different in treated animals from that in the controls.

3. LIPOSOMES COATED WITH HEAT AGGREGATED GAMMA GLOBULINS

Weissmann *et al.* (1975) proposed a sophisticated strategy to stimulate the endocytic process of the lysosomal system. These authors first showed that leucocytes take up immune precipitates in the presence of heat inactivated serum (Weissmann *et al.*, 1971), and that aggregated immunoglobulins are easily associated with liposomes by both electrostatic and hydrophobic interactions (Weissmann *et al.*, 1974). Liposomes loaded with horseradish peroxidase were coated with heat aggregated isologous IgM. Brought into contact with phagocytes of the smooth dogfish (*Mustellus canis*), these liposomes were endocytosed by the cells which acquired peroxidase-positive phagosomes. No morphological evidence of fusion between the plasma membrane and the liposomes could be found. The uptake at 30 °C of aggregated IgM-coated liposomes which contained horseradish peroxidase exceeded that of the free enzyme by 100-fold and was about twice as efficient as the uptake of horseradish peroxidase presented in uncoated liposomes or in liposomes coated with native IgM.

Cohen *et al.* (1976) tried to determine whether ligand–receptor interaction could engender the selective uptake by deficient cells of enzyme-laden liposomes. Liposomes containing highly purified hexosaminidase A were coated with aggregated human IgG in order to provide for ligand–receptor interaction with surface Fc receptors of human polymorphonuclear leucocytes (PMNs). PMNs were isolated from Tay–Sachs patients, genetically deficient in hexosaminidase A, and exposed to liposomes laden with the purified enzyme and coated with the heat aggregated IgG. The incorporation of enzyme in these cells was about four times higher than in experiments with uncoated liposomes, or with liposomes coated with native IgG which engage the Fc receptor with less avidity. The introduction of enzyme into PMNs was not due to an adsorption process of the liposomes on the cell surface. Indeed, the addition of cytochalasine B, which prevents the phagocytosis, blocked the uptake of the lipidic spherules. In addition, ultrastructural evidence for the fusion between the lysosomes and the endocytic vesicles which contained the liposomes was presented.

4. LIPOSOMES BEARING ANTIVIRAL ANTIBODIES

Magee and Miller (1972) showed that it is possible to protect cultured ML cells from Coxsackie A-21 virus infection by the use of liposomes containing human IgG with a high neutralizing titre. The lipid spherules were brought in contact with the cells, and the latter were rinsed before addition of the virus. The protective effect was obtained only with liposomes composed of sphingomyelin, cholesterol, and stearylamine, which attached to the cells almost instantly. Free IgG, or IgG entrapped in liposomes containing dicetylphosphate instead of stearylamine, were totally ineffective because they did not attach tightly to the cells and were thus rinsed off with the buffer before the infection of the cells with the virus.

It is worth-while noting that when associated with the lipid spherules a significant amount of IgG keeps its antiviral properties. It would be very interesting to know the fate of these liposomes brought in contact with the cells. Do they simply stick to the plasma membrane? Do they fuse and become incorporated within the membrane? Or do they take the route of endocytosis as a lysosomotropic agent (de Duve *et al.*, 1974)? Ultrastructural studies would probably answer this question.

REFERENCES

Bangham, A. D., Standish, M. M. and Watkins, J. C. (1965). Diffusion of univalent ions across the lamellae of swollen phospholipids, *J. Mol. Biol.*, **13**, 238.
Bangham, A. D. (1968). Membrane models with phospholipids, *Progr. Biophys. Mol. Biol.*, **18**, 29.
Cohen, C. M., Weissmann, G., Hoffstein, S., Awasthi, Y. C. and Srivastava, S. K. (1976). Introduction of purified hexosaminidase A in Tay–Sachs leukocytes by means of immunoglobulin-coated liposomes, *Biochemistry*, **15**, 452.
de Barsy, Th. (1976). La glycogénose type II. Approche thérapeutique. Thesis Oyez, Louvain, 154 pp.
de Barsy, Th., Jacquemin, P., Devos, P. and Hers, H. G. (1972). Rodent and human acid α-glucosidase. Purification, properties and inhibition by antibodies. Investigation in type II glycogenosis, *Eur. J. Biochem.*, **31**, 156.
de Barsy, Th., Devos, P. and Van Hoof, F. (1974). The cellular distribution of liposomes in the liver of new-born rats, *Trans. Biochem. Soc.*, **3**, 159.
de Barsy, Th., Devos, P. and Van Hoof, F. (1976). A morphological and biochemical study of the fate of antibody-bearing liposomes, *Lab. Invest.*, **34**, 273.
de Duve, C., de Barsy, Th., Poole, B., Trouet, A., Tulkens, P. and Van Hoof, F. (1974). Lysosomotropic agents, *Biochem. Pharmac.*, **23**, 2485.

Kataoka, T., Williamson, J. R. and Kinsky, S. C. (1973). Release of macromolecular markers (enzymes) from liposomes treated with antibody and complement. An attempt at correlation with electron microscopic observations, *Biochem. and Biophys. Acta,* **298**, 158.

Magee, W. E. and Miller, O. V. (1972). Liposomes containing antiviral antibody can protect cells from virus infection. *Nature,* **235**, 339.

Sessa, G. and Weissmann, G. (1968). Phospholipid spherules (liposomes) as a model for biological membranes, *J. Lip. Res.,* **9**, 310.

Weissmann, G., Zurier, R. B., Spieler, P. J. and Goldstein, I. M. (1971). Mechanism of lysosomal enzyme release from leukocytes exposed to immune complexes and other particles. *J. Exp. Med.,* **134**, 149.

Weissmann, G., Brand, A. and Franklein, E. C. (1974). Interaction of immunoglobulins with liposomes. *J. Clin. Invest.,* **53**, 536.

Weissmann, G., Bloomgarden, D., Kaplan, R., Cohen, C., Hoffstein, S., Collins, T., Gottlieb, A. and Nagle, D. (1975). A general method for the introduction of enzymes by means of immunoglobulin-coated liposomes, into lysosomes of deficient cells, *Proc. Nat. Acad. Sci. USA,* **72**, 88.

long-chain, charged amphiphiles such as fatty acids or naturally occurring negatively charged phospholipids (Bangham *et al.*, 1974; Papahadjopoulos, 1968). The surface properties of liposomes can also be altered by incorporating other classes of lipids such as glycolipids (Haywood, 1974), as well as glycoproteins (Juliano and Stamp, 1976; Redwood *et al.*, 1975), which would alter the surface chemistry of liposomes as well as their surface charge. In addition, the surface properties of liposomes can be modified by adding numerous other proteins which can bind electrostatically to the surface and/or partially penetrate into the hydrophobic interior of the bilayer (Kimelberg, 1976a), further increasing the potential for interactions with cell surfaces. The fluidity of the liposome bilayer can also be altered by varying the saturation of the fatty acyl groups of the phospholipid components or by adding cholesterol (Kimelberg, 1977; Marsh, 1975; Papahadjopoulos and Kimelberg, 1974).

The other important property of liposomes essential for their use as drug carriers is that they are in the form of 5 to 50 μm diameter multilamellar structures (Papahadjopoulos and Miller, 1967) with each lamella consisting of a lipid bilayer which forms a sealed vesicle. In this form, or the much smaller 250 to 500Å diameter unilamellar vesicles produced by ultrasonication (Huang, 1969; Papahadjopoulos and Kimelberg, 1974; Papahadjopoulos and Watkins, 1967), they can entrap small molecular species such as ions (Bangham *et al.*, 1965) and larger molecules such as proteins (Kimelberg and Lee, 1969; Sessa and Weissmann, 1970). The leakage of the trapped components out of the liposomes is also a critical factor in their use in encapsulating substances for pharmacological purposes. The capture and efflux of these components vary and are dependent both on the species of the entrapped molecules and the composition and fluidity of the lipid bilayer (Bangham *et al.*, 1965; De Gier *et al.*, 1968; Papahadjopoulos and Watkins, 1967). The addition of cholesterol both decreases the fluidity of the lipid bilayer and the efflux of a number of entrapped species (Papahadjopoulos and Kimelberg, 1974). The presence of a charged component will generally increase the capture of an oppositely charged substance (Bangham *et al.*, 1965; Papahadjopoulos and Watkins, 1967) while, other things being equal, the presence of a similarly charged component in the lipid bilayer will decrease the efflux of an entrapped component. In practical terms it would be very important for entrapped species not to leak out of liposomes too readily so that, once prepared, an entrapped species would remain inside liposomes for a reasonable length of time. Thus the types of materials which can be entrapped in liposomes are quite variable, and in addition to ions and proteins as mentioned above a number of drugs have also been successfully encapsulated (Gregoriadis, 1976). It would appear then that liposomes, if well tolerated *in vivo*, could prove to be potentially very useful as drug carriers.

A number of studies have now shown that the distribution of liposome-entrapped substances *in vivo* can be quite different from that of the corresponding free forms. Descriptions of many of these studies and their applications are discussed in other chapters in this volume and in recent reviews (Colley and Ryman, 1976; Fendler and Romero, 1977; Gregoriadis, 1976; Tyrrell *et al.,* 1976). Two important potential uses of liposome-entrapped drugs *in vivo* are: (1) they could be used as a means for controlled release of small quantities of drug over long periods of time, possibly also associated with decreased metabolic breakdown of the trapped drug; and (2) they could function to direct drugs to particular tissues. Whether this can be achieved by unmodified liposomes or whether particular techniques for 'homing' of these liposomes to target organs are necessary is discussed in Chapter 2. There is clearly an advantage to the use of liposome-entrapped drugs since the pharmacokinetics of a drug need not be altered by chemically modifying the drug, which may in turn modify its biological effects, but by altering its liposomal carrier. Since, however, between such an idea and its reality falls the shadow of biological complexity, the success and applicability of such a technique needs to be demonstrated in a convincing number of instances.

2. STUDIES OF LIPOSOMES AS CARRIERS FOR ANTICANCER DRUGS

Since many cancers are resistant to chemotherapy, it would be of great importance if liposomes proved to be useful as a means of increasing the effectiveness of anticancer drugs by exploiting one or other of the properties mentioned above, and recently a number of promising preliminary studies showing increased effects of liposome-entrapped antitumour drugs have been published. Actinomycin D entrapped in the aqueous phase within neutral liposomes (lecithin+cholesterol at a mole ratio of 1 : 1) has been shown to be less toxic and more effective than the free drug against Ehrlich Ascites tumour cells in mice *in vivo* (Rahman *et al.,* 1974). A 78% increase in survival times at drug concentrations of 0.75 mg/kg was found. Gregoriadis and Neerunjun (1975) entrapped actinomycin D in the lipid phase of negatively charged liposomes consisting of egg lecithin, cholesterol, and phosphatidic acid (molar ration 7 : 2 : 1) by co-evaporating the actinomycin D and lipid mixture in chloroform, and this preparation was also found to increase the survival of mice bearing intraperitoneal AKR-A cells. A maximum increase in survival of 90% after intraperitoneal (i.p.) injection was found. More significant effects have been achieved with liposome-entrapped cytosine arabinoside (1-β-D arabinofuranosylcytosine) injected intraperitoneally, which has been reported to be as effective at 500 times less concentration than free cytosine arabinoside in increasing the survival of mice bearing ascitic

L1210 cells (Kobayashi *et al.,* 1975). This treatment resulted in up to a 281% increase in mean survival times compared to 89% for free cytosine arabinoside. These effects were all obtained with the large non-sonicated multilamellar liposomes. In the three studies mentioned neutral, negatively charged, and positively charged liposomes were all used. Mayhew *et al.* (1976) have recently studied the effects of cytosine arabinoside entrapped in small (300–500 Å) unilamellar, sonicated, negatively charged liposomes consisting of phosphatidylcholine plus phosphatidylserine at a 4 : 1 mole ratio, in DBA/2/Ha mice bearing ascitic L1210 cells. They found 100% increases in the mean survival times of these mice with doses of cytosine arabinoside of 10 mg per kilogram.

In contrast to these results Fendler and Romero (1976) have reported only a 24% increase in mean survival times of L1210-bearing mice after intraperitoneal injection of azaguanine entrapped in non-sonicated positively charged (dipalmitoyl lecithin, cholesterol, and stearylamine in a 6 : 2 : 1.4 mole ratio) liposomes, at a dose of 0.76 mg per mouse (19–22 g) per day. Azaguanine entrapped in sonicated liposomes was totally ineffective. Mean survival times were 104% of the controls which received no drug. In this study, moreover, the liposome-entrapped drug was less effective than the free drug which gave a 49% increase in mean survival time relative to untreated tumour-bearing controls, at a dose of 1.0 mg/mouse/day. Thus, although there are a number of promising results for the *in vivo* effectiveness of liposome-entrapped anticancer drugs against tumours, there is also considerable variability in these effects. This may be dependent on a number of variables including the type of drug and the nature and location of the tumour. All the work quoted above used intraperitoneal and ascitic tumours rather than solid tumours. The other variables are the size and composition of the liposomes, and although it appears that the large non-sonicated liposomes are, if anything, more effective, there is clearly insufficient evidence for any firm conclusions.

These effects have been correlated, in certain cases, with the permeability properties of the entrapped species and distribution of the liposome-entrapped drug. Encapsulation of actinomycin D in the lipid phase of liposomes by co-evaporating lipid and drug and then adding the aqueous swelling medium was found to greatly increase the retention of the drug in plasma after i.v. injection in the rat (Gregoriadis, 1973). Subsequently it was found that the retention of actinomycin D in the plasma was less if the drug was entrapped in the aqueous interior of liposomes by adding drug with the aqueous swelling medium (Rahman *et al.,* 1975). This was attributed to the relatively high leakage of actinomycin D entrapped in the aqueous phase out of the liposomes. These results imply a lack of equilibrium between the drug in the lipid and aqueous phases, and seem to make a distinction between binding of the drug within and transport through the lipid bilayer. Marked leakage has also been noted for penicillin (Gregoriadis, 1973) and small cations in the presence of soluble proteins (Kimelberg and Papahadjopoulos, 1971). A comparison of the distribution of liposome-entrapped $^{86}Rb^+$ and $^{22}Na^+$ after injection into mice showed that their distribution more closely followed that of the corresponding free ion rather than ^{3}HDPPC-labelled liposomes (Kimelberg *et al.*, 1975). This suggested that considerable leakage of the entrapped ions might be occurring in the bloodstream and it was found that mouse serum caused a marked increase in ion efflux from the liposomes after 2 hours exposure *in vitro*.

Tissue uptake of liposome-entrapped substances after intravenous (Gregoriadis and Ryman, 1972; Jonah *et al.*, 1975) or intraperitoneal (Kimelberg *et al.*, 1975) injection has been found to be localized predominantly in tissues of the reticuloendothelial system, such as liver, spleen, and lung. There is no reason for anticancer drugs to be an exception to this pattern and liposome-entrapped actinomycin D (Gregoriadis, 1973) and methotrexate (Colley and Ryman, 1975; Kimelberg, 1976b; Kimelberg *et al.*, 1976) have been shown to generally follow this pattern, although the uptake of liposome-entrapped methotrexate was reduced when it was entrapped in small sonicated liposomes (Kimelberg *et al.*, 1976). There was a marked decrease in the clearance rate of the entrapped methotrexate from blood (Colley and Ryman, 1975; Kimelberg, 1976b; Kimelberg *et al.*, 1976), in agreement with previous work using liposome-entrapped penicillin and actinomycin D (Gregoriadis, 1973). One major cause of this in the case of methotrexate was shown to be a greatly decreased renal excretion (Kimelberg, 1976b).

Although conclusions as to the practical usefulness of liposome-entrapped anticancer drugs must be resolved by *in vivo* experiments, studies on their interactions with cultured tumour cells *in vitro* are likely to prove useful predictors of their behaviour *in vivo*. Since *in vitro* systems are more clearly defined and controllable they can provide valuable information on mechanisms of liposome uptake and the effects of the entrapped drugs. Such studies will, in turn, undoubtedly provide useful information for designing the optimal conditions under which liposome-entrapped drugs may be effective *in vivo*. There have been a number of studies on the interaction of liposomes with cells *in vitro* (see Papahadjopoulos and Poste, this volume), but only a few studies on the effects of liposome-entrapped anticancer drugs. Recently it has been reported that liposome-entrapped actinomycin D has an equal effect on inhibiting RNA synthesis and cell growth, at 200- and 120-fold lower concentrations than the free drug respectively, in an actinomycin-D-resistant Chinese hamster cell line (Papahadjopoulos *et al.*, 1976; Poste and Papahadjopoulos, 1976). Since this line was thought to be resistant due to decreased uptake of the drug it was suggested that these results supported the concept of a decreased membrane transport of the drug, which was effectively bypassed by the liposome-entrapped drug. Since, however, only a fivefold increased uptake of the drug was found, it was also suggested that the liposome-entrapped drug was being directed to more effective intracellular sites. Mayhew *et al.* (1976) compared the effects of liposome-entrapped cytosine arabinoside on L1210 cells both *in vivo* and in suspension culture. Again, an approximately fivefold increased uptake of the liposome-entrapped drug was found *in vitro*. In contrast to the results with the Chinese hamster line and actinomycin D, studies on its effectiveness showed that growth of the L1210, and also Ehrlich Ascites and SV403T3 cells, was inhibited at essentially the same concentrations for both the free and liposome-entrapped drug. Notwithstanding these *in vitro* effects there was a 200% increase in mean survival time of L1210 cells growing *in vivo* at concentrations at which the free drug showed essentially no effect (Mayhew *et al.*, 1976).

It is clear that quite variable results have so far been obtained and it becomes important to determine whether differences in the size and/or composition of liposomes, the route of administration, and whether the drug is entrapped in the internal aqueous compartments or in the lipid bilayer are important variables. Two equally important variables are: (1) whether the effectiveness of liposome entrapment is dependent on the type of anticancer drug used; and (2) whether certain tumours are more susceptible than others. It can readily be seen that such studies could have almost limitless complexity, comparable to or even surpassing the complexity existing in current studies on the anticancer effects of free drugs. As a preliminary approach to these problems, we have chosen to study the widely-used anticancer drug methotrexate (MTX), and have studied its entrapment, distribution, and effectiveness in several different systems. By using this drug as a model we have attempted to determine the type of general effects that entrapment in liposomes is likely to have on the pharmacokinetics and effectiveness of chemotherapeutic drugs, both with regard to increased effectiveness and possible limitations on the use of liposome-entrapped drugs *in vivo*. These studies and their implications for the behaviour of liposome-entrapped anticancer drugs, and their relation to the studies and results I have just briefly reviewed, will form the remaining part of this chapter.

3. PREPARATION AND PHYSICAL PROPERTIES OF LIPOSOME–ENTRAPPED METHOTREXATE (MTX)

The techniques and results obtained for the entrapment of MTX within liposomes serve as a good example for the entrapment of water-soluble, charged species within the aqueous interior of liposomes. Other considerations will of course apply for the entrapment of lipid-soluble drugs, which are usually mixed with the lipids prior to evaporation of the organic solvent. Subsequent exposure of this drug mixture to buffer is likely to result in the drugs being entrapped within the lipid bilayer. The preparation of liposomes is amply discussed in other chapters in this volume. In our studies we evaporate organic solvent from the lipids, vortex-mix the dry lipids with buffer containing MTX, and sonicate in a closed vessel so that the liposomes can be prepared in an anaerobic atmosphere (Papahadjopoulos and Kimelberg, 1974). This technique necessitates the use of a bath-type sonicator, and the lower energy of this type of sonication compared to sonication using a probe requires much longer sonication times of 1–2 hours and careful placement of the tube in the bath for maximum agitation. Maintenance of a totally anaerobic atmosphere allows such extended times of sonication to be employed and the mixture can be sonicated at room temperature or higher, above the

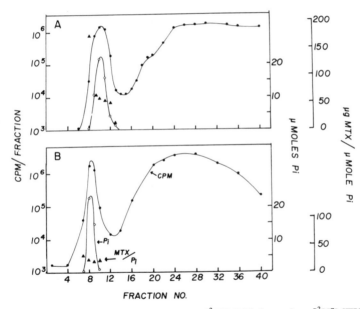

Figure 1. Separation of liposome-entrapped [^{3}H]MTX from free [^{3}H]MTX. 2 ml of the lipid mixture (see text) was eluted through a Sephadex G–50 (coarse) column at an elution rate of 4 ml/minute. The column contained 10 g Sephadex and the bed size was 2.2 × 34 cm. The fractions were collected as 5-ml volumes. A; vortex-mixed liposomes; B, sonicated liposomes. (·) ^{3}H radioactivity representing [^{3}H]MTX. (o) P_i liberated by perchloric acid hydrolysis, representing lipid phosphorus. (▲) The ratio of MTX in μg per μmol P_i for the fractions indicated. 25 mg of unlabelled MTX were present in the original swelling mixture. Reproduced by permission of Cancer Research Inc. From Kimelberg *et al.* (1976)

transition temperature of phospholipids containing saturated fatty acyl chains necessary for liposome formation by such phospholopids, by heating the water in the bath. Separation of free and entrapped material can then be achieved by gel filtration, extensive dialysis, and/or centrifugation in the case of the non-sonicated liposomes.

Figure 1 shows the elution profile of methotrexate entrapped in sonicated and non-sonicated liposomes on a G-50 Sephadex column. Liposomes of the following composition were used; 64.6 μmol of egg phosphatidylcholine, 35 μmol of cholesterol and 19.5 μmol of stearylamine in usually 2 ml of 130 mM NaCl, 4 mM KCl and 20 mM L-histidine, pH 7.4 containing 25 to 36 mg MTX and ~ 100 μCi of purified [3', 5', 9(n)-^{3}H] MTX. Under these conditions 10.3% of the added MTX was captured by the non-sonicated and 5.0% captured by the sonicated liposomes respectively. This gave 0.2 and 0.1% MTX/μmol of recovered lipid phosphorus for the non-sonicated liposomes respectively. There is always a small degree of retention of positive liposomes on the G-50 Sephadex column used for separating liposomes and free methotrexate. Reduction of the lipid concentration to half these amounts reduced the total capture by about 40 to 50%, thus giving the same capture per μmol of lipid. Altering the positive charge to a negative charge by replacing stearylamine with phosphatidylserine also reduced capture by about 50%. Unlike the positive liposomes, these negative liposomes showed no retention on the Sephadex column (Kimelberg, 1976b).

It is important to establish that when liposomes are injected *in vivo* they remain largely impermeable to the entrapped species. If there is a marked increase in permeability due to, for instance, the interactions with plasma constituents that have recently been demonstrated (Black and Gregoriadis, 1976; Tyrrell *et al.*, 1977), it could mean that after a short period of time a large fraction of the captured species would, in fact, be in the free form. We have already provided evidence that this does occur after injection into mice of ^{22}Na$^+$ or ^{86}Rb$^+$ entrapped in non-sonicated liposomes consisting of egg phosphatidylcholine, bovine brain phosphatidylserine, and cholesterol in a 4 : 1 : 3 ratio (Kimelberg *et al.*, 1975). In the case of MTX, *in vitro* experiments showed that liposomes of the above composition had a very low permeability to [^{3}H]MTX and this was only increased by a maximum of two- to fourfold in the presence of up to 60% v/v of human serum. These results are shown in Table 1. These considerations are relevant to whether one requires a liposome to quantitatively direct its contents to particular target tissues, in which case a very low permeability to the entrapped species is desirable, or whether one is simply using the liposomes as a depot for sustained release. In the latter case, one would like a finite but still low rate of efflux of the entrapped species. Variations in composition such as omission of cholesterol would alter liposomes by

Table 1 Permeability of stearylamine liposomes to [³H]methotrexate *in vitro*

		Per cent of total [³H]methotrexate diffusing per hour in presence of:			
Type of liposome	Time (hours)	No serum	20% serum	40% serum	60% serum[c]
Sonicated[a]	1	0.97	1.11	1.32	0.95
	2	0.43	0.55	0.69	0.63
	3	0.27	0.37	0.49	0.45
	4	0.21	0.28	0.38	0.36
Non-sonicated[a]	1	0.97	2.16	1.77	1.93
	2	0.44	1.28	1.21	1.30
	3	0.23	0.66	0.72	0.70
	4	0.14	0.43	0.47	0.80
Free [³H]methotrexate[b]	1	40.8			17.6
	2	29.3			11.1
	3	17.6			7.4
	4	15.0			—

Permeability of free methotrexate or methotrexate entrapped in liposomes. This was measured by dialysis technique. Per cent of total refers to the [³H]methotrexate diffusion in 1 hour as a percentage of the amount present at the start of the hour period.
[a] Average of two determinations.
[b] Average of four determinations.
[c] Human serum.
From Kimelberg (1976b). Reproduced by permission of Elsevier/North Holland Biomedical Press.

varying their permeability towards entrapped species. Also, as mentioned previously, the permeability does vary markedly with the nature of the entrapped molecules.

Separation of free and entrapped material by gel filtration results in considerable dilution of the liposomes, which elute in a 5 to 10 ml volume. This may be undesirable in small animal studies where it is necessary to inject small volumes of ~ 0.1 ml. These large volumes can, of course, be concentrated by various ultrafiltration procedures. It is also possible to maintain a minimal volume by separating the free species from the entrapped species by bulk dialysis, as was indeed done in the original studies by Bangham *et al.* (1965), if the entrapped species is relatively impermeable, as in the case of MTX. Using overnight bulk dialysis and the same composition of liposomes as described above, we have obtained the same percentage capture as after the more rapid gel filtration method, 5 to 6% for sonicated liposomes, showing that very little of the entrapped MTX leaked out over the bulk dialysis period. Subsequent dialysis of these liposomes for short periods of time showed the same low efflux rates as found for liposomes after gel filtration. This enabled us to maintain very small volumes for injection into small experimental animals such as mice or for intracerebroventricular injection into rats or monkeys, where volumes of 10–20 μl in the case of rats and 0.3 to 0.4 ml in the case of monkeys were necessary.

For practical use free and liposome-entrapped material could be routinely separated by methods similar to those that have just been outlined. However, a small but finite leakage of entrapped drugs like MTX would result in gradual loss of the entrapped material from inside the liposomes. Thus it would be far more convenient to inject the total mixture of free and liposome-entrapped drug, which could be reconstituted just prior to use. Such a procedure can be viewed as giving an initial loading dose due to the free drug and, as will be described in the following section, maintaining a slow, prolonged infusion due to the entrapped drug. Thus, sterile ampoules could easily be prepared containing the dried lipids as a thin film on their internal surface. Injection of a sterile solution of the free, water-soluble drug prior to use, followed by vigorous mixing with or without subsequent sonication in a bath-type sonicator, can then provide a sterile mixture of free drug and 10–20% of the drug entrapped in liposomes, dependent on the amount of lipid. This can be drawn up into a sterile syringe in the normal manner and injected. We will discuss later some studies using such a mixture of free and entrapped MTX on L1210-bearing mice. Lipid-soluble drugs could be present in the dry lipid film and upon reconstitution with water would be quantitatively incorporated into the lipid bilayer, as previously mentioned.

4. PHARMACOKINETICS OF LIPOSOME-ENTRAPPED MTX

4.1. After Intravenous Injection

It is now well established that the entrapment of a number of biologically active substances inside liposomes markedly influences their subsequent distribution after injection *in vivo*. One of the most noticeable effects is an increased retention of such substances in the plasma. This has been shown for actinomycin D and penicillin (Gregoriadis, 1973), EDTA (Rahman *et al.*, 1973), pertechnetate, 99m TcO_4 (McDougall *et al.*, 1974) and monovalent cations (Kimelberg *et al.*, 1975). This effect is also shown very well by MTX (Colley and Ryman, 1975; Kimelberg, 1976b; Kimelberg *et al.*, 1976). Figure 2 shows the effects of entrapment of [³H]MTX in positively charged liposomes on the clearance of ³H radioactivity from the bloodstream after intravenous injection in a primate (Cynomolgus monkey, *Macaca fascicularis*). It can be seen that this effect is most marked for [³H]MTX entrapped in sonicated liposomes, and entrapment in⸱ non-sonicated, positively charged liposomes has less of an effect. It has also

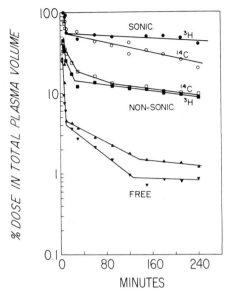

Figure 2. Radioactivity levels in plasma after intravenous injection of liposome-entrapped [³H]MTX containing [¹⁴C]cholesterol or free [³H]MTX, in Cynomolgus monkeys.

Upper graph: 10 ml of sonicated, positively charged liposomes containing 1.34 mg MTX (5.4% of the added MTX) and 50 μmol of egg phosphatidylcholine with other components in the same proportion as described in the text for Figure 1 plus 7.8 μCi [¹⁴C]cholesterol, were injected intravenously into a 3.74 kg monkey over 4.9 minutes. •, ³H radioactivity; ○, ¹⁴C radioactivity.

Middle graph: 10 ml of non-sonicated, positively charged liposomes containing 1.29 mg MTX (5.2% added MTX but about half of the lipid added for the sonicated liposomes) and 5.1 μCi [¹⁴C]cholesterol were injected intravenously into a 3.12 kg monkey over 4.9 minutes. ■ , ³H radioactivity; □ , ¹⁴C radioactivity.

Lower graph: ▲ , 111.3 mg free MTX and approximately 100 μCi [³H]MTX in 10 ml volume were injected intravenously into a 4.42 kg monkey over 4.9 minutes. ▼, 5 ml containing 19.4 mg free MTX and approximately 100 μCi [³H]MTX were injected intravenously into a 3.88 kg monkey over a 4.9 minute period. All the results are shown as the percentage of the total injected dose of [³H]MTX or [¹⁴C]cholesterol present in the total plasma compartment at the indicated times. Reproduced by permission of Elsevier/North Holland Biomedical Press. From Kimelberg (1976b)

been shown (Kimelberg, 1976b) that [³H]MTX in negatively charged, sonicated liposomes shows increased clearance from the blood compared to positively charged, sonicated liposomes.

Since MTX is cleared very rapidly by renal excretion (e.g., see Kimelberg *et al*., 1977a), it seemed likely that one of the most important effects of liposomes leading to an increased retention of MTX in the plasma could be inhibition of renal excretion. Such an effect was in fact

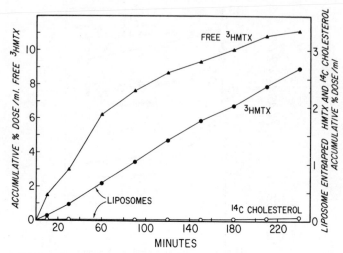

Figure 3 Urinary excretion of free and liposome-entrapped [³H]MTX in Cynomolgus monkeys. [³H]MTX plus MTX entrapped in positively charged, sonicated liposomes of the same composition as in Figures 1 and 2 and containing [¹⁴C]cholesterol, or free [³H]MTX were injected intravenously. Urine was collected continuously from a catheter inserted via the urethra into the bladder. The urine was collected as separate aliquots over the time periods indicated. The data are expressed as accumulative excretion in per cent initial dose/ml. Data taken from Kimelberg and Atchison (1978). Reproduced with permission of the New York Academy of Sciences

observed, as shown in Figure 3. Positively charged, sonicated [¹⁴C]cholesterol-labelled liposomes containing [³H]MTX were injected intravenously and it can be seen that much less of the liposome-entrapped [³H]MTX was excreted compared to free [³H]MTX. Furthermore even less of the ¹⁴C was excreted, suggesting that the ³H radioactivity seen in the curve may have derived from [³H]MTX which had leaked out of liposomes. This could have occurred in the plasma or possibly after interaction of liposomes with kidney tubule cells. We have previously shown that, in contrast to the high proportion of ³H-containing breakdown products of [³H]MTX in the plasma, ³H radioactivity appearing in the urine after intravenous injection of free [³H]MTX in Cynomolgus monkeys largely represents intact MTX for up to 4 hours, suggesting selective excretion of intact MTX (Kimelberg *et al.*, 1977a). The average percentage dose excreted for each time period collected over the 4 hour period in Figure 3 was 0.29 and 0.006%/ml for ³H and ¹⁴C radioactivity after injection of liposomes, and 1.23% for ³H after injection of free [³H]MTX. Although the decrease in per cent of the total ³H excreted was thus only fourfold, the actual decrease in renal clearance was much greater. Renal clearance is a measure of the excretion by the kidney in relation to the actual blood levels and is given by the equation $U.V/P$ where U is the concentration of the substance in the urine, V is the volume of urine produced and P is the concentration of the substance in the plasma. Since the reduced excretion was occurring in the face of much greater plasma concentrations for the liposome-entrapped [^{3}H]MTX as compared to free [^{3}H]MTX, the effect of liposome entrapment in reducing the renal clearance was approximately 100-fold for sonicated liposomes (Kimelberg *et al.*, 1976).

It appears from numerous observations that entrapment of substances in liposomes influences their tissue uptake, especially by liver and spleen (see reviews by Gregoriadis, 1976, and Tyrell *et al.*, 1976). We have found marked increases in the tissue uptake of liposome-encapsulated MTX and values for representative tissues, including liver and spleen, are shown in Table 2. Markedly increased uptake compared to the free form was found for liver and spleen, with no other tissue showing comparable effects (Kimelberg, 1976b; Kimelberg *et al.*, 1976). Increased uptake of the large, non-sonicated liposomes was especially evident for spleen. This effect of size on uptake by tissues other than spleen was, however, variable and was not seen in later studies (Kimelberg, 1976b). Increased tissue uptake may in part be responsible for the increased clearance of the larger liposomes from the plasma (see Figure 2 and Juliano and Stamp, 1975). In agreement with other studies (Gregoriadis, 1973), lower uptake of liposome-entrapped [^{3}H]MTX by intestine compared to the free form, as well as low kidney uptake in agreement with the lowered excretion, was found.

A further important consequence of injecting liposome-entrapped substances is that the entrapped substance can be protected from metabolic

Table 2 Percentage of total [^{3}H]MTX injected per gram of tissue 4 hours after a single injection in a Cynomolgus monkey

Tissue	Sonicated liposomes	Non-sonicated liposomes	Free
Liver	0.029 ± 0.01	0.18 ± 0.02	0.034 ± 0.002
Spleen	0.081 ± 0.016	0.68 ± 0.10	0.004 ± 0.001
Bone marrow	0.002 ± 0.001	0.056 ± 0.008	0.032 ± 0.016
Ileum	0.001	0.004 ± 0.002	0.023 ± 0.012
Kidney	0.004	0.020 ± 0.005	0.022 ± 0.003

Data for $n = 4$ (2 determinations from 2 separate monkey) ± S.E.M. The values are for total ^{3}H radioactivity as a percentage of the total dose of [^{3}H]MTX injected. The results are corrected for plasma content remaining after a standard procedure of rinsing the tissue in excess saline, and blotting. Plasma content in per cent per gram was 24% (liver); 11% (spleen); 18% (bone marrow); 3% (ileum), and 17% (kidney). The plasma content of the tissues was determined after the animal was sacrificed 20 minutes after intravenous injection of [^{125}I]albumin.
  Data taken from Kimelberg *et al.* (1976).

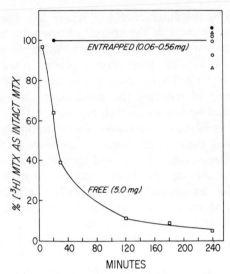

Figure 4 Breakdown of free and liposome-entrapped MTX in plasma. The results represent the amount of MTX, calculated from [^{3}H]MTX levels from experiments of the type shown in Figure 2, which actually represent intact MTX as determined by dihydrofolate reductase assay, at varying times after intravenous injection. Plasma containing liposome-entrapped MTX was first pretreated with 0.2% (v/v) Triton X-100 to lyse the liposomes releasing free MTX which is then able to inhibit the enzyme. The doses of MTX given are shown on the graph. The curve for free MTX represents the results from one experiment while the curve for liposome-entrapped MTX is for MTX entrapped in sonicated, positively charged liposomes and shows results from three separate experiments indicated by the different symbols used

degradation. We have found metabolism of MTX to be quite significant in the Cynomolgus monkey (Kimelberg *et al.*, 1977a), in contrast to the relatively low metabolism found for a variety of other species (Johns and Valerino, 1971). Figure 4 shows that after i.v. injection in Cynomolgus monkeys there is a rapid breakdown of free MTX, such that after 4 hours the levels indicated by ^{3}H radioactivity only represent 3–4% intact MTX. In contrast MTX entrapped in liposomes is almost completely protected against such metabolic degradation. This effect was also found for MTX taken up by tissues, although here metabolism was more marked. This is not surprising since some breakdown of the liposomes during the process of incorporation of liposomes into tissues is to be expected. The percentage intact MTX after injection of MTX entrapped in sonicated and non-sonicated liposomes was 29% and 20% for the liver and 66% and 22% for the spleen. The comparable figures after injection of free MTX were 5% and 6% and 3% and 8% respectively (Kimelberg, 1976b). The site of metabolism of methotrexate in the monkey was not determined, but by analogy with the rabbit (Johns and Valerino, 1971) is quite likely to be in the liver. Recently, similar protection against breakdown of liposome-entrapped polyuridilic acid by bovine pancreatic ribonuclease *in vitro* (Kulpa and Tinghitella, 1976) and polynucleotides *in vivo* (Magee *et al.*, 1976) have been reported.

From these studies and others briefly summarized in the introduction, some general principles concerning the distribution of liposomes after injection *in vivo* can be derived:

(1) The levels of the entrapped material found in plasma will correspond to that found for liposomes themselves, unless there is considerable leakage of the material out of the liposomes while in the blood (Gregoriadis, 1973; Kimelberg *et al.*, 1975; Rahman *et al.*, 1975). In the case of a substance like methotrexate which is rapidly excreted the levels can be appreciably higher than the free form, and in the case of a drug subject to metabolic breakdown such metabolism can be prevented resulting in even higher levels of the intact drug. Conversely, it has been found in the case of a substance such as serum albumin, which is normally maintained at high levels in the plasma, that encapsulation within liposomes can in fact increase its disappearance from plasma (Gregoriadis and Ryman, 1972).

(2) Excretion of the substance in urine can be markedly inhibited.

(3) Tissue uptake can be greatly influenced, although this uptake seems to involve preferentially tissues of the reticuloendothelial system and primarily liver and spleen. This is clearly a response to the particulate nature of liposomes, and it has been found that the uptake of larger colloid particles is greater than the uptake of smaller particles (Saba, 1970). Our studies have mainly involved distribution in a primate, Cynomolgus monkey, but the results do respond quite closely to those of others using other experimental animals such as rats or mice. In a later section on the effectiveness of liposome-entrapped methotrexate I will show also some data on its distribution in mice after intravenous injection.

4.2. After Intraperitoneal Injection

The studies mentioned above were concerned with the distribution of liposome-entrapped MTX after intravenous injection into monkeys. We have also studied the distribution after intraperitoneal injection, in this case in mice. These data are summarized in Table 3 where the distribution of sonicated and non-sonicated liposome-entrapped [³H]MTX after intraperitoneal injection is compared in a number of different tissues with the distribution after intraperitoneal injection of free [³H]MTX. As can be seen, the results are qualitatively the same as found after intravenous injection of free and liposome-entrapped [³H]MTX. These include

Table 3 Distribution of [³H]MTX and [¹⁴C]cholesterol after i.p. (Intraperitoneal) injection of free [³H]MTX and [³H]MTX entrapped in sonicated and non-sonicated liposomes in DBA/2 mice
(Per cent dose/ml or g)

Tissue	Time after injection (hours)	Free ³H	Sonicated liposomes ³H	Sonicated liposomes ¹⁴C	Non-sonicated liposomes ³H	Non-sonicated liposomes ¹⁴C
Plasma	1	1.2	12.5	8.4	5.9	4.6
	4	1.9	6.3	4.2	5.7	4.6
Liver	1	10.7	7.9	9.5	1.6	1.7
	4	2.7	12.2	17.3	9.2	10.1
Spleen	1	0.6	6.8	8.3	32.3	26.6
	4	0.4	8.0	14.8	83.5	93.5
Kidney	1	3.7	3.6	2.0	2.0	1.3
	4	1.4	2.7	2.7	2.2	2.4
Small Intestine	1	6.7	3.5	1.9	0.8	1.0
	4	0.6	3.1	3.1	2.8	2.5
Brain	1	0.09	0.3	0.2	0.1	0.1
	4	0.12	0.2	0.3	0.2	0.2

Results not corrected for blood content.
Sonicated liposomes, average of two mice. Rest—single experiments.
Results are per cent dose/g and not computed on the basis of the total organ uptake.

increased retention in the plasma, increased uptake into liver, especially at later times, and a low uptake into brain. Again, the uptake of non-sonicated liposomes into spleen is greatly enhanced. The uptake into tissues in both mice and monkeys is expressed per gram of tissue, but of course in mice this represents a much higher proportion of the total tissue or even an amount greater than the total weight of the tissue.

4.3. After Intracerebral Injection

As mentioned in the studies above and as found in previous studies (Jonah *et al.*, 1975; Kimelberg *et al.*, 1975; Kimelberg *et al.*, 1976), direct injection into the systemic circulation does not seem to cause increased uptake into the central nervous system (CNS) possessing an intact blood–brain barrier. Since it may be possible that liposome-entrapped substances could have increased effects within the CNS, direct injection would seem necessary in order to obtain significant amounts of liposome material in the normal CNS. Some preliminary studies using this mode of injection have recently appeared (Adams *et al.*, 1976; Adams *et al.*, 1977). These workers found that although some liposomes were well tolerated by the animals, other liposomes which contained stearylamine or dicetylphosphate caused seizures and resultant death within a few minutes after injection. In contrast to these results, we have found that, after injection of stearylamine-containing liposomes directly into the lateral cerebral ventricles of monkeys and rats, no obvious toxicity was obtained. However, the toxic results of Adams *et al.* (1976, 1977) were found with doses of 5 to 10 mg of lipid per mouse, which were presumably of an average weight of 20 to 30 g. We injected a total of 75 μmol of liposomes consisting of phosphatidylcholine, cholesterol, and stearylamine in a 1 : 0.52 : 0.22 ratio which comes to a total weight of lipid of 45 mg for an average 2.9 to 3.7 kg monkey. Thus the comparative doses were, taking an average 20 g weight for the mouse and a 2.9 kg weight for the monkey, 250–500 mg lipid/kg for the mice but only 13 mg lipid/kg for the monkey experiments. Thus, the around 30-fold higher doses used in the mice were probably responsible for the toxic results found in these experiments but not in the ones with the monkey. In more recent experiments on rats, injecting sonicated, positively charged liposomes at doses of 24 mg lipid/kg, also into the left lateral ventricle, caused no toxicity for at least 60 days, at which time the experiment was terminated (Tracey and Kimelberg, unpublished observations). Also the fact that the liposomes in the mice experiments were injected directly into the cerebral tissue may have been a factor. Adams *et al.* (1977) found after injection of negative liposomes that there was extensive haemorrhagic necrosis at the injection site. In contrast, histological examination of monkey and rat tissue after injection showed no detectable histological abnormalities in our experiments.

The levels of ^{3}H radioactivity found after direct injection of liposome-encapsulated [^{3}H]MTX into the CSF of Cynomolgus monkeys are summarized in Table 4. It can be seen that, compared to the levels found after injection of free [^{3}H]MTX, increased levels of liposome-entrapped [^{3}H]MTX were found 24 and 96 hours after injection in both the CSF and CNS tissue. Again, this was associated with protection against metabolic breakdown of MTX, and this was more evident for MTX in CSF. The values for percentage intact MTX associated with [^{3}H]MTX levels are shown in Table 4 as the numbers in brackets. Since the breakdown of free MTX in the CNS occurs much more slowly than the breakdown found after intravenous injection (Kimelberg *et al.*, 1977a, 1978 and Figure 4), it seems possible that the ^{3}H found in CNS is due to the re-uptake of MTX products containing ^{3}H from MTX which has been removed from the CNS and has been metabolized systemically. MTX metabolites containing ^{3}H do cross the blood–brain barrier quite readily after i.v. injection of MTX reaching isotopic equilibrium between plasma and CSF after 4 hours, while intact

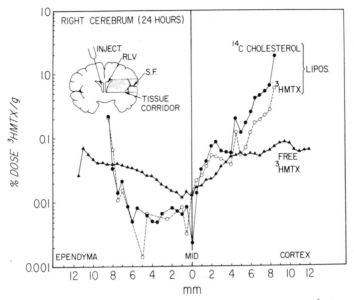

Figure 5 Levels of free [³H]MTX and liposome-entrapped [³H]MTX plus [¹⁴C]cholesterol at increasing distances from the ependymal surface 24 hours after intracerebroventricular injection. Free (1.72 mg/MTX, 100 μCi [³H]MTX) and liposome-entrapped [³H]MTX (0.42 mg MTX 2.8 μCi [³H]MTX) were injected into the left lateral ventricle. Immediately after sacrifice the entire brain, cerebellum, and cerebrum were removed. After freezing for 20 seconds in liquid nitrogen until just before the brain had become brittle a coronal section approximately 0.5 cm thick was cut beginning at the tip of the lateral ventricle. A tissue corridor approximately 0.8 cm wide was then cut from the ventricle laterally through the caudate nucleus, internal capsule, and Sylvian tissue to the cortical surface. A posterior view of this section is shown in the figure. After storage at −40°C for 3 days, 0.5 mm or 1 mm sections were cut using a freezing microtome. Each section was then digested in protosol, and ³H and ¹⁴C radioactivity determined. Reproduced by permission of Cancer Research Inc. From Kimelberg *et al.* (1978)

MTX does not (Kimelberg *et al.*, 1977a). The efflux of both free and liposome-entrapped MTX from CNS to plasma occurs at quite an appreciable rate (Kimelberg *et al.*, 1977b, 1978).

Figure 5 shows the distribution of ³H radioactivity within a corridor of brain tissue 24 hours after injection of liposome-entrapped [³H]MTX and free [³H]MTX into the lateral ventricles of Cynomolgus monkeys (see also Kimelberg *et al.*, 1978). It can be seen that there are marked regional differences in this distribution with very high levels being found at the ependymal and cortical surface of the tissue–CSF interface, consistent with the higher levels found for liposome-entrapped [³H]MTX in CSF.

However, the diffusion of liposome-entrapped methotrexate within brain tissue seems to be slower than the diffusion of free methotrexate, since in the middle areas of the tissue corridor the levels of ^{3}H radioactivity found after injection of liposome-entrapped [^{3}H]MTX are less than for free [^{3}H]MTX. These results suggest that MTX remains largely entrapped within liposomes in the CNS, at least for up to 24 hours. Similar regional differences might well be found when comparable determinations are made in systemic tissue, and thus the levels and effects of liposome-entrapped substances need not necessarily be uniform within a tissue.

Although these studies were initiated because liposomes do not appear to cross the intact blood–brain barrier, solid tumours of the CNS are known to have a local breakdown of the blood–brain barrier (Pardridge *et al.*, 1975). This should allow passage of larger substances such as liposome-entrapped material into the tumour and this, coupled with the higher plasma levels obtained, might result in greater effectiveness against solid tumours of the CNS.

In the case of MTX there is no compelling reason for trying other routes of administration at present. However, in the case of certain other substances there is clearly an advantage to an oral route of administration. Gregoriadis *et al.* (1976) have briefly reported that entrapment of insulin in phosphatidylinositol liposomes does seem to cause significant biological effects, in contrast to oral administration of free insulin which has no discernible effect.

So far, our studies have established details of the considerable effects that entrapment in liposomes has on the pharmacokinetics and distribution of MTX *in vivo*. It might be predicted that the greatly increased plasma levels of the intact drug obtained could lead to increased effectiveness against tumours. This assumes, however, that liposome-entrapped MTX is available to interact with malignant tissue, and perhaps shows some degree of preferential uptake compared to the intact free form. Thus, the subsequent sections of this review will be concerned with summarizing some of our more recent work on the effectiveness of liposome-entrapped MTX both *in vitro* and *in vivo*.

5. CHEMOTHERAPEUTIC EFFECTS OF LIPOSOME-ENTRAPPED MTX

5.1. Effects on the Growth of C$_6$ Glioma Cells *In Vitro*

The effects of free and liposome-entrapped MTX on the growth of C$_6$ glioma cells growing as monolayers in the presence of MTX at various concentrations are shown in Figure 6. The cells were seeded at 10^5 cells/dish on day 1 and the media was not changed over the entire growth period. When media was changed every 3 days a very similar growth rate

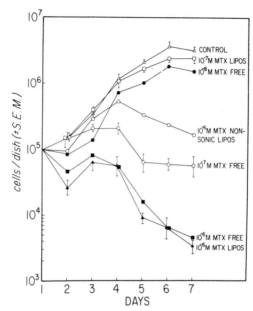

Figure 6 Effect of free and liposome-entrapped MTX on the growth of C_6 glioma cells. Cells were grown in Ham's F10 medium plus 15% horse and 2.5% foetal calf serum and penicillin + streptomycin, in the presence of free or liposome-entrapped MTX containing [^{3}H]MTX and [^{14}C]cholesterol as indicated. On the days shown 0.1 ml samples of media were taken, and the cells were then washed three times in cold phosphate-buffered saline. The cells were then removed by trypsin treatment and the number of viable cells excluding Trypan blue were counted. The cell numbers obtained are shown in the figure. ^{3}H and ^{14}C radioactivity were also determined and these results are shown in Table 5. LIPOS, sonicated positively charged liposomes, NON-SONIC, non-sonicated positively charged liposomes

with a saturation density of 4×10^6 cells/dish was found. The cells showed almost complete inhibition of growth at 10^{-7} M and marked decreases in cell number at 10^{-6} M free MTX. It can be seen that MTX entrapped in sonicated, positively charged liposomes and added to the cultures at a final concentration of 10^{-6} M was only marginally more effective in inhibiting cell growth than the free 10^{-6} M MTX. However, 10^{-6} M MTX entrapped in multilamellar non-sonicated liposomes of the same composition was much less effective than free 10^{-6} M MTX. In contrast to the effect of 10^{-7} M free MTX, cell growth in the presence of 10^{-7} M MTX entrapped in sonicated liposomes was not significantly different from the control. Both sonicated and non-sonicated liposomes of identical composition but not containing MTX, and added at the highest concentrations used in the experiments, had no effect on the growth rate. The fact that

Table 5 Uptake of [^{3}H]MTX and [^{14}C]cholesterol in glioma cells
treated with 10^{-6}M MTX
(Per cent of total added taken up per 10^5 cells)

Day	Free ^{3}H	Sonicated liposomes		Non-sonicated liposomes	
		^{3}H	^{14}C	^{3}H	^{14}C
2	0.42	0.15	0.71	0.42	0.94
3	0.32	0.38	1.16	0.21	0.49
4	0.40	0.58	2.62	0.17	0.45
5	0.94	2.90	3.31	0.23	0.75
6	1.31	2.31	4.23	0.36	1.46
7	1.74	1.16	5.00	0.46	1.21

The concentration of MTX in liposomes was 22.8 and 65.5 nmol/μmol lipid phosphate for sonicated and non-sonicated liposomes respectively. The liposomes were composed of 21.5 μmol egg PC, 10.0 μmol cholesterol, and 5.0 μmol stearylamine in 1.5 ml of buffer. Thus in the case of a final concentration of 10^{-6}M MTX, 219 and 76 nmol of lipid phosphate were added to each dish (5.0 ml total volume and initially 10^5 cells) for the sonicated and non-sonicated liposomes respectively.

liposome-entrapped MTX at a concentration of 10^{-6} M had an effect on cell growth after 1 day, and more significantly, the fact that liposome-encapsulated MTX at 10^{-7} M had no effect, suggests that the results seen are not due to free drug leaking out of the liposomes.

The uptake of ^{3}H and ^{14}C radioactivity expressed per 10^5 cells from free 10^{-6} M [^{3}H]MTX, and 10^{-6} M [^{3}H]MTX entrapped in [^{14}C]cholesterol-labelled liposomes is shown in Table 5. We have not determined how much of this radioactivity represents intact MTX and cholesterol. The uptake of ^{3}H radioactivity was less for non-sonicated liposomes especially at later times, consistent with the decreased effects on cell growth. It can be seen that the percentage uptake into glioma cells of ^{14}C radioactivity was greater than liposome-encapsulated [^{3}H]MTX. The data in Table 5 do not indicate the site of uptake and do not, for instance, distinguish between adsorption to the cell surface or intracellular localization. The amount of uptake does, however, correspond to the effects on cell growth and when liposome-entrapped MTX was less effective than free MTX it was taken up less. The increased uptake of ^{14}C relative to ^{3}H could be due to exchange of cholesterol without uptake of liposomes or 'leaky' fusion, based on various proposals by others as previously discussed (Kimelberg, 1976b). Exchange of cholesterol could be either direct, occurring during reversible adsorption of liposomes to the cell surface, or indirect via plasma lipoproteins (Black and Gregoriadis, 1976).

5.2. Effects on L1210 Cells *In Vivo*

Kobayashi *et al.* (1975) and Mayhew *et al.* (1976) have reported that treatment of L1210 tumour-bearing mice, with cytosine arabinoside encapsulated within positively and negatively charged (20% phosphatidylserine in phosphatidylcholine) liposomes respectively, resulted in a two- to four-fold increase in the mean survival times of the mice. These results were obtained at concentrations of cytosine arabinoside (10 to 50 mg/kg) which, in the free form, caused no increased survival. In contrast, L1210 tumour-bearing mice are quite sensitive to methotrexate,

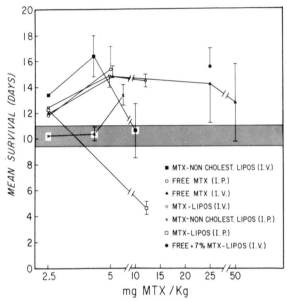

Figure 7 Effects of free and liposome-entrapped MTX injected intravenously or intraperitoneally on the survival of L1210 tumour-bearing mice. 20–25 g mice were injected intraperitoneally with 1×10^5 L1210 cells. 24 hours later free or liposome-entrapped MTX was injected by various routes at the doses indicated. *LIPOS: sonicated, positively charged liposomes consisting of 21.5 μmol egg phosphatidylcholine, 10 μmol cholesterol, and 5 μmol stearylamine in 1.5 ml of the same media as used in Figure 1.* They contained about 0.016 mg MTX/μmol egg phosphatidylcholine captured in a media initially containing 18.2 mg MTX/ml. *NON CHOLEST LIPOS: sonicated liposomes without cholesterol consisting of 64.5 μmol egg phosphatidylcholine and 10 μmol stearylamine.* They contained 0.017 mg MTX/μmol phosphatidylcholine. After gel filtration both types of liposomes were concentrated using Americon 24 centriflo ultrafilters to volumes permitting the injection of around 0.2 ml to give the final doses indicated. Routes of administration are also shown in the figure (from Kimelberg and Atchison, 1978).

showing a 30% increase in mean survival time at a dose of 15 mg/kg increasing to 40% increase in mean survival time at a dose of 250 mg/kg (Chabner *et al.*, 1972). At doses higher than this the drug is toxic. It was of interest therefore to see if the survival of L1210 tumour-bearing mice was increased over these values by methotrexate entrapped within liposomes. The results from a number of experiments using methotrexate entrapped in both sonicated, positively charged liposomes containing cholesterol, and also MTX in the same liposomes not containing cholesterol are shown in Figure 7. Also, administration of liposomes by the intraperitoneal route (I.P.) was compared with intravenous injection (I.V.). The hatched line in Figure 7 represents the range of survival times for control animals injected intraperitoneally with 10^5 L1210 cells per mouse.

It can be seen that with free MTX we achieved a 50% increase in mean survival times at 5 to 15 mg of MTX per kg, essentially in agreement with published data (Chabner *et al.*, 1972), and a 20% increase in mean survival time at a dose of 2.5 mg of MTX per kg. Free MTX injected intraperitoneally had the same effect as free MTX injected intravenously up to 5 mg/kg. In contrast, MTX encapsulated in sonicated liposomes containing cholesterol and injected intraperitoneally was quite toxic, causing a 50% decrease in mean survival time at a dose of 12 mg MTX per kg. When injected intravenously however, the identical dose caused the same increase in survival as free MTX injected intravenously. Doses higher than 10–15 mg/kg for liposome-entrapped MTX could not be studied easily because of limitations imposed by the low percentage capture obtained (2 to 5% for these sonicated liposomes depending on the amount of lipid). Thus, liposome-entrapped MTX is at least fivefold more toxic than cytosine arabinoside entrapped in non-sonicated, positive liposomes containing cholesterol which were found to have no toxicity when injected intraperitoneally in doses up to 50 mg/kg (Kobayashi *et al.*, 1975). This difference might in part be due to the fact that cytosine arabinoside leaks out of liposomes more rapidly than does MTX. It has been reported (Juliano, 1977) that 3–5% of the drug is lost from cytosine arabinoside–liposome complexes per hour, and this might well be further increased in the presence of serum proteins. We therefore made liposomes of the same composition as used previously, but without cholesterol. As expected these liposomes showed 5 to 6 times more leakage of the entrapped MTX compared to liposomes containing cholesterol in the presence of 50% (v/v) serum. Consistent with the above reasoning, such liposomes when injected intraperitoneally were less toxic than liposomes containing cholesterol as shown in Figure 7. When liposomes not containing cholesterol were injected intravenously a marked increase in mean survival time was found at a relatively low dose of about 4 mg/kg. However, these liposomes were also more toxic at higher levels of 12

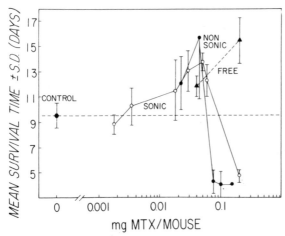

Figure 8 Effectiveness of sonicated and non-sonicated liposomes on the survival of L1210 tumour-bearing mice after intraperitoneal injection. Experimental conditions were the same as in Figure 7 except all liposomes were positively charged and contained cholesterol. In all experiments the liposomes were injected intraperitoneally. Doses are expressed per mouse, with an average weight of 22 g and a range of 19–25 g

mg/kg (Figure 7). A mixture of free and entrapped MTX was only slightly more effective than the free form alone (Figure 7).

Figure 8 compares the effects of positively charged, non-sonicated cholesterol-containing liposomes with positively charged, sonicated cholesterol-containing liposomes, after both were injected intraperitoneally. In this case the dosage is given in mg MTX/mouse and shown on a log scale to accommodate the wide range of doses used. Since the average weight of the mice was 20 g the values can be multiplied by 45 to give the dose in mg/kg. An approximately 50% increase in mean survival times was found for MTX in both sonicated and non-sonicated liposomes at slightly lower concentrations of about 2 to 3 mg/kg compared to free MTX, which was not evident in the previous figure. However, considerable toxicity was again found when the dose was raised to 5 to 10 mg/kg giving a narrow therapeutic index. Injection of the same liposomes not containing MTX at the highest dose of lipid used, equivalent to 8 μmol PC/mouse, showed no toxicity for up to 3 months, when observations were ended. Thus, increases of 50 to 60% in mean survival times, comparable to the maximum effects found for free MTX (Chabner *et al.*, 1972), were found for liposome-encapsulated MTX at doses five to ten times less than the concentration of free MTX required to achieve the same effect, but the therapeutic index for cholesterol-containing liposomes given intraperitoneally was small. The best results in terms of toxicity seem to be achieved with MTX entrapped either in liposomes containing cholesterol, or not containing cholesterol, injected intravenously.

These results compare to the 80% increase in the survival of mice bearing Ehrlich Ascites tumour cells (Rahman *et al.*, 1974), and about a 50% increase in the survival of mice bearing AKR-A tumour cells (Gregoriadis and Neerunjun, 1975) using liposome-entrapped actinomycin D. As previously mentioned cytosine arabinoside entrapped in liposomes has been reported to increase the survival of L1210 tumour-bearing mice by up to 100% (Mayhew *et al.*, 1976) and 280% (Kobayashi *et al.*, 1975) when given in sonicated negative or positive, and non-sonicated positive liposomes respectively. It should also be noted that whereas free MTX causes 50–60% increases in survival times at doses of 5–10 mg/kg, free actinomycin D and cytosine arabinoside require much higher doses before they show any effects.

6. CONCLUSIONS

Using MTX as a model these studies have shown that entrapment of drugs in liposomes can result in greatly increased levels of the intact drug being maintained *in vivo*. This is achieved by decreasing both excretion and metabolism. It would be very advantageous, however, to also reduce non-specific uptake of the entrapped drug into spleen and liver as this should make more drug available for the target tissue, as well as decreasing the possibility of toxicity. Maintaining increased levels is an advantage for some anti-cancer drugs since, theoretically, if cytotoxic levels can be maintained long enough so that all cancer cells are exposed during DNA synthesis the entire cell population can be eradicated. As we have seen, however, with liposome-entrapped MTX as with free MTX there is toxicity at higher doses, presumably due to the well-recognized low specificity of MTX and the susceptibility of some normal cells. Decreased liver and spleen uptake might be achieved by first injecting a large dose of liposomes not containing any drugs to achieve reticuloendothelial blockade, such that a second dose of colloids is taken up to a much less extent (Saba, 1970). However, it has been found that pretreatment with carbon particles actually increased the uptake by liver of a subsequent dose of liposomes, although there were suggestions that liposomes might now be taken up more by hepatocytes than Kupffer cells (Gregoriadis and Neerunjun, 1974). Also, it has been found recently that liposomes previously exposed to spleen cells are much less readily taken up by a variety of mammalian cells (Dunnick *et al.*, 1976), and liposomes coated with some polyamino acids are both more and less readily taken up by the liver *in vivo* (Dunnick *et al.*, 1975). Extension of such preliminary studies and incorporating other components such as glycolipids (e.g. Surolia and Bachhawat, 1977) could be of interest.

Thus, entrapment in liposomes can make much greater levels of the drug potentially available for interaction with the target tissue. In the case of the C_6 glioma cells *in vitro* however, entrapment in liposomes was found not to increase uptake of MTX compared to the free form. Consistent with this liposome-entrapped MTX was found to have equal or less effects in inhibiting cell growth. The percentage uptake of ^{14}C from [^{14}C]cholesterol-labelled liposomes of 7% per 10^6 cells after 24 hours that we obtained can be compared to the 0.2–20% incorporation reported by others for liposomes and other cell types for 10 minutes to 2 hour incubation times (Dunnick *et al.*, 1976; Magee *et al.*, 1974; Weissmann *et al.*, 1975). Thus, it appears that the lack of an enhanced effect of liposome-entrapped MTX compared to the free form is not due to a reduced uptake of liposomes by the C_6 cells compared with others, but rather a decreased uptake compared to free MTX, as shown in Table 5. The sensitivity of the C_6 cells to $\sim 10^{-6}$ M MTX is similar to the sensitivity to MTX inhibition by a number of cell types (Hryniuk and Bertino, 1971), so that the cells are neither unusually sensitive nor resistant to MTX. Increased effects and uptake of liposome-entrapped material may therefore only occur with substances to which cells are normally not very permeable, such as cAMP (Papahadjopoulos *et al.*, 1974) and proteins such as horseradish peroxidase (Magee *et al.*, 1974), or for cells which have acquired resistance due to reduced transport of the drug, such as an actinomycin-D-resistant line in which the liposome-entrapped drug was 100-fold more effective than the free drug (Papahadjopoulos *et al.*, 1976). If such transport defects are responsible for some types of drug resistance *in vivo* then this effect, coupled with increased levels and decreased metabolism, should lead to markedly increased effectiveness.

In our experiments with L1210 cells *in vivo* it was clear that although similar increased levels have been seen in plasma both in mice and in monkeys (Kimelberg and Atchinson, 1978), this did not lead to increased effectiveness against the L1210 cells *in vivo*. This is in contrast to studies with cytosine arabinoside where up to a four-fold increased effectiveness was seen *in vivo* (Kobayashi *et al.*, 1975; Mayhew *et al.*, 1976), although the liposome-entrapped drug did not show an increased effectiveness *in vitro* (Mayhew *et al.*, 1976). However, cytosine arabinoside is rapidly metabolized as well as being rapidly cleared in mice (Camierier and Smith, 1965; El Dareer *et al.*, 1977). By analogy with MTX we might expect both these effects to be reduced for liposome-entrapped cytosine arabinoside, and decreased clearance for liposome-entrapped cytosine arabinoside has recently been shown (Juliano, 1977). In contrast, although a similar 100-fold increased level of [^3H]MTX was found in both mice and monkeys there was less metabolism of free MTX in plasma in mice (Kimelberg and Atchison, 1978). Also, the L1210 cells *in vivo* take up slightly less of the liposome-entrapped than the free drug (Kimelberg and Atchison, 1978). Thus, it appears that liposome entrapment is most effective, at the present level of liposome technology, when the action of the free drug is severely diminished both by rapid clearance and metabolism. Entrapment of a drug in liposomes can prevent or markedly reduce both these effects resulting in bloodstream levels of the intact drug, which, by analogy with the behaviour of MTX, can be increased by several orders of magnitude. From the few studies presently available, however, the effectiveness of liposome-entrapped drugs cannot be readily predicted but each case has to be determined separately. Lowered excretion and reduced metabolisn will clearly be important in making more of the drug potentially available either in the systemic circulation or in the CSF of the central nervous system. The next challenge is to increase the specific uptake by target cells, while at the same time reducing non-specific uptake by other tissue. Preliminary experiments on 'homing' of liposomes by adding heat-aggregated immunoglobulin G (Weissmann *et al.*, 1975) or specific antibodies (Gregoriadis, 1975; Gregoriadis, 1977) have been quite successful *in vitro*, but one of the complications for *in vivo* use is that liposomes in plasma rapidly adsorb serum proteins (Black and Gregoriadis, 1976) altering their subsequent interactions with cells and perfused liver (Tyrrell *et al.*, 1977). Thus, successful targeting of liposomes *in vivo* will clearly require considerable ingenuity and expertise.

Acknowledgements

I should like to thank Elvira Graham for her patience and skill which made the preparation and typing of this manuscript a more enjoyable and efficient enterprise than it otherwise would have been. I should also like to gratefully acknowledge the collaboration and assistance of Michael Atchison, Sandra Biddlecome, Robert Bourke, Eric Reiss, Thomas Tracy, and Robert Watson in various aspects of the studies included in this review.

REFERENCES

Adams, D. H., Wisniewski, H. M., Joyce, G. and Richardson, V. (1976). *Trans. Amer. Soc. Neurochem.*, **7**, 127.

Adams, D. H., Joyce, G., Richardson, V. J., Ryman, B. E. and Wisniewski, H. M. (1977). *J. Neurol. Sciences*, **31**, 173.

Bangham, A. D., Standish, M. M. and Watkins, J. C. (1965). *J. Mol. Biol.*, **13**, 238.

Bangham, A. D., Hill, M. W. and Miller, N. G. A. (1974). In *Methods in*

Membrane Biology, 1, p.1. (ed. E. D. Korn), Plenum Press, New York and London.

Black, C. D. V. and Gregoriadis, G. (1976). Biochem. Soc. Trans., 4, 253.

Camierer, G. W. and Smith, C. G. (1965). Biochem. Pharmacol., 14, 1405.

Chabner, B. A., Johns, D. G. and Bertino, J. R. (1972). Nature, 239, 395.

Colley, C. M. and Ryman, B. E. (1975). Biochem. Soc. Trans., 3, 157.

Colley, C. M. and Ryman, B. E. (1976). Trends in Biochemical Sciences, 1, 203.

De Gier, J., Mandersloot, J. D. and Van Deenen, L. L. M. (1968). Biochim. Biophys. Acta, 150, 666.

Dunnick, J. K., McDougall, I. R., Aragon, S., Goris, M. L. and Kriss, J. P. (1975). J. Nucl. Med., 16, 483.

Dunnick, J. K., Rooke, J. D., Aragon, S. and Kriss, J. P. (1976). Cancer Res., 36, 2385.

El Dareer, S. M., Mulligan, L. T., White, V., Tillery, K., Mellett, L. B. and Hill, D. L. (1977). Cancer Treat. Rep., 61, 395.

Fendler, J. H. and Romero, A. (1976). Life. Sci., 18, 1453.

Fendler, J. H. and Romero, A. (1977). Life Sci., 20, 1109.

Gregoriadis, G. (1973). FEBS Letters, 36, 292.

Gregoriadis, G. (1975). Biochem. Soc. Trans., 3, 613.

Gregoriadis, G. (1976). New Eng. J. Med., 295, 704.

Gregoriadis, G. (1977). Nature, 265, 407.

Gregoriadis, G. and Neerunjun, E. D. (1974). Eur. J. Biochem., 47, 179.

Gregoriadis, G. and Neerunjun, E. D. (1975). Res. Commun. Chem. Path. Pharmacol., 10, 351.

Gregoriadis, G. and Ryman, B. E. (1972). Eur. J. Biochem., 24, 485.

Gregoriadis, G., Dapergolas, G. and Neerunjun, E. D. (1976). Biochem. Soc. Trans., 4, 256.

Haywood, A. M. (1974). J. Molec. Biol., 83, 427.

Hryniuk, W. M. and Bertino, J. R. (1971). Ann. N.Y. Acad. Sci., 186, 330.

Huang, C. (1969). Biochemistry, 8, 344.

Johns, D. G. and Valerino, D. M. (1971). Ann. N.Y. Acad. Sci., 186, 378.

Jonah, M. M., Cerny, E. A. and Rahman, Y. -E. (1975). Biochim. Biophys. Acta, 401, 336.

Juliano, R. L. (1977). Biophys. J., 17, 130a.

Juliano, R. L. and Stamp. D. (1975). Biochem. Biophys. Res. Commun., 63, 651.

Juliano, R. L. and Stamp, D. (1976). Nature, 261, 235.

Kimelberg, H. K. (1976a). Molec. Cell. Biochem., 10, 171.

Kimelberg, H. K. (1976b). Biochim. Biophys. Acta, 448, 531.

Kimelberg, H. K. (1977). In Cell Surface Reviews, 3, p.205 (eds. G. Poste and G. L. Nicolson), Elsevier/North-Holland Biomedical Press.

Kimelberg, H. K. and Atchison, M. A. (1978). Ann. N.Y. Acad. Sci., 308, 395.

Kimelberg, H. K. and Lee, C. P. (1969). Biochem. Biophys. Res. Commun., 34, 784.

Kimelberg, H. K. and Papahadjopoulos, D. (1971). J. Biol. Chem., 246, 1142.

Kimelberg, H. K., Mayhew, E. and Papahadjopoulos, D. (1975). Life Sci., 17, 715.

Kimelberg, H. K., Tracy, T. F., Biddlecome, S. M. and Bourke, R. S. (1976). Cancer Res., 36, 2949.

Kimelberg, H. K., Biddlecome, S. M. and Bourke, R. S. (1977a). Cancer Res., 37, 157.

Kimelberg, H. K., Tracy, T. F., Kung, D., Watson, R., Yen, J., Reiss, F. L. and Bourke, R. S. (1977b). Trans. Amer. Soc. Neurochem., 8, 77.

Kimelberg, H. K., Tracy, T. F., Watson, R. E., Kung, D., Reiss, F. L. and Bourke, R. S. (1978). *Cancer Res.*, **38**, 706.

Kobayashi, T., Tsukagoshi, S. and Sakurai, Y. (1975). *Gann*, **66**, 719.

Kulpa, C. F. and Tinghitella, T. J. (1976). *Life Sci.*, **19**, 1879.

Magee, W. E., Goff, C. W., Schoknecht, J., Smith, M. D. and Cherian, K. (1974) *J. Cell. Biol.*, **63**, 492.

Magee, W. E., Talcott, S. X., Straub, S. X. and Vriend, C. Y. (1976). *Biochim. Biophys. Acta*, **451**, 610.

Marsh, D. (1975). In *Essays in Biochemistry*, **11** (eds. P. N. Campbell and W. N. Aldridge), Academic Press, London, New York and San Francisco.

Mayhew, E., Papahadjopoulos, D., Rustum, Y. M. and Dave, C. (1976). *Cancer Res.*, **36**, 4406.

McDougall, I. R., Dunnick, J. K., McNamee, M. G. and Kriss, J. P. (1974). *Proc. Nat. Acad. Sci. USA*, **71**, 3487.

Papahadjopoulos, D. (1968). *Biochim. Biophys. Acta*, **164**, 240.

Papahadjopoulos. D. and Kimelberg, H. K. (1974). In *Process in Surface Science*, **4**, p. 141 (ed. S. G. Davison). Pergamon Press, Oxford.

Papahadjopoulos, D. and Miller, N. (1967). *Biochim. Biophys. Acta*, **135**, 624.

Papahadjopoulos, D. and Watkins, J. C. (1967). *Biochim. Biophys. Acta*, **135**, 639.

Papahadjopoulos, D., Poste, G. and Mayhew, E. (1974). *Biochim. Biophys. Acta*, **363**, 404.

Papahadjopoulos, D., Poste, G., Vail, W. J. and Biedler, J. L. (1976). *Cancer Res.*, **36**, 2988.

Pardridge, W. M., Connor, J. D. and Crawford, I. L. (1975). In *Critical Reviews in Toxicology*, **3**, pp.159–199 (ed. L. Goldberg), CRC Press, Cleveland, Ohio.

Poste, G. and Papahadjopoulos, D. (1976). *Nature*, **261**, 699.

Rahman, Y. -E., Rosenthal, M. W. and Cerny, E. A. (1973). *Science*, **180**, 300.

Rahman, Y. -E., Cerny, E. A., Tollaksen, S. L., Wright, B. J., Nance, S. L. and Thomson, J. F. (1974). *Proc. Soc. Exptl. Biol. Med.*, **146**, 1173.

Rahman, Y. -E., Kisieleski, W. E., Buess, E. M. and Cerny, E. A. (1975). *Europ. J. Cancer*, **11**, 883.

Redwood, W. R., Jansons, V. K. and Patel, B. C. (1975). *Biochim. Biophys, Acta*, **406**, 347.

Saba, T. M. (1970). *Arch. Intern. Med.*, **126**, 1031.

Sessa, G. and Weissmann, G. (1970). *J. Biol. Chem.*, **245**, 3295.

Surolia, A. and Bachhawat, B. K. (1977). *Biochim. Biophys. Acta*, **497**, 760.

Tyrrell, D. A., Heath, T. D., Colley, C. M. and Ryman, B. E. (1976). *Biochim. Biophys. Acta*, **457**, 259.

Tyrrell, D. A., Richardson, V. J. and Ryman, B. E. (1977). *Biochim. Biophys. Acta*, **497**, 469.

Weissmann, G., Bloomgarden, D., Kaplan, R., Cohen, C., Hoffstein, S., Collins, T., Gotlieb, A. and Nagle, D. (1975). *Proc. Nat. Acad. Sci. USA*, **72**, 88.

Liposomes in Biological Systems
Edited by G. Gregoriadis and A. C. Allison
© 1980, John Wiley & Sons, Ltd.

CHAPTER 9

Liposomes as Carriers of Polynucleotides

Wayne E. Magee

1. **Introduction**   249

2. **Preparation of liposomes containing polyribonucleotides**   251

3. **Interaction with cells**   254

4. **Biological activity in animals**   256

5. **Fate of polynucleotide-containing liposomes in animals**   257

6. **Conclusions and future prospects**   262

   References   263

1. INTRODUCTION

Our interest in liposomes resulted from reflections on the possibility of designing vesicles which might resemble membrane-enclosed viruses. In pursuing this analogy as far as possible (Figure 1), one should be able to design particles that: (*a*) attach preferentially to cells of interest; (*b*) fuse with the cellular membrane, emptying the contents of the particle into the cytoplasm; or alternately (*c*) be taken up by phagocytosis and enter the cell in phagocytic vacuoles. In the latter case, subsequent events would depend upon whether ingested material remained in the vacuole or was released from it. Our initial studies showed that liposomes could be prepared with antiviral antibody entrapped inside and that these particles attached readily to cells in tissue culture (Magee and Miller, 1972). The cells were protected from infection by the virus towards which antibody was directed.

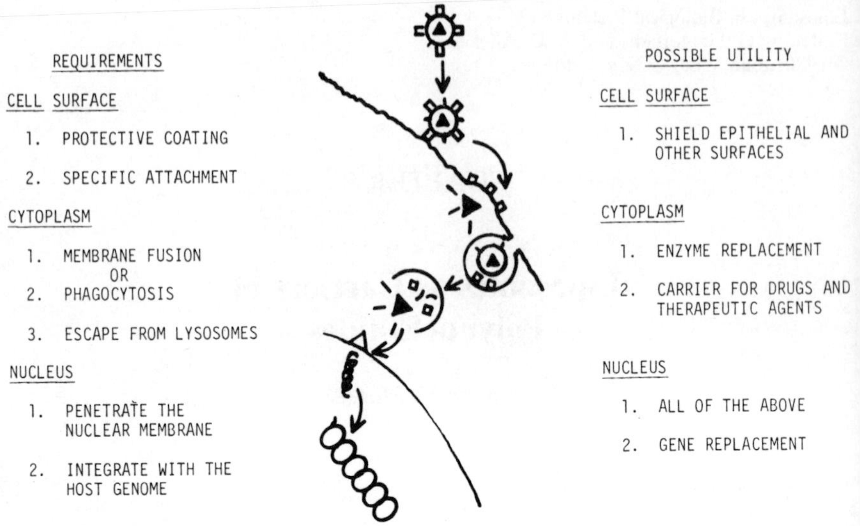

Figure 1 Interactions of membrane-enclosed viruses with cells. Listed on the left are requirements and types of interactions of virus components which are observed with various viruses during the infection process. Shown on the right are possible ways in which synthetic virus-like particles might be used to deliver materials to various cellular compartments

A subsequent study showed that protein-containing, cationic liposomes prepared from sphingomyelin, cholesterol, dicetylphosphate, and stearylamine (S–C–DCP–SA), and containing entrapped horseradish peroxidase, interacted with cells in several different ways. Clumped particles remained on the exterior of cells, some individual liposomes were phagocytized and some appeared to have fused with the cellular membrane (Magee *et al.*, 1974). Other investigators have further defined optimal lipid compositions which may promote fusion with the cellular membrane (see Poste, this volume, Poste *et al.*, 1976, Pagano and Weinstein, 1978).

A more direct analogy to the virus model might consist of liposomes which contain a biologically active nucleic acid trapped inside. We elected to prepare liposomes containing the synthetic double-stranded polyribonucleotide, polyinosinic : polycytidylic acid (poly(I) : poly(C)). Our choice was governed by several factors: (1) The compound has been shown to be a potent inducer of interferon in the animal, although undesirable side effects were observed (see Finter, 1973). (2) Our previous research interest included studies of interferon and its mode of action (Magee and Levine, 1970; Magee and Griffith, 1972). (3) Radiolabelled polynucleotides were available which facilitated quantitative studies.

It is important to note that these experiments were carried out with multilamellar liposomes that had been treated briefly with sonic vibration to break up large aggregates. We have been unable to prepare small unilamellar vesicles with sufficient amounts of incorporated poly(I) : poly(C) for study. Mayhew *et al.* (1977) have prepared large, unilamellar vesicles containing entrapped poly(I) : poly(C).

2. PREPARATION OF LIPOSOMES CONTAINING POLYRIBONUCLEOTIDES

The compositions of several liposome preparations used in our initial studies (Straub, *et al.*, 1974) are given in Table 1. A small amount of [^{14}C] cholesterol was incorporated into each to provide a radioactive marker. Several of the preparations showed a loss of [^{14}C]cholesterol as a result of the formation of some small particles during the sonic treatment. Liposomes also were prepared using [^{14}C]poly(I):poly(C), and stearylamine-containing liposomes were found to incorporate the polymer almost quantitatively. The partial loss of cholesterol from sonicated liposomes (Table 1) did not result in any decrease in the amount of [^{14}C] poly(I):poly(C) trapped because both S–C–DCP–SA and S–C–DCP–SA (no sonic) contained similar, high levels. The stoichiometry of poly(I) : poly(C) incorporation has been examined by preparing positively charged liposomes with increasing concentrations of [^{14}C]poly(I):poly(C) in the aqueous phase (Table 2). A maximum of 2 mg of the polymer became associated with 20 mg of lipid, although the per cent incorporated declined with increasing concentration of poly(I):poly(C) in the aqueous phase. Negatively charged liposomes lacking stearylamine (S–C–DCP) retained only 8–9% of the added polyribonucleotide, in keeping with the percentage of aqueous phase that becomes trapped inside liposomes during their preparation.

Quite different results were obtained by Kulpa and Tinghitella (1976) who reported only 15–18% association of poly (U) with either dicetylphosphate- or stearylamine-containing liposomes prepared with dipalmitoyl phosphatidylcholine and cholesterol. Possible explanations for their results include their use of a lower ratio of lipids to aqueous phase and extended sonication times which may have resulted in the generation of smaller vesicles and depolymerization of poly (U). The authors present data showing about a threefold decrease in incorporation with increasing time of sonication (to 10 minutes).

We have examined the proportion of polyribonucleotide associated with the exterior of positively charged liposomes. The amount of radioactivity which became acid soluble with time after incubation of [^{14}C]poly(C)-containing liposomes with 20 μg/ml pancreatic RNase was determined. The results showed that only 5% of the incorporated poly(C) was susceptible to nuclease digestion. Incubation of either [^{14}C]poly(I):poly(C)-

Table 1 Attachment of liposomes to L-929 cells[a]

Phospholipid	Composition		Cholesterol		
	Dicetyl-phosphate	Stearyl-amine	Incorporated (%)	Attached[b] (%)	Attached[b] (%)
Sphingomyelin	+	++	62.6	5.9,	6.0
Sphingomyelin (no sonic)	+	++	99.9	36.3,	37.8
Sphingomyelin (no dicetylphosphate)	−	++	54.4	20.0,	19.3
Sphingomyelin (no stearylamine)	+	−	55.5	<0.1,	<0.1
Lecithin (dipalmitoyl)	+	++	82.2	12.9,	11.7
Phosphatidylethanolamine	+	++	99.9	86.3,	86.8
Sphingomyelin–lecithin–phosphatidyl-ethanolamine (1 : 1 : 1)	−	++	56.4	31.2,	27.8

[a]In each case, 43 mg of phospholipid, 8 mg cholesterol, and 6 mg stearylamine and/or 3 mg dicetylphosphate (as indicated) were dissolved in chloroform–methanol, evaporated to thin films and resuspended in 1 mg/ml poly(I) : poly(C) and a small amount of phosphate buffer. The liposomes were sonically treated with a microprobe for 2 minutes, 15 seconds at a time with intermittent cooling and washed three times by centrifugation at $26,000 \times g$ for 30 minutes. The particles were resuspended in 5 ml of phosphate-buffered saline. The symbols + and ++ reflect relative concentrations.
[b]Cell monolayers were incubated with 0.05 ml of each liposome preparation (all contained [4-^{14}C]cholesterol) in 2.0 ml of Hanks solution for 2 hours at 37°C. (Reproduced from Straub et al. (1974) by permission of the American Society for Microbiology)

Table 2 Saturation of positively charged liposomes with poly(I) : poly(C)

Amount added (mg)	Average % incorporated	Amount incorporated (mg)
1.0	87	0.87
2.5	82	2.05
5.0	42	2.10
6.85	22	1.51

Each preparation contained S–C–DCP–SA (total of 20 mg) taken up in 1.0 ml of aqueous phase; 2 mg SA were present.

[^{14}C]poly(C)-containing liposomes with mouse serum showed that less than 2% of either polymer become acid soluble during a 4 hour incubation at 37 °C. A similar experiment with [^{14}C]poly(C)-containing negatively charged liposomes showed that 20% of the polymer was susceptible to RNase digestion. These results seemed rather surprising, but it must be noted that because of their relatively low content of polymer, only about 0.5 μg RNA/mg lipid was susceptible to RNase action while a 5% hydrolysis indicated that 1.5 μg RNA/mg lipid were released from positively charged vesicles. Kulpa and Tinghitella (1976) gave two sets of experimental data showing 37% or 75% susceptibility of poly(U) in positively charged particles to hydrolysis and 30%- or 35% for negatively charged particles. Mayhew *et al.* (1977) did not test for the amount of polymer which might be attached to the exterior of large, unilamellar liposomes, although the authors argue that it should be very low because of the negative charge of the liposomes.

An alternative explanation as to why only a low percentage of polymer could be released from the surface of positively charged liposomes by RNase might be that the electrostatic interaction between stearylamine and poly(C) prevented enzymatic hydrolysis. This possibility appears to be ruled out by the observation of Kulpa and Tinghitella (1976) who claim that incubation of empty liposomes with poly(U) did not result in the formation of any complexes which were resistant to hydrolysis by RNase.

Most of the studies concerned with the biological activity of polyribonucleotide-containing liposomes were carried out with S–C–DCP–SA (or S–C–SA) positively charged particles or S–C–DCP negatively charged particles. From the preceding discussion, the salient properties of these two types of liposomes are as follows:

(1) The positively charged liposomes had a high polymer/lipid ratio (typically, the S–C–DCP–SA liposomes contained 370 μg poly(I) :

poly(C) and 12 mg total lipid per ml) and 5% of the polymer was surface associated.

(2) The negatively charged liposomes had a low polymer/lipid ratio (typically the S–C–DCP liposomes contained 33 μg poly(I) : poly(C) and 12 mg total lipid per ml) and a maximum of 20% of the polymer was surface associated.

3. INTERACTION WITH CELLS

Liposomes of various composition were prepared containing [^{14}C] cholesterol as a marker and their adsorption to cells in tissue culture determined (Table 1). Approximately 600 μg of lipid were added to each monolayer of cells in 60 mm dishes. All of the preparations also contained poly(I):poly(C). Less than 0.1% of the added radioactivity became attached to cells in 2 hours when the liposomes carried a negative charge. Positively charged liposomes attached readily, and 20% of S–C–SA liposomes attached while 6% of S–C–DCP–SA became cell associated. A non-sonicated preparation containing larger aggregates of phospholipid absorbed to a greater percentage (36%). Microscopically visible clumps were attached to cells in the latter case.

Liposome preparations appeared to be relatively non-toxic to cells in tissue culture when observed for short periods. Quite a different picture emerged when observations were extended over the 2 day period required for the viral resistance assay. After challange with 100 PFU of vesicular stomatitis virus, cells were overlaid with agar-containing medium and incubated at 37 °C for 48 hours before staining with a vital stain. The standard preparation was toxic when individual 60 mm dishes were treated with 300 μg lipid or more (0.025 ml). The same degree of toxicity was observed whether liposomes contained only poly(I):poly(C) at 37 or 370 μg/ml or poly(I) at 370 μg/ml. Plaque reductions were observed with poly(I)-containing liposomes only when toxic levels of lipid were approached, confirming this compound's lack of activity for interferon induction regardless of the mode of presentation to cells.

The standard preparation of liposomes protected cells from virus infection at one-seventh the toxic concentration (5 μg poly(I):poly(C); 43 μg lipid gave a 50% reduction in plaques). Liposomes containing dipalmitoyl phosphatidylcholine instead of sphingomyelin gave an identical activity/toxicity ratio. In contrast to these results, 100 μg/ml of poly(I):poly(C) were required to give a 50% plaque reduction. The activity of the free polymer was greatly potentiated (to 0.1 μg/ml) by a pretreatment of cells with DEAE–dextran (Straub *et al.*, 1974).

Pretreatment of cells with DEAE–dextran did not potentiate activity of the standard preparations of liposomes (± twofold). An exception was found in the case of negatively charged liposomes containing dicetylphosphate and lacking stearylamine. These liposomes were inactive and non-toxic to levels of 1,800 μg lipid/dish, an observation that correlated with their failure to adsorb to cells (<0.1%). In DEAE–dextran pretreated cells, activity was noted at 1.6 μg poly(I):poly(C) and toxicity at double this level (3.3 μg; 1,220 μg lipid/dish). It can be assumed that increased quantities of the negatively charged liposomes become cell-associated as the result of the DEAE–dextran treatment of the cells.

The significance of an endpoint of 5 μg poly(I):poly(C) for the positively charged particles in view of the observed toxicity at 37 and 55 μg is difficult to assess. It is apparent that the poly(I):poly(C) was not presented to cells in the most optimal fashion for interferon induction; it is, however, quite possible that activity is directly correlated with only the amount of poly(I):poly(C) attached to the exterior of the particles (susceptible to RNase). Several lines of evidence have suggested that the polymer stimulates interferon induction via a cell surface interaction (DeClercq and DeSomer, 1972; Taylor-Papadimitriou and Kallos, 1973).

More favourable results in tissue culture have been reported by Mayhew *et al.* (1977) using poly(I):poly(C) entrapped in large, unilamellar liposomes prepared from phosphatidylserine. When compared to free poly(I) : poly(C), from three to nine times as much polymer became cells associated, when presented to the cells in the liposome entrapped form. About 10^6 cells were incubated with 1 μmol of lipid and from 1–4% became cell-associated. No cellular toxicity was observed at this level. The induction of resistance to virus infection in human fibroblast cells was more efficient using the encapsulated agent by about the same ratio as observed for increased uptake by the cells. Thus, these liposomes were less toxic than those used by us, and the human fibroblasts were more sensitive to induction of viral resistance by poly(I) : poly(C) than were mouse L-cells. The salient point in our experiments was that incubation of cells with entrapped poly(I) : poly(C) was much less effective for interferon induction than was a pretreatment of cells with DEAE–dextran, followed by the free polymer. These results emphasized the importance of interaction of poly(I):poly(C) with the cell surface for induction.

Mayhew *et al.* (1977) suggest that their phosphatidylserine liposomes most likely fused with the cell membrane and liberated poly(I):poly(C) into the cytoplasm. Considerably more experimental evidence must be accumulated, however, before any conclusion can be reached concerning the question of whether induction of interferon and cellular resistance to viruses by poly(I):poly(C) takes place exclusively at the cell surface or whether the inducer must enter the cell. An interesting corollary to this question concerns the suggestion that cytotoxicity of poly(I):poly(C) may itself be mediated by the interaction of the polymer with cellular receptors on the surface of cells (DeClercq and DeSomer, 1975). Theoretically, such an interaction could be circumvented by a vesicle that fused with the cell membrane.

4. BIOLOGICAL ACTIVITY IN ANIMALS

Both positively and negatively charged liposomes containing poly(I):poly(C) have been shown to be potent inducers of interferon in the mouse (Straub *et al.*, 1974; Magee *et al.*, 1976). Groups of animals were injected intravenously with liposomes or free poly(I):poly(C) (Figure 2) and levels of interferon in serum were determined at various times. Peak production of interferon occurred between 4 and 8 hours after injection of free poly(I) : poly(C) at 10–100 μg/mouse. Liposomes (S–C–DCP–SA; 37 μg poly(I):poly(C)/mouse) induced higher levels of circulating interferon (note logarithmic scale) which persisted for longer times.

Additional experiments established that free poly(I):poly(C) and liposomes containing the polymer gave parallel dose–response curves with the liposome-enclosed agent showing 10–20 times the activity of the free

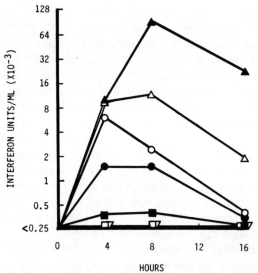

Figure 2 Interferon in the sera of mice after intravenous injection of poly(I):poly(C), poly(I), saline, or liposomes containing poly(I):poly(C). The sera from four mice were pooled for each time period and assayed for interferon. Symbols: ●, 10 μg; ○, 20 μg; △, 100 μg of poly(I) : poly(C) per mouse; ▽ 100 μg of poly(I); ▲, sphingomyelin liposomes [37.2 μg of poly(I) : poly(C)]; ■ sphingomyelin liposomes prepared with one-tenth concentration of poly(I) : poly(C) [3.7 μg of poly(I) : poly(C)]; and □, saline. (Reproduced from Straub *et al.* (1974) by permission of the American Society for Microbiology)

polymer whether given in positively charged (S–C–DCP–SA or L–C–DCP–SA) or negatively charged particles. S–C–DCP–SA liposomes also were active when injected intraperitoneally or intramuscularly. Negative liposomes did not produce a prolonged stimulation of the interferon response, while useful levels of interferon (>2,000 units/ml) were detected at 48 hours post-injection when positively charged particles were injected by either of the three routes.

5. FATE OF POLYNUCLEOTIDE-CONTAINING LIPOSOMES IN ANIMALS

Multilamellar liposomes containing poly(I):poly(C) were cleared very rapidly from the blood of mice following intravenous injection. Within 3 minutes, 88% of the dose had disappeared. These measurements were

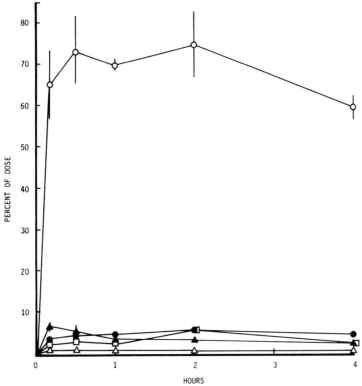

Figure 3 The localization of sphingomyelin liposomes [containing 29 μg of [^{14}C]poly(I):poly(C)] in organs of the mouse after intravenous injection. Symbols: $\circ$, liver; $\blacktriangle$, lung; $\bullet$, spleen; $\square$, muscle; and $\triangle$, kidney. (Reproduced from Straub *et al.* (1974) by permission of the American Society for Microbiology)

made on whole blood with S–C–DCP–SA liposomes containing [^{14}C] poly(I):poly(C) after preliminary measurements showed that the liposomes adsorbed to or co-sedimented with erythrocytes (Straub *et al.*, 1974). Juliano and Stamp (1975) have measured plasma clearance rates in rats and found that large liposomes were cleared much more rapidly than unilamellar vesicles. By 10 minutes, 65% of the radioactivity of the injected dose was in the liver (Figure 3). About 7% was found initially in the lungs and radioactivity recovered in the spleen rose to 6% of the dose by 2 hours. As would be expected, radioactivity reached the liver more slowly when liposomes were given intraperitoneally (Figure 4). Residual radioactivity which could be washed out of the peritoneal cavity declined from 85% at 10 minutes to only 8% of the dose by 4 hours.

Figure 5 summarizes distribution data of this type for liver and spleen when poly(I):poly(C) was injected as the free polymer or entrapped in positively or negatively charged liposomes. The times selected for presentation (10 minutes following intravenous injections for liver and 4 hours for the remaining data) generally reflect the times of highest recovery of radioactivity of the dose in the liver and spleen. The original publications should be consulted for additional details. It is apparent that high recoveries of the injected dose were obtained in liver when [^{14}C]

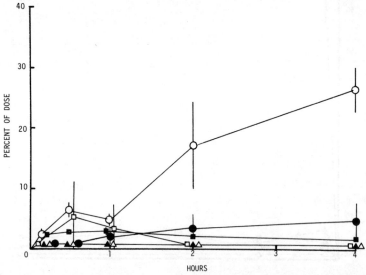

Figure 4 The localization of spingomyelin liposomes [containing 29 μg of [^{14}C]poly(I):poly(C)] in organs of the mouse after intraperitoneal injection. Symbols: ○ , liver; ▲ , lung; ● , spleen: ■ , muscle; △ , kidney; and □ , omentum. (Reproduced from Straub *et al.* (1974) by permission of the American Society for Microbiology)

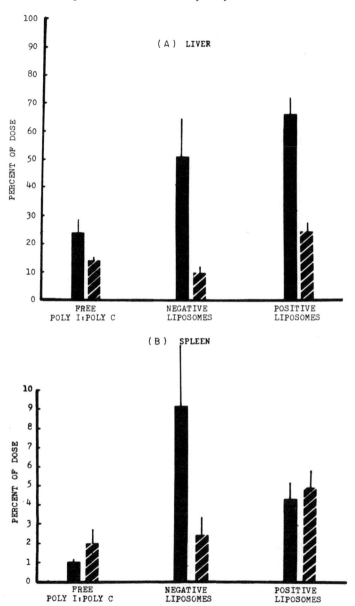

Figure 5 The localization of radioactivity in liver (A) and spleen (B) following injection of [^{14}C]poly(I):poly(C) as the free polymer or entrapped in negatively or positively charged liposomes. Solid bars, intravenous injections; cross-hatched bars, intraperitoneal injections. Data for intravenous injection in liver were taken 10 minutes after injection, and for intraperitoneal injections, at 4 hours. Data for spleen (B) were taken at 4 hours. Data from Straub *et al.* (1974) and Magee *et al.* (1976)

Table 3 Average recovery of polymeric [^{14}C]Poly(I):Poly(C) at 4 hours after intravenous injection

| Organ | Dosage | Fraction of the dose | | | Ratio: liposome/ free |
		Total	Acid insoluble	High mol. wt.	
Liver	Free	0.29	0.087	0.051	—
	Neg. liposome	0.42	0.23	0.16	3.1
	Pos. liposome	0.66	0.26	0.24	4.7
Spleen	Free	0.014	0.0068	0.0046	—
	Neg. liposome	0.069	0.040	0.034	7.4
	Pos. liposome	0.045	0.017	0.015	3.3

From Magee *et al.*, 1976.

poly(I):poly(C) was given intravenously in either encapsulated form, and poor uptake was observed following intraperitoneal injection of negatively charged particles (Figure 5A). Encapsulation also led to increased uptake of polymer by the spleen, especially following intravenous injection of negatively charged liposomes. Jonah *et al.* (1975) also have observed that negatively charged liposomes (containing EDTA) were taken up to a higher degree by spleen than were positively charged particles.

The results just discussed dealt with the distribution of total radioactivity of the dose taken up by various organs in the mouse. Of more interest is the determination of how encapsulation of polyribonucleotides might delay or prevent hydrolytic breakdown of the polymers. This is especially true in the case of the present experiments where the interferon response was greatly extended over that seen when free poly(I):poly(C) was injected. For these experiments, groups of animals were injected with the free or encapsulated [^{14}C]poly(I):poly(C) and total RNA was extracted from liver and spleen at 4 hours after intravenous injection. The amount of [^{14}C] poly(I) remaining in high molecular weight form was estimated by sucrose density gradient centrifugation (Table 3). The liver was found to contain three times as much high molecular weight material when poly(I) : poly(C) was given in negatively charged liposomes and five times as much when given in positively charged liposomes compared to that obtained when the free polymer was injected. Similarly, the ratios were seven and three for spleen for negatively and positively charged particles, respectively.

This type of analysis was extended to longer times for positively charged liposomes injected intravenously or intraperitoneally (Figure 6). Note that even at 48 hours, over 4% of the dose was recovered in high molecular weight form in liver and 1% from spleen when liposomes were given

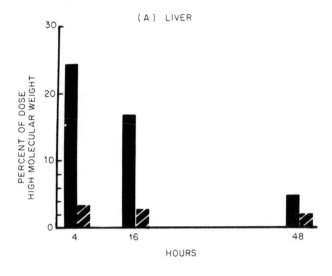

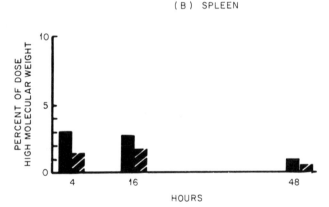

Figure 6 Recovery of high molecular weight [^{14}C]poly(I) from pooled samples of liver (A) and spleen (B) following injection of [^{14}C]poly(I):poly(C) entrapped in positively charged liposomes. Solid bars, intravenous injections; cross-hatched bars, intraperitoneal injections. Data from Magee *et al.* (1976)

intravenously. Similar measurements carried out following intraperitoneal injections showed 2% of the dose in liver and 0.5% in spleen at 48 hours. The per cent of high molecular weight material in liver never exceeded 4.3% of the dose following intraperitoneal injections.

From this it is evident that the radioactivity accumulating in the liver following intraperitoneal injections (reaching 22–28% of the dose for positively charged liposomes) (Figure 4) consisted mostly of low molecular weight metabolites of [^{14}C]poly(I).

These data do not provide proof concerning the mechanism of how positively charged liposomes stimulate the prolonged production of interferon in the mouse, but they do show that intact polymer is detectable for at least 48 hours. Thus, it seems likely that the continuing presence of intact inducer is necessary to obtain the response. It is well established that repeated injections of inducers of interferon lead to an unresponsive state in the animal in which no further interferon is produced (see Finter, 1973). We have found that repeated intravenous injections of encapsulated poly(I) : poly(C) also lead to the hyporeactive state, indicating that the prolonged response observed with a single injection cannot be augmented by multiple injections given at later times.

6. CONCLUSIONS AND FUTURE PROSPECTS

In common with other animal studies using multivesicular liposomes, our results show that particles were taken up primarily by the liver with lesser amounts going to spleen and lung. This distribution proved to be particularly advantageous because these organs are the ones most frequently implicated for interferon production (Finter, 1973; Magee and Griffith, 1972). The data also clearly indicated that polyribonucleotides are protected from hydrolytic cleavage in the body for extended periods when given in encapsulated form. In terms of the virus model discussed above, it should be feasible to incorporate any species of nucleic acid into liposomes of widely differing properties and expect that the nucleic acid will be protected while in the circulation and be delivered to various organs of the body.

For maximum utility, a vastly enhanced degree of homing to tissues of interest will be necessary. Initial progress in this direction has been made by incorporating cell-specific antibody into liposomes (Gregoriadis and Neerunjun, 1975). In agreement with our earlier data (Magee and Miller, 1972), these workers found appreciable amounts of antibody to be located at the surface of the particles. Furthermore, an increased uptake by cells towards which the antibody was directed was obtained in tissue culture experiments (Gregoriadis and Neerunjun, 1975; Magee *et al.*, 1978). Juliano and Stamp (1976) have reported increased homing using liposomes with surface attached lectins.

It would be most desirable to be able to retain the option of whether liposomes will be phagocytized or will fuse with target cells *in vivo*. Present evidence suggests that in animals, liposomes are taken up almost exclusively by phagocytosis by macrophagic elements of the reticuloendothelial system. In order to avoid this filtering mechanism liposomes should be relatively small in size, lack surface properties that trigger the phagocytic process, and have surface groups that promote a high degree of binding to the desired tissue. Highly fusogenic liposomes would present the hazard of extensive interaction with red blood cells and capillary walls, unless they also possessed a very high degree of tissue specificity. Hopefully, each of these desirable traits may be designed into phospholipid vesicles as research in this area continues.

Acknowledgement

This work was supported by Public Health Service Grants AI-10828 and AI-1310601 from the National Institute of Allergy and Infectious Diseases.

REFERENCES

DeClercq, E. and DeSomer, P. (1972). *J. Gen. Virol.*, **16**, 435.
DeClercq, E. and DeSomer, P. (1975). *J. Gen. Virol.*, **27**, 35.
Finter, N. B. (1973). *Interferon and Interferon Inducers*, American Elsevier, New York.
Gregoriadis, G. and Neerunjun, E. D. (1975). *Biochem. Biophys. Res. Commun.*, **65**, 537.
Jonah, M. M., Cerny, E. A. and Rahman, Y. E. (1975). *Biochim. Biophys. Acta.*, **401**, 336.
Juliano, R. L. and Stamp, D. (1975). *Biochem. Biophys. Res. Commun.*, **63**, 651.
Juliano, R. L. and Stamp, D. (1976). *Nature (London)*, **261**, 235.
Kulpa, C. A. and Tinghitella, T. J. (1976). *Life Sci.*, **19**, 1879.
Magee, W. E. and Levine, S. (1970). *Annal. New York Acad. Sci.*, **173**, 362.
Magee, W. E. and Griffith, M. J. (1972). *Life Sci.*, **11**, 1081.
Magee, W. E. and Miller, O. V. (1972). *Nature (London)*, **235**, 339.
Magee, W. E., Goff, C. W., Schoknecht, J., Smith, M. D. and Cherian, K. (1974). *J. Cell. Biol.*, **63**, 492.
Magee, W. E., Talcott, M. L., Straub, S. X. and Vriend, C. Y. (1976). *Biochim. Biophys. Acta*, **451**, 610.
Magee, W. E., Cronenberger, J. H. and Thor, D. E. (1978). *Cancer Res.*, **38**, 1173.
Mayhew, E., Papahadjopoulos, D., O'Malley, J. A., Carter, W. A. and Vail, W. J. (1977). *Mol. Pharm.* **13**, 488.
Pagano, R. E. and Weinstein, J. N. (1978). *Ann Rev. Biophys. BioEng*, **7**, 435.
Poste, G., Papahadjopoulos, D. and Vail, W. J. (1976). In *Methods in Cell Biology*, Vol. **14**, p. 34. (ed. D. M. Prescott), Academic Press, New York.
Straub, S. X., Garry, R. F. and Magee, W. E. (1974). *Infec. Immun.*, **10**, 783.
Taylor-Papadimitriou, J. and Kallos, J. (1973). *Nature, New Biol.*, **245**, 143.

Liposomes in Biological Systems
Edited by G. Gregoriadis and A. C. Allison
©1980, John Wiley & Sons, Ltd.

CHAPTER 10

Liposomes and Chelating Agents

Y. E. Rahman

1. **Introduction**   266

2. **Problems and possible solutions of chelation therapy in metal poisonings**   266

3. **Preparation and characterization of liposomes containing chelating agents**   270
   3.1. Preparation   270
   3.2. Size determination   272
   3.3. Tests for stability   272
   3.4. Dose determination of chelating agents   273
   3.5. Discussion   274

4. **Oxicity of liposomes**   275
   4.1. Liposomes without chelating agents   275
   4.2. Liposomes with chelating agents   277
   4.3. Discussion   278

5. **Distribution of [^{14}C] EDTA transported by liposomes**   282
   5.1. At the tissue level   282
   5.2. At the cellular level   282
   5.3. At the subcellular level   287
   5.4. Discussion   287

6. **Liposome-encapsulated chelating agents for toxic metal removal**   289

7. **Summary**   294

   References   295

1. INTRODUCTION

The complex civilizations of man have been founded to a large extent on metal technology. Ever since times of antiquity, man has been contaminating himself and his environment with metals through mining, smelting, casting, and machining processes. During the last few decades, the progress of modern technology has constantly accelerated the contamination of our environment by heavy metals and other pollutants, leading to increasing hazards to human health.

The ideal approach to the problem of preventing metal poisoning in man would be a complete avoidance of human contact. Since high levels of hazardous metals are already present in the environment, this ideal is no longer attainable. However, effective treatments should be available for the large number of human populations already affected. Among the drugs used for treatment of metal poisoning are chelating agents. These drugs are chemicals that have the capability to bind the metal ions to form a more soluble complex of the metal–chelate, thereby allowing the toxic metal to be excreted from the human body. Although several metal chelators are now in clinical use, their therapeutic effectiveness is rather limited because of malabsorption, toxic side effects, and rapid degradation and excretion from the human body. For better treatment of metal poisonings, substantial improvements over the present available therapeutic methods is required. New approaches, both in drug design and drug delivery system, are also needed.

In this report, I describe a new approach to the delivery of metal chelators, with the aim of increasing their therapeutic efficacy. The foundation of this approach is cell biology, particularly in the areas of membrane chemistry, membrane movement, and cellular enzymology. The significant progress achieved in this field during recent years has made my approach to the metal toxicity problem possible.

2. PROBLEMS AND POSSIBLE SOLUTIONS OF CHELATION THERAPY IN METAL POISONINGS

An 'ideal' chelating agent for a given toxic metal should have the following characteristics:

(1) high stability constant for the metal ion;
(2) high specificity for the metal ion, relative to other essential metal ions present in the animal body;
(3) high stability against enzymatic degradation in the animal circulation prior to tissue uptake;
(4) low toxicity of drug and drug-metal complex (the latter should be less toxic than the metal);

(5) high efficiency in promoting the metal excretion from the animal body (this requires that the chelating agent reaches the sites of metal deposits, and forms an excretable metal–chelate complex).

Among the chelating agents so far investigated, the synthetic polyaminopolycarboxylic acids such as ethylenediaminetetraacetic acid (EDTA) and diethylenetriaminepentaacetic acid (DTPA) are prominent (Catsch, 1964) because of: (a) their relatively high affinity for a large number of metal ions; (b) their water solubility; and (c) their resistance to metabolic breakdown by animal tissues.

Another group of commonly used chelating agents contains sulphydryl compounds. Of this group, 2,3-dimercaptopropanol (BAL) and D-penicillamine (PA) are being used for removal of mercury (Alajouanine et al., 1957; Williams and Bridge, 1958; Aposhian, 1960; Magliulo, 1974; Perrin and Agarwal, 1976), lead (Magliulo, 1974; Perrin and Agarwal, 1976; Foreman, 1961; Vitale et al., 1973), arsenic (Perrin and Agarwal, 1976; Peters et al., 1945; Brieger, 1960), gold (Magliulo, 1974; Perrin and Agarwal, 1976), and copper (Perrin and Agarwal, 1976; Walshe, 1956; Scheinberg and Sternlieb, 1960) from man.

Some naturally occurring substances are also known to exhibit high specificity for binding metal. Among them, desferrioxamine (DF) has been used for primary or secondary iron overload in man (Moeschlin and Schnider, 1963; Wohler, 1963; Smith, 1964; Walshe et al., 1965; Hallberg et al., 1966; Thomson et al., 1967; Cumming et al., 1969; Lukens and Newman, 1971; Modell and Beck, 1974). This compound is obtained from ferrioxamine B, a product derived from *Streptomyces pilosus* by chemical removal of its complex-bound trivalent iron. DF is not only the most potent but also by far the most specific ferric complexing agent now in clinical use.

Even though the use of EDTA and DTPA in therapy of metal poisonings, including radionuclides such as plutonium (Pu), has become acceptable during the last 20 years, there are serious limitations in their usefulness. The first is that these chelating agents are essentially unable to penetrate cellular membranes (Catsch, 1964; Foreman, 1960), so that they are unable to reach the metal deposits within the cells. This limitation results in the low efficacy of EDTA and DTPA for removing intracellular toxic metals. Secondly, these drugs are rapidly excreted (Catsch, 1964; Foreman et al., 1953), making it necessary to give them in closely repeated injections. Third, toxic side effects have been reported after repeated doses of EDTA or DTPA (Foreman et al., 1956; Fahey et al., 1961; Fairbanks et al., 1963; Barry et al., 1974; Morgan and Smith, 1974; Planas-Bohne and Ebel, 1975). Higher toxicity in the foetus than in the adult has also been observed (Fischer et al., 1975; Mays et al., 1976).

The undesirable properties of BAL include its low solubility in water, local irritation, and its rapid degradation and oxidation in the animal body (Perrin and Agarwal, 1976). In addition, redistribution in the body of mercury [inorganic mercury (Fitzsimmons and Kozelka, 1950; Berlin and Lewander, 1965; Magos, 1968), methylmercury (Berlin and Ullberg, 1963; Berlin *et al.*, 1965) or phenylmercury (Berlin and Ullberg, 1963; Berlin *et al.*, 1965; Berlin and Rylander, 1964)] and cadmium after administration of BAL has been reported. In the case of organic mercury, an enhanced toxic effect on the brain has been induced as a result of such chelation therapy (Berlin and Ullberg, 1963; Berlin *et al.*, 1965; Berlin and Rylander, 1964; Chenoweth, 1968). While PA has the advantage of being absorbed by the gastrointestinal tract and of being equally effective when given by mouth and by the intravenous route (Chenoweth, 1968; Selander, 1967), this chelating agent is less potent than BAL or the polyaminopolycarboxylic acids, and toxic effects have also been reported (Perrin and Agarwal, 1976; Selander, 1967).

DF is now the chelating agent of choice for treatment of acute iron poisoning and diseases due to iron overload, including transfusional haemosiderosis in Cooley's anaemia (Perrin and Agarwal, 1976; Moeschlin and Schnider, 1963; Wohler, 1963; Smith, 1964; Walsh *et al.*, 1965; Hallberg *et al.*, 1966; Thomson *et al.*, 1967; Cumming *et al.*, 1969; Lukens and Newman, 1971; Modell and Beck, 1974). However, it is rapidly degraded in the plasma (Keberle, 1964). Other unfortunate characteristics are that it is not easily taken up by the cells of the critical organs, e.g. liver, spleen, and bone marrow (Bobeck-Rutsaert *et al.*, 1972), and it is rapidly excreted in the urine (Keberle, 1964; Bobeck-Rutsaert *et al.*, 1972; Constantoulakis *et al.*, 1974).

To date, attempts have been made to improve the therapeutic efficacy of many chelating agents. The usual approaches are:

(1) New syntheses of chelating agents, based on structural design (*a*) to obtain ligands that form metal complexes with high stability constants and with a better selectivity for specific metal ions (Muller, 1970; Lehn and Sauvage, 1971; Dietrich *et al.*, 1973; Jones *et al.*, 1975; MacDonald *et al.*, 1976); and (*b*) to increase the lipid solubility, with the hope of inducing a higher uptake by tissue cells (Catsch, 1961; Markley, 1963; Karesh *et al.*, 1977).

(2) Modifications of the mode of drug administration in order to counteract the rapid excretion of the chelating agents. For example, the use of continuous infusion, either by the subcutaneous (Propper *et al.*, 1976) or intravenous route (Hussain *et al.*, 1976).

(3) Use of ion-exchange resins to complex specific metals in the gastrointestinal system (Perrin and Agarwal, 1976; Clarkson *et al.*, 1973). The therapeutic value of such an approach has not yet been evaluated.

Recently I introduced yet another approach—the use of liposomes as carriers to transport chelating agents into tissue cells. Results have been encouraging (Rahman *et al.*, 1973; Rahman and Rosenthal, 1973; Rahman *et al.*, 1974b; Rosenthal *et al.*, 1975; Rahman and Wright, 1975). The advantages of this approach are the following:

(1) The encapsulation of chelating agents within liposomes protects the drug from enzymatic degradation during transport to the target organs.

(2) Liposomes containing chelating agents are efficiently taken up by cells of the reticuloendothelial system, where particulate toxic metals are also mainly located (Rahman and Wright, 1975; De Barsy *et al.*, 1976; Wright and Rahman, 1976).

(3) Chelating agents transported by liposomes can be directed to the appropriate target organs, thereby minimizing possible drug toxicity to other organs and allowing the dose of the chelating agent to be reduced (Rosenthal *et al.*, 1975).

(4) Most toxic metals, particularly in their particulate form, are mainly localized in lysosomes of phagocytic cells (Rahman and Lindenbaum, 1964; Polliak and Rachmilewitz, 1973; Goldfischer, 1963). Since liposomes, when injected intravenously into animals, are also associated with lysosomes (Rahman and Wright, 1975; de Barsy *et al.*, 1976; Gregoriadis and Ryman, 1972; Rahman *et al.*, 1974a; Wisse *et al.*, 1976; de Duve *et al.*, 1974), direct contact between the intracellular toxic metals and the liposome-transported chelating agents can be achieved. In this way, efficient excretion of the soluble metal–chelate complex can be accomplished (Rahman *et al.*, 1973).

(5) Because liposomes are made of lipids, immunological reactions are not likely to be induced after repeated injections.

(6) Because phospholipids are common constituents of all living cells, they are readily assimilated.

(7) Surface characteristics of liposomes can be modified by varying the lipid constituents, in order to achieve delivery of a given chelating agent to a specific tissue. For example, the surface charge of the liposomes can be altered (Jonah *et al.*, 1975), or specific chemical groups can be inserted on the surface (Gregoriadis and Neerunjun, 1975; Weissmann *et al.*, 1975; Juliano and Stamp, 1976; Gregoriadis, 1977; Jonah *et al.*, 1979).

During the last few years, I have used the liposome approach to remove toxic metals from experimental animals. An overview of present results is reported here.

3. PREPARATION AND CHARACTERIZATION OF LIPOSOMES CONTAINING CHELATING AGENTS

3.1. Preparation

The methods- used to prepare unilamellar and multilamellar liposomes containing chelating agents are mainly based on the original method described by Bangham (Bangham *et al*., 1965). However, certain aspects specific to preparations of liposomes containing chelating agents merit some comments. To date, I have succeeded in encapsulating the following chelating agents within liposomes:

(1) Ethylenediaminetetraacetic acid (EDTA)

$$HOOC-H_2C \diagdown N-CH_2-CH_2-N \diagup CH_2-COOH$$
$$HOOC-H_2C \diagup \qquad\qquad\qquad \diagdown CH_2-COOH$$

(2) Diethylenetriaminepentaacetic acid (DTPA)

$$HOOC-H_2C \diagdown N-CH_2-CH_2-N-CH_2-CH_2-N \diagup CH_2-COOH$$
$$HOOC-H_2C \diagup \qquad |_{CH_2-COOH} \qquad\qquad \diagdown CH_2-COOH$$

(3) D-Penicillamine (PA)

$$CH_3-\overset{\overset{\displaystyle CH_3}{|}}{C}-\overset{\overset{\displaystyle H}{|}}{C}-COOH$$
$$\qquad\quad |_{SH} \quad |_{NH_2}$$

(4) Desferrioxamine (DF)

(5) Phthalyltetrathioacetic acid (PTTA)

For DTPA, only multilamellar liposomes have been prepared in our laboratory. A 25% aqueous solution of DTPA, in the form of $CaNa_3DTPA$, and sealed in sterile ampoules (Geigy Chem Co., Ardsley, NY), is usually used. After the liposomes are made by the stirring method, a suspension of DTPA-liposomes in the original 25% DTPA is obtained. In order to recover the non-trapped DTPA solution for re-use purposes, we collect the liposomes by centrifugation instead of gel filtration. After a centrifugation at 800 x g for 5 minutes in the suspending high density 25% DTPA solution, the liposomes are collected at *the top* of the solution as a white band. This layer of liposomes can be easily removed with a Pasteur pipette. Washing is accomplished by several centrifugations and resuspensions in 0.9% saline. In this medium, the DTPA-liposomes are readily sedimented to the *bottom* of the tube by centrifuging at 800 x g for 5 minutes. Neutral liposomes, prepared with a mixture of phosphatidylcholine (PC) and cholesterol, are mostly used in our experiments, although liposomes of positive surface charge (prepared by adding stearylamine to the lipid mixture), and of negative charge (by adding phosphatidylserine, phosphatidic acid, or dicetylphosphate to the lipid mixture) have also occasionally been used.

For the preparation of liposomes containing [^{14}C] EDTA (Amersham Searle Corp., Arlington Heights, Ill.), solutions of CaNa$_2$[^{14}C] EDTA at concentrations ranging from 5 to 25% were used. After the liposomes are formed, the suspension is subjected to collection and washing processes similar to those described for DTPA-liposomes. The EDTA-liposomes, of neutral, positive, or negative surface charge are collected after centrifugation at the top of the suspending medium. Because a large proportion of these EDTA-liposomes do not sediment well in normal saline (Jonah *et al.*, 1975), they are washed with a *non-radioactive* EDTA solution. For *in vivo* studies, with unilamellar liposomes, the washed EDTA-liposomes are prepared by sonication of multilamellar liposomes, and the unincorporated EDTA solution is removed from liposomes by gel filtration on Sephadex G-50.

We have also prepared liposomes containing EDTA or DTPA with various lipid compositions, (Jonah *et al.*, 1975), including glycolipids (Jonah *et al.*, 1979). The per cent incorporation of EDTA or DTPA within liposomes usually varies from 0.5 to 2%.

For PA-liposomes, various concentrations of aqueous solutions of PA have been used. Liposomes have been prepared with a mixture of PC and cholesterol; about 20–30% of the total PA is incorporated within these liposomes.

DF-liposomes have been prepared with DF solutions varying from 5 to 12% in concentrations; it should also be easy to prepare solutions of higher concentration. Liposomes of neutral, positive, or negative surface charge have been made. The per cent incorporation of DF within these liposomes varies from 6 to 30%.

PTTA-liposomes have been prepared with 5–10% aqueous solutions of PTTA. So far only a mixture of PC and cholesterol has been used for these liposomes.

3.2. Size Determination

Sizes of unilamellar liposomes are determined by electron microscopy after negative staining. We use a modified method based on those of Bangham and Horne (1964) and Papahadjopoulos *et al.* (1974). The unilamellar liposomes are stained for 10 minutes with 0.1% uranyl acetate, pH 4.0, on 400-mesh grids pretreated with 0.1% bovine serum albumin. Direct measurements of 500 to 1,000 liposomes from several representative micrographs usually are made. Unilamellar liposomes containing DTPA, prepared by a 30 minute sonication, ranged from 400 to 600 Å in diameter.

Sizing of multilamellar liposomes has presented some difficulties. Initially, we measured the diameters of 2,000 liposomes directly on light microscope microphotographs (Rahman *et al.*, 1974b) and determined the size–range distribution. This method not only lacks accuracy, particularly for liposomes smaller than 1 μm in diameter, but is also time consuming and tedious. We explored the feasibility of using an electron microscopic technique, but found it impractical due to the necessity of preparing a great many electron micrographs to obtain suitable liposome measurements. Recently, we have developed a method based on the procedure developed by Kubitschek for sizing micro-organisms (Kubitschek, 1958; Kubitschek, 1969). The system consists of a Coulter counter equipped with a 400-channel analyser. Liposomes in normal saline pass through a minute aperture (10–15 μm) through which an electric current flows. The passage of a relatively non-conducting particle leads to an increase in electrical resistance, giving rise to a transient increase of voltage across the aperture. The amplitude of the voltage pulse is proportional to the volume of the liposomes. Thus the distribution of pulse amplitudes represents the relative distribution of the volumes of the liposomes being analysed. Latex particles of known sizes are used as standards.

3.3. Tests for Stability

Early in our liposome studies, we found that liposomes prepared with partially degraded phospholipids tend to aggregate in small clumps and that leakage of encapsulated chelating agent increases with the degree of lipid oxidation. Aggregation of liposomes is probably due to lysophosphatides present in the phospholipids used to prepare liposomes. Lucy and co-workers (Poole *et al.*, 1970; Ahkong *et al.*, 1975) have demonstrated that membrane fusion can be induced by lysophosphatides. Increases in membrane permeability have also been correlated with the degree of membrane lipid oxiation (Klein, 1970). For potential clinical use, the importance of being able to prepare *stable liposomes* is only too evident. The first step is to use extreme care to prevent degradation and oxidation of stored phospholipids. Additions of certain antioxidants such as α-tocopherol, butylated hydroxyanisole (BHA), or butylated hydroxytoluene (BHT) can be made to the stored phospholipids without apparent interference with liposome formation.

Leakage of 40 to 45% of [^{14}C] EDTA from liposomes has been consistently observed (Figure 1). The surface charge of the liposomes does not seem to be a factor determining the rate of EDTA leakage with time. The [^{59}Fe]DF-liposomes, on the other hand, are more stable than the EDTA-liposomes; only about 5% of the [^{59}Fe]DF leaked out during a 14-day period.

3.4. Dose Determination of Chelating Agents

For experimental chelation therapy, when liposomes containing chelating agents are given to animals, the dosage of the encapsulated drug must be determined. We have used different radioactive tracers, the choice depending upon the particular chelating agent. Our methods for determining the administration dosage of the encapsulated drug are as

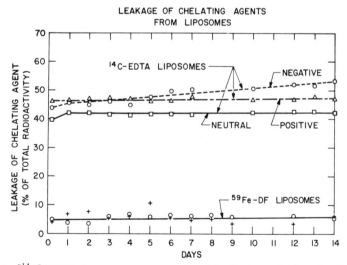

Figure 1 [^{14}C]EDTA liposomes were made with dipalmitoyl phosphatidylcholine and cholesterol (Chol), at a molar ratio of 1 : 1. Five mole per cent of phosphatidylserine (PS) was added to prepare the negatively charged liposomes; and 5 mole per cent of stearylamine (StAm) for the positively charged liposomes. [^{59}Fe]DF liposomes were made with DPPC and Chol, at a molar ratio of 1.5 : 1. Symbols (o, +) represent two separate experiments. The first time point was at 4 hours

follows:

EDTA—Since radiolabelled 2-[^{14}C]EDTA is commercially available, liposomes are prepared with this material adjusted to pH 7.4. Two or three separate radioactive liposome preparations are made at the same time and in the same manner as is used for the non-radioactive liposomes. For tissue distribution analysis, each mouse receives a liposome suspension containing between 50,000 and 100,000 dpm of the radioactive drug.

DTPA—Radiolabelled [^{45}CaNa$_3$]DTPA is prepared as follows to determine the dose of DTPA-liposomes. A 25% concentration of the non-radioactive DTPA solution in the acid form is first adjusted to pH 7.2 with concentrated NaOH. Then CaCl$_2 \cdot$ 2H$_2$O with a tracer amount of ^{45}CaCl$_2$ is added to form a [^{45}Ca]DTPA solution with a final DTPA/Ca molar radio of 1:1. The pH of the final solution is readjusted to 7.2 for liposome preparations. The radioactivity of [^{45}Ca]DTPA is used to determine the amount of drug encapsulated within liposomes. However, after liposomes are injected into animals and taken up by cells, [^{45}Ca]DTPA is released from the liposomes, and the ^{45}Ca rapidly exchanges with other calcium ions in the animal body. [^{45}Ca]DTPA liposomes are therefore not suitable for long-term tissue distribution studies.

PA—A trace amount of ^{45}CaCl$_2$ is added to the aqueous PA solution to be used for liposome preparation. For experimental chelation therapy, the radioactivity of [^{45}Ca]PA is used to determine the amount of drug incorporated within liposomes. No studies on tissue distribution of liposomal PA have been done to date.

DF—Radioiron-59 is used to label DF. Aqueous solutions of DF with a trace amount of added ^{59}FeCl$_3$ were used to determine the amount of DF incorporated within liposomes. However, only short-term (up to 24 hours) tissue distribution studies of liposomal DF have been done, because interpretation of studies employing radioiron labels is soon complicated by isotope exchange *in vivo*, and subsequent redistribution of the isotope.

PTTA—Calcium-45 is used to label PTTA for the purpose of dose determination. No tissue distribution studies have been done with this new chelating agent.

3.5. Discussion

The mean diameter of unilamellar liposomes, made of neutral phospholipids alone, was approximately 250 Å (Huang, 1969). However, when unilamellar liposomes were made with mixtures of phospholipid and cholesterol, Johnson found the mean diameter to be about 350 Å (Johnson, 1973). In our preparations of chelating agent liposomes, unilamellar liposomes made with PC and cholesterol at a weight ratio of 3 : 1 have a mean diameter ranging from 400 to 600 Å (Rahman and

Wright, unpublished results). Because particles of this size have limited inside volume, our *in vivo* experiments have been carried out only with multilamellar liposomes, which have a mean diameter 10 to 30 times larger. Although the precise total inside volume of a multilamellar liposome is difficult to estimate, they can encapsulate sufficient drug for effective therapy. The sizes of multilamellar liposomes prepared by stirring are rather heterogeneous. Juliano and Stamp have shown that the rate and site of *in vivo* uptake of small and large liposomes may be different (Juliano and Stamp, 1975). A new technique has recently been described by Deamer *et al.* (1976) that yields liposomes less heterogeneous in size, and with a single lipid bilayer. These liposomes have a mean diameter considerably larger than that of unilamellar liposomes obtained by the conventional sonication method.

We have also attempted, so far with limited success, to separate multilamellar liposomes into groups of more homogenous size by serial filtrations through filters made of different materials and by various gradient centrifugation.

One of the requirements for clinical application of liposomes is that sufficient amount of drug be encapsulated. The total amount of chelating agent that could be encapsulated is determined by: (1) the volume of the aqueous space in the centre and between the lipid bilayers of the liposomes; and (2) the solubility of the chelating agent. The higher the solubility of the chelating agent in aqueous medium, the higher the concentration of encapsulated chelating agent that could be obtained. However, drugs that are soluble in lipid solvents can also be incorporated into liposomes as part of the lipid bilayers; a larger total amount of drug can usually be incorporated under such conditions (Rahman *et al.*, 1975). New chelating agents attached with long chain hydrocarbons, as synthesized by Karesh and co-workers (Karesh *et al.*, 1977; Eckelman *et al.*, 1975), could be incorporated into the lipid bilayers.

4. TOXICITY OF LIPOSOMES

4.1. Liposomes Without Chelating Agents

Before liposomes can be introduced for clinical use as a drug delivery system, the possible toxic side effects of liposomal lipids, given in the form of spheroid particles, should be carefully examined. For this purpose, we inject into mice liposomes containing the common electrolyte, KCl. Signs of possible acute and subacute toxicity, as well as gross and microscopic pathological changes in certain major organs are being sought. The following results have so far been obtained after intravenous injection of

KCl-liposomes, made of PC/cholesterol, into young-adult CF # 1 female mice. The mice were observed for 2 weeks after liposome administration.

(1) No immediate or delayed toxicity was observed in mice after an intravenous injection of 5–50 mg of lipids as KCl-liposomes.

(2) There was no significant body weight change.

(3) There was no weight change in major organs, i.e., liver, spleen, kidney, lung, heart, brain, thymus. Histological studies of these organs are underway.

(4) Electron microscopic examination of the liver disclosed liposomes within hepatocytes and Kupffer cells 15 minutes after liposome injection. At 24 hours no striking morphological changes were seen in the hepatocytes, but vacuoles with liposome-like inclusions appeared in some of the Kupffer cells. Liver morphology was normal 1 week after KCl-liposome injection (Rahman and Wright, 1975).

(5) The protein content and levels of acid phosphatase, alkaline phosphatase, and glutamic dehydrogenase in liver, kidney, lung, and spleen were analysed 4 hours, 1, 3, and 7 days after injections. Acid phosphatase is a lysosomal enzyme, while alkaline phosphatase and glutamic

Table 1   Alkaline phosphatase activity of mouse tissues[a]

	Time after liposome injection	Tissues			
		Liver	Kidney	Lung	Spleen
Control	0	1.47 ±0.21	764 ± 131	69.1 ± 4.4	6.82 ± 2.37
Mice receiving KCl-liposomes	4 hours	2.08 ±0.71	864 ± 52	86.2 ± 4.4	6.08 ± 1.02
	1 day	3.84 ±0.02	847 ± 81	81.4 ±15.2	12.37 ± 0.56
	3 days	3.64 ±0.20	873 ± 59	66.6 ± 1.6	10.45 ± 0.10
	7 days	2.88 ±0.30	761 ± 19	80.3 ± 7.1	10.87 ± 3.10
Mice receiving DTPA-liposomes	1 day	4.37 ±0.40	953 ± 51	52.2 ± 4.2	9.47 ± 2.03
	3 days	9.34 ±0.42	1096 ± 110	64.1 ± 4.8	12.69 ± 0.82
	7 days	5.20 ±0.03	1058 ± 23	88.8 ± 4.6	9.60 ± 0.90

[a]Alkaline phosphatase activity is expressed in μg phosphate/mg protein/hour. Each group contains five mice. Values are mean enzyme activity ± the standard error of the mean.

dehydrogenase are both zinc-requiring enzymes. The total alkaline phosphatase activity was significantly increased in the liver and spleen, while a moderate increase was observed in kidney and lung (see upper part of Table 1). However, no changes were observed in protein content or in enzymatic activity of either acid phosphatase or glutamic dehydrogenase.

4.2. Liposomes with Chelating Agents

Liposomes containing either EDTA or DTPA and made of PC/cholesterol were used for toxicity studies in mice after intravenous injection. The following observations were made:

(1) There was no immediate or delayed toxicity. However, death due to pulmonary embolisms occurred when *aggregated* liposomes were injected (Rahman *et al.*, 1974b).

(2) There was no significant change in body weight 1 to 7 days after injection of DTPA-liposomes.

(3) A consistent increase in spleen weight was observed after a single or

ble 2 Spleen Weight Increase after Injection of Mice with DTPA Encapsulated in Liposomes[a]

	Route	Dose CaNa$_3$DTPA (mg/kg, each injection)	Number injections (once weekly)	Number of treated groups	Spleen weight ratio[b] Mean	Range
n-encapsulated DTPA	iv or ip	100 to 1000	1–4	12	0.96	0.89–1.10
capsulated KCl[c]	iv		1–4	5	1.01	0.90–1.09
capsulated DTPA	iv	25	1	1	1.06	—
	iv	50	1	3	1.34	1.27–1.46
	iv	100	1	6	1.55	1.29–1.95
	iv	100	2–4	5	2.68	2.31–2.91
	ip	100	1	2	1.50	1.42–1.59

liposomes were made of phosphatidylcholine and cholesterol, 3 : 1, and injected intravenously into
e which had received ~1 μCi/kg of 'mid-range' polymeric plutonium 3 days previously. All mice
e killed 7 days after the last injection of DTPA. Control mice received equivalent injection(s) of
er saline or KCl solution. Each treated or control group contained four to six mice (usually five
e). Data from five experiments are included.
e spleen weight ratio is the average wet spleen weight of each treated group divided by the average
spleen weight of the appropriate control group. In cases where data from more than one treated
p are included, the mean and range of the individual group means are given.
imals given encapsulated KCl received KCl-liposomes with or without an additional single injection
,000 mg/kg of CaNa$_3$DTPA. No significant spleen weight changes were observed. From Rosenthal
., 1975. (Reproduced by permission of Academic Press, Inc.)

K

multiple injections of DTPA-liposomes that contained at least 50 mg DTPA/kg (Table 2). Preliminary histological study indicated that EDTA-liposomes resulted in vacuolation of splenic medullary cells. No comparable vacuolation was found after injection of KC1-liposomes. No change in wet weight of other organs was noted.

(4) Since the liver takes up more liposomes than any other organ, attention has been focused on this organ. We have shown that liposomes can be phagocytized by hepatocytes as well as by Kupffer cells (Rahman and Wright, 1975). Increased numbers of lysosomes and autophagic vacuoles, particularly within the Kupffer cells, were observed at 15 and 24 hours after EDTA-liposome injection. In some cells, extensive areas of focal cytoplasmic degeneration were also seen (Figure 2). The morphology of the liver cells returned to normal about 7 days after liposome injection. A striking increase in macrophages was usually observed in the liver sinusoids 12 hours after an EDTA-liposome injection (Figure 3). This macrophage activation was not observed after KCl-liposome injections.

(5) The protein content as well as the acid phosphatase activity of liver, kidney, lung, and spleen remained unchanged from 1 to 7 days after DTPA-liposome injection. Alkaline phosphatase and glutamic dehydrogenase were analysed. The glutamic dehydrogenase in all four tissues was unchanged. However, alkaline phosphatase activity showed a threefold increase at 1 day and more than sixfold increase at 3 days. A moderate but significant increase was also observed in kidney and spleen (Table 1).

4.3. Discussion

Based on the limited data we have so far obtained, lipids given in the form of KCl-liposomes and in the usual required amount for *in vivo* studies, do not seem to be toxic to mice. However, still unexplained is the 1.5 to 2.6-fold increase in alkaline phosphatase activity of liver and spleen 4 hours to 7 days after a single injection of KCl-liposomes (Table 1). Changes in activity of the zinc-requiring enzyme, i.e. alkaline phosphatase, during the cell growth cycle and proliferative stage of various cells have been reported (Fennel, 1951; Bourne, 1956; Moog et al., 1966). The intestinal and serum alkaline ˈphosphatase levels also show significant changes during absorption of certain amino acids (Triantaphyllopoulos and Tuba, 1959). Further investigations are necessary before we can understand the mechanisms whereby KCl-liposomes stimulate alkaline phosphatase activity.

The biological changes observed in mice treated with liposomes containing EDTA or DTPA include: (1) an increase in the wet weight of the spleen; (2) striking mobilization of macrophages of unknown origin to

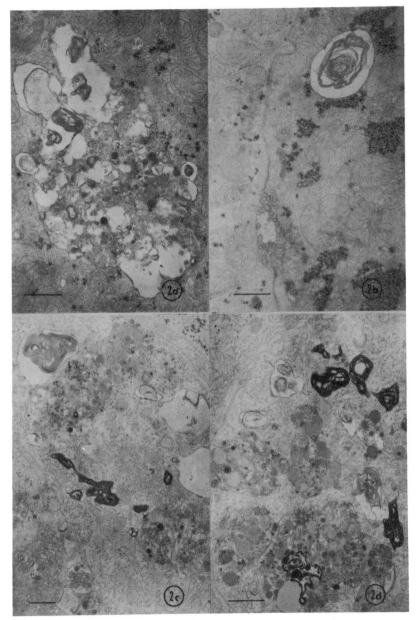

Figure 2 Twenty-four hours after injection of EDTA-liposomes, the liver shows several morphological changes. The hepatocytes have large areas of cytoplasmic degeneration containing remnants of liposomes (Figure 2a). Single liposomes enclosed in a vacuolar area are found in the region of the bile canaliculus (Figure 2b). The Kupffer cell cytoplasm contains large autophagic vacuoles and liposomes in close association with these vacuoles (Figures 2c and 2d). Figures 2a and 2b, × 10,000. Figure 2c, × 7,200. Figure 2d, × 10,000. From Rahman and Wright, 1975

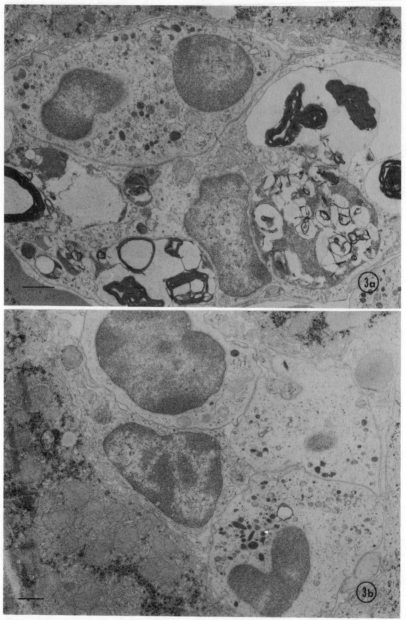

Figure 3 Twelve hours after injection of EDTA-liposomes, the sinusoids are filled with macrophages and engorged Kupffer cells. The montage (Figure 3a) shows a macrophage filled with dense granules. Most of the figure is occupied by a Kupffer cell with large vacuolar areas containing liposomes. The sinusoid (Figure 3b) contains parts of four macrophages. Figure 3a, × 8,800. Figure 3b, × 7,200. From Rahman and Wright, 1975

liver sinusoids, observed 12 hours after injection of EDTA-liposomes; (3) a significant increase of alkaline phosphatase activity in the liver and spleen of mice after DTPA-liposome injections. The above described changes were observed only after injection of liposomes containing EDTA or DTPA; no such changes were observed after injection of either of the chelating agents in the non-encapsulated form or of liposomes containing KCl. These changes, therefore, probably are associated with the successful transport of the EDTA or DTPA into the cells.

When given in the non-encapsulated form, EDTA and DTPA have been reported to cause the following adverse side effects, either in experimental animals or in human patients: (1) imbalance of calcium and magnesium metabolism (Muller-Eberhard *et al.*, 1963); (2) increased zinc excretion in the urine (Slobodien *et al.*, 1973; Spencer and Rosoff, 1966; Perry Jr. and Schroeder, 1957; Perry Jr. and Perry, 1959; Catsch *et al.*, 1968); (3) kidney damage (Foreman *et al.*, 1956; Morgan and Smith, 1974; Foreman and Nigrovic, 1968); (4) systemic toxic side effects (Fairbanks *et al.*, 1963; Barry *et al.*, 1974); (5) foetal toxicity (Fischer *et al.*, 1975; Mays *et al.*, 1976); and (6) inhibition of the synthesis of DNA, RNA, and proteins in the regenerating liver (Gabard, 1974). It is important to point out, however, that most of the toxic effects of non-encapsulated EDTA and DTPA, as described above, have been attributed to the chemical form used, i.e., $Na_2CaEDTA$ or $Na_3CaDTPA$ or to the repeated injections of high levels. Recent reports have claimed that, when EDTA or DTPA is given in the form of a zinc complex—$Na_2ZnEDTA$ or $Na_3ZnDTPA$, no toxic effects have been observed (Planas–Bohne and Ebel, 1975; Fischer *et al.*, 1975; Gabard, 1974; Catsch, 1968; Catsch and von Wedelstaedt, 1965).

With liposomes as carriers, it has now become possible to introduce a significant amount of chelating agent into cells. The question of their possible harmful effects on the intracellular ion metabolism unavoidably arises. In view of the unchanged activity of glutamic dehydrogenase and the increased activity of alkaline phosphatase, it appears that the high intracellular concentration of EDTA or DTPA introduced by liposomes does not result in the removal of protein-bound trace elements such as zinc. However, studies on the total excretion of metal ions, before and after administration of liposomes containing chelating agents, probably will be more useful for determining the overall effects of a given liposomal chelating agent on ion metabolism.

Among the clinically useful chelating agents the polyamino-polycarboxylic acids, such as EDTA, DTPA, are known to cause the most severe imbalance of ions. Intracellular zinc ions are particularly vulnerable. The use of EDTA or DTPA in the form of a zinc complex ($Na_2ZnEDTA$ or $Na_3ZnDTPA$) rather than the calcium salt to prepare liposomes may hopefully reduce this toxic side effect. Other chelating agents with high specificity towards a given metal, for example DF, are much less likely to cause severe imbalance of ion metabolism.

5. DISTRIBUTION OF [^{14}C]EDTA TRANSPORTED BY LIPOSOMES

5.1. At the Tissue Level

When tissue levels of liposome-encapsulated [^{14}C]EDTA were compared to those of non-encapculated [^{14}C]EDTA, the most significant findings were: (1) higher levels of [^{14}C]EDTA in most organs, particularly the liver and the spleen; (2) longer retention of [^{14}C]EDTA; and (3) decreased urinary excretion of [^{14}C]EDTA (Tables 3 and 4).

Most of our tissue distribution studies were done with neutral liposomes made of a mixture of PC and cholesterol. By changing the lipid constituents, some modifications of the tissue distribution pattern could be obtained. For example, the highest [^{14}C]EDTA concentrations we observed in the liver were achieved by using liposomes made of phospholipids extracted from mouse brain and cholesterol or of PC, galactosyl cerebroside, and cholesterol (weight ratio of 1 : 1 : 1) (Jonah *et al.*, 1979); the lowest uptake was obtained by using liposomes made of PC, gangliosides, and cholesterol (approximate weight ratio, 6 : 1 : 3) (Jonah *et al.*, 1979). Uptake of [^{14}C]EDTA by spleen and bone marrow was highest from liposomes with a negative surface charge, while uptakes by lung and brain were highest from positively charged liposomes. The total uptake in the brain, however, was very low (Jonah *et al.*, 1975). A striking result has been that spleen and bone marrow on one hand, and lung and brain on the other, show similar uptake patterns with liposomes made of different lipids (Jonah *et al.*, 1975; Jonah *et al.*, 1979).

5.2. At the Cellular Level

We have examined the cellular uptake of chelating agents delivered by liposomes, qualitatively by electron microscopy and quantitatively by cellular fractionation. The former technique has shown that liposomes occur in both hepatocytes and Kupffer cells within minutes after injection (Figure 4a,b) (Wright and Rahman, 1976). Fractionation by gradient centrifugation of organs into cell types has so far been attempted only with spleen and bone marrow (Rahman *et al.*, 1977). One hour after mice were given an intravenous injection of liposomes containing [^{14}C]EDTA, spleen cells were dispersed in isotonic saline and then separated on a linear gradient of 10–30% bovine serum albumin in isotonic saline. After centrifugation, each fraction was examined for: (1) [^{14}C]radioactivity; (2) cell number determined with a Coulter counter; and (3) cell type, identified by injected intravenously[a]

Time after injection	Brain	Blood[b]	Kidneys	Liver
5 minutes	0.616 ± 0.223	27.642 ± 2.722	1.954 ± 0.271	24.602 ± 5.577
15 minutes	0.343 ± 0.026	8.450 ± 2.167	1.288 ± 0.083	38.667 ± 3.508
1 hour	0.283 ± 0.034	2.418 ± 0.619	0.630 ± 0.059	37.353 ± 4.722
6 hours	0.257 ± 0.039	1.001 ± 0.240	0.446 ± 0.019	40.981 ± 1.833
12 hours	0.163 ± 0.023	0.468 ± 0.059	0.443 ± 0.032	38.845 ± 4.746
18 hours	0.185 ± 0.016	0.915 ± 0.104	0.428 ± 0.038	26.169 ± 4.701
1 day	0.237 ± 0.021	0.544 ± 0.065	0.363 ± 0.021	24.137 ± 2.263
2 days	0.124 ± 0.018	0.757 ± 0.210	0.348 ± 0.028	20.946 ± 1.235
3 days	0.107 ± 0.006	0.803 ± 0.025	0.305 ± 0.036	9.387 ± 0.749
7 days	0.052 ± 0.007	0.463 ± 0.152	0.162 ± 0.019	3.794 ± 1.173
17 days	0.030 ± 0.006	0.330 ± 0.042	0.060 ± 0.007	0.731 ± 0.365

Time after injection	Spleen	Lungs	Total in tissues shown
5 minutes	3.179 ± 0.133	37.851 ± 2.836	95.843 ± 1.065
15 minutes	8.188 ± 1.478	25.674 ± 2.658	82.611 ± 1.063
1 hour	18.030 ± 2.505	13.601 ± 3.482	72.316 ± 4.600
6 hours	11.454 ± 1.233	9.862 ± 0.566	64.002 ± 1.500
12 hours	6.709 ± 0.965	7.636 ± 0.562	54.263 ± 4.155
18 hours	9.275 ± 2.100	8.374 ± 0.453	45.347 ± 2.333
1 day	11.305 ± 0.806	7.127 ± 0.530	43.712 ± 1.275
2 days	6.791 ± 1.280	4.670 ± 0.529	33.636 ± 2.117
3 days	7.003 ± 0.452	3.601 ± 0.748	21.206 ± 0.433
7 days	1.315 ± 0.128	0.291 ± 0.102	6.078 ± 1.182
17 days	0.142 ± 0.039	0.066 ± 0.022	1.359 ± 0.429

[a] Values are mean per cent of injected ^{14}C radioactivity ± the standard error of the mean. Each group contains four mice, except those at 5 and 15 minutes (three mice each) and at 12 hours (five mice). The liposomal membranes were composed of phosphatidylcholine and cholesterol, 3 : 1. The liposomes were filtered once through at 1.2 μm Millipore filter.
[b] Activity in the estimated total blood volume, 2 cm³, as calculated from two 100 μl samples from each mouse. From Rahman et al., 1974b.

Table 4 Distribution and retention in mouse tissues of non-encapsulated [14C]EDTA after intravenous injection[a]

Time after injection	Brain	Blood[b]	Kidneys	Liver
5 minutes	0.157 ± 0.018	13.218 ± 0.515	7.134 ± 0.826	1.802 ± 0.101
15 minutes	0.090 ± 0.020	5.024 ± 0.673	2.681 ± 0.176	0.972 ± 0.041
1 hour	0.055 ± 0.006	0.917 ± 0.153	0.355 ± 0.028	0.394 ± 0.012
6 hours	0.043 ± 0.003	0.560 ± 0.160	0.165 ± 0.019	0.316 ± 0.045
1 day	0.034 ± 0.003	0.602 ± 0.144	0.077 ± 0.005	0.326 ± 0.039
3 days	0.034 ± 0.003	0.040 ± 0.010	0.061 ± 0.003	0.222 ± 0.016

Time after injection	Spleen	Lungs	Total in tissues shown
5 minutes	0.125 ± 0.012	0.663 ± 0.054	23.189 ± 1.299
15 minutes	0.103 ± 0.001	0.337 ± 0.024	9.208 ± 0.880
1 hour	0.033 ± 0.007	0.041 ± 0.003	1.795 ± 0.151
6 hours	0.036 ± 0.007	0.031 ± 0.008	1.151 ± 0.206
1 day	0.042 ± 0.004	0.041 ± 0.010	0.971 ± 0.202
3 days	0.028 ± 0.003	0.028 ± 0.003	0.374 ± 0.023

[a] Values are mean per cent of injected ^{14}C radioactivity from four mice ± the standard error of the mean.
[b] Activity in the estimated total blood volume, 2 cm^3, as calculated from two 100 μl samples from each mouse.
From Rahman *et al.*, 1974b.

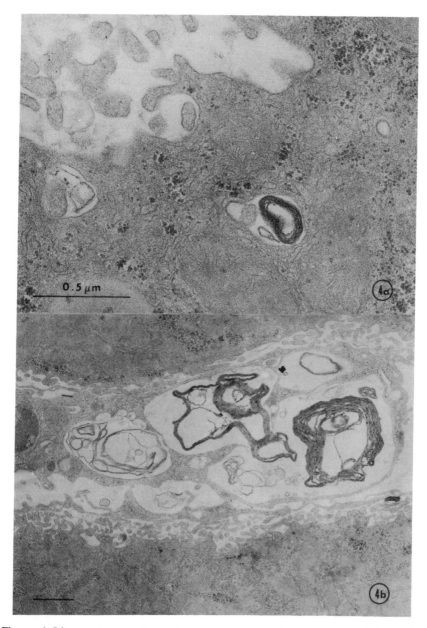

0.5 μm

4a

4b

Figure 4 Liposomes are shown in the cytoplasm of a hepatocyte (Figure 4a), and a Kuffer cell (Figure 4b). Figure 4a, × 25,600. Figure 4b, × 14,400. From Rahman and Wright, 1975

light microscopy after Giemsa staining. Liposome-transported [^{14}C]EDTA
was found exclusively in fractions containing lymphocytes and reticular
cells (Figure 5).

Cellular fractionation of tissues containing populations of mixed cell
types, for example the bone marrow, resulted in less satisfactory separation
(Rahman *et al*., 1977). Even though several clearly defined bands of cells
could be observed in the gradient after centrifugation, considerable
overlapping of various morphologic types was found. However, preliminary
results indicated that fractions containing megakaryocytes and
polymorphonuclear leucocytes contained the highest radioactivity.

A determination of the amount of [^{14}C]EDTA transported by liposomes
in liver cells will be undertaken. Techniques to fractionate parenchymal
and Kupffer cells have made significant progress in recent years (Berry and
Friend, 1969; Mills and Zucker-Franklin, 1969; Berg *et al*., 1972; Seglen,
1976; Munthe-Kaas *et al*., 1976), and we plan to use these new techniques.

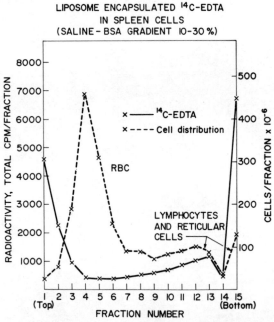

Figure 5 Distribution of liposome-transported[^{14}C]EDTA in spleen cells. One
hour after mice were given an intravenous injection of liposomes containing
[^{14}C]EDTA, spleen cells were teased and dispersed in isotonic saline, and were
then separated on a linear gradient of 10–30% bovine serum albumin in isotonic
saline. The gradient was centrifuged at 650 rpm in an International PR-2
centrifuge with a swinging bucket No. 269. Fifteen 3-ml fractions were removed.
Each fraction was examined for ^{14}C radioactivity, cell count, and cell type
identification

5.3. At the Subcellular Level

Only the mouse liver has been examined subcellularly. Subcellular fractions were obtained by sucrose gradient centrifugation from livers of mice 1 to 24 hours after they had received an intravenous injection of liposomes containing [^{14}C]EDTA. At all intervals, the [^{14}C]EDTA activity was mainly in the supernatant (Figure 6).

5.4. Discussion

The most significant advantages of using liposomes to transport chelating agents are: (1) that there is a higher uptake of these metal chelators by cells than when liposomes are not used; and (2) the retention of chelating agents is prolonged so that the therapeutic index of the drugs is increased.

High uptake of liposomes has been shown in organs rich in reticuloedothelial cells, such as the liver, spleen, and bone marrow (Rahman *et al.*, 1974a; Gregoriadis and Ryman, 1972; Rahman *et al.*, 1974b;

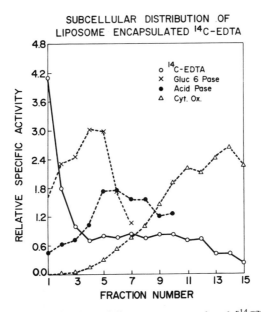

Figure 6 Subcellular distribution of liposome-encapsulated [^{14}C]EDTA in mouse liver. One to 24 hours after mice were given an intravenous injection of liposomes containing [^{14}C]EDTA, livers were removed and homogenized. The liver homogenate was then centrifuged on a sucrose gradient of 10–30%, at 4,200 rpm for 70 minutes in an International PR-2 centrifuge with a swinging bucket No. 269. Marker enzymes for mitochondria, lysosomes, microsomes, and ^{14}C radioactivity were determined in each fraction

Jonah *et al.*, 1975). These are also the major organs where toxic heavy metals are accumulated. Intracellularly, liposome-transported substances are localized within lysosomes (De Barsy *et al.*, 1976; Gregoriadis and Ryman, 1972; Wisse *et al.*, 1976; Rahman *et al.*, 1974b), where particulate heavy metals also are stored. Thus, a desirable contact between metal chelator and toxic metal can be achieved. The finding of liposomal EDTA primarily in the supernatant fraction of the liver (Figure 6) does not necessarily preclude the fusion between the EDTA-liposomes and lysosomes. By virtue of its anionic nature, EDTA may have been excluded by lysosomes soon after the fusion occurred. Due to this fusion, the brief contact between the liposome-transported chelating agent and the heavy metals within lysosomes may be sufficient to induce the formation of a more soluble metal–chelate complex. This phenomenon has recently been discussed by de Duve and co-workers (1974).

Liposome encapsulation of chelating agents improves the uptake of these drugs by the critical organs on one hand, and because contact between the chelator and the metal accumulated within lysosomes is facilitated on the other hand, the potential usefulness of liposomes as carriers for chelating agents is obvious.

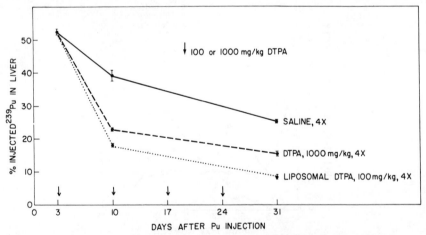

Figure 7 Effect of one to four injections of liposome-encapsulated DTPA or of non-encapsulated DTPA on the amount of Pu in the liver. Injections were given at 3, 10, 17, and 24 days after injection of Pu, as indicated by the arrows. Nonencapsulated DTPA was given intraperitoneally at 1000 mg/kg at each injection; for liposome-encapsulated DTPA, a dose of 100 mg/kg was injected intravenously at each injection, and the liposomes were filtered through a 1.2 μm Millipore filter. From Rosenthal *et al.*, 1975. (Reproduced by permission of Academic Press, Inc.)

6. LIPOSOME-ENCAPSULATED CHELATING AGENTS FOR TOXIC METAL REMOVAL

We have used liposome encapsulation of chelating agents to remove various toxic metals from mouse tissues and compared the therapeutic efficacy of this new drug delivery system to that of the conventional non-encapsulated form. These studies have been done mainly with plutonium-239 and lead-210. A few experiments were done with mercury-203 and colloidal gold-198. The results are summarized below:

(1) Encapsulated DTPA, given to mice 3 days after Pu injection, removed an additional fraction of Pu from within the liver cells that had not been removed by the non-encapsulated, free form of DTPA (Figure 7) (Rahman *et al.*, 1973; Rosenthal *et al.*, 1975). When given 24 days rather than 3 days after Pu, liposomal DTPA had an even greater advantage over non-encapsulated DTPA.

(2) Liposome-encapsulated DTPA removed more Pu from the skeleton than did the non-encapsulated drug (Figure 8) (Rosenthal *et al.*, 1975).

(3) Significantly greater urinary excretion of Pu occurred after liposomal DTPA treatment than after treatment with non-encapsulated DTPA (Figure 9) (Rahman *et al.*, 1973). There was no difference in faecal excretion (Figure 10).

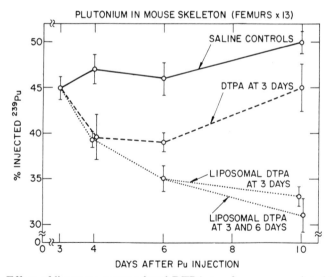

Figure 8 Effect of liposome-encapsulated DTPA or of non-encapsulated DTPA on the skeletal content of Pu (the amount in both femurs × 13). Liposome-encapsulated DTPA, 100 mg/kg, was injected intravenously at 3 days, or at 3 and 6 days, after injection of Pu. Non-encapsulated DTPA, 100 mg/kg, was injected intraperitoneally at 3 days after Pu. From Rosenthal *et al.*, 1975. (Reproduced by permission of Academic Press, Inc.)

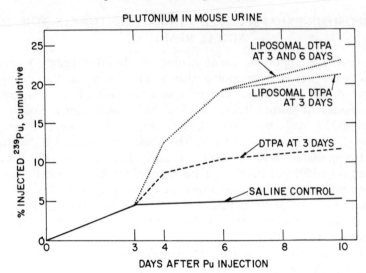

Figure 9 Cumulative excretion of Pu in the urine of mice treated with liposome-encapsulated or non-encapsulated DTPA, at a dose of 100 mg/kg, at 3 days, or at 3 and again at 6 days, after injection of Pu. From Rahman *et al.*, 1973

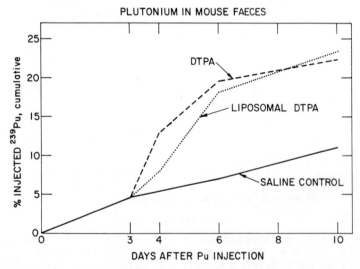

Figure 10 Cumulative excretion of Pu in the faeces of mice given a single treatment of liposome-encapsulated or non-encapsulated DTPA at a dose of 100 mg/kg, at 3 days after injection of Pu. From Rahman *et al.*, 1973

Table 5 Lead content in mouse tissues (7 days after an intravenous injection of ^{210}Pb and 4 days after a single treatment)

	Mean per cent injected dose of ^{210}Pb $\pm$ S.E.[a]				
	Skeleton	Liver	Spleen	Kidney	Lung
Saline	25.42 ± 1.72	1.25 ± 0.18	0.085 ± 0.005	0.84 ± 0.12	0.20 ± 0.08
Non-encapsulated DTPA (100 mg/kg)	25.19 ± 1.52	1.68 ± 0.20	0.072 ± 0.010	0.82 ± 0.14	0.11 ± 0.02
Liposome-encapsulated DTPA (100 mg/kg)	21.12 ± 0.66	1.06 ± 0.16	0.018 ± 0.004	0.55 ± 0.55	0.11 ± 0.02

[a]Each value is obtained from a group of five mice.

(4) DTPA encapsulated within liposomes was equally effective for Pu removal when given either intravenously or intraperitoneally (Rosenthal *et al*., 1975).

(5) The therapeutic effectiveness of liposomal DTPA was unchanged when the liposomes were stored for 3 days before use (Rosenthal *et al*., 1975).

(6) When DTPA was given in the form of liposomes, a dose of 25 mg/kg was not significantly less effective for Pu removal than was a dose of 100 mg/kg (Rosenthal *et al*., 1975).

(7) Liposome-encapsulated DTPA also removed significantly more lead from liver, spleen, kidney, and lung than non-encapsulated DTPA, although very low levels of lead were generally found in these soft tissues (Table 5).

(8) When radioactive lead, in the form of $^{210}Pb(NO_3)_2$, was injected into mice, the highest Pb burden was found in the skeleton. Single or multiple treatments with liposome-encapsulated DTPA, starting 3 days after Pb injection, were significantly more effective for removal of Pb from the skeleton than were treatments with the non-encapsulated free form of DTPA (Figure 11).

(9) In the kidney, most of the lead was in nuclei; DTPA given in the form of liposomes 10 hours after Pb injection prevented Pb deposition in that site (Figure 12).

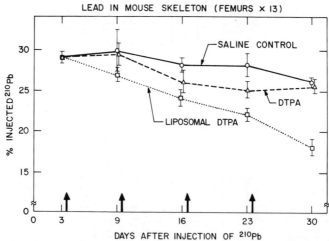

Figure 11 ^{210}Pb content in the whole skeleton of mice after multiple treatments with (1) saline solution ○———; (2) non-encapsulated DTPA solution (100 mg/kg) △------; (3) Liposome-encapsulated DTPA (100 mg/kg), □...... The treatments were given at 3, 9, 16, and 23 days after the ^{210}Pb injection, as indicated by arrows. Five mice in each group were killed on these days. The error bar indicates 2 standard errors of the mean

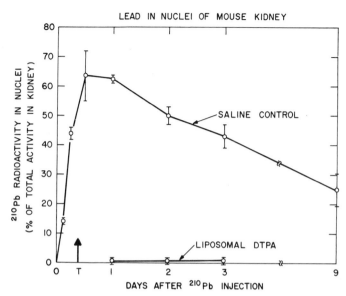

Figure 12 Prevention of lead deposition by liposome-encapsulated DTPA in nuclei of mouse kidney. Ten hours after receiving lead $[^{210}Pb(NO_3)_2]$ mice were given an intravenous injection of liposomes containing DTPA, at a dose of 50 mg/kg. Kidney nuclei were isolated by the method of Blobel and Potter (1966)

(10) Injected colloidal ^{198}Au localized mainly in liver. Liposomal DTPA was more effective in promoting faecal excretion of Au than was the non-encapsulated form (Figure 13).

(11) The major deposition site of inorganic mercury is the kidney. Liposomal DTPA, given 3 days after Hg injection, removed ~ 38% of the Hg burden in the kidney, while only ~ 15% was removed by the non-encapsulated DTPA.

These results were obtained mostly with DTPA in the form of calcium salt, a comparatively non-specific chelating agent, and as mentioned earlier, Ca-DTPA is more toxic to animals than Zn-DTPA (Foreman *et al.*, 1956; Fairbanks *et al.*, 1963; Morgan and Smith, 1974; Fischer *et al.*, 1975; Mays *et al.*, 1976; Muller-Eberhard *et al.*, 1963; Gabard, 1974). Therefore DTPA in the zinc form may be used in the future.

Among other chelating agents known to be more specific for certain metal ions, DF and PTTA are currently being investigated. Tissue distribution and retention studies of liposome-encapsulated DF have shown that desferrioxamine can be selectively transported to the critical organs where iron is stored (Guilmette *et al.*, 1978); long retention of DF in these organs has also been obtained (Guilmette *et al.*, 1978). Tests to determine the efficacy of liposomal PTTA in mercury removal are also under way.

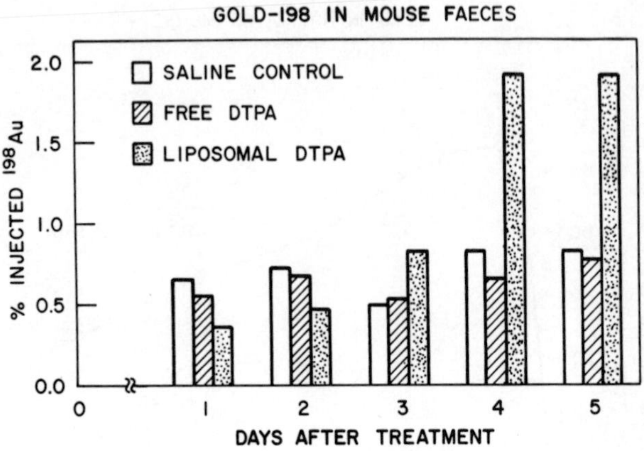

GOLD-198 IN MOUSE FAECES

Figure 13 Excretion of colloidal gold (^{198}Au) in mouse faeces. Three days after receiving ^{198}Au, four mice in each group were given an intravenous injection of saline, liposome-encapsulated DTPA, or non-encapsulated DTPA. The DTPA was given at a dose of 100 mg/kg. The results are presented as the average per cent injected dose per mouse per day, derived from the combined faeces of two groups of five mice each

The potential of liposome encapsulation in chelation therapy of human diseases that are caused by pathological accumulation of heavy metals is promising. A detailed discussion of this subject will be presented elsewhere (Rahman, 1979).

7. SUMMARY

The preparation of liposomes containing various chelating agents is described. The sizes of unilamellar liposomes were determined by conventional electron microscopy after negative staining. Rapid measurement of the sizes of multilamellar liposomes was performed by a Coulter transducer equipped with a multichannel analyser. The stability of liposomes was tested by leakage of chelating agent with time. The concentration of chelating agents encapsulated within liposomes was determined by the binding of a radioactive metal ion to the chelating agent before liposome preparation.

Liposomal lipids, given in the form of KCl-liposomes, showed no immediate or delayed toxicity to mice. A moderate increase of alkaline phosphatase activity of the liver and spleen occurred from 4 hours to 7 days after KCl-liposome injection.

The following changes were observed in mice receiving liposomes containing either EDTA or DTPA: (1) a 1.3- to 3-fold increase in the wet weight of the spleen 1 week after single or multiple injections of

DTPA-liposomes containing at least 50 mg/kg of DTPA; (2) striking mobilization to liver sinusoids of macrophages of unknown origin observed 12 hours after injection of EDTA-liposomes; (3) a significant increase of alkaline phosphatase activity in the liver and spleen of mice after receiving DTPA-liposomes.

The encapsulation of chelating agents in liposomes significantly altered the tissue distribution of these agents and prolonged their retention in the body of mice. Tissues rich in reticuloendothelial cells, where particulate heavy metals accumulate also had the highest uptake of liposomes; parenchymal cells in various organs took up liposomes as well. The high uptake of liposomes in reticuloendothelial tissues and within cells is therapeutically advantageous in removing toxic metals. As a consequence, the liposome encapsulation of chelating agents has great promise for future metal chelation therapy.

Acknowledgements

The author thanks Drs. M. P. Finkel, M. W. Rosenthal, and J. F. Thomson for reading this manuscript and providing helpful suggestions and criticism. Excellent assistance during the course of this work from E. A. Cerny, B. J. Wright, M. M. Jonah, E. H. Callahan, K. M. Strathy, and D. W. Karl is also gratefully acknowledged. Work from the author's laboratory was supported in part by a Grant from the National Institute of Arthritis, Metabolism and Digestive Diseases (AM 21592) and by the U.S. Department of Energy under Contract No. W-31-109-ENG-38.

REFERENCES

Ahkong, Q. F., Fisher, D., Tampion, W. and Lucy, J. A. (1975). *Nature*, **253**, 194.

Alajouanine, T., Castaigne, P., Cambier, J. and Fournier, E. (1957). *Arch. Mad. Prof.*, **18**, 557.

Aposhian, V. H. (1960). In *Metal Binding in Medicine*, p.290, Lippincott, Philadelphia and Montreal.

Bangham, A. D. and Horne, R. W. (1964). *J. Mol. Biol.*, **8**, 660.

Bangham, A. D., Standish, M. M. and Watkins, J. C. (1965). *J. Mol. Biol.*, **13**, 238.

Barry, M., Flynn, D. M., Letsky, E. A. and Risdon, R. A. (1974). *Brit. Med. J.*, **2**, 16.

Berg, T., Boman, D. and Seglen, P. O. (1972). *Exp. Cell Res.*, **72**, 571.

Berlin, M. and Lewander, T. (1965). *Acta Pharmac. Tox.*, **22**, 1.

Berlin, M. and Ullberg, S. (1963). *Nature*, **197**, 84.

Berlin, M. and Rylander, R. (1964). *J. Pharmac. Exp. Ther.*, **146**, 236.

Berlin, M., Jerksell, L. -G. and Nordberg, G. (1965). *Acta Pharmac. Tox.*, **23**, 312.

Berry, M. N. and Friend, D. S. (1969). *J. Cell Biol.*, **43**, 506.

Blobel, G. and Potter, V. R. (1966). *Science*, **154**, 1662.

Bobeck-Rutsaert, M. M., Wiltink, W. F., Op Den Kelder, A. M., Van Eijk, H. G. and Leijne, B. (1972). *Acta Haemat.*, **48**, 125.

Bourne, G. H. (1956). In *The Biochemistry and Physiology of Bone*, Chapter IX, Academic Press, New York.

Brieger, H. (1960). In *Metal Binding in Medicine*, p.200, Lippincott, Philadelphia and Montreal.

Catsch, A. (1961). *Int. J. Appl. Rad. Isotop.*, **11**, 131.

Catsch, A. (1964). In *Radioactive Metal Mobilization in Medicine*, p.30, Thomas, Springfield, Il.,

Catsch, A. (1968). In *Dekorporierung Radioaktiver und stabiler Metallionen*, p.25, München.

Catsch, A. and von Wedelstaedt, E. (1965). *Experientia*, **21**, 210.

Catsch, A., Harmuth-Hoene, A. -E., Havlicek, F. and Carpy, S. (1968). In *Diagnosis and Treatment of Deposited Radionuclides*, p.413, Excerpta Medica Foundation, New York.

Chenoweth, M. B. (1968). *Clin. Pharmacol. Ther.*, **9**, 365.

Clarkson, T. W., Small, H. and Norseth, T. (1973). *Arch. Environ. Health*, **26**, 173.

Constantoulakis, M. et al. (1974). *Ann. N.Y. acad. Sci.*, USA. **232**, 193.

Cumming, R. L. C., Millar, J. A., Smith, J. A. and Goldberg, A. (1969). *Brit. J. Haemat.*, **17**, 257.

Deamer, D. W., Hill, M. W. and Bangham, A. D. (1976). *Biochim. Biophys. Acta*, **443**, 629.

De Barsy, T., Devos, P. and Van Hoof, F. (1976). *Laboratory Investigation*, **34**, 273.

de Duve, C., De Barsy, T., Poole, B., Trouet, A., Tulkens, P. and Van Hoof, F. (1974). *Biochem. Pharmacol.*, **23**, 2495.

Dietrich, N., Lehn, J. M. and Sauvage, J. P. (1973) *Tetrahedron*, **29**, 1647.

Eckelman, W. C., Karesh, S. M. and Reba, R. C. (1975). *J. Pharmaceutical Sci.*, **64**, 704.

Fahey, J. L., Rath, C. E., Princiotto, J. V., Brick, I. B. and Rubin, M. (1961). *J. Lab. Clin. Med.*, **57**, 436.

Fairbanks, V. F., Warson, M. D. and Beutler, E. (1963). *Brit. Med. J.*, **1**, 1414.

Fennel, R. A. (1951). *J. Elisha Mitchell Sci. Soc.*, **67**, 219.

Fischer, D. R., Mays, C. W. and Taylor, G. N. (1975). *Health Phys.*, **29**, 780.

Fitzsimmons, J. R. and Kozelka, F. L. (1950). *J. Pharmac. Exp. Ther.*, **98**, 8.

Foreman, H. (1960). In *Metal Binding in Medicine*, p.82, Lippincott, Philadelphia and Montreal.

Foreman, H. (1961). *Fed. Proc.*, **20**, Suppl. 10, 191.

Foreman, H. and Nigrovic, V. (1968). In *Diagnosis and Treatment of Deposited Radionuclides*, p.419, Excerpta Medica Foundation, New York.

Foreman, H., Vier, M. and Magee, M. (1953). *J. Biol. Chem.*, **203**, 1045.

Foreman, H., Finnegan, C. and Lushbaugh, C. C. (1956). *J.A.M.A.*, **160**.

Gabard, B. (1974). *Biochem. Pharmacol.*, **23**, 901.

Goldfischer, S. (1963). *Am. J. Path.*, **43**, 511.

Gregoriadis, G. (1977). *Nature*, **265**, 407.

Gregoriadis, G. and Neerunjun, E. D. (1975). *Biochem. Biophys. Res. Commun.*, **65**, 537.

Gregoriadis, G. and Ryman, B. E. (1972). *Biochem. J.*, **129**, 123.

Guilmette, R. A., Cerny, E. A. and Rahman, Y. -E. (1979) *Life Sci.*, **22**, 313.

Guilmette, R. A., Parks, J. E. and Lindenbaum, A. (1979). *J. Pharm. Sci.*, **68**, 194.

Hallberg, L., Hedenberg, L. and Weinfeld, A. (1966). *Scand. J. Haemat.*, **3**, 85.

Huang, C. (1969). *Biochemistry*, **8**, 344.

Hussain, M. A. M., Flynn, D. M., Green, N., Hussein, S. and Hoffbrand, A. V. (1976). *Lancet.*, **2**, 1278.

Johnson, S. M. (1973). *Biochim. Biophys. Acta*, **307**, 27.

Jonah, M. M., Cerny, E. A. and Rahman, Y. -E. (1975). *Biochim. Biophys. Acta*, **401**, 336.

Jonah, M. M., Cerny, E. A. and Rahman, Y. -E. (1979) *Biochim. Biophys. Acta*, **541**, 321.

Jones, M. M., Banks, A. J. and Brown, C. H. (1975). *J. Inorg. Nucl. Chem.*, **37**, 761.

Juliano, R. L. and Stamp, D. (1975). *Biochem. Biophys, Res. Commun.*, **63**, 651.

Juliano, R. L. and Stamp, D. (1976). *Nature.*, **261**, 235.

Karesh, S. M., Eckelman, W. C. and Reba, R. C. (1977). *J. Pharmacol. Sci.*, **66**, 225.

Keberle, H. (1964). *Problems of Cooley's Anemia*, Ann. N.Y. Acad. Sci., **119**, Art. 2, 758.

Klein, R. A. (1970). *Biochim. Biophys. Acta*, **210**, 486.

Kubitschek, H. E. (1958). *Nature*, **182**, 234.

Kubitschek, H. E. (1969). In *Methods in Microbiology*, p.593, Academic Press.

Lehn, J. M. and Sauvage, J. P. (1971). *Chem. Commun.*, 440.

Lukens, J. N. and Neuman, L. A. (1971). *Blood*, **38**, 614.

MacDonald, J. S., Jones, M. M. and Harrison, R. D. (1976). *Pharmacology*, **18**, 124.

Magliulo, A. (1974). *Chemistry*, **47**, 25.

Magos, L. (1968). *Br. J. Indust. Med.*, **25**, 152.

Markley, F. F. (1963). *Int. J. Rad. Biol.*, **7**, 405.

Mays, C. W., Taylor, G. N. and Fisher, D. R. (1976). *Health Phys.*, **30**, 249.

Mills, D. M. and Zucker-Franklin (1969). *Am. J. Pathol.*, **54**, 147.

Modell, C. B. and Beck, J. (1974). *Third Conference on Cooley's Anemia*, Ann. N.Y. Acad. Sci. **232**, 201.

Moeschlin, S. and Schnider, U. (1963). *New Engl. J. Med.*, **269**, 57.

Moog, F., Vire, H. R. and Grey, R. O. (1966). *Biochim. Biophys. Acta*, **113**, 336.

Morgan, R. M. and Smith, H. (1974). *Toxicology*, **2**, 153.

Muller, W. H. (1970). *Naturwiss.*, **57**, 248.

Muller-Eberhard, U., Erlandson, M. E., Ginn, H. E. and Smith, C. H. (1963). *Blood*, **22**, 209.

Munthe-Kaas, A. C. *et al.* (1976). *Exp. Cell Res.*, **99**, 146.

Papahadjopoulos, D., Poste, G., Schaeffer, D. E. and Vail, W. J. (1974). *Biochim. Biophys. Acta*, **352**, 10.

Perrin, D. D. and Agarwal, R. P. (1976). In *Metal Induced Toxicity and Chelation Therapy*, p.361, Thomas, Springfield, Il

Perry, Jr., H. M. and Perry, E. F. (1959). *J. Clin. Invest.*, **38**, 1452.

Perry, Jr., H. M. and Schroeder, H. A. (1957). *Amer. J. Med.*, **22**, 168.

Peters, R. A., Stocken, L. A. and Thompson, R. H. S. (1945). *Nature*, **156**, 616.

Planas-Bohne, F. and Ebel, H. (1975). *Health Phys.*, **29**, 103.

Polliak, A. and Rachmilewitz, E. A. (1973). *Brit. J. Haemat.*, **24**, 319.

Poole, A. R., Howell, J. I. and Lucy, J. A. (1970). *Nature*, **227**, 810.

Propper, R. D., Shurin, S. B. and Nathan, D. G. (1976). *New Engl. J. Med.*, **294**, 1421.

Rahman, Y. -E. (1979). In *Lysosomes in Biology and Pathology*, Vol. 6, (in press).

Rahman, Y. -E. and Lindenbaum, A. (1964). *Radiat. Res.*, **21**, 575.

Rahman, Y. -E. and Rosenthal, M. W. (1973). *Radiat. Res.*, **55**, 516.

Rahman, Y. -E. and Wright, B. J. (1975). *J. Cell Biol.*, **65**, 112.

Rahman, Y. -E., Rosenthal, M. W. and Cerny, E. A. (1973). *Science*, **180**, 300.

Rahman, Y. -E., Cerny, E. A., Tollaksen, S. L., Wright, B. J., Nance, S., Wright, B. J., Nance, S. L. and Thomson, J. F. (1974a). *Proc. Soc. Exp. Biol. Med.*, **146**, 1173.

Rahman, Y. -E., Rosenthal, M. W., Cerny, E. A. and Moretti, E. S. (1974b). *J. Lab. Clin. Med.*, **83**, 640.

Rahman, Y. -E., Kisieleski, W. E., Buess, E. M. and Cerny, E. A. (1975). *Europ. J. Cancer*, **11**, 838.

Rahman, Y. -E., Tollaksen, S. L., Nance, S. L., Miller, M., Wright, B. J., Cerny, E. A. and Thomson, J. F. (1977). In *Methodological Surveys in Biochemistry*, Vol. 6, p. 401. Horwood, Chichester, G.B.

Rosenthal, N. W., Rahman, Y. -E., Moretti. E. S. and Cerny, E. A. (1975). *Radiat. Res.*, **63**, 262.

Scheinberg, I. H. and Sternlieb, I. (1960). *Pharmacological Reviews*, **12**, 355.

Seglen, P. O. (1976). In *Methods in Cell Biology*, Vol. **XIII**, 4, p.29. Academic Press, New York, N.Y.

Selander, S. (1967). *Brit. J. Indust. Med.*, **24**, 272.

Slobodien, M. J. , Brodsky, A., Ke, C. H. and Horm, I. (1973). *Health Physics*, **24**, 327.

Smith, R. S. (1964). *Problems of Cooley's Anemia*, Ann. N.Y. Acad. Sci., **119**, Art. 2, 776.

Spencer, H. and Rosoff, B. (1966). *Health Physics*, **12**, 475.

Thompson, R. B., Owen, D. M. and Bell, W. N. (1967). *Amer. J. Med. Sci.*, **253**, 453.

Triantaphyllopoulos, E. and Tuba, J. (1959). *Canad. J. Biochem.*, **37**, 711.

Vitale, L. F., Rosalinas-Bailon, A., Folland, D., Brennan, J. F. and McCormick, B. (1973). *Pediatric Pharmacology and Therapeutics*, **83**, 1041.

Walsh, J. R. (1956). *Amer. J. Med.*, **21**, 487.

Walsh, J. R., Mass, R. E., Smith, F. W. and Lange, V. (1965). *Gastroenterology*, **49**, 134–140.

Weissmann, G., Bloomgarden, D., Kaplan, R., Cohen, C., Hoffstein, S., Collins, T., Gotlieb, A. and Nagle, D. (1975). *Proc. Nat. Acad. Sci.*, USA **72**, 88.

Williams, N. E. and Bridge, H. G. T. (1958). *Lancet*, **2**, 602.

Wisse, E., Gregoriadis, G. and Daems, W. Th. (1976). In *The Reticuloendothelial System in Health and Disease : Functions and Characteristics*, p. 237, Plenum, New York.

Wohler, F. (1963). Acta Haemat. (Basel), **30**, 65.

Wright, B. J. and Rahman, Y. -E. (1976). *J. Cell Biol.*, **70**, 19a.

Liposomes in Biological Systems
Edited by G. Gregoriadis and A. C. Allison
© 1980, John Wiley & Sons, Ltd.

CHAPTER 11

Liposomes as Steroid Carriers in the Intra-articular Therapy of Rheumatoid Arthritis

*Ian H. Shaw and John T. Dingle**

1. **Introduction**   299

2. **Steroid retention in egg-yolk phosphatidylcholine liposomes**   304

3. **Steroid retention in synthetic liposomes**   309

4. **Effect of synovial fluid on liposomal retention and stability of entrapped steroid**   310

5. **Intra-articular liposomal therapy**   315
    5.1. Liposomal size and joint tissue localization of entrapped steroid   315
    5.2. Therapeutic assessment of intra-articular liposome administration in arthritis   319

6. **Conclusions**   320

    References   321

1. INTRODUCTION

Rheumatoid arthritis is a very painful and crippling disease of major national and international importance. Over half a million people, three

*This work was carried out in collaboration with D. P. Page-Thomas, C. G. Knight and N. C. Phillips at the Strangeways Research Laboratory, Cambridge; B. L. Hazleman at Addenbrookes Hospital, Cambridge; J. L. Gordon at the Institute of Animal Physiology, Cambridge and J. S. Lowe, E. H. Turner, G. Jones, F. J. T. Fildes and J. E. Oliver at I.C.I. Pharmaceutical Division, Alderley Park, Cheshire.

times as many women as men (Arthritis and Rheumatism Council, 1977), suffer from the disease in the United Kingdom. Duthie (1969) described the disease as a 'subacute or chronic non-suppurative, inflammatory polyarthritis affecting mainly the peripheral synovial joints, normally in a symmetrical fashion, running a prolonged course of exacerbation and remission, and accompanied by systemic disturbance'. The brunt of the disease is borne by the articulating joints although common systemic manifestations include a raised erythrocyte sedimentation rate, sub-cutaneous nodules, vasculitis, anaemia, neuropathy, cachexia, pulmonary, and ocular disease (Carwile LeRoy, 1974). Many rheumatoid patients have an auto-antibody (rheumatoid factor) in their serum (Ruddy, 1974a), an observation that has led to the proposal that rheumatoid arthritis may be an auto-immune disease. In rheumatoid arthritis part of the enlarged synovial membrane, the pannus, extends over the articular cartilage and erosion of the underlying tissue results. This characteristic synovial pro-liferation in rheumatoid disease causes the patient to suffer pain, stiffness, and loss of function of the affected joints. This is followed in more severe cases, by destruction of the sub-chondrial bone and progressive joint deformity will ensue with advancing disease.

Despite the introduction of new anti-inflammatory drugs, therapeutic techniques, and improved surgical procedures, the therapy and management of rheumatoid arthritis is still only symptomatic at the very best. The pharmacological treatment of rheumatoid arthritis is usually aimed at alleviating pain and inflammation in an attempt to allow severely diseased patients a degree of mobility which would otherwise be impossible.

The pharmacological treatment of rheumatoid disease is often associated with unwanted side effects which appear as a consequence of the chronic therapy these patients require. Occasionally the side effects are serious and necessitate the withdrawal of the drug. It has been estimated that about 50% of all iatrogenic deaths reported to the Committee on Safety of Medicines result from medication of rheumatic conditions (Watson Buchanan et al., 1977).

Corticosteroids, first introduced by Hench et al. (1950), are still among the most effective anti-rheumatic agents. Systemic administration of steroids brings about a dramatic amelioration of the disease. However, prolonged administration of steroids gives rise to systemic side effects, the more serious of which include myopathy, increased susceptibility to infection, osteoporosis, adrenal suppression leading to an inability to respond to stress and dependence (Koch-Weser, 1976; Dinning, 1976; Askari et al., 1976). As a consequence of their low therapeutic index, corticosteroids are limited to controlling acute episodes of severe chronic rheumatoid disease.

Hollander *et al*. (1951) reported that the intra-articular injection of 25 mg hydrocortisone (cortisol) acetate into rheumatoid knee joints gave a prompt but transient alleviation of the symptoms in over 80% of all treated joints. Despite the large dose, the duration of the beneficial effect varied greatly from 48 hours to many weeks.

The transient effect of intra-articular corticosteroid therapy was associated with a variety of systemic effects suggesting the rapid loss of steroid from the joint space (Oka, 1956). Young *et al*. (1954) reported that 21% of 148 patients given local steroid injections had systemic as well as articular effects 2 to 20 hours after injection. Wilson *et al*. (1955) found that 60 minutes after the local injection of 50 mg hydrocortisone acetate only 14% remained in the joint. Significant amounts of steroid were also recovered from the contralateral uninjected arthritic joint after 30 minutes, an observation which could explain the post-injection general anti-rheumatic effect reported by several workers (Ward and Manson, 1953; Bilka, 1967; Goetzl *et al*., 1974; Koehler *et al*., 1974).

Attempts to reduce these systemic effects by prolonging the synovial localization and retention of the steroid and thereby extending the duration of local anti-rheumatic effect, led to clinical trials of higher esters and analogues of hydrocortisone (Hollander *et al*., 1954; Hollander, 1955). These studies suggested that hydrocortisone tertiary butyl acetate was the most effective ester although this was questioned by Chandler *et al*. (1958) who, unlike the previous investigators, performed a double blind cross-over trial, and found no significant difference between esters.

The introduction of more potent steroids such as prednisolone, triamcinolone, and dexamethasone (Halden and Kendall, 1962; Will and Murdoch, 1960; Bilka, 1967) into local rheumatoid therapy did not reduce the incidence of systemic effects such as generalized anti-inflammatory action and adrenal suppression (Koehler *et al*., 1974).

Local adverse articular reactions have been reported following intra-articular administration. Hollander *et al*. (1954) reported a temporary exacerbation after injection as did Bilka (1967). Increased pain, swelling, temperature, and tenderness manifest themselves within a few hours (Hollander, 1972). Severe post-injection arthropathy was first reported by Chandler and Wright (1958) and a Charcot-like arthropathy was observed by Steinberg *et al*. (1962). As a result, a more conservative use of local corticosteroid therapy was suggested and the procedure even condemned by Bently and Goodfellow (1969) who reported extensive articular degenerative changes and malfunction following prolonged repeated injections of steroid. However, a recent study of normal primate joints failed to support the claim that intra-articular steroids are deleterious to cartilage (Gibson *et al*., 1976).

As a consequence of the foregoing observations the practice of intra-articular corticosteroid therapy in rheumatoid arthritis still remains controversial. The technique is generally considered only to be an adjuvant treatment (Dick-Smith, 1974) and is restricted to controlling acute mono- or diarticular episodes or when regular systemic therapy is contraindicated.

Modifying the steroid molecule in an attempt to improve the retention within rheumatoid tissue has been of little success in the past. One of us (J. T. Dingle) postulated that presenting the steroid to the tissue, encapsulated within a proven biodegradable pharmacological carrier such as a liposome, may eliminate many of the problems associated with intra-articular therapy. As arthritic synovium is actively phagocytic and is essentially within a closed cavity, it seemed an ideal target tissue for a liposomal drug-delivery system. Consequently, a collaborative study was initiated between a group in Cambridge and a group at Imperial Chemical Industries Limited Pharmaceutical Division, Alderley Park, Cheshire.

After systemic administration, liposomes of different size and charge have repeatedly been shown to localize, to a variable extent, within the liver and spleen (Gregoriadis, 1973; McDougall *et al.*, 1974; Colley and Ryman, 1975; Jonah *et al.*, 1975; McDougall *et al.*, 1975) as well as the lungs, kidneys, and non-specific cells of the reticuloendothelial system. Unlike the systemic therapeutic administration of liposomes, as being proposed for the treatment of lysosomal storage diseases (Gregoriadis *et al.*, 1971; Ryman, 1974), cancer chemotherapy (Gregoriadis *et al.*, 1974), heavy metal poisoning (Rahman *et al.*, 1974), hyperglycaemia (Patel and Ryman, 1976), and for use in radiosotopic scanning (Caride *et al.*, 1976), intra-articular administration is not severely handicapped by rheological factors and the problems of attaining selective tissue targeting (Gregoriadis, 1975).

We considered that local therapy with a liposomal carrier system should allow the use of very small quantities of an anti-inflammatory steroid, with a consequent reduction in any systemic effect. The nature of the carrier would retard the systemic absorption of the entrapped steroid while facilitating phagocytosis by, or fusion with, the lining cells of the joint cavity (Figure 1).

Our reasons for selecting cortisol as the most suitable corticosteroid for initial experiments on liposomal entrapment were twofold. Firstly, the extracellular release of proteolytic enzymes capable of breaking down connective tissue components (Fell and Dingle, 1963) has been implicated in the pathogenesis of arthritis and other connective tissue diseases (Dingle, 1962; Dingle, 1966; Weissmann, 1972). Low concentrations of cortisol (0.1 μg) are known to protect cultured cartilaginous limb bones against both enzyme release and matrix degradation (Fell and Thomas, 1961). Secondly, a stabilizing effect of cortisol has been demonstrated on lysosomes (Weissmann and Dingle, 1961) from liver (Ignarro, 1971a) and

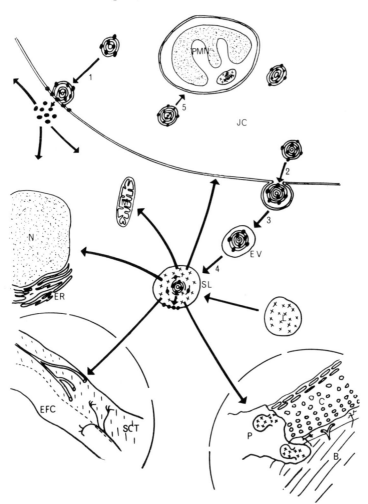

Figure 1 Mechanisms of action of liposomes as drug carriers in the intra-articular therapy of rheumatoid arthritis. Multilamellar liposomes containing an entrapped anti-inflammatory drug are injected into the joint cavity (JC) where they associate with the hyperplasic synovium (1, 2) and the infiltrating polymorphonuclear leucocytes (PMN) of the synovial fluid (5). Cellular uptake of the liposomes is either by fusion (1) with the cell membrane, or by endocytosis (2) forming an endocytic vacuole (EV) (3) and ultimately a secondary lysosome (SL) (4). Following liposomal degradation within the lysosomes the free drug can act on the various cell components including the inflammatory sites such as the vascular beds of the subsynovial connective tissue (SCT) and infiltrating pannus (P) where it degrades the cartilage (C) and underlying bone (B). Nucleus (N); endoplasmic reticulum (ER); mitochondria (M); lysosome (L); external fibrous capsule (EFC)

leucocytes (Nakanishi and Goto, 1975; Ignarro, 1971b), an organelle repeatedly shown to associate with systemically administered liposomes (Gregoriadis and Ryman, 1972a; Gregoriadis and Ryman, 1972b; Segal *et al.*, 1974; de Barsy *et al.*, 1976).

2. STEROID RETENTION IN EGG-YOLK PHOSPHATIDYLCHOLINE LIPOSOMES

Our preliminary concern was to devise a liposomal carrier system that would retain steroid at physiological temperatures. The incorporation and retention of entrapped radiosotopic markers or steroid was assessed *in vitro* by either dialysis (Papahadjopoulos *et al.*, 1971), or washing the suspension at 50,000×*g* (Shaw *et al.*, 1976) every 24 hours and counting residual radioactivity. The liposome components were dried down by rotary evaporation from chloroform and hydrated (Bangham and Horne, 1964) in phosphate-buffered saline (5 mM, pH 7.35) at 30 °C. The resultant multilamellar liposomes were washed three times by centrifugation at 50,000×*g* for 10 minutes to remove an unentrapped marker or steroid.

The capacity of negatively charged egg-yolk phosphatidylcholine liposomes to entrap a hydrophilic marker was demonstrated by the

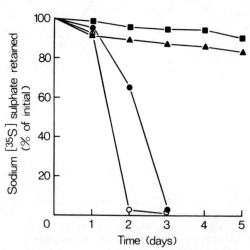

Figure 2 Effect of cholesterol on the retention of sodium [^{35}S]sulphate in egg-yolk phosphatidylcholine liposomes at 37 °C. Liposomes were prepared from 8 mg egg-yolk phosphatidylcholine, 1 mg phosphatidic acid, 20 μg sodium [^{35}S]sulphate (1.9 μCi) and 1 mg (○), 2 mg (●), 6 mg (▲) and 8 mg (■) cholesterol. The initial radioactivity was measured and the preparation (2 ml) dialysed against phosphate-buffered saline (900 ml, pH 7.35) at 37 °C. Residual radioactivity was determined every 24 hours

Table 1 [^{3}H]cortisol esters entrapped within negatively charged egg-yolk phosphatidylcholine (EYPC) liposomes containing various concentrations of cholesterol

Cortisol Derivative	C21 Side chain*	Liposomal formulation (mg/ml)			
		Steroid	EYPC	Cholesterol	Phosphatidic Acid
Alcohol (cortisol)	R–OH	0.10 (0.70 μCi)	8.0	2.0 – 8.0	1.0
Succinate	R–O–C–CH$_2$CH$_2$COONa ($=$O)	1.00 (0.70 μCi)	8.0	1.5 – 8.0	1.0
Acetate	R–O–C–CH$_3$ ($=$O)	0.18 (1.34 μCi)	8.0	3.0 – 6.0	1.0
Phosphate	R–O–P–(OH)$_2$ ($=$O)	0.75 (0.12 μCi)	8.0	1.5 – 6.0	1.0
Cyclohexyl ester	R–O–C–C$_6$H$_{11}$ ($=$O)	0.50 (0.40 μCi)	8.0	1.5 – 6.0	1.0

The liposomal lipids were made up in chloroform and dried down by rotary evaporation under nitrogen at 30 °C. The dried lipid film was hydrated with 5 mM phosphate-buffered saline, pH 7.35. The liposome preparation was washed three times by centrifugation at 50,000 g for 10 minutes.
*where R = cortisol

Liposomes in Biological Systems

incorporation of sodium [^{35}S]sulphate (20 μg, 1.9 μCi) in the presence of 1, 2, 6 and 8 mg cholesterol. The retention of sodium [^{35}S]sulphate at 37 °C was markedly enhanced by the presence of cholesterol (Figure 2).

Hydrophilic esters of cortisol were entrapped within egg-yolk phosphatidylcholine liposomes of differing cholesterol concentration (Table 1) in order to determine the optimum parameters for steroid incorporation and retention. The liposomes were made negative by the incorporation of phosphatidic acid.

With the exception of cortisol cyclohexyl ester, liposomal incorporation of cortisol and cortisol C21 esters was less that 10% regardless of the cholesterol concentration (Table 2). Cortisol phosphate incorporation was, however, enhanced with increasing concentrations of cholesterol.

The liposomal retention of cortisol esters at 37 °C is illustrated in Figure 3. Retention of cortisol (A) and the esters (B,C,D) was very limited and variable at all cholesterol concentrations. No liposomal cortisol acetate was detectable after 24 hours. Cortisol (A) and cortisol phosphate (D) readily diffused out of the liposomes within 24 and 48 hours. At low concentrations of cholesterol, the loss of cortisol succinate (B) and cyclohexyl ester (C) was slightly retarded. The failure of egg-yolk phosphatidylcholine liposomes to retain esters of cortisol at 37 °C was thought to be due in part to the mixed hydrophobicity and hydrophilicity exhibited by these compounds. At 37 °C egg-yolk phosphatidylcholine is above the phase transition temperature (-10 °C) and exists in a fluid state, consequently the liposomes are more permeable (de Gier *et al.*, 1968).

At the suggestion of Dr. C. G. Knight we decided to entrap a hydrophobic C21 ester of cortisol, cortisol octanoate (Junkmann and Suchowsky, 1960). [^{3}H]cortisol octanoate (0.54 mg, 0.59 μCi) was entrapped within 1 ml of liposomes containing 8 mg of egg-yolk phosphatidylcholine, 1 mg egg-yolk phosphatidic acid, and 1.5, 3.0, 4.5 and

Table 2 The effect of cholesterol on the percentage incorporation of cortisol esters into negative egg-yolk phosphatidylcholine liposomes

Steroid	Initial steroid conc. (mg/ml)	Cholesterol concentration (mg/ml liposomes)						
		1.5	2.0	3.0	4.0	4.5	6.0	8.0
Cortisol	0.10	–	3.6	–	2.6	–	–	2.3
Cortisol succinate	1.00	1.0	–	1.2	–	1.4	2.5	4.2
Cortisol acetate	0.18	–	–	1.0	–	1.0	1.0	–
Cortisol phosphate	0.75	4.3	7.1	–	7.4	–	10.0	–
Cortisol cyclohexyl ester	0.50	25.0	–	10.0	–	14.0	18.0	–

Liposomes were prepared as described in the text. After washing by centrifugation in phosphate-buttered saline the initial radioactivity was determined.

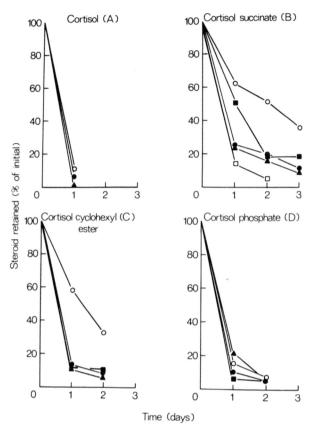

Time (days)

Figure 3 Effect of cholesterol on the retention of esters of cortisol within egg-yolk phosphatidylcholine liposomes at 37 °C. Liposomes were formulated as described in Table 1. Initial radioactivity was measured and the preparations (2 ml) dialysed against phosphate buffered saline (900 ml, pH 7.35) at 37 °C. Residual radioactivity was determined every 24 hours.

(A) CORTISOL
Retention of cortisol within liposomes containing 2.0 mg (o), 4.0 mg (●) and 8.0 mg (▲) of cholesterol.

(B) CORTISOL SUCCINATE
Retention of cortisol succinate within liposomes containing 1.5 mg (o), 3.0 mg (●) 4.5 mg (▲), 6.0 mg (■) and 8.0 mg (□) of cholesterol.

(C)   CORTISOL CYCLOHEXYL ESTER
Retention of cortisol cyclohexyl ester in liposomes containing 1.5 mg (o), 3.0 mg (●), 4.5 mg (▲) and 6.0 mg (■) of cholesterol.

(D) CORTISOL PHOSPHATE
Retention of cortisol phosphate within liposomes containing 1.5 mg (o), 3.0 mg (●) 4.5 mg (▲) and 6.0 (■) of cholesterol

Liposomes in Biological Systems

6.0 mg cholesterol. Liposomal incorporation of the C8 ester was inversely related to the cholesterol concentration. Initial entrapment of the steroid was 42.1, 37.6, 13.3, and 12.5% for liposomes containing 1.5, 3.0, 4.5, and 6.0 mg cholesterol respectively. Stevens and Green (1972), studying the relationship between testosterone ester side chain structure and liposomal incorporation, demonstrated optimum steroid incorporation with the C8 ester, testosterone octanoate. The inverse relationship between cholesterol and cortisol octanoate as regards liposomal incorporation may be due to the structural similarities between the molecules. Cholesterol, a natural membrane sterol, also has a C8 side chain although the chain is shorter than the octanoate due to branching (Stevens and Green, 1972). However, the difference in physical characteristics between the molecules must also be considered.

The retention of cortisol octanoate at 37 °C was also inversely related to the cholesterol concentration (Figure 4). In liposomes containing less than 3 mg cholesterol, over 0.14 mg (70%) of the entrapped steroid was still liposome-associated after 4 days. Demel *et al.* (1968) found that the rate of efflux of entrapped glucose was strongly retarded by the incorporation of cholesterol. The permeability of the liposomes was also related to the degree of unsaturation of the acyl chains, an observation confirmed by de Gier *et al.* (1968).

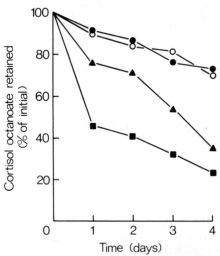

Figure 4 Effect of cholesterol on the retention of [³H]cortisol octanoate within egg-yolk phosphatidylcholine liposomes at 37 °C. Liposomes were prepared from 8 mg egg-yolk phosphatidylcholine, 1 mg phosphatidic acid, 0.54 mg [³H]cortisol octanoate (0.59 μCi), and 1.5 mg (○), 3.0 mg (●), 4.5 mg (▲) and 6.0 mg (■) of cholesterol. The initial radioactivity was measured and the preparations (2 ml) dialysed against phosphate-buffered saline (900 ml, pH 7.35) at 37 °C. Residual radioactivity was determined every 24 hours

Liposomal permeability changes induced by cholesterol are dependent on an intact sterol side chain, the planar sterol nucleus, and the 3β-hydroxy group (Demel *et al.*, 1972). This structure–activity relationship led to the view that the reduced permeability is due to an increase in packing and decreased mobility of the hydrocarbon chains of the bilayer phosphatidylcholine.

The series of experiments involving liposomes prepared from egg-yolk phosphatidylcholine illustrated the importance of bilayer stability and entrapped drug form at temperatures above that of the phase transition temperature of the constituent lecithin.

3. STEROID RETENTION IN SYNTHETIC LIPOSOMES

Papahadjopoulos *et al.* (1974) suggested the cellular fate of an entrapped molecule was related to the physical state of the liposome carrier. Investigating the effects of entrapped cyclic-AMP they found that liposomes in the liquid–crystalline state fuse with the outer cell membrane releasing their contents into the cytoplasm. Liposomes in the gel phase were endocytosed and localized in the lysosomes (Figure 1).

The synthetic saturated lecithins dimyristoyl, dipalmitoyl, and distearoyl phosphatidylcholine exhibit phase transition temperatures of 23.9, 41.4, and 54.9 °C respectively (Mabrey and Sturtevant, 1976). At physiological temperatures dimyristoyl phosphatidylcholine liposomes will therefore exist in the fluid state while those of dipalmitoyl and distearoyl phosphatidylcholine will be below the gel–liquid crystalline transition temperature and have a more ordered structure (as reviewed by Poste *et al.*, 1976).

To determine the most stable synthetic liposome composition for the entrapment and retention of anti-inflammatory steroid at physiological temperatures, negatively charged liposomes containing entrapped cortisol octanoate were prepared from dimyristoyl, dipalmitoyl, and distearoyl phosphatidylcholine as described by Shaw *et al.* (1976).

Cortisol octanoate was released from all liposome preparations incubated at 37 °C and the rate of loss was related to the fatty acid chain length of the liposomal lecithin. Cortisol octanoate was released from dimyristoyl phosphatidylcholine liposomes at a much greater rate than from otherwise similar dipalmitoyl or distearoyl phosphatidylcholine liposomes containing 6 mg lecithin, 3 mg cortisol octanoate, and 1 mg phosphatidic acid per ml (molar ration of 7:4.3:1.2). After 3 days, 34.1% (1.02 mg) of the entrapped steroid ester was associated with the liposomes.

In an attempt to improve the *in vitro* retention of steroid ester within liposomes of defined physical characteristics, the incorporation of a cortisol ester with a longer, more compatible side chain was considered. Cortisol

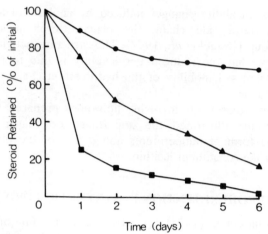

Figure 5 Retention of [³H]cortisol, [³H]cortisol octanoate, and [³H]cortisol palmitate in dipalmitoyl phosphatidylcholine liposomes at 37 °C. Liposomes were prepared from 6 mg of dipalmitoyl phosphatidylcholine, 1 mg phosphatidic acid, and 3 mg of [³H]cortisol (■), [³H]cortisol octanoate (▲) or [³H]cortisol palmitate (●) as described in the text. The initial radioactivity was measured. At 24 hour intervals the liposome suspension was washed by centrifugation and resuspended in fresh 5 mM phosphate-buffered saline, pH 7.35. (From Shaw *et al.*, 1976)

palmitate was therefore entrapped within dipalmotoyl phosphatidylcholine liposomes and the steroid retention assessed at 37 °C.

Increasing the chain length of the substituent group on C21 of cortisol caused a marked enhancement of steroid ester retention at 37 °C in dipalmitoyl phosphatidylcholine liposomes prepared with 30% steroid (Figure 5). Initial incorporation of the palmitate ester was 1.80 mg/ml compared to 1.76 mg/ml for the octanoate ester and 1.21 mg/ml for cortisol. After 3 days incubation at 37 °C, 0.15 mg of cortisol (12%), 0.71 mg of cortisol octanoate (40%), and 1.27 mg of cortisol palmitate (71%) remained entrapped within the liposomes (Shaw *et al.*, 1976). The need for a compatible hydrophobic side chain to enhance liposomal retention of cortisol and cortisol esters was clearly demonstrated by the rapid loss of the free alcohol from dipalmitoyl phosphatidylcholine liposomes.

4. EFFECT OF SYNOVIAL FLUID ON LIPOSOMAL RETENTION AND STABILITY OF ENTRAPPED STEROID

Having established a relatively stable liposomal–steroid carrier complex in our test system, we then turned our attention to an environment more in common with active rheumatoid arthritis, that of synovial fluid.

Normal diarthrodial joints lined with a synovial membrane contain very little synovial fluid (0.1–0.4 ml) but enough to facilitate articulation and nutrition of the avascular cartilage. Synovial fluid contains hyaluronate but substances with a molecular weight greater than 160,000, such as immunoglobulins, fibrinogen, and α_2-macroglobulin, are normally excluded Sledge, 1975). In the pathological state the volume of synovial fluid can increase dramatically. Volumes greater than 200 ml have been aspirated from rheumatoid knee joints (Gardner, 1972). Arthritic synovial fluid often reflects the degree of inflammation in the synovium and cartilage, and being easily obtainable, has received considerable attention (for a recent review see Medicis *et al.*, 1976). Rheumatoid synovial fluid is usually turbid, has a tendency to clot, and is heavily infiltrated with polymorphonuclear leucocytes, the majority of which contain intracytoplasmic inclusions (Broderick *et al.*, 1976). The protein content of the fluid in rheumatoid arthritis is often in excess of 4g% (Ruddy, 1974b) and viscosity of the fluid is reduced, an observation shown to correlate with the degree of synovitis (Reimann, 1976). The source of elevated lysosomal enzymes found in rheumatoid synovial fluid is thought to be infiltrating leucocytes (Weissmann, 1972), the hyperplasic synovium or pannus (Dingle, 1962; Weissmann, 1972) and possibly the cartilage itself (Gardner, 1972). Intra-articular injections of steroids have been shown to bring about a reduction in the enhanced levels of lysosomal enzymes and infiltrating cells found in rheumatoid synovial fluid (Greiling *et al.*, 1971). Swedlund *et al.* (1974) have demonstrated elevated levels of the proteolytic enzyme inhibitor α_1-antitrypsin in rheumatoid synovial fluid.

Unlike the systemic administration of liposomes, intra-articular injection in active rheumatoid arthritis involves introducing the carrier into a pathological environment of excess protein and enzymes, many of which may interact with the drug-carrying liposome. Of particular interest to intra-articular liposomal administration is the ability of preformed liposomes to interact with a wide variety of proteins (as reviewed by Tyrell *et al.*, 1976). Black and Gregoriadis (1976) demonstrated that egg-yolk phosphatidylcholine liposomes associated with α_2-macroglobulin in human plasma. Binding of protein to liposomes can also increase the rate of efflux of entrapped markers (Poste *et al.*, 1976), an effect thought to parallel the extent of protein ingression into the lipid bilayer (Papahadjopoulos and Kimelberg, 1973). Eytan *et al.* (1976), however, incorporated mitochondrial proteins into preformed unilamellar liposomes at room temperature without any apparent adverse structural effects.

In preliminary studies we investigated the stability and retention of the liposome-entrapped steroid in the presence of cell-free synovial fluid. Synovial fluid was kindly provided by Dr. B. L. Hazleman. The knee joints of patients suffering from active rheumatoid arthritis were aspirated under aseptic conditions. Infiltrating cells were removed by centrifugation.

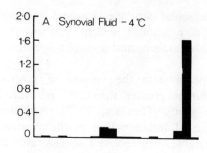

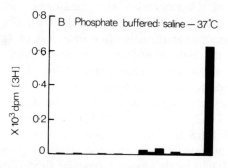

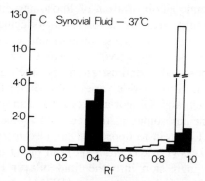

Figure 6 Radiochromatograms illustrating the effect of rheumatoid synovial fluid on the stability of [³H]cortisol octanoate and [³H]cortisol palmitate entrapped within liposomes. Negatively charged egg-yolk phosphatidylcholine liposomes containing 1.5 mg [³H]cortisol octanoate (shaded histograms) were incubated in cell-free rheumatoid synovial fluid at 4 °C (A) and phosphate-buffered saline at 37 °C (B) for 16 hours. Negatively charged dipalmitoyl phosphatidylcholine liposomes containing 1.5 mg [³H]cortisol palmitate (C, open histogram) were incubated with cell-free rheumatoid synovial fluid at 37 °C for 16 hours. Portions were chromatographed as described in the text

Negatively charged egg-yolk phosphatidylcholine liposomes containing 1.5 mg [³H]cortisol octanoate and dipalmitoyl phosphatidylcholine liposomes containing 1.5 mg [³H]cortisol palmitate were incubated in 80% synovial fluid at 4 and 37 °C. After 16 hours, portions of the incubate were applied to a silica gel thin layer chromatography plate and eluted with chloroform:glacial acetic acid (9:1, v/v). After elution the plate was cut into sections (2 × 0.5 cm) and radiochromatograms plotted after scintillation counting (Figure 6).

Cortisol octanoate incubated at 4 °C in synovial fluid was relatively stable after 16 hours (Figure 6A). A similar radiochromatogram was obtained for cortisol palmitate liposomes. Both steroids had an *Rf* value of 0.9–1.0. At 37 °C, in phosphate-buffered saline, liposomal cortisol octanoate (Figure 6B) and cortisol palmitate remained intact. The effect of rheumatoid synovial fluid on liposomal cortisol octanoate and cortisol palmitate is clearly seen from Figure 6C. There was no detectable hydrolysis of cortisol palmitate after 16 hours, however 80% of the cortisol had reverted to cortisol (*Rf* 0.35–0.45). In a study with negative, positive, and neutral egg-yolk phosphatidylcholine liposomes containing cortisol octanoate, we found no difference in the rate of hydrolysis of the ester linkage upon incubation in synovial fluid at 37 °C.

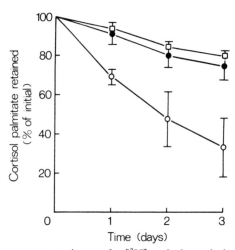

Figure 7 Percentage retention of [³H]cortisol palmitate in dipalmitoyl phosphatidylcholine liposomes at 37 °C in the presence of 50% synovial fluid (○), phosphate-buffered saline (5 mM, pH 7.35) (●) and 2.7% bovine serum albumin (□). Liposomes were prepared from 6 mg dipalmitoyl phosphatidylcholine, 1 mg phosphatidic acid, and 3 mg [³H]cortisol palmitate. The initial radioactivity was measured and the preparations (5 ml) dialysed against phosphate-buffered saline (900 ml, pH 7.35) at 37 °C. Residual radioactivity was determined every 24 hours

Retention of [^{3}H]cortisol palmitate within negatively charged dipalmitoyl phosphatidylcholine liposomes in the presence of 50% synovial fluid (with a total protein content of 2.7%) and 2.7% bovine serum albumin in phosphate-buffered saline at 37 °C was assessed by dialysis. Liposomes (2.5 ml) and synovial fluid (2.5 ml) were thoroughly mixed and placed in a dialysis bag. After counting the initial radioactivity, the suspension was dialysed against 900 ml phosphate-buffered saline (pH 7.35) at 37 °C. Every 24 hours the dialysate was changed and residual radioactivity determined.

Rheumatoid synovial fluid accelerated the rate of release of entrapped cortisol palmitate from dipalmitoyl phosphatylcholine liposomes (Figure 7) at 37 °C. After 24 hours 70 ± 3% of steroid was retained in comparison to 90 ± 4% and 92 ± 2% in the presence of phosphate buffered saline and 2.7% bovine serum albumin respectively. After 3 days 34 ± 15% of the steroid remained within the liposomes incubated in synovial fluid. The inability of bovine serum albumin, in a concentration equivalent to that of the protein content of the synovial fluid, to influence liposomal retention of steroid would suggest more specific factors are involved in steroid leakage. Sogar and Zull (1975) have presented X-ray data supporting the view that bovine serum albumin does not affect negative liposomal bilayer organization or permeability. In a previous study (Sweet and Zull, 1970), however, glucose efflux was enhanced upon interaction with bovine serum albumin. Kimelberg (1976) found that multilamellar liposomes showed a small increase in permeability to methotrexate in the presence of human serum albumin whereas sonicated liposomes were mainly permeable.

The degree of bilayer fluidity may be an important factor in regulating the penetration of a protein or an enzyme into the liposome. The susceptibility of phospholipid bilayers to phospholipases has been shown to depend on the degree of unsaturation of the fatty acyl chains and the concentration of cholesterol (Jain and Cordes, 1973). Both these factors are known to influence the phase transition temperature of liposomes (Poste *et al.*, 1976; Shimshick and McConnell, 1973). Papahadjopoulos *et al.* (1973) observed a large increase in permeability of preformed liposomes to Na$^+$ after the addition of a variety of proteins. These protein-induced permeability changes were markedly reduced by the incorporation of cholesterol into the vesicles. The diffusion rate of Na$^+$ from phosphatidylserine vesicles incubated in the presence of human serum albumin was reduced 61-fold upon the addition of cholesterol. The induced diffusion of entrapped marker was also reduced when the liposomes were incubated below their respective melting temperatures.

The resistance of cortisol palmitate to hydrolysis by rheumatoid synovial fluid, unlike that of the octanoate ester, is as yet unexplained. It would appear that cortisol palmitate release is brought about by an action on the liposomal bilayer rather than altering the hydrophobicity of the entrapped steroid. Steroid readily escapes from egg-yolk phosphatidylcholine liposomes containing cortisol octanoate when incubated in rheumatoid synovial fluid at 37 °C. Within 3 hours, 60% of the incorporated steroid had escaped from the liposomes (Shaw and Dingle, unpublished observation). Differences in the rate of liposome steroid loss may therefore reflect the penetrability of the liposomal bilayers as well as the stability of the entrapped steroid ester.

These preliminary results clearly illustrate the need for a more detailed study of liposomal–synovial fluid interactions if the system is to be considered as a drug carrier. However, prior to the intra-articular injection of pharmacological agents, it is usual to aspirate excess synovial fluid from the joint cavity (Jubb and Hazleman, 1976). This procedure would obviously be advantageous in intra-articular liposome therapy.

5. INTRA-ARTICULAR LIPOSOMAL THERAPY

5.1 Liposomal Size and Joint Tissue Localization of Entrapped Steroid

The systemic clearance of liposomes of various sizes and charges has provided much information in regard to the optimum liposomal parameters required for tissue localization. Gregoriadis and Neerunjun (1974) found that negatively charged liposomes were cleared from rat plasma faster than those of neutral or positive charge. More than 80% of the liposomes containing dicetyl phosphate had been cleared from the circulation within 30 minutes. This rapid clearance of negatively charged liposomes was also confirmed by Juliano and Stamp (1975), and more recently by Kimelberg (1976) using primates. Recently Adams *et al.* (1977) demonstrated that liposomes made negative by the incorporation of dicetyl phosphate induced epileptic seizures and necrosis when injected intracerebrally in mice. Toxicity following the administration of dipalmitoyl phosphatidylcholine liposomes, or liposomes containing phosphatidic acid, was limited to mechanical damage at the site of injection. As a consequence of the foregoing observations, negatively charged liposomes containing phosphatidic acid were assessed *in vivo* as vehicles for intra-articular steroids.

Evidence that multilamellar vesicles are more appropriate for local therapy was presented by Segal *et al.* (1975) after intratesticular administration in rats. Sonicated liposomes readily escaped from the site of injection via the lymphatics and circulation. However, the fact that the liposomes were administered into a non-phagocytic environment must be considered. Multilamellar liposomes are also cleared faster from the bloodstream than those of the unilamellar variety (Juliano and Stamp, 1975; Kimelberg, 1976).

Upon hydration of a dried lipid film, a heterogeneous population of multilamellar liposomes with a wide size distribution are formed. In an initial study we attempted to fractionate a preparation of liposomes into 'large' (LML) and 'small' (SML) multilamellar liposomes in order to determine the optimum liposomal size for steroid presentation to arthritic tissue.

Negatively charged dipalmitoyl phosphatidylcholine liposomes containing [^{3}H]cortisol palmitate were fractionated by repeated centrifugation through Ficoll (1%) in 5 mM phosphate-buffered saline at pH 7.35 as illustrated in Figure 8. After fractionation, the liposomes were sized by Normarski differential interference contrast microscopy and electron microscopy. For contrast microscopy portions of each liposome fraction were examined under oil immersion. The microscope was fitted with a monofilar eyepiece to aid sizing. Preparations for electron microscopy were negatively stained

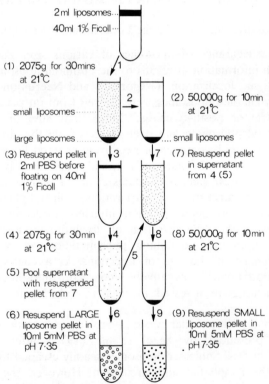

Figure 8 The separation of a heterogeneous preparation of multilamellar liposomes into two size distributions by centrifugation through Ficoll

with ammonium molybdate and electron micrographs of each preparation taken at ×30,000 to facilitate sizing.

The size distributions, as assessed by the two techniques, of fractionated and unfractionated liposome preparations are presented in Table 3. Determination of liposomal size was dependent on the technique used. In all three preparations contrast microscopy resulted in a higher mean liposome diameter. It is conceivable that the liposomes undergo partial dehydration during electron microscopy resulting in a smaller mean diameter (Glauert, personal communication). The most striking difference in size was that observed for the heterogeneous preparation. A five-fold difference in mean diameter was recorded between the two techniques. With reservation, we regarded the liposomes sized by contrast microscopy at room temperature to be more representative of the true liposomal diameter. The SML preparation was seen to contain many small vesicles below the resolving power of the light microscope sizing technique. Caution must therefore be exercised in accepting what may be an artificially high mean diameter for the SML preparation. In a previous study an attempt was made to determine the average diameter of egg-yolk phosphatidylcholine liposomes by means of a Coulter counter. Working within the lower limits of the counter's capacity the mean liposome diameter of a heterogeneous preparation was determined as 0.8 μm (J. L. Gordon, unpublished observation). These results do indicate that the technique employed for determining liposomal size may have considerable influence on the results observed.

A 4-day polycation–polyanion complex induced arthritis (Page-Thomas, 1977) in Old English rabbits was selected as the most suitable model for the assessment of intra-articular liposomal uptake. Each arthritic knee received, by injection through the supra-patellar ligament, 0.5 ml of

Table 3 Size distribution of dipalmitoyl phosphatidylcholine liposomes containing cortisol palmitate

Liposome preparation	Contrast Microscopy		Electron Microscopy	
	Observations	Diameter (μm) $\bar{x} \pm$ S.E.	Observations	Diameter (μm) $\bar{x} \pm$ S.E.
Heterogeneous	80	0.93 ± 0.48	200	0.18 ± 0.01
LMLs	50	1.08 ± 0.31	199	0.59 ± 0.02
SMLs	90	0.34 ± 0.21	138	0.16 ± 0.01

Liposomes were prepared from 6 mg dipalmitoyl phosphatidylcholine, 3 mg cortisol palmitate and 1 mg phosphatidic acid. After three washes the liposome preparation was fractionated by centrifugation through 1% Ficoll as illustrated in Figure 8. The mean liposome diameter was determined for fractionated and unfractionated preparations by Normarski differential interface contrast microscopy using a monofilar eyepiece and electron microscopy. LMLs—'large' multilamellar liposomes; SMLs— 'small' multilamellar liposomes liposome preparation containing cortisol, as [³H]cortisol palmitate, as follows: unfractionated (248 μg cortisol, 4.35 μCi); LML (222 μg cortisol, 3.90 μCi) and SML (178 μg cortisol, 3.31 μCi).

At post-mortem 2 hours after the intra-articular injection of liposomes, each joint was washed out *in situ* with saline. After centrifugation the joint fluid and supernatant were counted for radioactivity. The joint tissue was dissected free, washed *in vitro*, and weighed (686 ± 63 mg). Weighed portions of excised tissue were digested by papain at 60 °C for 20 hours. Portions of the digest were counted in Triton X-100 scintillant.

There was no quantitative difference ($p > 0.05$) between joint tissue localization of [³H]cortisol palmitate after intra-articular injection of heterogeneous, large and small multilamellar liposome preparations (Figure 9). Washing the excised tissue before digestion accounted for less than 1% of the injected steroid in all groups. The inability to recover the majority of the injected steroid could be due to a combination of factors. Liposomal escape from the joint space via the bloodstream or lymphatics, steroid efflux from the liposomes *in vivo*, and failure to excise all of the arthritic tissue must be considered.

These results suggested there was no advantage to be gained in using a liposome preparation of defined size for the tissue localization of liposomal steroid ester after intra-articular injection.

Data on the size exclusion limits of joints have come from the

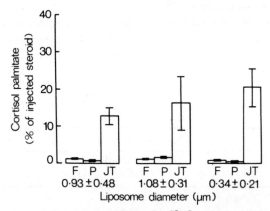

Figure 9 Percentage distribution of liposomal [³H]cortisol palmitate following the intra-articular injection of sized unsonicated liposome preparations into acutely arthritic rabbit joints. Liposomes were prepared, fractionated, and sized as described in the text. Four days after the induction of a bilateral experimental arthritis each arthritic joint received an injection of sized liposomes (0.5 ml). After 2 hours, the localization of liposomal [³H]cortisol palmitate was assessed in the supernatant (F) and pellet (P) from the joint fluid and *in vivo* wash and the arthritic joint tissue (JT)

intra-articular use of colloids as a means of radiosynovectomy. Ingrand (1973) presented evidence to suggest that gold particles with a diameter greater than 0.3 μm did not escape via the lymphatics. In one study 35.5% of the patients showed lymphatic spreading of colloidal particles of 20 nm. In two further studies, increasing the particle diameter to 30 nm reduced this spreading to 19 and 22.2%. However, caution must be exercised in relating this data to optimum liposome size. In attempts to reduce the extra-articular absorption of radioactive colloids, patients undergoing synovectomy are often pre-medicated with intra-articular steroids and local anaesthetics (Goode and Howe, 1973). Similarly, post-synovectomy splinting and bed rest will influence particle escape from the joint space (Roberts and Gillespie, 1973). Indeed, it has been suggested that there is no relationship between particle size and extra-articular spreading (Gumpel, personal communication). An added complication is the observation in experimentally induced arthritis in rabbits, that articular retention of [90]Yttrium was dependent on the formation of the colloid (Gumpel *et al.*, 1973).

5.2 Therapeutic Assessment of Intra-articular Liposome Administration in Arthritis

A preliminary assessment of the anti-inflammatory potential of liposome-entrapped steroid was made on the acute experimental arthritis in rabbits (Dingle *et al.*, 1978). A bilateral polycation–polyanion complex induced arthritis was established in the knee joints of Old English rabbits. The choice of an acute articular inflammatory model was made in view of the unsuitable nature of the chronic models at present available (Page-Thomas, 1977).

Four days after the induction of the arthritis, 0.5 ml of negatively charged dipalmitoyl phosphatidylcholine liposomes containing 20 μg cortisol, as cortisol palmitate, were injected into one joint. Changes in the degree of inflammation were qualified by regularly measuring joint diameter (Davis, 1971; Blackham *et al.*, 1975) and the temperature of the joints. Changes in joint temperature were monitored by either bolometery (Collins and Ring, 1972; Blackham *et al.*, 1974) or thermography (Collins *et al.*, 1974) in a room of constant ambient temperature. The treated joint was compared with the contralateral untreated joint.

Following the induction of experimental arthritis, there was a progressive increase in articular cutaneous temperature and joint diameter. After the intra-articular injection of liposomes containing cortisol palmitate there was a reduction in joint temperature and diameter. In comparison to the untreated joint, this anti-inflammatory effect lasted for 3 days. Liposomes prepared in the absence of steroid had no detectable pharmacological effect. Evidence that the C16 ester of cortisol possesses pharmacological activity in rheumatoid arthritis has been demonstrated by Hollander (1955) who assessed the local anti-inflammatory efficacy of a series of esters; among them cortisol palmitate. In fifteen rheumatoid patients the mean duration of ester activity was 7 days compared with that of 5 days for the free alcohol after a single intra-articular injection of 37.5 mg steroid.

In comparison to liposome-incorporated steroid, 20 μg cortisol, as cortisol acetate, was administered to arthritic rabbits. No therapeutic effect was established with free steroid at a concentration equivalent to that within the liposomes.

The reduction in joint size and temperature demonstrated by a liposome–steroid preparation containing 20 μg cortisol, as cortisol palmitate, represents in relation to body weight, a reduction of some 30 to 50 times the effective clinical dose. It would therefore appear that the use of liposomes as steroid carriers may bring about a reduction in the systemic toxicity as predicted.

Studies on articular localization of lecithin and steroid, after administration, were carried out using [^{3}H]dipalmitoyl phosphatidylcholine and [^{3}H]cortisol palmitate. The results of these studies have been published in full (Shaw *et al.*, 1979). In brief, in 4- and 8-day arthritic synovium, liposomes, as monitored by [^{3}H]dipalmitoyl phosphatidylcholine retention, were associated with the tissue 2 hours after adminstration. Twelve hours after intra-articular injection there was no significant change in liposomal retention by the tissue.

Steroid retention by arthritic joint tissue *in vivo* was dependent on the chronicity of the tissue. Maximum incorporation of steroid was seen by 2 hours. After the injection of 20 μg cortisol, as cortisol palmitate within liposomes, 10.0 ± 2.0 μg was associated with the 4-day tissue and 6.35 μg with 8-day tissue after 2 hours. Eight hours after treatment there was no significant difference in the concentration of steroid retained by 4-day tissue (8.2 ± 1.0 μg) when compared with the 2-hour tissue level. In 8-day tissue there was a significant loss of steroid 8 hours after injection, the steroid concentration being 1.8 ± 0.2 μg. The ability of the more advanced arthritic tissue to retain liposome-entrapped steroid may be a consequence of the hydrolysis of the C21 ester by the more developed pathological tissue. We are looking further at the phenomenon.

6. CONCLUSIONS

It would appear from our preliminary studies on acute arthritis that liposomes may be suitable carriers for anti-inflammatory steroids. By manipulation of the structural lecithins, stable carriers with variable biodegradable properties could be formulated. This would enable one to prolong the release of the entrapped steroid. By using more potent steroids, such as dexamethasone, and indeed mixtures of steroids, the efficacy of the liposome preparations could be altered. The assessment of the carrier system in a suitable chronic arthritis will provide more conclusive information on the need to manipulate the liposome–steroid complex.

The use of liposomes as drug carriers in intra-articular therapy need not be restricted to that of steroids. In order to reduce the extra-articular spread of isotopes used for radiochemical synovectomy it is necessary for the patients to rest, receive local steroids and post-injection splinting. The liposomal encapsulation of radioisotopes may be of value in these circumstances (Sledge, personal communication).

Steroid encapsulated into liposomes would also provide a suitable vehicle for the local treatment of various necrotizing diseases of the eye. In a situation analogous to that of the joint, soluble steroids administered locally as drops, rapidly escape from the orbit into the systemic circulation (Watson, personal communication). Liposome encapsulation may therefore retard the escape of the steroids.

The use of liposomes as drug carriers in local therapy has considerable potential, particularly in the treatment of rheumatoid arthritis. By extending our studies into chronic models we ultimately hope to develop for use in man, a carrier system which will considerably prolong the efficacious effect of local anti-inflammatory steroids and markedly reduce the systemic and local toxicity.

Acknowledgements

I. H. Shaw was supported by a Medical Research Council Studentship and J. T. Dingle is a member of the external staff of the Medical Research Council.

REFERENCES

Adams, D. H., Joyce, G., Richardson, V. J., Ryman, B. E. and Wisniewski, H. M. (1977). *J. Neurol. Sci.,* **31**, 173.
Arthritis and Rheumatism Council (1977). *Rheumatism: The Price We Pay*, ARC, London.
Askari, A., Vignos, P. J. and Moskowitz, R. W. (1976). *Amer. J. Med.,* **61**, 485.
Bangham, A. D. and Horne, R. W. (1964). *J. Mol. Biol.,* **8**, 660.
Bentley, G. and Goodfellow, J. W. (1969). *J. Bone Jt. Surg.,* **51B**, 498.
Bilka, P. J. (1967). *Minn. Med.,* **50**, 483.
Black, C. D. V. and Gregoriadis, G. (1976). *Biochem. Soc. Trans.,* **4**, 253.
Blackham, A., Farmer, J. B., Radziwonik, H. and Westwick, J. (1974). *Brit. J. Pharmacol.,* **51**, 35.
Blackham, A., Radziwonik, H. and Shaw, I. H. (1975). *Agent. Action,* **5**, 519.

Broderick, P. A., Corvese, N., Pierik, M. G., Pike, R. F. and Mariorenzi, A. L. (1976). *J. Bone Jt. Surg. USA.*, **58A**, 396.

Caride, V. J., Taylor, W., Cramer, J. A. and Gottschalk, A. (1976). *J. Nucl. Med.*, **17**, 1067.

Carwile LeRoy, E. (1974). In *Rheumatoid Arthritis*, p.99, (ed. E. D. Harris), Medcom, New York.

Chandler, G. N. and Wright, V. (1958). *Lancet*, **2**, 661.

Chandler, G. N., Wright, V. and Hartfell, S. J. (1958). *Lancet*, **2**, 659.

Collins, A. J. and Ring, E. F. J. (1972). *Brit. J. Pharmacol.*, **44**, 145.

Collins, A. J., Ring, E. F. J., Cosh, J. A. (1974). *Ann. rheum. Dis.*, **33**, 113.

Davis, B. (1971). *Ann. rheum. Dis.*, **30**, 509.

de Barsy, T., Devos, P. and Van Hoof, F. (1976). *Lab. Invest.*, **34**, 373.

Demel, R. A., Kinsky, S. C., Kinsky, C. B. and van Deenen, L. L. M. (1968). *Biochim. Biophys. Acta*, **150**, 655.

Demel, R. A., Bruckdorfer, K. R. and van Deenen, L. L. M. (1972). *Biochim. Biophys. Acta*, **255**, 322.

de Gier, J., Mandersloot, J. G. and van Deenen, L. L. M. (1969). *Biochim. Biophys. Acta*, **266**, 561.

Dick-Smith, J. B. (1974). *Med. J. Aust.*, **1**, 539.

Dingle, J. T. (1962). *Proc. Roy. Soc. Med.*, **55**, 109.

Dingle, J. T. (1966). In *Modern Trends in Rheumatology*, p.110 (ed. A. G. S. Hill), Butterworths, London.

Dingle, J. T., Gordon, J. L., Hazleman, B. L., Knight, C. G., Page-Thomas, D. P., Phillips, N. C., Shaw, I. H., Fildes, F. J. P., Oliver, J. E., Jones, G., Turner, E. H. and Lowe, J. S. (1978). *Nature* (London) **271**, 372.

Dinning, W. J. (1976). *Postgrad. Med. J.*, **52**, 634.

Duthie, J. J. R. (1969). *Textbook of Rheumatic Diseases*, 4th ed., p.259. (ed. W. S. C. Copeman). Livingstone, Edinburgh.

Eytan, G. D., Matheson, M. J. and Racker, E. (1976). *J. Biol. Chem.*, **251**, 6831.

Fell, H. B. and Dingle, J. T. (1963). *Biochem. J.*, **87**, 403.

Fell, H. B. and Thomas, L. C. (1961). *J. Exp. Med.*, **114**, 343.

Gardner, D. L. (1972). In *Pathology of Rheumatoid Arthritis*, p.84, Arnold, London.

Gibson, T., Burry, H. C., Poswillo, D. and Glass, J. (1976). *Ann. rheum. Dis.*, **36**, 74.

Goetzl, E. J., Bianco, N. E., Alpert, J. S., Sledge, C. B. and Schur, P. H. (1974). *Ann. rheum. Dis.*, **33**, 62.

Goode, J. D. and Howey, S. (1973). *Ann. rheum. Dis.*, **32** (suppl.), 43.

Gregoriadis, G. (1973). *FEBS Lett.*, **36**, 292.

Gregoriadis, G. (1975). *Biochem. Soc. Trans.*, **3**, 613.

Gregoriadis, G. and Neerunjun, D. E. (1974). *Eur. J. Biochem.*, **47**, 179.

Gregoriadis, G. and Ryman, B. E. (1972a). *Biochem. J.*, **129**, 123.

Gregoriadis, G. and Ryman, B. E. (1972b). *Eur. J. Biochem.*, **24**, 485.

Gregoriadis, G. , Leathwood, P. D. and Ryman, B. E. (1971). *FEBS Lett.*, **14**, 95.

Gregoriadis, G., Swain, C. P., Wills, F. J. and Tavill, A. S. (1974). *Lancet*, **1**, 1313.

Greiling, H., Kisters, R., Eberhard, A. and Stuhlsatz, H. W. (1971). In *Rheumatoid Arthritis: Pathogenic Mechanisms and Consequences in Therapeutics*, p. 173, (eds. W. Müller, H. G. Harwerth and K. Fehr). Academic Press, London.

Gumpel, J. M., Hasp, R. and Loewi, G. (1973). *Ann. rheum. Dis.*, **32**, (Suppl., 11.

Halden, G. and Kendall, P. H. (1962). *Ann. Phys. Med.*, **6**, 178.

Hench, P. S., Kendall, E. C., Slocumb, C. H. and Polley, H. F. (1950). *Arch. Inter. Med.*, **85**, 545.

Hollander, J. L. (1955). *Ann. N.Y. Acad. Sci.*, **61**, 511.

Hollander, J. L. (1972). In *Arthritis and Allied Conditions*, 8th Edn. (eds. J. L. Hollander and D. L. MacCarthy), p.517, Lea and Febiger, Philadelphia.

Hollander, J. L., Brown, E. M., Jessar, R. A. and Brown, C. Y. (1951). *J. Amer. Med. Ass.*, **147**, 1629.

Hollander, J. L., Brown, E. M., Jessar, R. A., Udell, L., Smukler, N. and Bowie, M. A. (1954). *Ann. rheum. Dis.*, **13**, 297.

Ignarro, L. J. (1971a). *Biochem. Pharmacol.*, **20**, 2847.

Ignarro, L. J. (1971b). *Biochem. Pharmacol.*, **20**, 2861.

Ingrand, J. (1973). *Ann. rheum. Dis.*, (Suppl.), 3.

Jain, M. K. and Cordes, H. K. (1973). *J. Membrane Biol.*, **14**, 119.

Jonah, M. M., Cerny, E. A. and Rahman, Y. E. (1975). *Biochim. Biophys. Acta*, **401**, 336.

Jubb, R. and Hazleman, B. L. (1976). *Hosp. Update*, **2**, 169.

Juliano, R. L. and Stamp, D. (1975). *Biochem. Biophys. Res. Commun.*, **63**, 651.

Junkmann, K. and Suchowsky, G. K. (1960). *Arzneimittelforschung*, **10**, 921.

Kimelberg, H. K. (1976). *Biochim. Biophys. Acta*, **448**, 531.

Koch-Weser, J. (1976). *N. Engl. J. Med.*, **295**, 30.

Koehler, B. E., Urowitz, M. B. and Killinger, D. W. (1974). *J. Rheumatol.*, **1**, 117.

Mabrey, S. and Sturtevant, J. M. (1976). *Proc. Nat. Acad. Sci. USA*, **73**, 3862.

McDougall, I. R., Dunnick, J. K., McNamee, M. G. and Kriss, J. P. (1974). *Proc. Nat. Acad. Sci. USA*, **71**, 3487.

McDougall, I. R., Dunnick, J. K., Goris, M. L. and Kriss, J. P. (1975). *J. Nucl. Med.*, **16**, 488.

Medicis, R.de., Reboux, J-F. and Lussier, A. (1976). *Pathol. Biol. Semaine, Hop.*, **24**, 641.

Nakanishi, M. and Goto, K. (1975). *Biochem. Pharmacol.*, **24**, 421.

Oka, M. (1956). *Ann. rheum. Dis.*, **15**, 327.

Page-Thomas, D. P. (1977). In *Rheumatoid Arthritis: Cellular Pathology and Pharmacology*, p.173, (eds. J. L. Gordon and B. L. Hazleman) North-Holland, Amsterdam.

Page-Thomas, D. P. (1977). In *Bayer-Symposium IV, Experimental Models of Chronic Inflammatory Disease*, p.353 (eds. L. E. Glynn and H. D. Schlumberger) Springer-Verlag, Heidelberg.

Papahadjopoulos, D. and Kimelberg, H. K. (1973). *Prog. Surf. Sci.*, **4**, 141.

Papahadjopoulos, D., Nir, S. and Ohki, S. (1971). *Biochim. Biophys. Acta*, **266**, 561.

Papahadjopoulos, D., Cowden, M. and Kimelberg, H. (1973). *Biochim. Biophys. Acta*, **330**, 8.

Papahadjopoulos, D., Mayhew, E., Poste, G. and Smith, S. (1974). *Nature*, **252**, 163.

Patel, H. M. and Ryman, B. E. (1976). *FEBS Lett.*, **62**, 60.

Poste, G., Papahadjopoulos, D. and Vail, W. J. (1976). In *Methods in Cell Biology*, **14**, p.23 (ed. D. M. Prescott), Academic Press, London.

Rahman, Y. E., Rosenthal, M. W., Cerny, E. A. and Moretti, E. S. (1974). *J. Lab. Clin. Med.*, **83**, 640.

Reimann, I. (1976). *Clin. Orthop. Related Res.*, **119**, 237.

Roberts, S. D. and Gillespi, P. J. (1973). *Ann. rheum. Dis.*, **32** (Suppl. 3), 46.

Ruddy, S. (1974a). In *Rheumatoid Arthritis*, p. 27 (ed. E. D. Harris), Medcom, New York.

Ruddy, S. (1974b). Ibid. p.58.

Ryman, B. E. (1974). In *Enzyme Therapy in Lysosomal Storage Diseases*, p.149, (eds. J. M. Tager, G. J. M. Hoogwinkel, W. Th. Daems), North-Holland, Amsterdam.

Segal, A. W., Wills, E. J., Richmond, J. E., Slavin, G., Black, C. D. V. and Gregoriadis, G. (1974). *Br. J. Exp. Path.*, **55**, 320.

Segal, A. W., Gregoriadis, G. and Black, C. D. V. (1975). *Clin. Sci. Mol. Med.*, **49**, 99.

Shaw, I. H., Knight, C. G. and Dingle, J. T. (1976). *Biochem. J.*, **158**, 473.

Shaw, I. H., Knight, C. G., Page Thomas, D. P., Phillips, N. C. and Dingle J. T. (1979). *Br. J. Exp. Path.*, **60**, 142.

Shimshick, E. J. and McConnnell, H. M. (1973). *Biochem. Biophys. Res. Commun.*, **53**, 446.

Sledge, C. B. (1975). *Ortho. Clin. N. Amer.*, **6**, 619.

Sogar, B. V. and Zull, J. E. (1975). *Biochim. Biophys. Acta*, **375**, 363.

Steinberg, C. L. R., Duthie, R. B. and Piva, A. E. (1962). *J. Amer. Med. Ass.*, **181**, 851.

Stevens, R. W. and Green, C. (1972). *FEBS Lett.*, **27**, 145.

Swedlund, H. A., Hunder, G. G. and Gleich, G. J. (1974). *Ann. rheum. Dis.*, **33**, 162.

Sweet, C. and Zull, J. E. (1970). *Biochim. Biophys. Acta*, **219**, 253.

Tyrrell, D. A., Heath, T. D., Colley, C. M. and Ryman, B. E. (1976). *Biochim. Biophys. Acta*, **457**, 259.

Ward, E. and Manson, H. L. (1953). *J. Lab. Clin. Med.*, **42**, 961.

Watson Buchanan, W., Rennie, J. A. N., Rooney, P. J. and Kennedy, A. C. (1977). In *Rheumatoid Arthritis: Cellular Pathology and Pharmacology*, p.77 (eds. J. L. Gordon and B. L. Hazleman), North-Holland, Amsterdam.

Weissmann, G. (1972). *N. Eng. J. Med.*, **286**, 141.

Weissmann, G. and Dingle, J. T. (1961). *Exp. Cell Res.*, **25**, 207.

Will, G. and Murdoch, W. R. (1960). *Brit. med. J.*, **1**, 94.

Wilson, H., Fairbanks, R., McEwen, C. and Ziff, M. (1955). *Ann. N.Y. Acad. Sci.*, **61**, 502.

Young, H. H., Ward, L. E. and Henderson, E. D. (1954). *J. Bone Jt. Surg.*, **36A**, 602.

Liposomes in Biological Systems
Edited by G. Gregoriadis and A. C. Allison
© 1980, John Wiley & Sons, Ltd.

CHAPTER 12

Liposomes as Diagnostic Tools

I. Ross McDougall

1. **Introduction**   325

2. **Method of production of liposomes**   326

3. **Diagnostic uses of liposomes**   327
    3.1. *In vitro* tests   327
    3.2. *In vivo* studies   329
        3.2.1. Radioactive pharmaceuticals and preparation of
                liposomes with entrapped radiopharmaceuticals   329
        3.2.2. Alteration of liposome permeability   331
        3.2.3. Demonstration that liposomes are intact in
                circulation   333
        3.2.4. Alteration of rate of clearance of liposomes from
                the circulation   333
        3.2.5. Direction of liposomes to target organs   336

4. **Logistic problems**   341

5. **Conclusions**   341

    References   342

1. INTRODUCTION

Liposomes are tiny spherules containing concentric aqueous compartments separated from one another, as well as from the external aqueous environment, by closed bilayers of amphipathic lipids. In general the lipids are phospholipids and they are orientated like the lipids in biomembranes (Danielli and Davson, 1935; Singer and Nicolson, 1972) with hydrophilic (polar) head groups facing outwards into the aqueous compartments and hydrophobic segments (non-polar) facing inwards out of contact with water. The number of aqueous compartments and lipid bilayers of the liposome can be altered by the method of production (*vide infra*) and may, in certain circumstances, be reduced to a single cavity, separated from the aqueous environment by a single lipid bilayer. In this discussion single compartmental spherules will be called vesicles and multicompartmental spherules liposomes.

The diagnostic value of these artifically produced spheres depends primarily on their ability to entrap a detectable marker molecule within their cavity or cavities. For *in vivo* detection it is preferable for the marker to be a gamma (γ) emitting radionuclide or radiopharmaceutical which can be detected by suitable devices, such as rectilinear scanner, or a gamma camera for investigations in experimental animals or patients. Less frequently non-radioactive markers such as spin labels can be entrapped, though these molecules cannot be used to detect the distribution of liposomes in intact animals.

Liposomes (or vesicles) have been employed *in vitro*, as a test system for detection of complement-aided immune lysis (Kinsky, 1972). They might also provide a method of carrying concentrated packages of diagnostic agents *in vivo*. At the time of writing, this latter approach is potential, rather than real, but because of the interest in new methods for early detection of disease *in vivo*, a considerable section of this chapter will concentrate on *in vivo* studies. One important aim of this approach would be localization of a radionuclide marker carried within liposomes or vesicles in primary neoplasms of small dimension, hopefully at a time when no metastases have occurred. There is theoretical and practical evidence that earlier diagnosis of such lesions would improve the outcome of treatment, which might well become curative, rather than palliative. It should be apparent, that if liposomes can be designed to seek out diseased target tissues *in vivo*, this would not only be of diagnostic significance but would also provide a novel method of introducing drugs (chemotherapy) or destructive radionuclides (β-emitters) for local therapy. Several review articles have dealt with the topic of liposomes as carriers of therapeutic agents such as the missing enzymes in lysosomal storage disorders (Weissmann, 1976; Gregoriadis, 1976).

2. METHOD OF PRODUCTION OF LIPOSOMES

Several authors have discussed in detail the method of production of liposomes (Huang, 1969; Gregoriadis *et al*., 1974; McDougall *et al*., 1974). In brief, amphipathic lipids are thoroughly dried and a suitable aqueous buffer solution is added. The lipids swell spontaneously and form bilayers encapsulating a proportion of the buffer solution. A variety of lipids have been used and a fuller description of these is outlined in a subsequent section of this chapter. Most investigators employ phosphatidylcholine and cholesterol as major constituents. Gregoriadis *et al.* (1974) favour dipalmitoyl lecithin : cholesterol : phosphatidic acid in a molar ratio of 7 : 2 : 1 as the basic liposome formula for their experiments. McDougall *et al.* (1974) use 44 μmol egg lecithin (prepared by the method of Singleton *et al.*, 1965) and 4 μmol gangliosides as the standard mixture to which other lipids or steroids are added. Whichever lipids are used, the formation of liposomes with entrapped buffer produces a milky-coloured solution. If the added buffer contains a water-soluble marker, a proportion of the marker will be enclosed within the liposomes and gel filtration or centrifugation are convenient techniques to separate the 'labelled' liposomes from the non-entrapped marker.

Production of single compartmental vesicles is achieved by subjecting liposomes to ultrasonic irradiation either using a probe or bath sonicator. The formation of vesicles is heralded by a clearing of the milky colour to produce a faintly opalescent solution. Prolonged sonication (2–3) hours of phosphatidylcholine liposomes produces vesicles with an external diameter of 250 Å (Huang 1969; Huang and Charlton 1972); sonication of liposomes containing phosphatidylcholine, gangliosides, and cholesterol for 1 hour, produces spherules of approximately 500 Å diameter (Dunnick *et al.*, 1975).

3. DIAGNOSTIC USES OF LIPOSOMES

3.1. *In Vitro* Tests

Liposome membranes have been shown to mimic natural membranes in their response to complement-induced immune lysis (Kinsky *et al.*, 1969). This property has been exploited as a test system for detection of specific circulating antibodies, by enclosing within liposomes a marker molecule, which can be detected when it is released after rupture of the liposomes' phospholipid bilayers.

The first experiments designed to demonstrate this property utilized liposomes made for lipids extracted from sheep erythrocyte membranes, with entrapped glucose as the marker molecule. Anti-sheep erythrocyte serum, plus complement, caused lysis of the 'sheep lipid' liposomes and the immune lysis was detected by the release of glucose (Haxby *et al.*, 1968). Spectrophotometry was found to be a sensitive method of measuring glucose released from liposomes. An increased absorbance occurred at 340 nm upon reduction of NADP in the presence of hexokinase, glucose-6-phosphate dehydrogenase, and cofactors. Any glucose which remained within liposomes was protected from this reaction and because of this Haxby *et al.* (1968) found it was unnecessary to separate the released glucose from the intact liposomes.

Using similar techniques for detecting lysis, Kinsky *et al.* (1969) were able to demonstrate that liposomes, made artificially from phosphatidylcholine (or sphingomyelin), cholesterol, and dicetyl phosphate (or stearylamine) with Forssman hapten incorporated within the lipid bilayers, were lysed by the addition of complement and antibody.

Further experiments have shown that lipid A, a lipopolysaccharide derived from the outer cell wall of *Salmonella minnesota* (Galanos *et al.*, 1971), can be used to sensitize liposomes. These sensitized liposomes provide a test system to detect antilipid A in rabbit serum (Kataoka *et al.*, 1971), lysis in the presence of specific antibody and complement being detected by glucose release. Complement, inactivated by heating, or serum lacking antilipid A, fails to cause lysis of the sensitized liposomes.

Alving *et al.* (1974) extracted lipids from *Schistosoma mansoni* worms and incorporated the extracted lipids into liposomes whose basic constituents were dipalmitolyl lecithin, cholesterol, and dicetyl phosphate in molar ratios of 2 : 1.5 : 0.22 The rate of release of entrapped glucose from the liposomes was employed as a marker as described above. When serum from monkeys previously exposed to *Schistosoma mansoni* and complement were added to liposomes, complement-dependent immune lysis of the liposomes occurred and glucose was released. In control experiments the omission of (1) *schistosoma mansoni* lipids from the liposome membrane, (2) serum containing specific antibody or (3) complement, produced no rupture of liposomes and no release of glucose.

An alternative and ingenious *in vitro* assay system using liposomes has been developed by Humphries and McConnell (1975). In their model, the enclosed marker molecule was tempocholine, an electron paramagnetic resonance spin label. Tempocholine is water soluble but membrane impermeable, therefore it can be entrapped within liposomes or vesicles and it does not leak across the lipid bilayers. Tempocholine enclosed within liposomes produces a characteristic broad paramagnetic resonance signal of small amplitude; this is because there is a high concentration of spin molecules which exchange signals because of their close proximity to one another. When the liposome membranes are ruptured, the tempocholine molecules are released and diluted in the external medium. This results in a readily detectable, qualitative and quantitative, alteration in the paramagnetic resonance spectrum (Kornberg and McConnell, 1971).

Humphries and McConnell (1975) entrapped tempocholine in liposomes, whose walls were made from lecithin, cholesterol, and dicetyl phosphate sensitized with bacterial lipopolysaccharide. Addition of specific lipopolysaccharide antibody and complement caused release of tempocholine, detected and quantitated by the changes in electron paramagnetic resonance spectrum described above. Although this form of liposome marker provides a very sensitive, quantitative assay for specific antibodies, the detecting instruments are very expensive and not widely available. This alone, may limit the diagnostic importance of the spin label system.

Liposome models for detection of complement immune lysis are of interest not only because they provide a novel test system but also because they demonstrate an unsuspected immune response to lipids. It appears that complement-induced lysis is not dependent on protein being present in biomembranes as had previously been suspected.

3.2. *In Vivo* Studies

The diagnostic use of labelled vesicles or liposomes in patients depends on certain important factors. It must be possible to entrap a suitable γ-emitting radionuclide or radiopharmaceutical in high concentration within the lipid spherules and the entrapped marker molecule should not leak across the lipid bilayer too rapidly. Liposomes must remain intact in the circulation and they should not be cleared too rapidly from the circulation by reticuloendothelial cells. The abnormal target tissue must show preferential uptake of liposomes compared to normal surrounding tissues, since detection and localization of the radionuclide is dependent on differential levels of activity between regions. Therefore, either the abnormal region must endocytose the liposomes at a greater rate, or the liposomes must be designed to seek out and attach to the pathological site. For use in patients, the lipid spherules must be non-toxic, sterile, and free from endotoxins. Each of these points will be discussed separately.

3.2.1. *Radioactive Pharmaceuticals and Preparation of Liposomes With Entrapped Radiopharmaceuticals*

The usefulness of a radiopharmaceutical *in vivo* is determined not only by its distribution but also by its physical characteristics. Of major importance is the type and energy of the emissions. Radionuclides which emit particulate radiations, alpha and beta, are undesirable for two reasons; they give a high radiation dose to the patient and they cannot be detected by imaging devices. Ideally, the radionuclide should be a pure gamma emitter with a monoenergetic γ-ray in the range 80–400 keV. Photons with energies below 80 keV are severely attenuated by biological tissues and cannot be detected, whereas those with energies greater than 400 keV are difficult to collimate and cause a loss of spatial resolution. The physical half-life of the nuclide is also important, if too short it will decay before it can be incorporated into liposomes or vesicles and radionuclides with long half-lives (months or years) subject the patient to prolonged and excessive radiation. Currently the two radionuclides most frequently used in nuclear medicine laboratories are ^{99m}Tc and ^{113m}In. ^{99m}Tc is usually dispensed as an anion, pertechnetate (^{99m}TcO$_4$), whereas ^{113m}In is a cation. Both of these radionuclides have physical characteristics which make them suitable for use in humans and both can be detected using a gamma camera or rectilinear scanner.

In the field of nuclear medicine the chemical form of the nuclide is also of prime importance since the aim is often to incorporate the radiotracer into compounds which will result in an alteration of the expected distribution of the radionuclide (Miller, 1975). For example, ^{99m}Tc as pertechnetate is actively concentrated by the thyroid but if it is attached to aggregates or spheres of albumin, 20–50 μm in diameter, the radiopharmaceutical will lodge in pulmonary capillaries after intravenous injection and can be used for lung scanning; when compounded with colloidal particles of sulphur which are avidly extracted from the circulation by reticuloendothelial cells in the liver and spleen these organs can be imaged or it can be combined to phosphates or phosphonates which carry the radiomarker to the skeleton and therefore can be used for bone imaging. Similarly, other radionuclides may be compounded in such a way that they are directed to specific target sites.

When liposomes or vesicles are considered as *in vivo* diagnostic agents, the physical properties of the entrapped radionuclide are important but in this situation biorouting is completely dependent on the *in vivo* distribution of the liposome. Therefore, the aim is to design liposomes which seek out specific target organs. The alternative to this is to make use of or alter the endocytic function of the cells under study.

The liposome may be made to entrap water-soluble radionuclides such as ^{99m}Tc simply by adding the ^{99m}Tc to the buffer solution used in the production. Liposomes with the ^{99m}Tc marker enclosed can be separated from the free ^{99m}Tc by Sephadex or Sepharose gel filtration. When this simple technique is undertaken only a small proportion of the radionuclide is trapped, therefore a large quantity of radionuclide is required at the start of production if sufficient ^{99m}Tc for scanning is to be encased within the liposomes.

It is also possible to prepare liposomes with an enclosed molecule onto which the radionuclide can be attached at some time after the liposomes have been formed. Veal (1976) has produced liposomes with entrapped transferrin (mol. wt. 90,000), the plasma protein which transports iron in the circulation. Transferrin has been shown to carry indium and other cations when these are injected intravenously. Vesicles or liposomes containing transferrin are labelled with indium very rapidly and in high concentration if the indium is added to preformed vesicles. Presumably the cation moves across the lipid bilayers into the central compartments where it attaches to the transferrin. Similarly ^{131}I has been attached to albumin entrapped in preformed liposomes using the monochloride method (Gregoriadis *et al.*, 1974). The longer half-life of ^{131}I (8 days) and the high energy emission make this radionuclide less than ideal for patient studies, but ^{123}I (half-life 13 hours) could be incorporated by a similar method. This approach for labelling is more successful in achieving a higher specific activity but by necessity it involves the use of a protein which is undesirable.

A third method of labelling liposomes is to attach a tracer molecule onto the outside of the preformed lipid spherule. Sometimes this can be done by simply adding the desired tracer molecule to the vesicle preparation and a proportion of the tracer attaches non-specifically. 1% of the antithyroglobulin labelled with ^{125}I added to vesicles consisting of phosphatidylcholine, cholesterol, and gangliosides remained attached Dunnick *et al.*, 1975). Chemical manipulations can be employed to increase the quantity of external marker which will remain attached to the external membrane (Dunnick *et al.*, 1976a), and these will be discussed more fully in the section devoted to homing devices.

3.2.2. Alteration of Liposome Permeability

Knowledge of the *in vitro* and *in vivo* permeability characteristics of the membrane to the entrapped marker is important, since concentration of released radionuclide in certain body tissues might erroneously be attributed to uptake of intact liposomes. The rate of elution of an entrapped marker from liposomes depends both on the nature of the enclosed molecule and the lipid bilayer of the liposomes. Molecular size and charge are important characteristics of the trapped substance. Small molecules cross lipid bilayers more rapidly than large ones and anions more rapidly than cations. Although the selectivity does not depend simply on molecular radius this general principle is true. Although the author recognizes that anions are more permeable and therefore less desirable than cations or larger radiopharmaceuticals for prolonged 'labelling' of the aqueous cavity of liposomes in some of the experiments to be described below ^{99m}Tc (pertechnetate) has been used. In situations where the same marker molecule is used, its rate of release from the central cavity can be altered by: (*a*) altering the lipid composition of the liposome membranes; or (*b*) altering their method of production. Vesicles made from phosphatidylcholine alone are relatively permeable to ^{42}K (Bangham *et al.*, 1965) and ^{99m}TcO$_4$ (McDougall *et al.*, 1974). The addition of dicetyl phosphate (Bangham *et al.*, 1965) or gangliosides markedly reduces the permeability. The permeability of vesicles made of phosphatidylcholine and

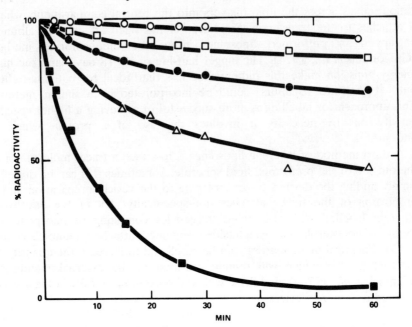

Figure 1 Rate of release of $^{99m}TcO_4$ from vesicles of different composition measured by dialysis.

Vesicle composition

o—o phosphatidylcholine, gangliosides and cholesterol
□—□ phosphatidylcholine and gangliosides (sonicated for 12 minutes)
●—● phosphatidylcholine and gangliosides (sonicated for 7 minutes)
△—△ phosphatidylcholine
■—■ no vesicles

(Reproduced from McDougall *et al.*, 1975, by permission of *Journal of Nuclear Medicine*)

gangliosides to $^{99m}TcO_4$ is not altered by addition of phosphatidylserine or phosphatidylethanolamine. Cholesterol appears to have a major role in reducing permeability of vesicles to $^{99m}TcO_4$ (Figure 1) probably by stiffening the membrane (Papahadjopoulos *et al.*, 1972, 1973a; Boggs and Hsia, 1972). It is of interest that if the concentration of cholesterol exceeds a critical proportion (ratio of cholesterol to phospholipid 0.43 to 1.0) the liposomes, after being taken up by tissue lysosomes, cannot be degraded (Johnson, 1975). This may also be related to the strengthening effect of cholesterol.

From a diagnostic point of view the fact that liposome walls are totally impermeable to an entrapped marker is not a disadvantage and neither is the fact that the marker fails to be released intracellularly—provided the label is a γ-emitting radionuclide. However, if the lipid spherules are to be employed to deliver therapeutic agents it is fundamental that the agent is released unaltered at the target site. As an example of impermeability of liposomes to larger molecules Colley and Ryman (1975) were unable to demonstrate significant leakage of entrapped methotrexate over several days. Similarly entrapped albumin (mol. wt. 60,000) shows little tendency to leave liposomes (Gregoriadis *et al.*, 1974a). Some molecules of intermediate size may not diffuse across liposome membranes, e.g. bleomycin (Dapergolas *et al.*, 1976), whereas others such as penicillin G do (Gregoriadis, 1973). Therefore in the search for the best combination of constituent lipids and entrapped carriers, trial and error will be of great consequence. It is unfortunate that the factors which result in reduction of liposome wall permeability are also the factors which accelerate clearance of liposomes from the circulation of experimental animals (*vide infra*).

3.2.3. *Demonstration that Liposomes are intact in Circulation*

In the previous section methods for reducing loss of tracer across the intact liposome wall were discussed and intactness of the liposome is obviously essential for this. Slight loss of entrapped marker *in vivo* might well be compatible with the use of liposomes diagnostically, but rupture of liposomes on exposure to the circulation would not. There is histological and autoradiographic evidence of intact liposomes in tissues after intravenous injection (Segal *et al.*, 1974; de Barsy *et al.*, 1975; de Barsy *et al.*, 1976) strongly suggesting that they had remained intact in the circulation. Using a spin label marker entrapped in a single compartmental vesicle injected intravenously into mice it has been possible to demonstrate that a proportion of those vesicles which remain in the circulation are intact and do retain the enclosed spin label (McDougall *et al.*, 1974).

3.2.4. *Alteration of Rate of Clearance of Liposomes from the Circulation*

If liposomes have any potential as carriers of diagnostic markers one of the most critical factors is that concerning their rate of extraction from the circulation. Rapid clearance of labelled liposomes from the blood would leave insufficient amounts of the dose to be concentrated in the target organ. Therefore any method which retains the spherules intact and within the blood would be advantageous. There is good evidence that particulate material injected intravenously is rapidly extracted from the circulation by reticuloendothelial cells, predominantly in the liver, but also in the spleen and bone marrow (Shingleton, 1971). Although there is some argument about the cells which maximally remove liposomes *in vivo*, there is no argument that the liver and spleen are the major organs of uptake (Gregoriadis, 1974a,b; McDougall *et al.*, 1974; Gregoriadis and Neerunjun, 1974). The evidence and inference is that reticulendothelial cells are the cells involved (de Barsy *et al.*, 1975; de Duve *et al.*, 1974). Gregoriadis (1974a) has shown that liposomes with negatively charged membranes consisting of dicetyl phosphate are cleared very rapidly from the circulation of a rat after intravenous injection; only 10% remained in the blood after 30 minutes, the major site of uptake being reticuloendothelial cells. Liposomes with neutral membranes are removed from the blood less rapidly than those with negatively charged membranes and positive liposomes are extracted even less rapidly. Three hours after intravenous injection in rats approximately one-half of liposomes containing sterylamine remain in the blood (Gregoriadis and Neerunjun, 1974). Colley and Ryman (1975) found the hepatic uptakes of positive and negative liposomes in the rat after 1 hour were 25% and 40% respectively. In addition to the effect of charge of the liposome wall on rate of clearance from the circulation, there is almost a direct relationship between the length of sonication, the hepatic uptake of liposomes, and their rate of clearance from the circulation of mice. It has been demonstrated that the size of the liposome decreases with the length of sonication and this also may be one of the factors which dictates uptake. Cholesterol incorporated into the liposome wall also increases hepatic and splenic uptake of liposomes which are very rapidly cleared from the circulations of mice. Single compartment vesicles made from dimyristoyl phosphatidylcholine are larger (900–1000 Å in diameter) than vesicles made from phosphatidylcholine containing longer fatty acids such as oleic or palmitic acids (Aragon, 1974). They show less hepatic uptakes but are concentrated to a greater extent by the spleen (McDougall and Dunnick, 1974).

To prevent rapid extraction of simple lipid liposomes from the circulation the spherules should have a positively charged membrane, a low, or absent, concentration of cholesterol and their size should not be excessively small, e.g. less than 500 Å.

In an effort to increase specificity of uptake of liposomes Dunnick *et al.* (1975) attached antibodies and polypeptides to vesicles. Serendipitously it was found that incorporation of polyamino acid chains of L-lysine or L-alanine reduced hepatic uptake of entrapped radioactive marker and such a mechanism might help retain liposomes in the circulation. Dunnick *et al.* (1976b) demonstrated that preformed vesicles, after interaction with cultured mammalian cells, were altered so that when these treated vesicles were injected intravenously in mice their rate of hepatic uptake was reduced. The conclusion was that some fraction from the cultured cells, probably a protein became incorporated in, or attached to the vesicle membrane and in some way inhibited its hepatic uptake. Therefore it is possible that manipulation of the chemical identity of the vesicle membrane might be advantageous in preventing rapid clearance. However, it is extremely unfortunate that the added protector is almost certainly a protein since this would increase the probability of immune reactions such as serum sickness or anaphylaxis on repeat exposure to the lipid–protein complex. Allison and Gregoriadis (1974) have shown that liposomes containing diphtheria toxoid augment the expected rise in circulating antibodies after exposure of mice to diphtheria toxoid. One possible method of overcoming the problem of immunization would be to use the patient's 'proteins' to treat liposomes, however, it would be totally impractical to culture some of the patient's cells, add vesicles to the cultured cells, and then inject the vesicles with entrapped marker into the patient. However, as a corollary of this suggested approach, Dunnick and Kriss (1976) have made vesicles by sonication of animal plasma and these vesicles made from native components are more resistant to hepatic clearance. If human plasma vesicles are found to be appropriate they would have several important advantages. Firstly, no foreign material would be used with the exception of the entrapped marker, which, in most instances would be widely used in nuclear medicine and proven to be non-toxic. These liposomes would hopefully circulate for a longer time and have prolonged exposure to the target site. Finally, it is conceivable that a natural serum factor, e.g. antibody against C.E.A., could be utilized to promote specific localization of the diagnostic package.

Figure 2 demonstrates that vesicles containing $^{99m}TcO_4$, injected intravenously in rats (or other experimental animals), are not handled like colloidal particles labelled with ^{99m}Tc. The figure shows serial computer processed gamma camera images of two rats, one injected with vesicles the other with [^{99m}Tc]sulphur colloid. The colloid shows a rapid peak of activity over the liver not seen in the rat injected with vesicles. In a similar experiment (Figure 3) the distribution of [^{99m}Tc]diphosphonate enclosed in vesicles is compared to [^{99m}Tc]diphosphonate which is rapidly cleared by the kidneys and appears in urine in the bladder. These pictures (Figures 2 and 3) also demonstrate to non-nuclear physicians the type of images possible in experimental animals (or patients). Figure 4 shows some computer manipulations which can be derived from the information. The curves demonstrate changes of radioactivity with time from areas of interest in the two rats shown in Figure 3. A, B, and C are areas of interest over the heart, liver, and bladder of the rat injected with the vesicles; D, E, and F are the equivalent regions from the control animal. It can be noted that blood clearance taken (or diphosphonate) from areas A and B is more rapid and there is also very rapid urinary excretion, F versus C.

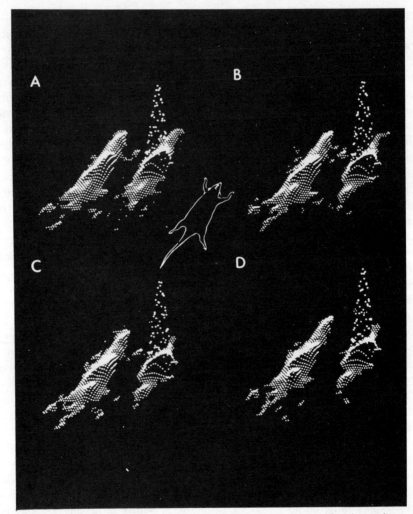

Figure 2 A, B, C, and D are gamma scintigrams made at 10 minute intervals of two rats. The rat on the left was injected intravenously with phosphatidylcholine–ganglioside vesicles containing $^{99m}TcO_4$, the rat on the right was injected with [^{99m}Tc]sulphur colloid. The animal injected with vesicles shows diffuse distribution of radioactivity with some concentration of activity in liver and bladder whereas the animal injected with colloid shows marked hepatic uptake

3.2.5. *Direction of Liposomes to Target Organs*

Provided a suitable marker can be retained within the liposome and the labelled liposome can be retained within the circulation, the next problem is to direct the liposome to the target organ. This requires two steps. Firstly, the liposome must leave the bloodstream by crossing capillary walls

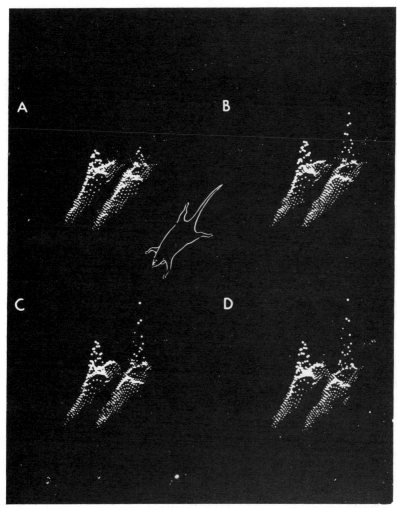

Figure 3 A, B, C, and D are sequential gamma camera images made at 10 minute intervals. Two rats are shown, the one on the left was injected intravenously with vesicles (phosphatidylcholine–gangliosides) containing [^{99m}Tc]diphosphonate, the one on the right injected with [^{99m}Tc]diphosphonate alone. Free [^{99m}Tc] diphosphonate is rapidly concentrated in the urinary bladder, whereas vesicles direct the same radiopharmaceutical to the liver

and basement membranes. Data referred to above, showing intact vesicles within cells *in vivo*, strongly suggest that they can cross capillaries. Indirect evidence has been obtained by injecting labelled vesicles intraperitoneally in mice. The label is found to distribute like intact vesicles rather than the free label and among the explanations for this, is the fact that intact

Liposomes in Biological Systems

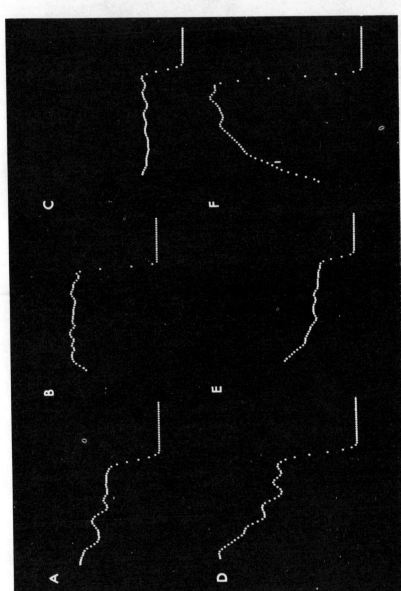

Figure 4 The figure shows curves of radioactivity versus time. A, B, and C correspond to areas of interest over the heart (blood pool), liver, and bladder from the rat injected with vesicles shown pictorially in Figure 3. The curves are generated using an area of interest from a computer oscilloscope. Similar areas of interest from the rat injected with [^{99m}Tc]diphosphonate demonstrate the more rapid blood clearance and rapid urinary accumulation of the free [^{99m}Tc]diphosphonate (D, E, and F).

vesicles can cross the peritoneum and enter into capillaries (McDougall *et al.*, 1975; Dapergolas *et al.*, 1976). $^{99m}TcO_4$ entrapped within vesicles injected subcutaneously in rats leaves the injection site slowly and concentrates in the kidneys, whereas free $^{99m}TcO_4$ injected subcutaneously in controls, rapidly enters the circulation and is concentrated in the stomach and thyroid. The ability of vesicles to travel from a subcutaneous injection site to the kidneys must be due to these particles gaining entrance to the circulation by crossing either lymphatic or capillary walls, albeit in the reverse direction for our requirements. Segal *et al.* (1975) also found that small, sonicated vesicles disappear from a subcutaneous injection site (rat testis) rapidly; they believed the distribution was via lymphatics. Large unsonicated liposomes remain at the site of subcutaneous injection considerably longer, presumably because they are too large to cross lymphatic capillary walls. Provided the particles can leave the circulation at the desired site there must be some mechanism to produce specificity of uptake at the target site. On the one hand the abnormal cell may have increased endocytic properties which could be used to advantage; many tumour cells have this property. More likely, however, the liposome will require to have characteristics such as incorporation of a probe which will provide selectivity.

Gregoriadis (1974a, b), Gregoriadis and Neerunjun (1975), Dunnick *et al.* (1975), Dunnick *et al.* (1976a) have carried out experimental work using immunoglobulins as the liposome probe. *In vitro*, liposome-associated IgG uptake by a specific cell type is increased if the specific anticell antibody is used (Gregoriadis and Neerunjun, 1975). Dunnick *et al.* (1976a) have shown that antithyroglobulin (Anti TG) complexed with vesicles is capable of fixing the vesicle Anti TG to thyroglobulin. The results of these investigations demonstrate that it is feasible to attach antibodies to vesicles and that a proportion of the attached antibody retains the capacity of recognizing its specific antigen. Weissmann *et al.* (1975) augmented liposome uptake by dogfish phagocytes by coating the phagocytes with dogfish IgM. It is possible that all immunoglobulins might be valuable in providing specificity.

Gregoriadis and Neerunjun (1975) have complexed the protein, fetuin, to liposomes to direct them to liver cells. Although the process was successful, it has been the author's experience that hepatic uptake can be augmented by altering the lipid composition of the vesicle wall and in general the problem is to prevent hepatic uptake, although in certain circumstances, e.g. in lysosomal storage diseases when the liver is primarily involved, liposomes could be designed to deliver packages of the missing enzyme to the liver.

There are other reports of proteins being incorporated into lipid bilayers of liposomes: these include rhodopsin (Montal and Korenbrot, 1973), albumin (Juliano and Stamp, 1975), polyamino acids (Shafer, 1974; Dunnick *et al.*, 1975), ATPase (Jilka *et al.*, 1975), and sialoglycoprotein (MacDonald and MacDonald, 1975). There is also a growing volume of information about protein–lipid interactions (Finean, 1973) and it seems probable that valuable contributions will be made, by further efforts to define specific probes and also to improve the techniques by which these are complexed with liposomes. It is probable that some of the techniques currently used are sufficiently strong to destroy or partially denature the protein moiety.

The next problem is to determine what happens when the liposome arrives at the target site. There are several possibilities. Firstly there may be no interaction, therefore the liposome would not be valuable either diagnostically or therapeutically. Secondly, the liposome membrane may fuse with the target cell membrane and produce three possible outcomes. (i) The fusion may cause rupture of the liposome with loss of the entrapped diagnostic agent into the extracellular fluid. This also would be of no value diagnostically. (ii) The liposome lipids and membrane lipids may exchange but the liposome cavity remains intact within the cell membrane surrounded by a bilayer of which the inner monolayer consists of vesicle lipids, the outer monolayer being a mixture of vesicle phospholipids and cell lipids (Pagano and Huang, 1974 and 1975). The vesicle with its marker still enclosed might break off from the target cell at a later time without having changed size, though a proportion of the target cell phospholipids would have exchanged for an equal proportion of vesicle lipids. At 37 °C using small sonicated vesicles and cultured cells *in vitro* this mechanism accounts for about 10% of uptake. (iii) The major interaction of 37 °C using cultured cells is complete fusion of vesicle bilayer with ejection of entrapped marker into the cell interior. This uptake is linear with time and strongly dependent on temperature (Huang *et al.*, 1974). Both the second and third mechanisms of uptake of vesicles could be used diagnostically since the specific localization of the γ-emitter, either in cell membrane or cell cytoplasm is of no significance. What is important is that the marker remains at the target site for sufficiently long to be visualized.

A final method of uptake is endocytosis of the complete lipid spherule which would then be complexed with lysosomes and degraded by phospholipases. *In vivo*, there is evidence that this mechanism is of importance (Segal *et al.*, 1974), although as mentioned above liposomes with a high concentration of cholesterol resist lysosomal degradation (Johnson, 1975). Therefore, endocytosed liposomes may or may not be degraded intracellularly but again this would not alter their diagnostic use. It is important to state that there may be a fundamental difference in uptake of vesicles by cells *in vivo* and *in vitro*. Huang *et al.* (1974) have shown *in vitro* that incorporation of vesicles into cells is not altered by inhibitors of energy metabolism and therefore it is improbable that endocytosis is important. *In vivo*, the vesicles might be altered by serum factors such as α_2-macroglobulin (Black and Gregoriadis, 1976) which could promote endocytosis. Huang *et al*. (1974) also found that large unsonicated liposomes did not fuse with cultured cells, and they suggest this is due to the low surface activity of the larger spheroids.

The topics of cell fusion and vesicle–cell fusion (Papahadjopoulos *et al*., 1973b) are ones which attract a lot of interest and ones which are fundamental to the use of liposomes and vesicles either as diagnostic or therapeutic agents. We require to have more information about cell receptors, endocytosis, and homing agents such as antibodies or hormones or perhaps mitogens such as concanavalin A.

4. LOGISTIC PROBLEMS

Before liposomes can be used in patients it is essential that they are sterile. Standard sterilization techniques, such as autoclaving, would be inappropriate because they would rupture the liposomes. Gregoriadis *et al*. (1974) incubated liposomes with antibiotics to maintain sterility and although this approach might be justifiable for pilot studies, it is not ideal for widespread use, because of fear of sensitivity reactions and because it is bad medicine to prescribe suboptimal doses of antibiotics which may mask the course of an infectious process. Perhaps the best approach will be preparation of liposomes under aseptic conditions or alternatively the preparation could be passed through an ultrafilter to remove bacteria. Endotoxins would not be removed by these methods and careful testing using animals and the Limulus test (Cooper *et al*., 1971) would be necessary.

5. CONCLUSIONS

Liposomes and vesicles have provided scientists with a model system to study membrane characteristics. Over the last few years the intriguing concept has been proposed that these biodegradable spherules could be used to encapsulate concentrated packages of diagnostic (or therapeutic) agents. There is a considerable volume of information about the best diagnostic radionuclidess and how to encapsulate them with liposomes or vesicles. Nevertheless before liposomes (vesicles) can be used with confidence in patients investigations will have to be extended so that the following three questions are answered.

(1) What is the best method of producing sterile liposomes?
(2) How can liposomes be directed to target sites?
(3) What factor dictate the rate of escape of liposomes across capillary walls?

M

REFERENCES

Allison, A. C. and Gregoriadis, G. (1974). Liposomes as immunological adjuvants. *Nature,* **252**, 252.

Alving, C. R., Joseph, K. C., Lindsley, H. B. and Schoenbechler, M. J. (1974). Immune damage to liposomes containing lipids from *Schistosoma mansoni* worms (38125), *Proc. Soc. Exp. Biol. Med.*, **146**, 468–461.

Aragon, S. (1974). Personal communication.

Bangham, A. D., Standish, M. M. and Watkins, J. C. (1965) Diffusion of univalent ions across the lamellae of swollen phospholipids, *J. Mol. Biol.*, **13**, 238–252.

Black, C. D. V. and Gregoriadis, G. (1976). Interaction of liposomes with blood plasma proteins, *Biochem. Soc. Trans.*, **4**, 253–256.

Boggs, J. M. and Hsia, J. C. (1972). Effects of cholesterol and water on the rigidity and order of phosphatidylcholine bilayers, *Biochem. Biophys. Acta*, **290**, 32–42.

Colley, C. M. and Ryman, B. E. (1975). Liposomes as carriers *in vivo* for methotrexate, *Biochem. Soc. Trans.*, **3**, 157–159.

Cooper, J. F., Levin, J. and Wagner, H. N. (1971). Quantitative comparison of *in vitro* and *in vivo* methods for the detection of endotoxin, *J. Lab. Clin. Med.*, **78**, 132–148.

Danielli, J. F. and Davson, M. (1935). A contribution to the theory of permeability of thin films, *J. Cell Comp. Physiol.*, **5**, 495–508.

Dapergolas, G., Neerunjun, E. D. and Gregoriadis, G. (1976). Penetration of target areas in the rat by liposome-associated bleomycin, glucose, oxidase, and insulin, *Febs Lett*, **63**, 235–239.

de Barsy, T., Devos, P. and Van Hoof, F. (1975). The cellular distribution of liposomes in the liver of newborn rats, *Biochem. Soc. Trans.*, **3**, 159–160.

de Barsy, Th., Devos, P. and Van Hoof, F. (1976). A morphologic and biochemical study of the fate of antibody-bearing liposomes, *Lab. Invest.*, **34**, 273–282.

de Duve, C., de Barsy, Th., Poole, B., Trouet, A., Tulkens, P. and Van Hoof, F. (1974). Lysosomatropic agents, *Biochem. Pharmacol.*, **23**, 2495–2531.

Dunnick, J. K. and Kriss, J. P. (1976). Studies of radiopharmaceutical-enclosing lipid–protein vesicles formed from native plasma components, *J. Nucl. Med.* (in press).

Dunnick, J. K., McDougall, I. R., Aragon, S., Kriss, J. P. (1975). Vesicle interaction with polyamino acids and antibody: *in vivo* and *in vitro* studies, *J. Nucl. Med.*, **16**, 483–487.

Dunnick, J. K., Badger, R. S., Takeda, Y. and Kriss, J. P. (1976a). Vesicle interactions with antibody and peptide hormone: Role of vesicle composition, *J. Nucl. Med.* (in press).

Dunnick, J. K., Rooke, J. D., Aragon, S. and Kriss, J. P. (1976b). Alteration of mammalian cells by interaction with artificial lipid vesicles, *Cancer Research*, **36**, 2385–2389.

Finean, J. B. (1973). Phospholipids in biological membranes and the study of phospholipid–protein interactions, in *Form and Function of Phospholipids*, p.171 (eds. G. B. Ansell, J. N. Hawthorne and R. M. C. Dawson), Elsevier Scientific Publishing Company, Amsterdam.

Galanos, C., Luderitz, O. and Westphal, O. (1971). Preparation and properties of antisera against the lipid—a component of bacterial lipopolysaccharides, *Eur. J. Biochem.*, **24**, 116–122.

Gregoriadis, G. (1973). Drug entrapment in liposomes, *FEBS Lett*, **36**, 292–296.

Gregoriadis, G. (1974a). Structural requirements for the specific uptake of macromolecules and liposomes by target tissues. In *Enzyme Therapy in*

Lysosomal Storage Diseases, pp.131–138, (eds. J. M. Tager, G. J. M. Hooghwinkel and W. Th. Daems), North Holland Publishing Company.

Gregoriadis, G. (1974b). Drug entrapment in liposomes: possibilities for chemotherapy, *Biochem. Soc. Trans.*, **2**, 117–119.

Gregoriadis, G. (1976). Carrier potential of liposomes in biology and medicine (First of two parts), *New Eng. J. Med.*, **295**, 704–710 and 765–770.

Gregoriadis, G. and Neerunjun, D. E. (1974). Control of the rate of hepatic uptake and catabolism of liposome-entrapped proteins injected in rats. Possible therapeutic applications, *Eur. J. Biochem.*, **47**, 179–185.

Gregoriadis, G. and Neerunjun, E. D. (1975). Homing of liposomes to target cells, *Biochem. Biophys. Res. Comm.*, **65**, 537–544.

Gregoriadis, G., Swain, C. P., Willis, E. J. and Tavill, A. S. (1974). Drug-Carrier potential of liposomes in cancer chemotherapy, *Lancet*, **1**, 1313–1316.

Hazby, J. A., Kinsky, C. B. and Kinsky, S. C. (1968). Immune response of a liposomal model membrane. *Proc. Nat. Acad. Sci.*, **61**, 300–307.

Huang, L. (1969). Studies on phosphatidylcholine vesicle. Formation and physical characteristics, *Biochemistry*, **8**, 344–351.

Huang, L. and Charlton, J. P. (1972). Studies on the state of phosphatidylcholine molecules before and after ultrasonic and gel-filtration treatments, *Biochem. Biophys. Res. Comm.*, **46**, 1600–1666.

Huang, L., Ozato, K. and Pagano, R. E. (1974). Interaction of phospholipid vesicles with mouse lymphocytes *in vitro*, *Carnegie Institute Yearbook*, **74**, 60–64.

Humphries, G. M. and McConnell, H. M. (1975). Antigen mobility in membranes and complement mediated immune attack, *Proc. Nat. Acad. Sci. USA,* **72**, 2483–2487.

Jilka, R. R., Martonosi, A. N. and Tillack, T. W. (1975). Effect of the purified $(Mg^{2+} + Ca^{2+})$ activated ATPase of sarcoplasmic reticulum upon the passive Ca^{2+} permeability and ultrastructure of phospholipid vesicles, *J. Biol. Chem.*, **250**, 7511–7524.

Johnson, S. M. (1975). The inability of macrophages to digest liposomes containing a high proportion of cholesterol, *Biochem. Society Trans.*, **3**, 160–161.

Juliano, R. L. and Stamp, D. (1975). The effect of particle size and charge on the clearance rates of liposomes and liposome-encapsulated drugs. *Biochem. Biophys. Res. Comm.*, **63**, 651–658.

Kataoka, T., Inoue, K., Galanos, C. and Kinsky, S. C. (1971). Detection and specificity of Lipid A antibodies using liposomes sensitized with Lipid A and lipopolysacharides, *Europ. J. Biochem.*, **24**, 458–461.

Kinsky, S. C. (1972). Antibody–complement interaction with lipid model membranes, *Biochim. Biophys. Acta*, **265**, 1–23.

Kinsky, S. C., Haxby, J. A., Zopf, D. A., Alving, C. R. and Kinsky, C. B. (1969). Complement-dependent damage to liposomes prepared from pure lipids and Forssman hapten, *Biochemistry*, **8**, 4149–4158.

Kornberg, R. D. and McConnell, H. M. (1971). Inside–outside transitions of phospholipids in vesicle membranes, *Biochemistry*, **10**, 1111–1120.

MacDonald, R. I. and MacDonald, R. C. (1975). Assembly of phospholipid vesicles bearing sialoglycoprotein from erythrocyte membrane, *J. Biol. Chem.*, **250**, 9206–9214.

McDougall, I. R. and Dunnick, J. K. (1974). Unpublished observations.

McDougall, I. R., Dunnick, J. K., McNamee, M. G. and Kriss, J. P. (1974). Distribution and fate of synthetic vesicles in the mouse. A combined radionuclide and spin label study, *Proc. Nat. Acad. Sci. USA*, **71**, 3487–3491.

McDougall, I. R., Dunnick, J. K., Goris, M. L. and Kriss, J. P. (1975). *In vivo* distribution of vesicles loaded with radiopharmaceuticals: A study of different routes of administration, *J. Nucl. Med.*, **16**, 488–491.

Miller, W. (1975). *Technetium 99m biorouting. Textbook of Nuclear Med. Technology* p.255, (Eds. P. J. Early, M. A. Razzak and D. B. Sodee) C. V. Mosby Company, St. Louis.

Montal, M. and Korenbrot (1973). Incorporation of rhodopsin proteolipid into bilayer membranes, *Nature*, **246**, 219–221.

Pagano, R. E. and Huang, L. (1974). Interaction of phospholipid vesicles with mammalian cells, *Carnegie Institution Year Book*, **74**, 54–60.

Pagano, R. E. and Huang, L. (1975). Interaction of phospholipid vesicles with cultured mammalian cells, *J. Cell Biol.*, **67**, 49–60.

Papahadjopoulos, D., Nir, S. and Ohki, S. (1972). Permeability properties of phospholipid membranes: effect of cholesterol and temperature, *Biochim. Biophys. Acta*, **266**, 561–583.

Papahadjopoulos, D., Cowden, M. and Kimelberg, H. (1973a). Role of cholesterol in membranes. Effects of phospholipid–protein interactions, membrane permeability and enzymatic activity, *Biochim. Biophys. Acta*, **330**, 8–26.

Papahadjopoulos, D., Poste, S. and Schaffer, B. E. (1973b). Fusion of mammalian cells by unilamellar lipid vesicles : influence of lipid surface charge, fluidity and cholesterol, *Biochim. Biophys. Acta*, **323**, 23–42.

Segal, A. W., Wills, J. E., Richmond, J. E., Slavin, G., Black, C. D. V. and Gregoriadis, G. (1974). Morphological observations on the cellular and subcellular destination of intravenously administered liposomes, *Brit. J. Exp. Path.*, **55**, 320–327.

Segal, A. W., Gregoriadis, G. and Black, C. D. V. (1975). Liposomes as vehicles for the local release of drugs, *Clin. Sci. Mol. Med.*, **49**, 99–106.

Shafer, P. T. (1974). The interaction of polyamino acids with lipid monolayers, *Biochim. Biophys. Acta*, **373**, 425–435.

Shingleton, W. W. (1971). Liver scanning, in *Nuclear Medicine*, 2nd edition, p.366. (ed. W. H. Bladm), McGraw-Hill Book Company, New York.

Singer, S. J. and Nicolson, G. L. (1972). The fluid mosaic model of the structure of cell membrane, *Science*, **175**, 720–731.

Singleton, W. S., Gray, M. S. and Brown, M. L. (1965). Chromatographically homogeneous lecithin from egg phospholipids, *J. Amer. Oil. Chem. Soc.*, **42**, 53–56.

Veal, N. (1976). Personal communication.

Weissmann, G. (1976). Experimental enzyme replacement in genetic and other disorders, *Hospital practice*, **11**, 49–58.

Weissmann, H., Bloomgarden, D., Kaplan, R., Cohen, C., Hoffstein, S., Collins, T., Gottlieb, A. and Nagle, D. (1975). A general method for the introduction of enzymes by means of immunoglobulin-coated liposomes into lysosomes of deficient cells. *Proc. Nat. Acad. Sci. USA*, **72**, 88–92.

Liposomes in Biological Systems
Edited by G. Gregoriadis and A. C. Allison
©1980, John Wiley & Sons, Ltd.

CHAPTER 13

The Use of Liposomes for studying Membrane Antigens as Immunogens and as Targets for Immune Attack

Gillian M. K. Humphries

1. **Introduction**   345

2. **Model membrane engineering**   347

3. **Immunogenicity**   355

4. **Immune attack on model membranes**   359

5. **Conclusions**   372

   References   373

1. INTRODUCTION

While cell–cell recognition appears to be a general property of the healthy cells of higher organisms, this faculty is particularly well demonstrated by cells of the immune system. Clearly there is information on the surface of cells which proclaims their identity: evidence of a membrane language. In order to carry out its role in defence of the host animal against foreign or diseased cells and tolerance of normal healthy tissue, the immune system must be able to 'read' membrane language and, based upon the information so obtained, to make a correct decision whether or not to mount an attack culminating in the destruction of unwanted cells. The various mechanisms of killing by cellular and/or humoral components of the system are not fully understood, but certainly in some (if not all) cases the primary event of the actual killing is impairment of the integrity of the doomed cell's membrane. A complete understanding of how targets are selected for destruction and how this objective is carried out, is clearly of great importance for the control of auto-immune disease, cancer, and tissue transplantation.

Three events which involve the *target* cell membrane are apparent: (*a*) recognition by afferent cells; (*b*) recognition by effector cells and/or humoral components; (*c*) infliction of membrane damage. If one makes the hypothesis that target cells are principally *passive* participants in their own destruction, then it is reasonable to suppose that they could be effectively replaced by model membrane structures such as liposomes, and that scientific examination of this type of simplified system would be illuminating. The purpose of this chapter is to present and review evidence supporting the claim that such model structures are, in fact, useful analogues of target cells, and to discuss the type of information that has been, or may be, gained by their use. Although it cannot be claimed that liposomes have already made extensive contributions to immunology, the potential benefits of using synthetic membranes with defined chemical and physical properties, to answer questions about the molecular bases of membrane language and membrane damage are already apparent.

What questions may we expect to be answered by the use of model membranes?

Stored messages generally require a 'reference frame' within which a limited number of types of symbol are displayed. Information is contained in a message as a consequence of: (*a*) the particular recognizable symbols used; (*b*) the quantity of each type of symbol used; (*c*) the spatial and temporal relationship of one symbol to another within the reference frame. For example, only about ninety symbols are generated by an ordinary typewriter. The number of times each is used will vary from page to page of a typewritten manuscript, but the information also depends, in this particular case, upon the fact that the symbols remain stationary within the two-dimensional confines of the paper (the reference frame) and are spatially related to each other in a special way.

If we regard the external surface of a cell membrane as a language reference frame, then molecular moieties recognizable by the immune system (epitopes) represent the symbols. The antigenic profiles of two types of cell, one bearing epitopes A and B, and one bearing C and D clearly differ chemically, one from the other, and we would expect them to be distinguished by an appropriate immune system. However, it is also possible that two cell types both of which bear the same set of epitopes might present antigenic profiles which are significantly different by virtue of purely *physical* variation such as the quantity, lateral distribution, and lateral mobility of the epitopes or, perhaps, the distance of the epitope from the surface of the membrane, its masking by another component, or effects caused by the charge on the surface of the membrane. All these types of physical variation have been suggested, at one time or another, as explanations for immune phenomena which cannot be accounted for by considering only the more obvious chemical differences between membranes.

A great deal of scientific work has been devoted to detecting tissue-specific antigens and studying their distribution and mobility (or susceptibility to redistribution) with a variety of mono- or polyvalent specific antibodies or lectins, usually labelled with either ferritin or a fluorescent marker (de Petris and Raff, 1972; de Petris *et al.*, 1973; Frye and Edidin, 1970). Specific restraints to the mobility of certain components by fibrous networks have been revealed (Nicolson and Painter, 1973). High specific affinities between various membrane components, particularly glycolipids and glycoproteins (Pinto da Silva and Branton, 1972) have been indicated. Based on such work, the current picture of a cell membrane is one which shows that the distribution of the various component molecules is not homogeneous and their mobilities are not equal. (See also Raff, 1976a).

It is difficult to obtain precise information as to the physical state of biological membrane components and even more difficult to vary these systematically. In order to investigate physical variations which might affect the information displayed by epitopes on a target cell surface (thereby changing afferent and/or efferent immune responses to that cell) it may prove helpful to use model 'cells' having membranes of known composition, bearing epitopes whose physical state can be monitored and variably controlled.

Infliction of membrane damage as a consequence of recognition by cellular and/or humoral components of the immune system may, or may not, be directly affected by the epitopes, but it *is* very likely to be affected by the nature of the target areas with respect to their susceptibility to damage. We can anticipate that requirements for successful damage might range from the presence of a specific component, e.g. an altered self-antigen (Zinkernagel and Doherty, 1974), to more general physical properties such as membrane fluidity or charge. Again, this problem may be elucidated by the use of defined model membrane systems.

2. MODEL MEMBRANE ENGINEERING

The ideal system for studying immune responses to membranes would mimic those of living cells in stability and (for many purposes) size. Each structure in a given preparation would have the same chemical and physical composition; the chemical composition would be that of the original mixture used for the preparation and the physical state of a component of interest (e.g. an epitope) could be readily determined. For some purposes it is necessary to trap marker molecules to monitor the integrity of the bilayers and so the method of preparation should allow for this. In order to maximize marker release as a function of the number of lytic events, structures should be as large as possible and single-compartmented. A model system having all these advantages has yet to be reported; for most purposes the liposome, first described by Bangham (see Chapter 1), is the best approximation available at this time. A feature of liposomes is the rather wide variability in size and shape which they exhibit. It is not easy to assess how serious a handicap to their use this is; its importance almost certainly varies with the application considered. Another property of liposomes which, in some cases, is undesirable is the existence of multiple internal compartments.

Continuous synthetic membrane structures other than liposomes include the following:

(1) small single-compartmented vesicles (diameter ~250–500 Å) which can be prepared by sonication and have potentially useful features such as simplicity of preparation and relatively homogeneous size in addition to the single compartment. However, they are far smaller than cells and the physical state of the lipids is affected by strain resulting from the smaller radius of curvature of the vesicles. They tend to fuse, either with each other (Van der Bosch and McConnell, 1975) or with biological membranes (Grant and McConnell, 1973), under conditions which facilitate their transition to lower energy, non-strained, 'extended' bilayers.

(2) large single-compartmented vesicles, with diameters of the order of microns, which may be prepared by dialysis of detergent solutions of suitable amphiphilic lipids. This method has proved very useful for reconstitution of membrane proteins, which are first dissolved in detergent together with the lipids (Kleeman and McConnell, 1976; Grant and McConnell, 1974). Advantages which could be useful for immunological applications are their size and the possibility of inclusion of membrane proteins, as well as the possession of a single compartment. However, the method of preparation is lengthy and the composition of the vesicles often varies unpredictably from that of the original mixture of membrane components.

Bilayers composed of a single amphiphilic lipid species exhibit, at a given pressure, a characteristic sharp (1–2 °C range) 'chain melting' or phase transition point; two phases, one solid and one fluid, exist only at that temperature. However, studies using several well-defined binary mixtures have clearly shown phase separations for wide characteristic ranges of temperature and composition. Using electron paramagnetic resonance (EPR) spectroscopy to monitor 'melting' by observing the partitioning of 2,2,6,6-tetramethyl piperidine-1-oxyl (TEMPO) between lipid and aqueous environments, phase diagrams (reminiscent of those used to describe mixtures of metals) have been constructed for several binary lipid systems. The dipalmitoyl phosphatidylcholine (DPPC) and dimyristoyl phosphatidylcholine (DMPC) diagram (Shimshick and McConnell, 1973a) has been verified by freeze-fracture electron microscopy of rapidly cooled membranes; lateral phase separation of visibly distinct solid and fluid areas is observed for membranes cooled from the middle of a phase transition (Grant *et al.*, 1974). During melting, the fluid phase is relatively rich in the component having the lower melting point (DMPC) and so, in this state, distribution of the two components is not homogeneous throughout the membrane. However, for the DMPC : DPPC system, homogeneity of composition does occur above and below the *range* of temperature corresponding to melting of the entire membrane.

A third component, glycophorin (a human erythrocyte glycoprotein), is excluded from the solid phase of DMPC : DPPC when there is a coexisting fluid phase (Grant and McConnell, 1974). Its selective concentration in the fluid phase, under these conditions, is another example of the redistribution of a membrane component by lateral phase separation. (See also Kleeman and McConnell, 1976.)

In other synthetic systems, data indicating coexistence of solid areas (or phases) of different composition (Shimshick and McConnell, 1973b) and fluid areas (or phases) of different composition (Wu and McConnell, 1975) have been obtained, i.e. solid–solid and fluid–fluid immiscibility, respectively.

A very important issue in biological and medical science is the role of cholesterol in membranes. Phosphatidylcholine (PC) : cholesterol membranes have been extensively studied with a view to determining this. Unfortunately various fundamental aspects are still unknown.

It is clear that cholesterol decreases the flexibility of the hydrocarbon chains of phospholipids at temperatures above their principal phase transition temperatures (Saito *et al.,* 1973; McConnell and McFarland, 1972). However, it has also been reported that cholesterol has a 'fluidizing' effect for PC below that characteristic temperature (Ladbrooke *et al.,* 1968). This latter effect is not as well understood or accepted. Whereas for PC alone, molecular order and membrane fluidity are clearly inversely related, this may not be the case for PC : cholesterol bilayers and this topic is therefore the subject of intense experimentation and debate.

Another intractable area of cholesterol chemistry is the phase behaviour of PC : cholesterol systems with respect to composition. Freeze-fracture studies of preparations having less than 20 mol % cholesterol have shown solid–solid immiscibility at temperatures below the phase transition point of the PC (Kleeman and McConnell, 1976). This has also been indicated by phase diagrams of DMPC : cholesterol and DPPC : cholesterol (Shimshick and McConnell, 1973b) and by scanning calorimetry (Mabrey and Sturtevant, see Kleeman and McConnell, 1976). Coexistence of pure PC and a PC : cholesterol phase having a molar ratio of 4 : 1 is suggested. The maximum amount of cholesterol which can be incorporated into PC in the presence of excess water is 50 mol % (Bourgès *et al.,* 1967). It is therefore apparent that solid solutions or complexes of cholesterol and PC exist only for the range 20–50 mol % cholesterol, although this does *not* imply that continuous variability of composition within this range necessarily exists. Outside this range, phases exceedingly rich in the appropriate dominant component coexist with a PC : cholesterol phase.

There have been a formidable number of communications reporting changes in the properties of PC : cholesterol membranes which occur as the cholesterol content is systematically increased through 33 mol % or thereabouts. A few of the more recent are the following: (*a*) incorporation of more than 33 mol % cholesterol suppresses the lytic effect of Triton (Inoue and Kitigawa, 1976); (*b*) fluorescence enhancement for the probe 8-anilino-1-napthalene sulphonate disappears at more than 33 mol % cholesterol (Tsong, 1975); (*c*) macrophages release the contents of liposomes having up to about 30 mol % cholesterol but not those having more (Johnson, 1975); (*d*) the shape of sonicated PC : cholesterol vesicles is changed from spherical to asymmetric beyond 32 mol % cholesterol (Newman and Huang, 1975). Undoubtedly a dramatic physical change becomes evident at around 33 mol % but the existence of a 2 : 1 PC : cholesterol complex, as suggested from calorimetric studies by Hinz and Sturtevant (1972) and X-ray diffraction studies by Engelman and Rothman (1972), has not been unequivocally established. Evidence for a 4 : 1 complex and a 1 : 1 complex between lecithin and cholesterol is strong. Possibly only phases of these two compositions can exist for the range 20–50 mol % cholesterol and 35 mol % represents the midpoint after which the 1 : 1 phase is dominant. If this were true, the situation could be analogous to a large terrain drying up after a flood and changing from a lake dotted with islands to land dotted with ponds. The principal characteristics of the terrain and transport across it would be governed by the dominant geographical feature.

Phase separations of charged lipids in synthetic bilayers can be triggered by alteration of pH, ionic strength, and the concentration of bivalent cations. These phenomena may have very important biological significance (for a recent review see Träuble and Eibl, 1975).

The study of phase separations in synthetic membranes has had at least two important consequences: (*a*) it has prompted experimental work supporting the hypothesis that such behaviour may be the basis of various structural and functional features of biological membranes (Linden *et al.,* 1973); (*b*) it has suggested the possibility of controlled systematic variation of the distribution and mobility of membrane components in appropriate synthetic bilayers with a view to their use as targets for immune responses (see also McConnell, 1975).

It is fortunate that competent immune systems recognize both natural and synthetic molecular moieties, as this allows the choice of an epitope capable of relaying information both to the immune system and to the scientist. Although it is likely that most of the important epitopes on living cells are parts of proteins or glycoproteins, there is frequently no reason why one should use proteins rather than lipids as the point of covalent attachment to epitopes when designing a model system; instead, the relative simplicity of lipids recommends them for this role in most cases.

Spin labels such as the stable paramagnetic nitroxide, TEMPO, have

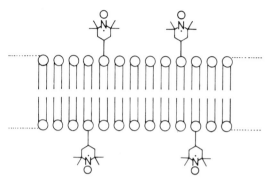

Figure 1 Diagrammatic representation of spin label lipid haptens in a lipid bilayer. (Reproduced from Brûlet *et al.*, 1977, by permission of Plenum Publishing Corporation)

been used extensively to investigate the kinetic and structural properties of synthetic and biological membranes. Labels are either covalently attached to a molecular species of interest, e.g. to the fatty acid chain of a phospholipid (Gaffney and McConnell, 1974), or non-covalently bound to the membrane, e.g. the partition of dissolved TEMPO between the aqueous and lipid compartments of the system (Shimshick and McConnell, 1973a). In either case their intended function is truly as 'labels' or probes; the scientist is interested only in what they are able to report about the membrane or its constituents and it is important that labels do not perturb the system significantly.

Recently, spin labels have found a radically new use as the epitopes of lipid haptens and conjugated proteins (Humphries and McConnell, 1976). Although the term 'label' has been retained for simplicity, it is not literally appropriate in this case, because the group is no longer being used as a probe but as a central component of the system. Figure 1 is a diagrammatic representation of spin label lipid haptens in a synthetic lipid bilayer. Chemical formulae of some phospholipid spin labels which have been prepared and shown to function as lipid haptens by their ability to bind TEMPO-specific IgG antibodies and exhibit complement-fixing activity when presented as components of lipid bilayers are given below.

Spin Label I

$$H_2C-O-{}^!CO-(CH_2)_{14}CH_3$$

$$CH_3(CH_2)_{14}-CO-O-CH$$

$$H_2C-O-\overset{\overset{O}{\parallel}}{\underset{\underset{O^-}{|}}{P}}-O-CH_2-CH_2-{}_+N$$

(prepared by the method of Kornberg and McConnell, 1971).

Spin Label II

$$CH_3(CH_2)_{14}-CO-O-CH \begin{array}{c} H_2C-O-CO-(CH_2)_{14}CH_3 \\ | \\ | \\ H_2C-O-\underset{\underset{O^-}{|}}{\overset{O}{\overset{||}{P}}}-O-CH_2-CH_2-\overset{H}{\underset{|}{N}}-CH_2-\overset{O}{\overset{||}{C}}-\overset{H}{\underset{|}{N}} \end{array}$$

(prepared as described by Brûlet and McConnell, 1976).

Spin Label III

$$CH_3(CH_2)_{14}-CO-O-CH \begin{array}{c} CH_2-O-CO-(CH_2)_{14}-CH_3 \\ | \\ | \\ CH_2-O-\underset{\underset{O^-}{|}}{\overset{O}{\overset{||}{P}}}-O-(CH_2)_2-NH-CO-(CH_2)_3-CO-NH \end{array}$$

(prepared as described by Brûlet and McConnell, 1977).

Electron paramagnetic resonance (EPR) spectroscopy may be used to monitor the physical state of these haptens in chemically defined bilayers (for a recent monograph on spin labelling see Berliner, 1975). Briefly, the type of information that can be obtained from such systems mostly relates to (*a*) rate of motion of and (*b*) rate of collisions between spin label epitopes. The rate of motion of the label is increased either by increasing the lateral motion of the entire molecule (see Figure 2) or by increasing the distance by which the nitroxide is separated from the surface of the bilayer. Rates of collision are increased either by increasing the lateral motion of the entire molecule or by decreasing the distance between adjacent nitroxides, even though the motion of the entire molecule is restricted. This latter effect can be achieved with homogeneously distributed haptens by increasing their concentration until collision is made inevitable (see Figure 3). If distribution is not homogeneous (i.e. the haptens are clustered) the collision rate may be high even though the overall concentration of hapten is low. An amphiphilic lipid bearing two head group spin labels has been shown to form clusters of six molecules under certain conditions of concentration, temperature, and bilayer composition (Rey and McConnell, 1977).

Interpretation of spectra may not always be simple: for example, line broadening with concomitant decrease in the amplitude of the first derivative signal displayed by the spectrometer, is effected either by decreasing the rate of motion or increasing the rate of collision (spin exchange broadening) of epitopes. However, the nature of the broadening is not identical, as demonstrated by spin label II in Figures 2 and 3. Whereas spin exchange broadening affects all three lines to approximately

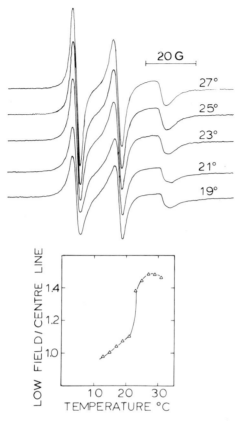

Figure 2 Spectral consequence of 'melting' carrier lipid bilayers: the electron paramagnetic resonance spectra of DMPC liposomes containing 0.5 mol % spin label hapten II, together with a plot of temperature versus the ratio of the amplitude of the low field line to that of the centre line. The principal phase transition temperature of DMPC is 23 °C. (It should be noted that melting the bilayers both sharpens the spectrum, by increasing the rate of motion, and broadens it, by increasing the collision rate of spin label haptens. In this instance, because the hapten is present at a low concentration in the membrane, the dominant effect is that due to increasing the rate of motion. When haptens are already sufficiently concentrated to show significant spin exchange broadening in the solid state, melting is accompanied by an appreciable increase in broadening.) (See text for further discussion)

the same extent, broadening as a consequence of immobilization affects the low field line to a greater extent than the centre line. Physical changes in spin label epitopes must frequently be accompanied by a variety of different types of spectral change which add together to give the paramagnetic resonance signal displayed, and are not easy to resolve. Also it is likely that in some cases, epitopes in a single preparation will exist in

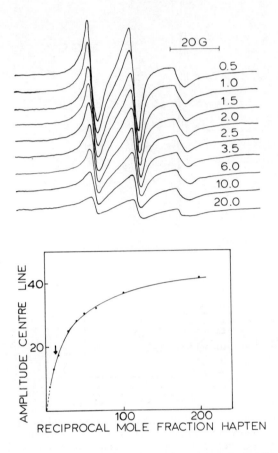

Figure 3 Spectral consequence of decreasing the spacing of epitopes in a 'solid' membrane: the electron paramagnetic resonance spectra of DMPC liposomes at 15 °C containing *equal amounts* of spin label hapten II at the various molar percentages (with respect to DMPC) indicated. Also shown, is a plot of the amplitude of the centre line (in arbitrary units) versus the reciprocal of the mole fraction of hapten present in the bilayers. This latter parameter is proportional to the average area of membrane available to each hapten. The arrow marks the value for which this average area is equal to (30 Å).[2] The distance by which the nitroxide is separated from the bilayer surface is close to 15 Å. The data indicate a random, monomolecular dispersion of this hapten in solid DMPC bilayers.

Spectra obtained using a Varian E12 spectrometer and variable temperature control accessory, interfaced with a Digital pdp8/e computer. Samples were prepared as specified but such that all had the same *overall* concentration of nitroxide (i.e. total lipid per ml liposome suspension was varied). Even so, because of the heterogeneous nature of lipid suspensions, spectra were integrated and normalized to the same spin concentration and then plotted at these new normalized values in order to measure comparable spectral parameters two or more well-defined physical states (see Rey and McConnell, 1977) giving rise to mixed spectra. Interfacing the spectrometer with a computer having programs for storing spectra, performing various mathematical operations, and controlling the plotter to generate new displays, is of primary importance for interpretation of many spectra derived from spin label haptens in lipid bilayers.

It is important to use target cell models far more amenable to chemical and physical definition than are cells themselves if much is to be learned about how the physical state of membrane antigens affects immune responses.

3. IMMUNOGENICITY

For several years the question whether induction of specific antibodies was due to 'instruction' or 'selection' by antigen was hotly debated. Followers of the 'instructive' theory held that the antigen acted as a template which was used to modify antibody synthesis to obtain the correct fit. However, by 1967, the very important Clonal Selection Theory of Burnet became generally accepted. This theory holds that lymphocytes differ from each other in the specificity of antigen receptors which they bear on their surfaces; antigen selects an appropriate lymphocyte by binding to its surface receptors and providing a signal for cell proliferation and the production of antibodies; each antibody-producing lymphocyte is capable of making only one type of antibody with a single or a small number of specificities for antigen.

Since 1967 it has become increasingly evident that mere binding of epitopes to B cells (the lymphocytes responsible for antibody production) is not sufficient to trigger antibody synthesis. Recent reviews of work in this area include those by Ada and Ey (1975), Goodman (1975), and Coutinho and Möller (1975). In brief, it appears that for effective stimulation of B cells an antigen-specific signal is required which is believed to consist of the presentation of a matrix of epitopes suitably spaced on the surface of macromolecules, multimolecular complexes, or cells (candidates are macrophages, T cells, or target cells). Induction of specific tolerance appears to be a closely related phenomenon in some cases (Feldman, 1971).

Some antigens, e.g. polymerized bacterial flagellins, apparently already have the correct structure to provide an antigen-specific stimulatory signal; these are classified as T-independent and typically display multiple repeating determinants. Most antigens are T-dependent, requiring help which is provided by the class of lymphocytes called T cells (or thymus-derived cells) and by macrophages. T-cell help is antigen-specific and generally directed to a part of the antigen different from that invoking the antibody. Typically, T-dependent antigens have more than one type of epitope. Soluble antigen-specific helper factors may be involved in organizing T-dependent antigens into spatial arrangements which form effective antigen-specific B-cell signals.

Non-specific helper factors are also thought to be required for effective B-cell stimulation. The suggestion that an activated complement component (C3) is involved in non-specific help is particularly intriguing. T-independent antigens and B-cell mitogens (i.e. substances such as polyanions which stimulate B cells non-specifically) generally activate the alternative pathway of complement fixation (APC); they are capable of activating C3, thereby triggering the rest of the pathway (Bitter-Suermann *et al.*, 1975). On the other hand, most T-dependent antigens only cause C3 cleavage in a very indirect way, i.e. by causing aggregation of IgG antibodies which are then capable of activating the classical pathway of complement fixation, of which C3 is the fourth component.

T-independent antigens selectively induce IgM synthesis; T-dependent antigens usually induce a low level of IgM initially but after a short time, the predominant antibody synthesized is IgG. Human serum albumin heavily substituted with dinitrophenyl is a T-dependent antigen, as is the lightly substituted compound, but the former (unlike the latter) both selectively induces IgM and is a potent APC activator. The suggestion has therefore been made, that APC-activating potential is not related to T-independence as such, but to the class of B cells that can be triggered by a given antigen (Bitter-Suermann *et al.*, 1975). This suggestion implies that 'selection' goes beyond specificity and that physical factors, such as the spatial arrangement of epitopes, determine not only whether an immune response will be made but, by selecting among various classes of lymphocytes specific for that epitope, determine the type of response that will be made. It should be noted that there is good evidence that B lymphocytes are first committed to IgM synthesis and at a later date switch to a commitment to IgG synthesis. However, it is not established whether this change takes place before or after exposure to antigen (see Smith, 1973).

Although the idea that there is a causal relationship between APC-activating activity and T-independence is appealing, there are apparent contradictions. Feldman and Pepys (1974) found that antibodies directed against C3 inhibited T-dependent, but not T-independent *in vitro* antibody responses. The interpretation was that T-dependent, but not T-independent, responses require C3. It has been suggested by Bitter-Suermann *et al.* (1974) that if APC-activating antigens are capable of using C3 more efficiently than are those whose effective presentation depends on a cooperating cell system, this paradox might be resolved. Macrophages and some, but not all, B cells have receptors for activated C3.

The structural features of antigens which influence different cellular immune responses are even less well understood than are those governing humoral responses (i.e. the production of antibodies). Cellular responses include the generation of helper and suppressor T cells and the generation of T cells which either specifically attack foreign (or 'altered self') cells or, when stimulated, cause the activation of nearby macrophages. Even the nature of the antigen receptor of T cells has been very controversial (Ada and Ey, 1975).

As cellular immunity appears to be more important for responses to grafts and tumours than humoral immunity, it is of great interest to know how it is influenced by various modes of antigen presentation. Optimal recognition of foreign antigens by T cells requires their presentation in association with major histocompatibility antigens. Recent work providing evidence of this has been reviewed by Raff (1976b).

In 1973, N. A. Mitchison suggested that cell membranes could be the basis for structural linkage of helper and antigenic determinants. This would obviate the need for covalent linkage of helper and antigenic determinants. He also suggested that a membrane could provide the necessary structure for presentation of antigen for multipoint binding by lymphocytes (see FEBS meeting report by Wallach *et al.*, 1973).

Current knowledge of immunogenicity has profited greatly from the use of synthetic antigens; for example, those in which dinitrophenyl is covalently attached to proteins such as haemocyanin or polymerized bacterial flagellin (Feldmann and Pepys, 1974), or to synthetic polymer beads (Trump, 1975; Inman, 1975).

Mixtures of natural lipid haptens, such as galactocerebroside or cardiolipin, together with carrier lipids, such as lecithin (or sphingomyelin) and cholesterol, have been used for many years to elicit antibody production in experimental animals (Rapport, 1970). More recently synthetic lipid haptens have been shown to elicit specific humoral and cellular responses in animals immunized with such haptens included in liposomal model membranes. The most extensive of such studies have been those by S. C. Kinsky and his colleagues using the 2,4-dini-trophenyl-ε-aminocaproyl and mono (*p*-azobenzenearsonic acid) tyrosyl derivatives of phosphatidylethanolamine (DNP-cap-PE and ABA-Tyr-PE respectively). Using DNP-cap-PE and derivatives or analogues, Uemura *et al.* (1974) have shown that, in quinea pigs, the immunogenicity of the dinitrophenyl group, as monitored by haemagglutination of trinitrophenylated sheep erythrocytes, is enhanced by: (*a*) its attachment to an amphiphilic molecule inserted in liposomal membranes, composed of sphingomyelin and cholesterol together with dicetyl phosphate at a molar ratio of 2.0 : 1.5 : 0.2; (*b*) increasing the distance between the epitope and the membrane; (*c*) using sphingomyelin rather than lecithin, together with cholesterol and dicetyl phosphate, as the carrier lipids (natural sphingomyelin is substituted with longer, more saturated fatty acids than egg lecithin: a fact probably accounting for the greater stability of liposomes prepared with the former lipid and hence probably accounting for this experimental finding); (*d*) using Freund's complete adjuvant rather than Freund's incomplete adjuvant (a lipopolysaccharide supplement was about as effective as the latter but in the absence of any of these agents there was no measureable response). Confirmation of the results obtained using the haemagglutination assay was given by using an assay based on the antibody–complement-mediated lysis of liposomes (to be discussed in the next section of this chapter).

The antibody-forming ability of cell suspensions prepared from the lymph nodes or spleens of guinea pigs immunized with liposomal membranes containing DNP-cap-PE has been examined using plaque assays which employ trinitrophenylated sheep erythrocytes (Uemura *et al.*, 1974). Both direct (IgM) and indirect (IgG) responses were observed. As determined by inhibition of plaque formation by systematic variation of the level of added ϵ-DNP-lysine, both IgG and IgM exhibited a very restricted range of avidities. This limited range was comparable with that shown by a mouse myeloma protein and quite different from the broad range of avidities elicited by immunization with dinitrophenylated guinea pig albumin. The interpretation is that DNP conjugated to phosphatidylethanolamine via amino caproic acid and non-covalently inserted in liposomal bilayers presents a far more uniform epitopic profile than does DNP conjugated to a protein, and is therefore capable of stimulating a very limited group of DNP-specific lymphocytes. The restricted nature of the IgG antibody response to liposomes was confirmed by examination of the isoelectric focusing patterns of the proteins. This phenomenon may have practical importance for production of homogeneous antibodies as well as being of theoretical interest.

In other interesting experiments by Kinsky's group, the effect of incorporating more than one type of epitope in the same bilayer has been studied (Kochibe *et al.*, 1975). Using the same carrier lipid mixture as previously employed with a single species of hapten, DNP-cap-PE and ABA-tyr-PE were jointly included in liposome bilayers by their addition together, at various concentrations, in the lipid mixture solution prior to evaporation of organic solvents. These 'hybrid' liposomes were then emulsified with Freund's complete adjuvant prior to injection in guinea pigs. In control experiments, liposomes containing each of the two haptens were separately prepared and emulsified with adjuvant prior to injection of their mixture (i.e. 'mixed' liposomes). In other controls, one or the other phospholipid hapten was replaced by addition of an equivalent amount of the appropriate deacylated, non-amphiphilic derivative to the aqueous solution used to suspend the dried lipids. These methods of liposome preparation were used to show that: (*a*) increasing amounts of ABA-tyr-PE stimulated the anti-DNP response to hybrid liposomes; (*b*) increasing amounts of DNP-cap-PE decreased the anti-ABA response to hybrid liposomes. Both help and inhibition were dependent on the presence of the appropriate epitopes attached to amphiphilic molecules and included in the same bilayers. These experiments are the correlate of observations made with more conventional synthetic antigens by other workers (see Kochibe *et al.,* 1975).

The help afforded by the inclusion of ABA-tyr-PE in liposomes suggests that this compound might be a particularly effective T-cell stimulator. This is borne out by the finding that ABA-tyr-PE, either free or present in liposomes, can be used to confer cellular immunity, as manifested by delayed hypersensitivity reactions to ABA-conjugated bovine serum albumin (ABA-tyr-PE in lipid bilayers; Nicolotti and Kinsky, 1975). It is interesting that this lipid hapten generates both humoral and cellular responses. Like ABA-tyrosine, the deacylated derivative of ABA-tyr-PE (i.e. ABA-Tyrosyl-glycerophosphorylethanolamine) confers cellular immunity without antibody formation. However, induction of cellular immunity by ABA-tyrosine and also by ABA-tyr-PE sensitized liposomes (presumably also by the deacylated derivative of ABA-tyr-PE and by ABA-tyr-PE not included in liposomes) is dependent upon administration of the antigen in Freund's complete adjuvant.

The delayed hypersensitivity reaction is generally considered an *in vivo* correlate of cell-mediated immunity and, therefore, such a response to model membranes suggests that they may be useful analogues of cells in studying cell-mediated recognition and attack against target cells.

A point which should be borne in mind when considering procedures with liposomes (e.g. the immunization of animals) is that if one uses a constant weight of liposomes and varies the weight of hapten included, then both the total quantity of hapten available to the system *and* its spacing on the membrane may differ. Experimental design should allow for testing of these two variables separately.

4. IMMUNE ATTACK ON MODEL MEMBRANES

At the present time, virtually all scientific effort in this field has been directed towards understanding antibody–complement-mediated immune attack on liposomes. As mentioned before, there are clearly two major membrane-related steps in such an attack, one being recognition by antibody and complement and one being the infliction of membrane damage. Recognition requires the binding of specific antibodies of an appropriate type in such a way that they are able to *initiate* complement fixation; damage requires an effective interaction between the activated later components of the complement cascade and the membrane. Taking examples from living cells and model systems it can be seen that these do not invariably occur together.

For activation of the first components of complement by the classical pathway it is necessary for two, or a smaller number, of IgG antibody molecules (of an appropriate subclass) to be found in close proximity on the surface of a cell (Borsos and Rapp, 1965a; see also Cohen, 1968, and Hyslop *et al.*, 1970, for similar results involving soluble antigens rather than membrane antigens); or, in the case of IgM antibodies, a single molecule will suffice (Borsos and Rapp, 1965b) but it is likely that this must be multiply bound to repeating epitopes on the cell surface (Ishizaka and Ishizaka, 1969; Cunniff and Stollar, 1968). Clearly the spacing and mobility of epitopes on a cell surface is of fundamental importance to whether antibodies will bind in such a way that they are unable to initiate complement fixation. Binding of antibody is necessary, but not always sufficient, for effective immune recognition in this system. This is a particularly promising area for investigation using model membranes and will be dealt with later in more detail.

Even if complement fixation has been successfully initiated, for living cells this does not necessarily mean that cell death will follow. It has been shown that there is a lack of correlation between the amount of C4 and C3 fixed, and cell lysis, for certain tumour lines (Ohanian and Borsos, 1975). Also, for Moloney virus-transformed cells, resistance to lysis, which varies with the growth phase of the cells, is not related to the amounts of C5 and C8 bound to the cells (Cooper *et al.*, 1974). It has been known for a long time that nucleated cells are less susceptible to the cytotoxic action of antibody and complement than erythrocytes and it has been suggested that the former might be capable of repairing membrane damage. This has been strongly supported by recent work. It is possible to prepare erythrocytes (Burakoff *et al.*, 1975) or tumour cells (Boyle *et al.*, 1976) to which all necessary components of complement are bound, but which are reversibly prevented from lysing or dying at low temperatures or in the presence of EDTA. However, in the case of tumour cells, but *not* erythrocytes, $3'5'$ cAMP is capable of *irreversibly* preventing cell death if the original amount of antibody used to initiate damage is not very great (see Boyle *et al.*, 1976). The effect is time, temperature, and cAMP dose dependent, suggesting that metabolic activity is required. Furthermore, metabolic inhibitors have been shown to enhance cytotoxicity (Segerling *et al.*, 1974). It should therefore be borne in mind, that living cells are probably *not* passive targets for antibody–complement-mediated attack; they may have a limited capacity for self-defence.

It is also possible that the susceptibility to damage is affected by physical features of the membrane, such as fluidity (as suggested by the reversible effect of temperature on cell death mentioned above) or charge, which has been suggested to explain the enhanced cytotoxicity observed when herpes simplex virus-infected cells are treated with neuraminidase (Tompkins *et al.*, 1976).

A phenomenon called 'reactive lysis' can be demonstrated either with erythrocytes, or with liposomes composed of egg lecithin together with a low concentration of either stearylamine or phosphatidic acid (Lachmann *et al.*, 1970). Intermediate activated complement components followed by terminal components are added to the liposomes and can be shown to cause membrane damage. No membrane-bound antigen or specific antibody is involved in this activity. Reactive lysis of erythrocytes can be modified by addition of polyanions or polycations (Baker *et al.*, 1975).

Binding of specific antibodies to lipid haptens in liposomal bilayers or uncharacterized aqueous suspensions of lipids (frequently termed 'floccules') is not at all new. In the important VDRL test for syphilis, antibodies found in positive sera agglutinate continuous bilayer structures formed by injecting an alcoholic solution of cholesterol, lecithin, and cardiolipin (the hapten) into saline. In general, lipid haptens do not bind antibodies well unless they are presented, together with carrier lipids such as lecithin or sphingomyelin and cholesterol, in the form of bilayers or micelles.

The binding of TEMPO-specific antibodies to spin label lipid haptens in the membranes of single-compartmented vesicles (prepared either by dialysis or sonication) is indicated by a reduction in amplitude of the paramagnetic resonance signal derived from unbound spin label epitopes and the concomitant appearance of a new signal, remarkable for 'the very wide splitting of the hyperfine extrema (79G) (see Figure 4). This new component of the spectrum is undoubtedly derived from antibody-bound labels which are strongly immobilized and, in addition, experience a strong, specific electrostatic interaction with the binding site of the antibody; the latter effect leads to an increase in charge separation about the nitroxide group with resulting increase in spin density on the nitrogen atom, and hence, increase in the hyperfine splitting, T_{zz}, characteristic of the spectrum. (For further characterization see Rey and McConnell, 1976.)

A direct assay for antibody binding to multicompartmented liposomes bearing spin label haptens is not feasible because of the high background of protected internal labels. However, one may assay for such binding by an inhibition method: incubating antibodies with liposomes and then removing these, together with bound antibody, prior to testing for residual binding capacity towards the small water-soluble labels, TEMPO or TEMPO-choline chloride, by EPR analysis. Using this method, Brûlet and McConnell (1976, 1977) have found that the specific IgG antibody (and Fab) binding capacity of hapten-bearing lecithin : cholesterol liposomes is a

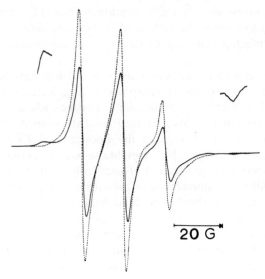

Figure 4 Electron paramagnetic resonance spectra of large, single-compartmented DMPC vesicles containing 2.5 mol % spin label lipid hapten III together with immunoglobulins from rabbit anti-TEMPO haemocyanin serum, (———), or from rabbit anti-human erythrocyte serum, (- - - -). The hyperfine extrema of the spectrum derived from antibody-bound labels are shown above the complete spectrum at a higher gain; a total splitting of 79G is observed. It should be noted that the decrease in sharp signal, caused by addition of specific antibodies is proportional to the number of haptens bound (i.e. about 40% of the total in this case). This result was obtained using unfractionated immunoglobulins. The specificity and affinity of antibodies raised to TEMPO-haemocyanin have recently been examined by Rey and McConnell (1976). (Reproduced from Brûlet *et al.*, 1977 by permission of Plenum Publishing Corporation)

non-linear function of cholesterol content, being markedly enhanced at concentrations greater than 20–33 mol % cholesterol. Furthermore, the use of spin labels I, II, and III has shown that binding is favoured by increasing the distance by which the epitope projects from the surface of the bilayer (Brûlet and McConnell, 1977). The cholesterol effect would be explained by a change in the fraction of haptens exposed at the liposomal surfaces which could occur if the structure of liposomes is affected by cholesterol content. Although examination by light microscope does not reveal noticeable differences between lecithin : cholesterol liposomes of various compositions, this question of hapten exposure is important and is currently under investigation. However, Brûlet and McConnell consider that the effect of cholesterol on antibody binding is more likely to be related to an increase in the distance by which the epitope projects from the surface of the bilayer when cholesterol content is increased.

Experimental evidence for this increased projection is provided by the shape of the spectrum derived from spin label II when included in bilayers having 50 mol % cholesterol; it appears that the motion of the TEMPO group is appreciably more isotropic in the presence of this high concentration of cholesterol than it is when included in fluid DMPC membranes (although rapid lateral motion is not indicated in the presence of 50 mol % cholesterol). In general, label II gives rise to spectra which are quite strongly affected by the restriction to isotropic motion of the nitroxide caused by its proximity to the bilayer. Label III (which has a longer hydrophilic side chain), when included in lecithin bilayers, gives rise to spectra which are both more typical of isotropic motion and similar to those given by label II in lecithin plus 50 mol % cholesterol.

Complement fixation has long been used as one of the principal means of studying lipid haptens. Complement fixation tests are based on the ability of certain classes of antibody, when suitably bound to their specific antigens (or polyvalent haptens), to deplete the lytic activity of fresh animal sera towards antibody-sensitized sheep erythrocytes. IgM and most of the subclasses of IgG are capable of complement fixation via the classical pathway.

Typically, IgM fixes complement most effectively in conjunction with antigens which display multiple repeating epitopes (Cunniff and Stollar, 1968) and is even capable of inhibiting complement fixation by IgG, probably because epitopes are not presented in a suitable fashion (Scott and Russell, 1972). However, it should be noted that Brown and Koshland (1975), using RNAase substituted with one or several haptens, find either form as effective as the other in inducing complement fixation by IgM, on a per epitope basis. Fixation is not induced by hapten alone. These findings are interpreted as showing that neither inter- not intramolecular cross-linking of IgM subunits by antigen is required to facilitate complement fixation, but that a carrier moiety (e.g. RNAase) is essential for the induction of a necessary conformational change in the immunoglobulin. The mode of action of the carrier is not understood. This work is, at first sight, somewhat at variance with that of Cunniff and Stollar (1968), who find that complement fixation mediated by IgM specific for adenosine is far more effective using denatured DNA as antigen that it is using adenosine-conjugated human serum albumin. As Brown and Koshland used hapten-conjugated proteins throughout (for which the epitopes must have exhibited a random spatial arrangement) it is still probable that complement fixation by IgM is facilitated by presentation of multiple repeating epitopes in a critical spatial configuration, although this is not essential.

Complement fixation by most subclasses of IgG antibodies depends upon their aggregation by heat, chemical treatment or, more physiologically, by cross-linking as the result of binding to specific antigens or multivalent haptens. Using a divalent hapten, Hyslop *et al.* (1970) have shown that aggregates of four or more IgG molecules are required for effective complement fixation. On the other hand, Borsos and Rapp (1965a) have shown that two IgG molecules in close proximity on the surface of a cell are required for complement-mediated lysis of sheep erythrocytes. Steric factors may be responsible for the apparent disparity between these findings. It is likely that only two IgG molecules are required, but that their Fc portions must be in close proximity (see also Cohen, 1968). An interesting unanswered question concerns how long the Fc portions must be in close proximity to initiate fixation. (For a review of the controversy regarding possible conformational changes due to antigen binding see Metzger, 1974). An anomalous finding has been the induction of IgG-mediated complement fixation by a monovalent hapten attached to a polycationic side chain (Goers *et al.*, 1975).

A great deal of work concerning lipid haptens has been done by M. M. Rapport (see Rapport, 1970). Complement fixation by such natural lipid haptens as cardiolipin and galactocerebroside has been shown to be not only dependent upon their suspension together with 'carrier' amphiphilic lipids, but also upon the composition of the mixture and the proportion of hapten used. The addition of cholesterol to lecithin : hapten mixtures effects a particularly dramatic improvement to complement fixing activity. In general, at least 60 mol % cholesterol has been used to prepare lipid suspensions suitable for studying complement fixation by natural lipid haptens. It should be noted that conditions favouring antibody binding are *not* necessarily the same as those favouring complement fixation (Rapport and Graf, 1967). As suggested by Rapport, it is likely that the carrier lipid effect is related to the mode of presentation of epitopes (i.e. their physical state).

Even before cardiolipin was known to be the active hapten in the reaction, addition of cholesterol to alcoholic extracts of beef heart was known to enhance the complement fixing activity of aqueous lipid suspensions of these extracts in the presence of antibodies found in syphilitic sera (Kolmer, 1928). Intrigued by this ancient empirical finding and by the work of Rapport and others, Humphries and McConnell (1975) adapted a version of the Kolmer Syphilis Test (US Public Health Service Publication no. 411, 1964) and used, instead of commercially available Kolmer antigen (cardiolipin : lecithin : cholesterol at molar ratios approximately 1 : 3 : 36), liposomes prepared from 3 mol % cardiolipin together with cholesterol, in the range 25–60 mol %, and DMPC or DPPC. The complement fixing activity of these liposomes was not linear with cholesterol content; for the range 25–35 mol %, it was at a low constant level characteristic of the serum, whereas, for the range 40–60 mol %, it increased with cholesterol content (particularly steeply for 40–50 mol %). The same profile was observed using either lecithin, and for several temperatures in the range 4–37 °C. The cholesterol concentration at which this dramatic change takes place (>35 mol %) is about the same as that at which so many changes in the structure and behaviour of lecithin : cholesterol bilayers have been reported. As mentioned in the Section 2 of this chapter, the molecular basis of these changes is unknown but in all probability is related to a change in the phase or phases represented at this concentration.

The inclusion of 3 mol % cardiolipin in lecithin : cholesterol bilayers has a marked effect on changes in TEMPO binding which occur as a function of temperature. As mentioned previously, changes in TEMPO binding (or partition) have been used to detect the onset and completion of melting for binary mixtures of lipids and, hence, to construct phase diagrams for these systems. The phase diagrams for cholesterol and either DMPC or DPPC, determined using this method by Shimshick and McConnell (1973b), are not fully understood. Problems of interpretation are discussed by Kleeman and McConnell (1976). However, in spite of these problems, it is evident that for cholesterol concentrations greater than 35 mol %, cardiolipin markedly lowers the temperature at which increase in TEMPO binding, as a function of temperature, is enhanced (Humphries and McConnell, 1975). This has been interpreted as showing that, for the temperatures used in the complement fixation experiments, cardiolipin is included in a relatively rigid cholesterol-rich phase when more than about 35 mol % cholesterol is present, and excluded from this rigid phase (possibly as clusters of pure cardiolipin) at lower concentrations of the steroid. Changes in hapten mobility, distribution, and perhaps projection of the head group from the membrane (if the behaviour is similar to that of spin label II) would attend such a phase change. Presentation of cardiolipin in the form of a display of multiple, spaced, repeating epitopes is, by analogy with the denatured DNA antigen mentioned earlier, likely to produce an effective antigen for induction of complement fixation by IgM. This work, which indicated that a biological phenomenon could be controlled by the physical state of a membrane component in synthetic bilayers, also stressed the advantages which would be gained by using an epitope capable of reporting directly upon its own physical state.

The IgG antibodies shown to bind specifically to spin label lipid hapten III (Humphries and McConnell, 1976) were also shown to fix complement in the presence of this hapten, presented either in DMPC or DPPC bilayers (Brûlet *et al.*, 1977). If complement fixation proceeded at 32 °C, midway between the principal phase transition points of DMPC (23 °C) and DPPC (41 °C), the amplitude of the peak of the biphasic response obtained, using a fixed amount of antibody and varying the amount of liposomes supplied, was very significantly greater for the case of 'fluid' (DMPC) liposomes than it was for the 'solid' (DPPC) liposomes. Furthermore, the positions of these peaks or equivalence points were not the same; far less 'fluid' (DMPC) than 'solid' (DPPC) liposomes were required for equivalence. These differences in behaviour were almost totally obliterated if fixation proceeded at 4 °C rather than at 32 °C; both types of liposomes were solid at 4 °C and exhibited virtually identical responses. Therefore, the inclusion of label III in fluid, rather than solid, bilayers enhances its ability to induce complement fixation by IgG antibodies.

If the same type of experiment is performed using DPPC liposomes incorporating different haptens (i.e. using labels I, II, and III), the amplitude of the biphasic response increases in the order I < II < III, in direct correlation with the distance of projection of the epitope from the bilayer surface. However, in this case, more of the very responsive label III liposomes are required for equivalence than are required with the other haptens. This suggests that label III is capable of binding a larger population of antibody molecules than are the others: a conjecture supported by antibody-binding experiments (Brûlet and McConnell, 1977). Alving *et al.*, 1974a, using four different galactosyl lipid haptens, found a correlation which may be significant, between the overall lengths of the molecules and their antigenicity and immunogenicity.)

In a slightly different type of experiment, a constant amount of liposomes (DMPC or DPPC) containing various concentrations of spin label hapten II (0.25–0.01 mol %) have been employed at 32 °C, to study complement fixation as a function of the amount of TEMPO-specific antibodies supplied (antibodies were purified by use of an affinity column) (Brûlet and McConnell, 1976). These studies have indicated that the induction of fixation by IgG is particularly strongly enhanced by fluid, rather than solid, carrier bilayers when the concentration of hapten in the plane of the membrane drops below that which ensures an average spacing sufficient to enable antibodies to bind with both sites, even to epitopes whose mobility in the plane of the membrane is restricted (i.e. about 0.1 mol %). These results are interesting because they suggest that use of a fluid, rather than solid, matrix for hapten presentation may potentiate IgG interactions necessary for the initiation of complement fixation, in more ways than by encouraging interliposomal binding leading to agglutination. Antibodies involved in such binding would probably be clustered and somewhat immobilized by virtue of their restriction to areas of membrane in close apposition. That such antibodies would be effective in complement fixation is reasonably predictable. However, it is not known how long two IgG molecules must be in close apposition in order to initiate complement fixation and it is quite possible, and is supported by the experimental work described, that IgG molecules bound to the *same* membrane via monovalent haptens and free to move fairly rapidly in the plane of the membrane are, by virtue of the fluidity of the matrix, in close apposition a sufficient length of time to initiate complement fixation. It should be noted that divalent binding of IgG, even to a fluid membrane, both concentrates and, in all probability, orients it. Because of the twofold rotational symmetry of the protein, and hence of the binding site positions, it is likely that it oscillates about the perpendicular to the membrane.

It should also be noted that, in all complement fixation studies undertaken so far by the McConnell group, depletion of *whole* guinea pig complement has been tested. Because an absolute requirement for all positive results has been the presence of specific antibodies known normally to fix complement via the classical pathway (together with liposomes which show no anticomplementary behaviour on their own), the assumption has been made that changes in the physical state of membrane haptens which modify induction of fixation, do so by modifying the ability of antibodies to react with the first component of complement. The validity of this assumption has yet to be proven. However, it has clearly been shown that an immunological phenomenon (the depletion of whole complement initiated by specific antibodies) can be controlled by manipulating the physical state of a reactant (the epitope) contained by synthetic bilayers.

A different approach to studying antibody–complement interactions with lipid haptens in liposomal bilayers has been taken by S. C. Kinsky and others who have followed his lead. In these types of experiment, immune lysis of liposomes is observed by determining the extent of release of a marker species (a membrane-impermeable, water-soluble molecule or ion) initially trapped between the bilayers of liposomes, on treatment with hapten-specific antibodies, of an appropriate type, and complement. Although this approach is appealing because of the close resemblance to haemolysis, it should be noted that two membrane-related phenomena are involved (as has been discussed previously). Unless a very standard formula is used for the carrier lipids, data are difficult or impossible to interpret because one is faced with the problem of deciding whether induction of complement fixation or damage to the membrane has been affected. Therefore, immune lysis of liposomes *on its own* is of limited use for studying the very interesting carrier lipid effects which are characteristic of the immunochemistry of lipid haptens.

For most studies of the immune lysis of liposomes, they have been prepared from a lipid mixture having lecithin (or sphingomyelin), cholesterol, and dicetyl phosphate, at a molar ratio 2.0 : 1.5 : 0.2, together with a low variable concentration of a lipid antigen or hapten. The marker molecule used is most commonly glucose, whose release may be monitored photometrically, without prior separation of lysed and unlysed liposomes, by adding appropriate enzymes and cofactors to the reactants such that released glucose is able to reduce NADP$^+$ (Kinsky, 1974). Unless otherwise stated, the following applies to liposomes of this type.

An immune response to such membranes was initially obtained using lipids extracted from sheep erythrocytes as the antigenic component, together with heated rabbit anti-sheep erythrocyte serum and unheated guinea pig serum as the sources of antibody and complement respectively. The response showed many features of immune lysis of erythrocytes even though, in some cases, liposomes lacking any detectable protein were used (Haxby *et al.*, 1968). The absence of a requirement for protein receptors or substrates, which was verified by later work, was a very important finding.

Pure Forssman hapten (a glycosphingolipid found in sheep erythrocyte membranes) was later used to sensitize liposomes having sphingomyelin as the phospholipid. Such liposomes are particularly resistant to glucose release by rabbit anti-sheep erythrocyte serum and complement unless they contain this hapten. An apparent threshold concentration of Forssman hapten, corresponding to about 0.04 mol % with respect to total lipids, was observed (i.e. 1 μg hapten per μmol sphingomyelin). The maximum effect appears to have been obtained at around 0.2 mol % hapten (Kinsky *et al.*, 1969). It is interesting that these concentrations are so close to that found to be required for effective whole complement depletion by IgG bound to spin label haptens in a 'solid' membrane (Brûlet and McConnell, 1976).

The maximum amount of glucose which could be released from cholesterol : sphingomyelin : dicetyl phosphate : Forssman hapten liposomes by immune attack, was directly related to hapten incorporation for a range of concentrations between about 0.04 and 0.2 mol % hapten. The amounts of antibody (in the presence of excess complement) and complement (in the presence of excess antibody) required to give these characteristic levels of marker release were inversely related to hapten incorporation. Furthermore, the time taken to achieve maximal release was inversely related to hapten incorporation.

A lag phase, which appears to correspond to the time required for effective binding of antibodies to liposomes, could be detected by varying the order of addition of reactants. The length of this lag phase was also inversely related to hapten incorporation; in the case of liposomes having about 0.08 mol % hapten it was of the order of 1 minute. This is a very interesting observation because one would predict that the rate for binding of antibodies to single epitopes is so fast as to be diffusion controlled. Therefore, the most likely explanation for the time lag is that it relates to constraints to the *multiple* binding of antibodies to epitopes. Such constraints would be imposed if: (*a*) lateral diffusion of haptens in the plane of the membrane is very slow; (*b*) epitopes are randomly distributed within the whole or a greater part of the plane of the membrane, such that the number of adjacent epitopes which are spaced to allow multiple binding of antibodies is a function of hapten incorporation (and hapten incorporation happens to be low). It is difficult to imagine that manifestation of such a lag phase could be consistent with rapid lateral diffusion of haptens in the plane of the membrane but it may reflect either their slow diffusion or rearrangements of antibodies such that they are multiply bound wherever possible.

Further studies by the Kinsky group employing globoside and galactocerebroside (Inoue *et al.*, 1971) and Lipid A and bacterial lipopolysaccharides (Kataoka *et al.*, 1971) were on the whole supportive of those using Forssman hapten.

The effect of immunoglobulin class and affinity on the initiation of complement-dependent damage to liposomal membranes has been investigated by use of dinitrophenylated phospholipids as lipid haptens, together with DNP-specific, low affinity IgM ($Ka \sim 10^5$ L.mol^{-1}), low affinity IgG ($Ka \sim 10^5$ L.mol^{-1}), and high affinity IgG ($Ka \sim 10^8$ L.mol^{-1}) (Six *et al.*, 1973). Two lipid haptens were prepared: DNP-PE, by direct coupling of the dinitrophenyl group to the amino function of phosphatidylethanolamine; and DNP-cap-PE, which has a similar structure except that ϵ-amino caproic acid is included as a spacer between phosphatidylethanolamine and the dinitrophenyl group. Rabbit antibodies were elicited by immunization with conjugated proteins containing ϵ-DNP-lysine as the principal antigenic determinant. It is predictable that the use of DNP-cap-PE, rather than DNP-PE, would favour antibody binding, either by virtue of some similarity between DNP-cap and DNP-lysine (as is the interpretation given by the authors) or simply because DNP projects further from the surface of the bilayer, in the case of the former lipid, as a result of its attachment to a relatively long, rather featureless chain. The prediction was borne out by experimental results; both high and low affinity IgG was absorbed better by liposomes which incorporated DNP-cap-Pe than by those which incorporated DNP-PE Similarly, the initiation of complement-mediated membrane damage was greatly facilitated by using DNP-cap-PE rather than DNP-PE. Significant complement-mediated marker release was effected only by high affinity IgG when the latter hapten was used. Therefore, in order to study other conditions required for effective initiation of membrane damage by the three antibody preparations, it was necessary to use liposomes containing DNP-cap-PE.

In the case of excess high affinity IgG, very low levels of hapten (~ 0.05–0.27 mol % with respect to total lipid) were required for sensitiz-ation. (This level of hapten incorporation is the same as was required for sensitization with pure Forssman hapten for lysis by haemolysin, probably containing specific antibodies mainly of the IgM class.) Lysis by IgM required a higher level of hapten and lysis by low affinity IgG required even more. Comparable release of glucose from liposomes having a high level of hapten incorporation was obtained using significantly less high affinity IgG than low affinity IgG. In this type of test the IgM was, on a weight for weight basis, about as effective as high affinity IgG and far more effective than low affinity IgG (hapten was at a level of about 2.7 mol %).

In the same paper, Six *et al*. report using a mouse myeloma IgA, with specificity for DNP, to sensitize liposomes to lysis by rabbit anti-myeloma protein antiserum and complement. Even though the antigen, in this case, was almost certainly confined to the outer surface of the liposomes, approximately six times more glucose was released than the outermost compartments would be expected to contain. This is thought to imply that inner layers of liposomes may be lysed by a method not requiring prior formation of antigen–antibody complexes on their surfaces.

Inoue *et al* (1971) have reported differences in the immune lysis of liposomes which are identical except that different phospholipids are employed for their preparation (together with the usual cholesterol and dicetyl phosphate). For example, liposomes prepared using an equimolar mixture of lecithin and sphingomyelin require less antiserum and guinea pig serum for half-maximal glucose release than do those prepared using either phospholipid alone; furthermore, 'lecithin' liposomes are more susceptible to lysis than 'sphingomyelin' liposomes. Although these difference also correlate with the inherent leakiness of such liposomes and their susceptibility to hypotonic or detergent-mediated lysis, it is thought that the phospholipid content may also have some bearing on either (or both) the initiation of complement fixation (including antibody binding) or infliction of membrane damage. Alving *et al*. (1974a, b), using the same methodology as the Kinsky group, report an inverse correlation between glucose release and phospholipid fatty acid chain length, when liposomes prepared with di-14:0 PC, di-16:0 PC, or di-18:0 PC (together with cholesterol and dicetyl phosphate) and incorporating galactocerebroside, are lysed with specific antiserum and complement. In the case of Forssman hapten, differential glucose release was not observed for this series of synthetic PCs. However, liposomes prepared with di-14:0 PC (DMPC), both absorbed more of a monoclonal immunglobulin with specificity for Forssman, and were more susceptible to lysis by this antibody (together with complement) than were liposomes prepared with beef sphingomyelin, which has far longer fatty acid chains. The interpretation given by the authors for these observations is that lipid haptens may be partially buried by bilayers having long fatty acid chains and that this effect might be particularly significant when the hydrophilic portion of the molecule is short. However, the rate of lateral diffusion of haptens in the plane of the membrane is not known, may not be insignificant, might affect various aspects of efferent recognition and the lytic sequence, and would almost certainly be modified by phospholipid content.

Haxby *et al*. (1969) have shown that release of glucose from haptenated liposomes by specific antiserum and complement is absolutely dependent upon complement components 2 and 8 and is stimulated by 9. Alving and Kinsky (1971) separated liposomes bearing either antibody alone or antibody plus proteins thought to be derived from complement components. As a result of a series of experiments using radiolabelled or enzyme-resistant phospholipids, it appears that complement-mediated membrane damage is not caused by degradation of membrane components. It is likely that increased permeability for marker molecules is a result of the insertion of activated complement components into the membrane. For a review of this work, see Kinsky (1972).

The molecular basis of the increased permeability is not known. Manfred Mayer, who has proposed that terminal complement components form a doughnut-shaped pore in the membrane (Mayer, 1972), has recently been concerned with the use of black lipid films to study the effect of 'reactive lysis' on conductance of membranes. If the C5b,6 complex is added first and then followed in sequence by C7, C8, and C9, a moderate increase in conductance is observed on addition of C8 and a large increase on addition of C9 (Michaels *et al*., 1976). Other workers favour the idea that, rather than forming discrete pores, insertion of terminal components gives rise to leaky patches of membrane due to a detergent-like action. Early experiments using large single-compartmented vesicles (for which the physical state of membrane lipids is monitored as a consequence of spin labels situated at various defined levels in the bilayer) have indicated a moderate change, detectable by head group labels, on addition of C7 to suitably primed membranes and a pronounced increase in disorder, detectable by labels situated in the hydrophobic interior, on subsequent addition of C8 and C9 (Alfred Esser, personal communication).

Immune haemolysis has been used as the basis for many clinical tests. Probably because of technical problems connected with using erythrocytes, most of these tests are obsolete. Substitution of erythrocytes by suitable synthetic continuous lipid membrane structures bearing appropriate epitopes might be used to test directly for antibodies or indirectly, by inhibition methods, for antigens or haptens. Furthermore, they might be used to test for whole complement depletion associated with the presence of antigen–antibody complexes, or even perhaps, for the detection of individual complement components. Release of glucose from lipid structures would not be useful because biological fluids used as reactants must first be dialysed to remove endogenous glucose. Similarly any other method which involves biological molecules in the detection mechanism *per se* (e.g. as a substrate or enzyme), is likely to encounter problems.

The EPR spectrum of nitroxide spin labels dissolved in a suitable solvent is markedly broadened by spin exchange (with concomitant decrease in amplitude) at concentrations of 10^{-1} M and above. If water-soluble membrane-impermeable molecules such as TEMPO choline chloride are trapped by liposomes or erythrocyte ghosts, lysis of these structures may be monitored by observing the increase in amplitude of the EPR signal (Humphries and McConnell, 1974). No prior separation of lysed and unlysed sacs is required and very small reaction volumes (50 μl or less) are used. As the method is not optical, neither turbidity nor colour of samples interferes. The sensitivity of the method is primarily dependent upon the quantity of labels which can be released by each lytic event. Large, stable, preferably single-compartmented vesicles capable of being loaded with spin labels and easily freed from external labels, should certainly provide the basis for useful clinical assays. There are technological problems, most likely not insoluble, connected with preparation of a suitable composition. Attachment of epitopes is unlikely to be a major problem. Very small amounts of exogenous egg albumin modified the immune lysis, by complement and rabbit anti-egg albumin, of egg albumin-coated erythrocyte ghosts loaded with TEMPO choline chloride. More recently the method has been used with liposomes to assay for Forssman glycolipid (Wei *et al.*, 1975) and for digoxin and thyroxin (Hsia *et al.*, 1976). Release of spin labels from liposomes has also been used to detect immune lysis of cholesterol, lecithin, cardiolipin liposomes (molar ratios 50 : 47 : 3 or 50 : 45 : 5) by Wasserman antibodies present in syphilitic serum together with complement (Humphries and McConnell, 1975; Vistnes *et al.*, 1976).

5. CONCLUSIONS

Biological membranes are principally held together by hydrophobic intermolecular associations which derive from attractions between the fluctuating or fixed, but weak, dipoles associated with molecules and collectively known as Van der Waals forces. Molecular interactions which result from these forces may be fairly long-lived or else short-lived, hence giving rise to dynamic structures which, nonetheless, may manifest considerable molecular order, as has been observed in the case of synthetic lipid bilayers. Structure also derives from interactions between the polar head groups of membrane molecules and components of the aqueous phase (or between the groups themselves). The majority of such bonds are also easily made and broken and contribute to the dynamic, but not random, nature of the structures they produce. It is reasonable to expect that biological membranes exhibit types of molecular ordering, such as phase separations and formation of molecular complexes (i.e. specific associations of molecules in ratios that are small whole numbers), as do synthetic membranes.

Immunology has historically been regarded as a branch of medicine because of its origin in the empirical treatment and prevention of disease. In recent years it has expanded enormously and, in many cases, has converged upon membrane biochemistry. Just as our understanding of the functioning of proteins and nucleic acid has advanced by knowledge of their structures, it is quite certain that a fundamental understanding of immunology will depend upon detailed knowledge of the subtle, dynamic structure of biological membranes. It is important to recognize that lipids contribute to the final structure in more ways than were envisioned by the original lipid bilayer theory and that investigation of these contributions constitutes an important ongoing area of biophysical chemistry.

Acknowledgements

This chapter is written from the laboratory of Harden McConnell and is substantially based on our discussions, for which I am very grateful. The work has been supported by NIH Fellowship 1 F32 A105291-01 ALY and NIH Grant no. 1 R01 A1 13587-01 BBCB. The manuscript has been very skilfully prepared by Laurie Doepel.

I would also like to express my gratitude for a too brief, but very interesting and educational time spent recently in the laboratories of Martin Raff and Avrion Mitchison at University College, London, supported by MRC Grant G. 975/895/c. The writing of this chapter was initiated during that time and has benefited from it.

Figures 1 and 4 are reproduced by kind permission of Plenum Press, having been previously published in the *Proceedings of the Nobel Symposium*, **34**.

REFERENCES

Ada, G. L. and Ey, P. L. (1975). In *The Antigens*, Vol. **III**, pp.189–269 (ed. Michael Sela), Academic Press, New York.

Alving, C. R., Fowble, J. W. and Joseph, K. C. (1974a). *Immunochemistry*, **11**, 475–481.

Alving, C. R., Joseph, K. C. and Wistar, R. (1974b). *Biochemistry*, **13**, 4818–4824.

Alving, C. R. and Kinsky, S. C. (1971). *Immunochemistry*, **8**, 325–343.

Baker, P. J., Lint, T. F., McLeod, B. C., Behrends, C. L. and Gerwurz, H. (1975). *J. Immunol.*, **114**, 554–558.

Berliner, L. (ed.) (1975). *Spin Labeling: Theory and Applications*, Academic Press, New York.

Bitter-Suermann, D., Hadding, U., Schorlemmer, H. -U., Limbert, M., Dierich, M. and Dukor, P. (1975). *J. Immunol.*, **115**, 425–433.

Borsos, T. and Rapp, H. J. (1965a). *J. Immunol.*, **95**, 559–566.

Borsos, T. and Rapp, H. J. (1965b). *Science*, **150**, 505–506.

Bourgès, M., Small, D. M. and Derchivian, D. G. (1967). *Biochim. Biophys. Acta*, **137**, 157–167.

Boyle, M. D. P., Ohanian, S. H. and Borsos, T. (1976). *J. Immunol.*, **116**, 1272–1279.

Brown, J. C. and Koshland, M. E. (1975). *Proc. Nat. Acad. Sci. USA*, **72**, 5111–5115.

Brûlet, P. and McConnell, H. M. (1976). *Proc. Nat. Acad. Sci. USA*, **73**, 2977–2981.

Brûlet, P. and McConnell, H. M. (1977). *Biochemistry*, **16**, 1209–1217.

Brûlet, P., Humphries, G. M. K. and McConnell, H. M. (1977). In *Structure of Biological Membranes*, pp.321–329. (eds. S. Abrahamsson and I. Pascher), Plenum Press, New York/London.

Burakoff, S. J., Martz, E. and Benacerraf, B. (1975). *Clin. Immunol. Immunopathol.*, **4**, 108–126.

Cohen, S. (1968). *J. Immunol.*, **100**, 407–413.

Cooper, N. R., Polley, M. J. and Oldstone, M. D. (1974). *J. Immunol.*, **112**, 866–868.

Coutinho, A. and Moller, G. (1975). *Adv. in Immunol.*, **21**, 113–236.

Cunniff, R. V. and Stollar, B. D. (1968). *J. Immunol.*, **100**, 7–14.

de Petris, S. and Raff, M. C. (1972). *Eur. J. Immunol.*, **2**, 523–535.

de Petris, S., Raff, M. C. and Mallucci, L. (1973). *Nature New Biol.*, **244**, 275–278.

Engelman, D. M. and Rothman, J. E. (1972). *J. Biol. Chem.*, **247**, 3694–3697.

Feldmann, M. (1971). *Nature New Biol.*, **231**, 21–23.

Feldmann, M. and Pepys, M. B. (1974). *Nature*, **249**, 159–161.

Frye, L. D. and Edidin, M. (1970). *J. Cell. Sci.*, **7**, 319–335.

Gaffney, B. J. and McConnell, H. M. (1974). *J. Mag. Resonance*, **16**, 1–28.

Goers, J. W., Schumaker, V. N., Glovsky, M. M., Rebek, J. and Müller-Eberhard, H. J. (1975). *J. Biol. Chem.*, **250**, 4918–4925.

Goodman, J. W. (1975). Antigenic determinants and antibody combining sites, in *The Antigens*, Vol. **III**, pp.127–187. (ed. Michael Sela), Academic Press, New York.

Grant, C. W. M. and McConnell, H. M. (1973). *Proc. Nat. Acad. Sci. USA*, **70**, 1238–1240.

Grant, C. W. M. and McConnell, H. M. (1974). *Proc. Nat. Acad. Sci. USA*, **71**, 4653–4657.

Grant, C. W. M., Wu, S. H. W. and McConnell, H. M. (1974). *Biochim. Biophys. Acta*, **363**, 151–158.

Haxby, J. A., Kinsky, C. B. and Kinsky, S. C. (1968). *Biochemistry*, **61**, 300–307.

Haxby, J. A., Gotze, O., Müller-Eberhard, H. J. and Kinsky, S. C. (1969). *Proc. Nat. Acad. Sci. USA*, **64**, 290–295.

Hinz, H. J. and Sturtevant, J. (1972). *J. Biol. Chem.*, **249**, 3697–3700.

Hsia, J. C., Chan, S. W. and Tan, C. T. (1976). Abstract TU-P27. VIIth International Conference on Magnetic Resonance in Biological Systems.

Humphries, G. K. and McConnell, H. M. (1974). *Proc. Nat. Acad. Sci. USA*, **71**, 1691–1694.

Humphries, G. K. and McConnell, H. M. (1975). *Proc. Nat. Acad. Sci. USA*, **72**, 2483–2487.

Humphries, G. K. and McConnell, H. M. (1976). *Biophys. J.*, **16**, 275–277.

Hyslop, N. E., Dourmashkin, R. R., Green, N. M. and Porter, R. R. (1970). *J. Exp. Med.*, **131**, 783–802.

Inman, J. K. (1975). *J. Immunol.*, **114**, 704–709.

Inoue, K., Kataoka, T. and Kinsky, S. C. (1971). *Biochemistry*, **10**, 2574–2581.

Inoue, K. and Kitigawa, T. (1976). *Biochim. Biophys. Acta*, **426**, 1–16.

Ishizaka, T. and Ishizaka, K. (1969). *J. Immunol.*, **102**, 1337.

Johnson, S. M. (1975). *Biochem. Soc. Trans.*, **3**, 160–161.

Kataoka, T., Inoue, K., Galanos, C. and Kinsky, S. C. (1971). *Eur. J. Biochem.*, **23**, 123–127.

Kinsky, S. C. (1972). *Biochim. Biophys. Acta*, **265**, 1–23.

Kinsky, S. C. (1974). *Methods in Enzymology*, **32**, 501–513.

Kinsky, S. C., Haxby, J. A., Zopf, D. A., Alving, C. R. and Kinsky, C. B. (1969). *Biochemistry*, **8**, 4149–4158.

Kleeman, W. and McConnell, H. M. (1976). *Biochim. Biophys. Acta*, **419**, 206–222.

Kochibe, N., Nicolotti, R. A., Davie, J. M. and Kinsky, S. C. (1975). *Proc. Nat. Acad. Sci. USA*, **72**, 4582–4586.

Kolmer, J. A. (1928). In *Serum Diagnosis by Complement Fixation*, pp.182–183, Lea and Febiger, Philadelphia.

Kornberg, R. D. and McConnell, H. M. (1971). *Biochemistry*, **10**, 1111–1120.

Lachmann, P. J., Munn, E. A. and Weissman, G. (1970). *Immunol.*, **19**, 983–986.

Ladbrooke, B. D., Williams, R. M. and Chapman, D. (1968). *Biochim. Biophys. Acta*, **150**, 333–340.

Linden, C. D., Wright, K. L., McConnell, H. M. and Fox, C. F. (1973). *Proc. Nat. Acad. Sci. USA*, **70**, 2271–2275.

Mayer, M. M. (1972). *Proc. Nat. Acad. Sci. USA*, **69**, 2954–2958.

McConnell, H. M. (1975). Lateral molecular motions in membranes, in *Functional Linkage in Biomolecular Systems*, pp.123–131 (eds. Schmitt, Schneider and Crothers), Raven Press, New York.

McConnell, H. M. and McFarland, B. G. (1972). *Ann. N.Y. Acad. Sci.*, **195**, 201–217.

Metzger, H. (1974). *Adv. Immunology*, **18**, 169–207.

Michaels, D. W., Abramovitz, A. S., Hammer, C. H. and Mayer, M. M. (1976). *Proc. Nat. Acad. Sci. USA*, **73**, 2852–2856.

Newman, G. C. and Huang, C. (1975). *Biochemistry*, **14**, 3363–3370.

Nicolotti, R. A. and Kinsky, S. C. (1975). *Biochemistry*, **14**, 2331–2337.

Nicolson, G. L. and Painter, R. G. (1973). *J. Cell. Biol.*, **59**, 395–406.

Ohanian, S. H. and Borsos, T. (1975). *J. Immunol.*, **114**, 1292–1295.

Pinto da Silva, P. and Branton, D. (1972). *Chem. Phys. Lipids*, **8**, 265–278.

Raff, M. C. (1976a). *Sci. Amer.*, **234**, 30–39.

Raff, M. C. (1976b). *Nature*, **263**, 10–11.

Rapport, M. M. (1970). In *Handbook of Neurochemistry*, Vol. **III**, pp.509–524 (ed. Abel Lajtha), Plenum Press, New York & London.

Rapport, M. M. and Graf, L. (1967). In *Methods in Immunology and Immunochemistry*, Vol. **I**, p.195 (eds. Williams and Chase), Academic Press, New York & London.

Rey, P. and McConnell, H. M. (1976). *Biochem. Biophys. Res. Comm.*, **73**, 248–254.

Rey, P. and McConnell, H. M. (1977). *J. Amer. Chem. Soc.* **99**, 1637–1642.

Saito, H., Schreier-Muccillo, S. and Smith, I. C. P. (1973). *FEBS Lett.*, **33**, 281–285.

Scott, R. M. and Russell, P. K. (1972). *J. Immunol.*, **109**, 875–877.

376   *Liposomes in Biological Systems*

Segerling, M., Ohanian, S. H. and Borsos, T. (1974). *J. Nat. Cancer Inst.*, **53**, 1411–1413.

Shimshick, E. J. and McConnell, H. M. (1973a). *Biochemistry*, **12**, 2351–2360.

Shimshick, E. J. and McConnell, H. M. (1973b). *Biochem. Biophys. Res. Comm.*, **53**, 446–451.

Six, H. R., Uemura, K. and Kinsky, S. C. (1973). *Biochemistry*, **12**, 4003–4011.

Smith, G. P. (1973). In *The Variation and Adaptive Expression of Antibodies*, pp.142–143, Harvard University Press, Cambridge, Massachusetts.

Tompkins, W. A. F., Seth, P., Gee, S. and Rawls, W. E. (1976). *J. Immunol.*, **116**, 489–495.

Träuble, H. and Eibl, H. (1975). Cooperative structural changes in lipid bilayers, in *Functional Linkage in Biomolecular Systems*, pp.59–90 (eds. Schmitt, Schneider and Crothers), Raven Press, New York.

Trump, G. N. (1975). *J. Immunol.*, **114**, 682–687.

Tsong, T. Y. (1975). *Biochemistry*, **14**, 5415–5417.

Uemura, K., Nicolotti, R. A., Six, H. R. and Kinsky, S. C. (1974). *Biochemistry*, **13**, 1572–1578.

Van der Bosch, J. and McConnell, H. M. (1975). *Proc. Nat. Acad. Sci. USA*, **72**, 4409–4413.

Vistnes, A. I., Rosenquist, E. and Henriksen, T. (1976). Abstract TU-P25. VIIth International Conference on Magnetic Resonance in Biological Systems.

Wallach, D., Knufermann, H. and Wunderlich, F. (1973). *FEBS Lett.*, **33**, 275–280.

Wei, R., Alving, C. R., Richards, R. L. and Copeland, E. S. (1975). *J. Immunol. Meth.*, **9**, 165–170.

Wu, S. H. and McConnell, H. M. (1975). *Biochemistry*, **14**, 847–854.

Zinkernagel, R. M. and Doherty, P. C. (1974). *Nature*, **251**, 547–548.

Liposomes in Biological Systems
Edited by G. Gregoriadis and A. C. Allison
© 1980, John Wiley & Sons, Ltd.

CHAPTER 14

Recent Progress in Liposome Research

Gregory Gregoriadis

1. Methodology   378

2. Interaction of liposomes with the biological environment   379

3. Applications in biology   382

4. Applications in medicine   385
   4.1. Enzyme therapy   385
   4.2. Metal storage diseases   386
   4.3. Antimicrobial therapy   386
   4.4. Cancer chemotherapy   387
   4.5. Arthritis   388
   4.6. Liposomes as immunological adjuvants   389
   4.7. Oral therapy   390

5. Targeting of liposomes   390

6. Applications in immunology   392

   References   394

In the interval which has elapsed between the submission of the last manuscript for this book and its going to press there have been further, rapid developments in liposome research which merit discussion. This 'added-in-proof' chapter deals with such developments and related information has been supplied in part by contributors to the book. Some of it is dealt with in a number of recent reviews (Juliano, 1978; Pagano and Weinstein, 1978; Kaye and Richardson, 1979; Portal *et al.*, 1979; Delattre, 1979; Papahadjopoulos, 1979; Dousset *et al.*, 1979; Gregoriadis, 1979 and 1980).

1. METHODOLOGY

The wide interest that liposomes have attracted as a means of drug delivery has brought into focus difficulties associated with the production of vesicles of defined sizes. Recently, Barenholtz *et al.* (1979) published a method for the preparation of small unilamellar liposomes (about 31–52 nm in diameter) by the use of the so-called French press. This procedure, subjecting dispersions to high hydraulic pressure, should be preferable to the classical sonication method when materials for entrapment are sensitive to ultrasonic irradiation. Small unilamellar liposomes with an average diameter of 50 nm have also been prepared by a method (Mortara *et al.*, 1978) employing dihexadecyl phosphate as the only lipid component. However, such vesicles as well as similar ones prepared from synthetic tetraalkylammonium amphiphiles (Kunitake and Okanata, 1977) are sensitive to salts, flocculating at concentrations of KCl as low as 5 mM. A method particularly suitable for membrane protein reconstitution studies produces liposomes, primarily unilamellar and homogenous in size, by solubilizing mixtures of egg phosphatidylcholine and cholesterol with cholate and subsequently removing the detergent by rapid (hollow fibre) dialysis (Rhoden and Goldin, 1979). The average diameter of the vesicles can vary from 38 to 128 nm depending on the amount of cholesterol used relative to the phospholipid, and the pH of the dialysate. In an approach similar to the above, cholate is added either to preformed small unilamellar liposomes or to a dry egg phosphatidylcholine film. In both cases formed vesicles are large unilamellar with an average diameter of 100 nm (Enoch and Strittmatter, 1979). Unilamellar vesicles of an even larger diameter (average 210 nm) have been produced (Schieren *et al.*, 1978) by an improved version of the ether vaporization method (Deamer and Bangham, 1976). In yet another method, large unilamellar and oligolamellar vesicles with augmented capacity for entrapment are formed by sonication of a phospholipid solution in an organic solvent in the presence of an aqueous buffer containing the solute for entrapment and subsequent evaporation of the organic solvent under reduced pressure (Szoka and Papahadjopoulos, 1978). Darszon *et al.* (1979) have used this approach (without added phospholipids) to prepare vesicles from rhodopsin–lipid complexes. Liposomes of defined size and homogeneity have been prepared by sequential extrusion of an heterogeneous population of multilamellar vesicles through polycarbonate membranes. Sequential extrusion through a 0.2 μm membrane gives a homogeneous size distribution with a mean diameter of 0.27 μm. This process maintains an 'acceptable' level of solute entrapment in the aqueous phase (Olson *et al.*, 1979).

Regarding separation of non-entrapped from liposome-entrapped solutes, a recently published simple method (Fry *et al.*, 1978) appears to shorten the ime interval required for such separation by centrifugation or dialysis: posomes applied on Sephadex G50 minicolumns are obtained after brief entrifugation at $100 \times g$ at the bottom of appropriate tubes. The 'second arrier' approach (see Chapter 2) for increased entrapment of solutes within he aqueous phase of liposomes has been applied by Mauk and Gamble 1979) who were able to incorporate large amounts of $^{111}In^{3+}$ (more than 0% of added material) in liposomes containing the indium chelate nitrilo-riacetic acid. Interestingly, transport of indium across the bilayers was ffected by the ionophore A23187. Entrapment of large amounts of adioactive indium by this method enabled application of the system in the nonitoring of liposomal stability by gamma-ray perturbed angular correla-ion techniques (Hwang and Mauk, 1977). Finally, methods have been ecently developed for the visualization of multilamellar liposomes carrying luorochromes in their lipid phase under fluorescence microscopy (van Rooijen and Nieuwmegen, 1978) and for the labelling and visualization of phospholipids at the ultrastructural level (Bayer *et al.*, 1979). The latter vorkers used biotinylated lipids specifically labelled with ferritin–avidin onjugates which can be detected by transmission microscopy.

2.   INTERACTION OF LIPOSOMES WITH THE BIOLOGICAL ENVIRONMENT

Control of the stability of liposomes is an important prerequisite for their effective use as drug carriers. Liposomal stability, defined here as the extent o which the carrier retains its drug contents *in vitro* and *in vivo*, is nfluenced by the biological environment with which liposomes come into contact and also by their structural characteristics as well as those of the entrapped drugs (see Chapter 2). Regarding liposomal structure and com-position, it has been observed (Krupp *et al.*, 1976) that upon contact with plasma, unilamellar cholesterol-free liposomes lose some of their phos-pholipid to high density lipoproteins (HDL). A similar observation has been made with cholesterol-poor liposomes (Scherphof *et al.*, 1978; Zierenberg and Betziny, 1979) and Damen *et al.* (1979) have suggested that the iposomal phospholipid blends with that of the lipoproteins. Loss of phos-pholipid is paralleled by the liberation of previously entrapped agents Scherphof *et al.*, 1978).

It has been shown already (Chapter 2) that solute permeability of the membranes of both small unilamellar (Kirby *et al.*, 1980) and small multi-amellar (Gregoriadis and Davis, 1979) liposomes in the presence of serum, plasma, and whole blood as well as in the blood of injected animals n vivo is drastically reduced upon enriching liposomes with cholesterol. It vas of interest to note that solute permeability of cholesterol-free or -poor iposomes in the presence of a biological fluid such as serum or blood, was not only considerable but also very rapidly occurring, at most within 2 min of mixing or injection (Gregoriadis and Davis, 1979; Kirby *et al.*, 1980). Since in similar liposomes solute permeability is increased in the presence of buffered (pH 7.2) saline over a period of hours only slightly, it became obvious that the action of excess cholesterol in abolishing permeability incurred by biological fluids was not simply the result of cholesterol-induced phospholipid packing which is known to reduce inward or outward diffusion of ions (Demel and de Kruyff, 1976). The suggestion was made (Gregoriadis and Davis, 1979; Kirby *et al.*, 1980) that cholesterol, by restricting the mobility of phospholipid (Demel and de Kruyff, 1976) prevented its subsequent loss to lipoproteins, probably by forming a bond with it. An additional finding was that the presence of blood cells (presumably erythrocytes) reduced the effect of serum in rendering cholesterol-free or -poor liposomes permeable to solutes (Gregoriadis and Davis, 1979; Kirby *et al.*, 1980). This was attributed to a preponderance of phospholipid movement between blood cells and lipoproteins over a similar one between liposomes and lipoproteins. We have now found that the hypotheses of prevention or diminution of phospholipid loss by cholesterol or blood cells are correct: studies with unilamellar liposomes containing 6-carboxyfluorescein as an aqueous marker and tritiated egg phosphatidylcholine have shown that upon their incubation with plasma and subsequent chromatography through an Ultrogel AcA 34 column, the loss of lecithin to high-density lipoproteins diminishes with increasing amounts of cholesterol in the liposome structure. Phospholipid loss, which is considerable for cholesterol-free liposomes, is also reduced when incubation is carried out in the presence of whole blood. Moreover, there is, in both cases, a parallel reduction of dye loss. Mobilization of egg lecithin to the HDL is not accompanied by a similar movement of 6-carboxyfluorescein indicating that only the phospholipid fraction of liposomes is removed rather than a portion of intact liposomes (C. Kirby, J. Clarke, and G. Gregoriadis, unpublished data). Similar observations have been made by J. Damen and G. Scherphof (unpublished data). These workers also observed that transfer of phospholipid to lipoproteins can be reduced even further if lecithin is replaced by sphingomyelin. The latter lipid (as well as cholesterol) has been reported to prevent loss of solutes from liposomes in the presence of serum or plasma (Finkelstein and Weissmann, 1979).

Scherphof *et al.* (1979) have found that with well-defined, saturated lecithins the formation in the presence of plasma of a radioactive lipoprotein from vesicles labelled with radioactive lecithin, was greatly enhanced by incubating at the gel to liquid–crystalline phase transition temperature of the phospholipid. J. Damen and G. Scherphof (unpublished observations) were, in addition, able to confirm the formation of the HDL-lecithin complex under *in vivo* conditions originally observed by Krupp *et al.* (1976). Within minutes after intravenous injection into rats of unilamellar liposomes label-led with ^{14}C-egg lecithin, more than 90% of the radioactivity in the plasma was associated with the HDL fraction. When the labelled lipoprotein complex was injected intravenously, a half-life of approximately 70 min was found, similar to that for unilamellar vesicles. An important question to be answered is the form in which unilamellar liposomes leave the circulation. Are they, for instance, eliminated as complexes with lipoproteins and, if so, how is this influenced by cholesterol?

Hoekstra and Scherphof (1979) have recently modified their standpoint regarding the fate of multilamellar liposomes in the presence of plasma. This group (Chapter 6) originally suggested disintegration of multilamellar vesicles caused by HDL. It is now believed (Hoekstra and Scherphof, 1979) that such vesicles are much less susceptible to lipoprotein attack than are unilamellar vesicles and that the massive release of entrapped solutes cannot be ascribed to HDL only but also to the adsorption of other plasma proteins onto the liposomal membrane. This causes a drastic permeability increase without changing the gross morphology of the vesicles and without rapid formation of a lipoprotein particle. Indeed, gross changes in solute per-meability rather than (multilamellar) liposome destruction upon contact with serum has already been proposed on the basis of studies on liposomal stability *in vitro* and *in vivo* (Gregoriadis and Davis, 1979). Hoekstra and Scherphof (1979) also believe that the observed considerable transfer of ^{14}C-lecithin from multilamellar vesicles to the hepatocytes *in vivo* is prob-ably not entirely mediated by the lipoprotein particles formed. They propose that primary uptake of multilamellar vesicles by the Kupffer cells is followed by partial breakdown of the liposomes and transfer of the lecithin to hepatocytes. Involvement of Kupffer cells in liposome uptake (Chapter 2) has been confirmed by electron microscopy using a tri-complex liver fixation method (Wisse *et al.*, 1978).

Regarding the uptake of liposomes by isolated hepatocytes, it was origi-nally suggested (Scherphof *et al.*, this book, p. 205) that the inhibitory effect of serum on such uptake was related to the formation of an HDL-like particle. However, further experiments by the same group have now found that serum greatly reduces the extent of stable absorption of liposomes onto the hepatocyte's surface and, in addition, inhibits the exchange of individual phospholipid molecules between vesicles and cells (Hoekstra *et al.*, 1980). In relation to this, it may be relevant that Blumenthal *et al.* (1977) have found that serum or albumin inhibit transfer of liposome-entrapped 6-carboxyfluorescein from its carrier to lymphocytes.

Very little work has been carried out on the effect of liposomes as such on the physiological state of treated animals (Chapter 2). In a recent report Bruni and co-workers (Bigon *et al.*, 1979) have extended their previous investigations (e.g. Bruni *et al.*, 1976) on the effect of phosphatidylserine-

o

liposomes *in vivo* and found that phosphatidylserine-induced glucose accumulation in the brain is due to reduced energy expenditure and therefore, to a decrease in carbohydrate consumption. In another study on the effect of liposomes of various lipid compositions on the function of platelets (Berdichevsky *et al*., 1979), it is shown that liposomes composed of phosphatidylethanolamine are more likely to decrease the aggregability of platelets than egg phosphatidylcholine liposomes. However, there is no harmful action of liposomes with either lipid composition on the function of platelets. These results support findings that after injection of egg phosphatidylcholine-cholesterol liposomes into a patient there was no change in platelet aggregability (Gregoriadis *et al*., 1979). An interesting observation has been made by Strejan *et al*. (1979) who showed the presence of naturally occurring antibodies (mainly the IgM antibody class) in the serum of normal rabbits against liposomes containing sphingomyelin in their structure. As the anti-liposome activity in the serum increased considerably after immunization of rabbits with a variety of unrelated antigens, the authors speculated that antigenic stimulation may trigger the activation of lymphocyte clones directed against autologous cell-membrane components that cross-react with artificial membranes containing sphingomyelin. These findings argue against the use of sphingomyelin-containing liposomes in man and reinforce the notion that phosphatidylcholines which give marginal (Strejan *et al*., 1979) or no (Hudson *et al*., 1979) humoral antibody response may be more safe in terms of toxicity than other phospholipids.

3. APPLICATIONS IN BIOLOGY

The use of liposomes as tools for the study or modification of biological systems *in vitro* has continued. Klein *et al*. (1978), for instance, found that cholesterol-rich dipalmitoyl phosphatidylcholine liposomes presented to rat kidney fibroblasts decreased the activity of the cell membrane enzymes adenylate cyclase and $(Na^+ + K^+)$-ATPase. The decrease in adenylate cyclase activity was directly proportional to the uptake of liposomal cholesterol, a finding which is consistent with the view that cholesterol controls the activity of some membranous enzymes. Capitani *et al*. (1979) on the other hand, found that DNA polymerase-A from calf thymus was stimulated in the presence of dioleoyl phosphatidylcholine, suggesting a role for phospholipids in the activity of DNA-related enzymes. Liposomes have also been used for the study of distribution, function, and properties of membrane-bound tubulin which seems to be selectively adsorbed onto dimyristoyl phosphatidylcholine (Caron and Berlin, 1979), for the uptake and utilization of free fatty acids (supplied by liposomes) by tumour cells in culture (Hosick, 1979), for studies of the interaction of lipids and proteins in viral membranes (Huang *et al*., 1979) and as acceptors for the assay of lipid glycosyltransferases (Cestelli *et al*., 1979).

Recent reports have described the use of liposome-entrapped plant toxins to circumvent resistance to toxin in various mammalian cell mutants (Nicolson and Poste, 1978; Gardas and Macpherson, 1979; Dimitriadis and Butters, 1979) and the uptake of liposomes and/or their contents by isolated plant protoplasts cultured *in vitro* (Cassells, 1978, Matthews *et al*., 1979). Furthermore, there has been progress in the possible use of liposomes as carriers of genetic information. Thus, Mannino *et al*. (1979) entrapped fragments of phage T7 DNA into large unilamellar vesicles. The entrapped DNA was resistant to nuclease digestion and the efficacy of its encapsulation was dependent upon the size of the DNA molecules. On the other hand, Fraley *et al*. (1979) and Dimitriadis (1979) encapsulated plasmid DNA into large unilamellar liposomes. Incubation of plasmid BR 322-containing liposomes with competent *Escherichia coli* cells in a standard transformation mixture resulted in the appearance of tetracycline-resistant colonies at a frequency of 1% of the control frequency (Fraley *et al*., 1979). Finally, Wilson *et al*. (1979) extended their work with liposomal poliovirus to show that poliovirus RNA entrapped in large unilamellar liposomes can be delivered efficiently into cells in an infectious form.

Attention is now given to the possibility of employing liposomes in the study of events associated with cell-mediated immune recognition. Several groups of investigators have shown that treatment of non-infected mouse cells with liposomes containing integral membrane glycoproteins extracted from the envelope of paramyxoviruses renders such cells susceptible to killing by synergeic virus-immune T lymphocytes (CTL) (Koszinowski *et al*., 1977; Sugamura *et al*., 1978; Poste *et al*., 1980). In contrast, allogeneic CTL do not kill liposome-treated cells. This is identical to the phenomenon of histocompatibility-mediated restriction of lymphocyte-mediated cytotoxicity seen in natural virus infection (see review by Zinkernagel, 1978). These results suggest, therefore, that modification of cells by liposome-derived antigens could provide an experimental system for studying the mechanism(s) of immune recognition by cytotoxic T lymphocytes.

This work has, at the same time, provided new information on the mechanism(s) of liposome-cell interaction *in vitro*. The ability of CTL to kill cells that are non-infected but are instead treated with liposomes containing viral antigens, indicates that the latter have been successfully incorporated into the plasma membrane of treated cells and are not merely bound to their outer surface: several studies have shown that CTL-mediated cytotoxicity is only evoked by target antigens which are integral components of the plasma membrane and that adsorption of exogenous antigens to the cell surface without assimilation into the plasma membrane is not sufficient to elicit lymphocyte cytotoxicity (Sugamura *et al*., 1978; Kurrie *et al*., 1979; Poste *et al.*, 1980). This, incidentally, is in contrast to the complement-dependent antibody-mediated cytotoxicity which can occur under conditions where the sensitizing antigen is merely bound to the cell surface (Forman and Finkelstein, 1977; Roitt, 1977). Poste *et al.* (1980) also found that liposome-mediated insertion of viral antigens into the plasma membrane of treated cells is accompanied by uptake of liposomal lipid. For instance, cells incubated with liposomes containing both viral antigens and a dinitrophenylated lipid hapten could be killed by either virus- or hapten-specific immune CTL. Poste *et al.* (1980) interpreted this as evidence of entire liposomal membrane assimilation into the plasma membrane of treated cells presumably following fusion between these structures.

Also of interest from the standpoint of how liposomes are incorporated into cells *in vitro* is the finding that the ability of liposomes containing viral antigens and lipid haptens to transfer these components to acceptor cells is significantly affected by the liposomal lipid composition (Poste *et al.*, 1980). Insertion of liposome-derived paramyxovirus antigens and lipid haptens into cells to render them susceptible to cytolysis by CTL was detected only when charged liposomes composed of phospholipids that are 'fluid' at 37 °C were used. In contrast, cells treated with identical concentrations of viral antigens and lipid haptens associated with neutral phosphatidylcholine liposomes were completely resistant to killing by CTL (Poste *et al.*, 1980). These results reinforce the evidence discussed earlier (Chapter 4) that neutral PC liposomes lack the ability to fuse.

A number of important immunologically active membrane molecules have been incorporated into the membranes of liposomes in the last two years, including: human and murine histocompatibility antigens (Curman *et al.*, 1978; Englehard *et al.*, 1978a,b; Turner and Sanderson, 1978); Ia allo-antigens (Littman *et ai.*, 1979) and eye muscle protein (Kriss and Mehdi, 1979). Liposomes containing these determinants have been used as model systems to study lymphocyte-mediated antigen recognition *in vitro* (Curman *et al.*, 1978; Kriss and Mehdi, 1979; Engelhard *et al.*, 1978b) and *in vivo* (Morein *et al.*, 1978) and to evaluate the capacity of these molecules to discharge additional functions as receptors for microorganisms (Helenius *et al.*, 1978; Klareskog *et al.*, 1978).

Liposomes have been profitably employed in recent studies of the interaction of lymphokines with their specific target cells. Higgins *et al.* (1979) and Poste *et al.* (1979a,b), for instance, showed that treatment of guinea pig macrophages enhances their ability to respond to the lymphokine referred to as macrophage activation factor (MAF). MAF is responsible for converting resting macrophages to an 'activated' state in which they exhibit an increased ability to kill microorganisms and tumour cells. Following activation by MAF, macrophages lose their surface receptor for this molecule and are thus refractory to reactivation by MAF (Poste and Kirsh, 1979). This has potentially important implications for macrophage-mediated defence reactions since it suggests that the microbicidal and tumoricidal activities of tissue macrophages are short lived and that maintenance of an effective level of macrophage-mediated resistance to microorganisms and tumour cells will require constant recruitment of new macro-phages from the circulation which are sensitive to activation by MAF. However, recent studies by Poste *et al.* (1979c) have shown that macrophages which have become refractory to reactivation by MAF can be activated by MAF entrapped in unilamellar liposomes. This work raises the intriguing question of whether liposome-encapsulated MAF could induce similar activation of tissue macrophages *in vivo* and provide a potential therapeutic modality for augmenting macrophage-mediated host defence reactions.

4.   APPLICATIONS IN MEDICINE

4.1   Enzyme Therapy

Continuing their studies on the use of liposomes as enzyme carriers in enzyme therapy, Hudson *et al.* (1979) evaluated the immune response of C3H/HeJ mice to liposomes containing bovine β-glucuronidase or buffer. It was found that liposomes (composed of dipalmitoylphosphatidylcholine, cholesterol and phosphatidic acid) acted as immunological adjuvants to the entrapped enzyme (an observation made already with a variety of proteins; Chapter 2), and that no antibodies to the carrier itself could be detected. In time course experiments the recovery of the liposomal enzyme activity in tissues was much lower in mice sensitized with the free or liposomal enzyme or even with the buffer-loaded liposomes than in unsensitized mice. This was attributed to the interaction of anti-β-glucuronidase antibodies with the enzyme followed by the rapid clearance and catabolism of the complexes in the tissues (enzyme-immunized mice) and to a cellular response to the liposomal carrier by phagocytic cells of the reticuloendothelial system (unsensitized mice). The latter suggestion was supported by the appearance of activated peritoneal macrophages after intraperitoneal sensitization with buffer-loaded liposomes. The observation of decreased enzyme recovery in the tissues of sensitized animals (presumably as a result of rapid uptake on catabolism of antigen–antibody complexes) is in contrast to previous findings (Chapter 2) in intact mice or in mice immunized with diphtheria toxoid and subsequently injected with the liposome-entrapped radioactive antigen showing no difference in the two groups in hepatic and splenic radioactivity levels. Such discrepancy could be explained if diphtheria toxoid, or at least its antigenic sites, were not as available on the liposomal surface for interaction with the relevant antibodies in the blood, as in the case of β-glucuronidase.

4.2 Metal Storage Diseases

Research on the possibility of using liposomes as carriers of chelating agents in the treatment of metal storage diseases has been further promoted by work (Young *et al*., 1979) in which intravenously given desferrioxamine-containing liposomes greatly improved ^{59}Fe excretion in iron-loaded ^{59}Fe-labelled mice. Compared to the short-lived effect of the free chelator, excretion of iron after a single dose was extended and lasted for up to 3 days. Furthermore, liposomes containing the ionophore A23187 and administered concurrently with DTPA caused iron excretion, whereas DTPA alone was ineffective.

4.3 Antimicrobial Therapy

Gruenberg *et al*. (1979) studied the interaction of *Trypanosoma brucei* with 'fluid' positively charged and 'solid' negatively charged liposomes. Both types of liposomes were labelled in their lipid phase with ^{14}C-stearic acid. According to the authors, the former type of vesicles underwent fusion with the membrane of the cell while the latter type was only adsorbed onto the membranes. These results are in considerable variance with those obtained earlier using the non-pathogenic trypanosome *Crithidia fasciculata* which was found to endocytose 'fluid' liposomes (Vakirtzi-Lemonias and Gregoriadis, 1978): radiolabelled albumin, used as a liposomal marker, was extensively and rapidly catabolized by the cells. Furthermore, in the experiments by Gruenberg *et al*. (1979) the use of a lipid marker (stearic acid) renders interpretation of the data difficult (see Chapter 4 for problems in elucidating mechanisms of cell–liposome interaction when lipid markers are used).

In work with malaria parasites, Alving *et al*. (1979) found that liposomes containing neutral glycolipids with a terminal glucose or galactose (i.e. glucosyl, galactosyl or lactosyl ceramide) prevented, upon intravenous injection, the appearance of erythrocytic forms of *Plasmodium berghei* in mice previously injected with sporozoites. These findings originated from efforts by Alving *et al*. (1979) to employ glycolipids for the targeting of liposomes to the hepatic parenchymal cells in the way that others have used fetuin and GM_1 gangliosides for a similar purpose (Chapter 2). However, glucosyl, galactosyl, and lactosyl caramide are not known to interact specifically with parenchymal cells. It is, therefore, unclear why Alving *et al*. (1979) have implicated hepatocyte receptors in the action of the three glycolipids. Indeed, GM_1 ganglioside which was effective in targeting liposomes to these cells (Surolia and Bachhawat, 1977) was not found active in suppressing sporozoite-induced malaria.

4.4 Cancer Chemotherapy

Additional evidence of improved survival time and number of survivors after treatment of ascites tumour-bearing animals with liposomal drugs (Chapter 2) has come from Shinozawa *et al.* (1979a) who showed that in mice inoculated with Ehrlich ascites carcinoma cells and treated intra-peritoneally with liposome-entrapped illudin S, survival time was nearly doubled when compared to treatment with the free drug. Furthermore, there were 6 survivors out of 10 twenty-four days later, whereas none survived after the same treatment with unentrapped illudin S. In recent work Rustum *et al.* (1979) have evaluated the antitumour activity of 1-β-D-arabinofuranosylcytosine (ara-C) entrapped in liposomes of different sizes and net surface charges. Results with mice inoculated intraperitoneally with L1210 leukaemia cells indicated that ara-C-containing multilamellar liposomes were more effective than were small or large unilamellar liposomes at comparable doses, and that positively and negatively charged multilamellar vesicles were equally effective. The latter were also active when both tumour cell transplant and treatment were carried out intravenously. The authors (Rustum *et al.*, 1979) suggest that their results could be explained by some type of depot system the effectiveness of which compares with that of continuous or multiple daily drug injections. In an earlier report by the same group (Kosloski *et al.*, 1978) methotrexate-containing small unilamellar liposomes were used intraperitoneally for the treatment of mice bearing methotrexate-resistant P1798 tumours and of rats bearing metho-trexate-sensitive Murphy–Sturm lymphosarcoma tumours. Both tumours were injected subcutaneously into the animal's flank and the effect of the treatment was monitored by measuring the diameter of the tumours. It was found that treatment which was ineffective with the free drug resulted in an 80% reduction of tumour mass when methotrexate was administered via liposomes. Similar but less impressive results were obtained with the lymphosarcoma in rats. Results with the methotrexate-resistant tumours are interesting in that drug resistance may have been bypassed by the liposomal carrier which, presumably, entered the target cells. However, as the liposomes used by Kosloski *et al.* (1978) were cholesterol-rich, a slow release of the entrapped methotrexate in the circulation (Kirby *et al.*, 1980) resulting in its prolongation of half-life may have been a critical factor. These experiments show for a second time (see treatment of asparagine-dependent tumours, Chapter 2) that solid tumours can be treated with liposomal drugs.

Experiments relevant to the chemotherapy of pulmonary metastases have been carried out recently by McCullough and Juliano (1979) who adminis-tered free or liposome-entrapped Ara-C into rats by intratracheal instilla-tion. It was found that whereas free drug left the lung rapidly to enter the systemic circulation, the entrapped drug persisted in the lung for a long period with little redistribution in other tissues. Furthermore, the liposomal drug suppressed incorporation of thymidine into the DNA of lungs but had little effect on this process in the gut and bone marrow. In contrast, free drug was effective in all three tissues. Another topical application of liposomes is that of lymph node localization and treatment (Segal *et al.*, 1975). This approach has now been used for the regional lymph node localization (and, possibly, treatment of lymph nodes containing tumour metastases) in rats injected with liposomes containing ^{99m}Tc and subsequently scanned by a γ-camera (Osborne *et al.*, 1979). Best results were obtained with small liposomes (33 nm mean diameter) of neutral or positive charge. The same group (Richardson *et al.*, 1978) have also used ^{99m}Tc-containing liposomes to study the potential of the carrier to transport drugs to solid tumours. In rats bearing Walker 256 carcinoma, uptake of the label (visualized in scintigrams) by the tumours was optimal with 'fluid' small unilamellar negatively charged liposomes. As with previous similar results (Chapter 2), it is by no means certain that localization of liposomal radioactivity in tumours was the outcome of actual liposome localization in the tissue: although liposomes can deliver their contents into tumour cells *in vitro*, it is not known whether liposomes can do so *in vivo* where transcapillary passage after intravenous injection is an obligatory step. With regard to the uptake of liposomal contents by tumours *in vitro*, a recent report by van Renswoude *et al.* (1979) suggests that ascites hepatoma cells take up small unilamellar liposomes mostly by fusion (see however, discussion by Poste in this book on pitfalls of current methods for the demonstration of fusion). Unfortunately, van Renswoude *et al.* (1979) carried out their experiments in the absence of serum and it may be that results obtained are of little relevance *in vivo*.

4.5 Arthritis

Shaw *et al.* (1979) have extended their work on the application of liposomes in the treatment of rheumatoid arthritis and found that cortisol palmitate-containing liposomes are stable in rheumatoid synovial fluid at 37 °C. Intra-articular injection of such liposomes into experimentally arthritic rabbits is followed by the recovery 2 h later of considerable proportions of the steroid and the lecithin components in the synovialis. The level of the liposomal steroid in the tissue was inversely related to the chronicity of inflammation and the degree and duration of its anti-inflammatory activity was greatest in the initial acute phase of the inflammation. These promising results have led to a preliminary clinical trial in patients with rheumatoid arthritis (de Silva *et al.*, 1979): intra-articular treatment with liposomal cortisol palmitate resulted in an improvement in both subjective and objective (e.g. infrared thermography of treated knees) indices of inflammation in the affected joint. Using a similar approach for the treatment of chronic articular rheumatism, Shinozawa *et al.* (1979b) have compared the absorption and distribution of liposome-entrapped prednisolone injected into the hip muscle of rats with that of the free steroid. As expected, liposomal prednisolone was retained by the injected tissue for longer periods of time.

4.6   Liposomes as Immunological Adjuvants

Work on the immunological adjuvant properties of liposomes has been pursued by Sakai *et al.* (1980) who were able to entrap Gross cell surface antigen (GCSAa) from lymphoma cells in multilamellar liposomes composed of dipalmitoyl phosphatidylcholine, cholesterol, and dicetylphosphate. Under defined conditions, 22–55% of the proteins of the cellular extract were associated with liposomes in proportion to the protein concentration of the extract and the amount of phospholipids used. In further work by the same group (Gerlier *et al.*, 1980) subcutaneous immunization of rats with the free antigen as such, in mixture with 'empty' liposomes or after emulsification with Freund's complete adjuvant (CFA) failed to produce significant levels of antibodies cytotoxic to GCSAa. On the other hand, after immunization with liposome-entrapped Nonidet P40-solubilized GCSAa emulsified with CFA there were high and persistent levels of cytotoxic antibodies. Although similar results were obtained without the presence of CFA, solubilization of the cells with Nonidet was, nevertheless, an important prerequisite for good antibody response. On the basis of this work, it would appear that the inclusion in liposomes of a solubilized tumour cell surface protein antigen can augment antibody response as potently as viable tumour cells.

The lipopolysaccharide constituent lipid A was used by Schuster *et al.* (1979) to investigate liposomes as carriers and adjuvants for enhancing the production of antibodies against lipid A. It was found that, as in the case of water-soluble antigens (Chapter 2), lipid A in liposomes produced a greater immune response against it than that obtained with lipid A alone. Of great interest was the finding that with lipid A-containing liposomes there was a concurrent immune response against the phosphatidylcholine and sphingomyelin components of the carrier. Although no antibodies were formed against the liposomal phospholipids in the absence of lipid A, in terms of therapeutic applications of liposomes, it is disquieting that a liposomal antigen is capable of inducing antibody response against its carrier. Finally, Yasuda *et al.* (1979) have devised a method by which the *in vivo* immunogenicity of sensitized liposomes can be replicated in an *in vitro* cell culture system.

4.7 Oral Therapy

Hashimoto and Kawada (1979) have entrapped insulin in egg phosphatidylcholine liposomes supplemented with various amounts of cholesterol and with dicetylphosphate or stearylamine. Best entrapment values (up to 48% of the hormone used) were obtained with positively charged liposomes. In the presence of pepsin, trypsin, and pancreatin, such liposomes were stable but they disintegrated to release insulin quantitatively in the presence of bile. In spite of their vulnerability to bile (which was, incidentally, minor with diluted bile) insulin-containing liposomes administered orally into rats in the third phase of acute alloxan diabetes reduced blood glucose levels considerably (by 30–70%) in 7 out of 11 animals for several hours. Furthermore, liposomal insulin increased the glucose tolerance in half the diabetic animals.

5. TARGETING OF LIPOSOMES

It is almost certain that preparation of target cell-specific liposomes will require association of a cell-recognizing molecule with the liposomal surface in a way that the relevant region(s) of the molecule become available for interaction with the respective moieties on the cell surface. Huang and Kennel (1979) have carried out a systematic investigation on the optimal conditions for the association of immunoglobulin G (IgG) from various species with liposomes. Their findings suggest that best entrapment values (up to 38% of the total IgG used) are obtained with negatively charged extensively sonicated vesicles. Similarly high association values were observed for goat $F(ab')_2$. Under the experimental conditions used, IgG-containing liposomes were found to aggregate considerably. They were, however, stable in terms of IgG loss in both phosphate-buffered saline or 50% foetal calf serum for up to 20 h at 37 °C. The substantial 'lipid degradation' which the authors observed in the presence of serum can be probably explained as loss of egg phosphatidylcholine from the cholesterol-poor liposomes to high density lipoproteins (see above and Chapters 2 and 6). Huang and Kennel (1979) also found that about 30–50% of the original (before sonication) antigen binding activity of IgG was recovered in the vesicles after sonication and most of it was available on their surface.

In experiments by another group (Leserman *et al.*, 1979) the system of liposomal antibody–(cellular) antigen interaction was reversed by incorporating the hapten N-dinitrophenylaminocaproyl phosphatidylethanolamine (DNP-Cap-PE) into (small unilamellar) carboxyfluorescein-containing liposomes which were subsequently exposed to murine myeloma tumour cells MOPC 315 secreting and also bearing on their surface an immunoglobulin with affinity for the antigen. Liposomes were found to bind specifically onto the cells because binding was abolished by an excess of soluble nitrophenyl derivatives, by omitting DNP-Cap-PE from the liposomes or by substituting the MOPC 315 cells with tumour cells lacking receptors for the DNP-Cap-PE. It was observed, however, that in spite of the vesicle–cell association, there was no increased delivery of carboxyfluorescein into the cell's interior. Such interiorization of liposomal contents (observed with HeLa cells exposed to liposomes bearing anti-HeLa antibodies, see Chapter 2), may depend not only on the experimental conditions but also on the endocytic capacity of cells.

Sinha and Karush (1979) have developed a method for the attachment of immunoglobulins and other proteins onto the liposomal surface. A phospho-lipid-containing alkylating reagent, N-(N^{a}iodoacetyl, N-dansyl lysyl)-phospha-tidylethanolamine is reacted with the protein, in this case a dimeric lambda-type Bence–Jones protein(λ2). Subsequent incubation of liposomes composed of dioleoyl- or dimirystoylphosphatidylcholine with the modified protein leads to the association of the latter with the liposomal surface. The accessibility of the protein was demonstrated by the agglutination of the vesicles with antisera against the human λ chain and the dansyl group. In yet another method (Torchilin *et al.*, 1978) a protein marker, α-chymotrypsin, was entrapped in, adsorbed on, or linked (via dimethylsuberimidate or glutaraldehyde) with the surface amino groups of dipalmitoyl phosphatidyl-ethanolamine-containing liposomes. Covalent coupling was found more efficient in terms of both amount of α-chymotrypsin incorporated and preservation of the protein's ability to interact with pancreatic trypsin inhibitor. This method was subsequently used (Torchilin *et al.*, 1979) to couple onto the surface of liposomes antibodies against canine cardiac myosin. The interaction of the antigen with the antibody-bearing liposomes was more efficient with small unilamellar vesicles than with the large multilamellar version. In preliminary work with targeting *in vivo*, Torchilin *et al* (1979) administered antibody-bearing liposomes (also containing ^{111}In) into dogs with myocardial infarction (left anterior descending coronary artery) via a catheter into the left main coronary artery. Gamma camera scintigrams showed preferential localization of ^{111}In radioactivity in the infarcted myocardium. This interesting finding could, however, be strengthened by demonstrating that free [111]In (leaking from the cholesterol-poor liposomes used) or non-specific anti-body-bearing liposomes fail to localize selectively in the diseased areas.

Targeted fusion of liposomes with cells has been attempted by Uchida *et al.* (1979). Spike proteins from HVJ (Sendai virus), known to promote cell-to-cell fusion, were incorporated into liposomes containing fragment A of diphtheria toxin. Fragment A is toxic to sensitive cells only when they become permeable to it. Electron microscopy indicated that the liposomal membranes were associated with the viral spikes on both sides. Such liposomes were capable of binding to mammalian cells (mouse L) and of subsequently releasing fragment A into the cytoplasm thus causing cell death. Uchida *et al.* (1979) suggest that the F protein of the virus (presumed to be involved in the fusion of the viral envelope to the cell membrane) may act in conjunction with the haemagglutinin moiety in causing liposomal membranes to fuse with the cell membranes.

Difficulties in targeting liposomes past the capillary barrier could be overcome by a recent suggestion (Yatvin *et al.*, 1978) that liposomes designed appropriately may release an entrapped drug 'near' target sites. The basic strategy of these workers was to design liposomes with a liquid-crystalline transition temperature (Tc) above physiological temperature but in a range attainable by mild local hyperthermia. On passing through the heated target area, liposomes (of which permeability to ions increases at their Tc) would be expected to release their drug contents at a rate greater than in other parts of the body, thus leading to higher local drug concentrations. After the system, namely neomycin-containing dipalmitoyl phosphatidylcholine-distearoyl phosphatidylcholine liposomes, was tested *in vitro* and shown to enhance killing of bacteria by heating such liposomes to their Tc, experiments were undertaken *in vivo* (Weinstein *et al.*, 1979). Liposomes as above but now containing radioactive methotrexate were given intravenously to mice bearing in their flanks Lewis lung tumours preheated by microwaves to 42 °C. Uptake of the drug after 4 and 20 h (when drug levels in the blood were already very low) was over fourfold greater than in various control animals. These results were consistent with the hypothesis that local heating leads to the release of methotrexate in the tumour area, the drug subsequently entering the tumour cells by normal transport mechanisms. However, as the authors comment (Weinstein *et al.*, 1979), this approach cannot deal with metastatic disease, a limitation also associated with radiotherapy and local hyperthermia. Another possible problem which may not apply in the use of methotrexate is the participation in drug uptake by normal rapidly dividing cells. Toxicity is the major obstacle in treating cancer and it would be worthwhile examining to what extent local hyperthermia prevents released drugs from reaching other areas in the body. Although tumours are in the vicinity of release, the bloodstream is expected to carry most of the liberated drug. This is illustrated by the results of Weinstein *et al.* (1979) showing a dramatic increase of liposome methotrexate clearance from the circulation when tumours are heated: only a fraction of the released drug enters the tumour.

6. APPLICATIONS IN IMMUNOLOGY

Contributions to the field of *in vivo* immunogenicity of hapten-carrying liposomes have continued. For instance, Dancey *et al.* (1979) used such liposomes, known to behave in mice as T-independent (TI) immunogens eliciting a primary IgM response (Yasuda *et al.*, 1977), to examine their relative immunogenicity when sensitized with dinitrophenylated phosphatidylethanolamine derivatives differing in the length of the spacer linking dinitrophenyl to the lipophilic moiety. In addition, *in vitro* work by Humphries (1979) has shown that multilamellar 'fluid' liposomes containing 1 mol % (with respect to the other liposomal lipids) of a synthetic dinitrophenylated lipid hapten behave as TI, adherent cell-dependent antigens for primary stimulation of hapten-specific IgM plaque-forming cells (PFC). At a higher hapten concentration (4 mol %) liposomes suppress the anti-dinitrophenyl PFC response to co-cultured immunogenic liposomes, but not the anti-sheep cell response to co-cultured sheep cells. This suppression is also TI. In view of the rapid rates of lateral diffusion of both receptors (surface immunoglobulin on the B cells) and ligands (DNP-cap-PA), it is proposed (Humphries, 1979) that stimulation is thermodynamically controlled and it occurs only when the liposomal and B-cell membrane surfaces bind reversibly. If the hapten concentration and/or intrinsic affinity of the ligand-receptor bonds are insufficient to permit effective binding of the surfaces, no stimulation can occur; on the other hand, if they are such that essentially irreversible binding takes place, tolerization ensues. Additional work by the same group (Humphries and McConnell, 1979) indicates that *in vitro* immune responses such as induction of PFC or allogenic stimulation in 'mixed lymphocyte cultures' (G. M. K. Humphries, unpublished data) are suppressed by low concentrations (about 10^{-7}M) of oxidized cholesterol. As cholesterol is readily oxidized atmospherically, this represents a significant hazard when interfacing cholesterol-containing membrane preparations with cellular components of the immune system *in vitro*.

Regarding the use of liposomes in complement fixation studies, Richards *et al.* (1979) investigated the influence of the membrane composition of liposomes on their interaction with C-reactive protein (CRP) and complement (C). It was shown that binding of CRP was greatest with highly positive liposomes. Both CRP-mediated consumption of haemolytic C and C-dependent glucose release from liposomes were strongly influenced by liposomal charge. Glucose release and, to some extent, consumption of haemolytic C were inversely related to phospholipid fatty acyl chain length. Richards *et al.* (1979) conclude that CRP-mediated complement consumption and membrane damage require an optimum membrane fluidity. These results supplement previous findings by Humphries and McConnell (1977) who studied complement depletion by IgM specifically bound to lipid haptens (Smith *et al.*, 1979) in synthetic lipid membranes. These authors found that complement depletion was enhanced by decreasing the average spacing between haptens, even though the total number of haptens available for binding remained constant. This is consistent with the hypothesis that IgM molecules must be bound to multiple antigenic determinants at a membrane surface to induce optimal interaction with complement (Humphries and McConnell, 1977).

Liposomes were also found (Cunningham *et al.*, 1979) to activate the alternative pathway of human complement. Activation was measured by incubating serum with liposomes and monitoring C3 conversion and component consumption. It was observed that C3 conversion did not require C1 or C2 of the classical pathway since it was occurring in serum from a C1r-deficient patient, serum from a C2-deficient patient and normal serum in buffer containing EGTA and $MgCl_2$. Activation of the alternative pathway by liposomes was dependent on their lipid composition, a positive surface charge being required to produce C3 conversion. In addition, both liposomal cholesterol content and phospholipid fatty acid chain length and degree of unsaturation influenced activation suggesting the importance of membrane fluidity. Regarding fluidity, Esser *et al.* (1979) found that activation of the first component of complement (C1) was enhanced when antibody (IgG) was bound to 'fluid' rather than 'solid' liposomes.

A dependence on the physical properties of liposomes similar to that of complement depletion, was observed by Hafeman *et al.* (1979) for superoxide production by human neutrophils after stimulation with liposomal membranes containing nitroxide spin-labelled lipids in the presence of antinitroxide antibodies. Superoxide production was strongly related to the lipid composition of liposomes and it was enhanced by unsaturated liposomal lipids or by the incorporation of cholesterol.

REFERENCES

Alving, C. R., Schneider, I., Swartz, G. M. and Steck, C. A. (1979). *Science*, **205**, 1142–1144.
Barenholtz, Y., Amselam, S. and Lichtenberg, D. (1979). *FEBS Lett.*, **99**, 210–214.
Bayer, E. A., Rivnay, B. and Skutelsky, E. (1979). *Biochem. Biophys. Acta*, **550**, 464–473.
Berdichevsky, V. R., Markosyan, R. A., Pozin, E. Ya., Smirnov, V. N., Suvorov, A. V., Torchilin, V. P. and Chazov, E. I. (1979). *Bull. Exp. Biol. Med.*, **88**, 141–143.
Bigon, E., Boarato, E., Bruni, A., Leon, A. and Toffano, G. (1979). *Br. J. Pharmac.*, **66**, 167–174.
Blumenthal, R., Weinstein, J. N., Sharrow, S. O. and Henkart, P. (1977). *Proc. Nat. Acad. Sci. USA*, **74**, 5603–5607.
Bruni, A., Toffano, G., Leon, A. and Boarato, E. (1976). *Nature*, **260**, 331–333.
Capitani, S., Mazzoti, G., Jovine, R., Papa, S., Maraldi, N. M. and Manzoli, F. A. (1979). *Mol. Cell. Biochem.*, **27**, 135–138.
Caron, J. M. and Berlin, R. D. (1979). *J. Cell Biol.*, **81**, 665–671.
Cassells, A. C. (1978). *Nature*, **275**, 760–762.
Cestelli, A., White, F. V. and Costantino-Ceccarini, E. (1979). *Biochim. Biophys. Acta*, **572**, 283–292.
Cunningham, C. M., Kingzette, M., Richards, R. L., Alving, C. R., Lint, T. F. and Gewurz, H. (1979). *J. Immunol.*, **122**, 1237–1242.

Curman, B., Östberg, L. and Peterson, P. A. (1978). *Nature*, **272**, 545–547.
Damen, J. Waite, M. and Scherphof, G. (1979). *FEBS Lett.*, **105**, 115–119.
Dancey, G. F., Isakson, P. C. and Kinsky, S. C. (1979). *J. Immunol.*, **122**, 638–642.
Darszon, A., Vandenberg, C. A., Ellisman, M. H. and Montal, M. (1979). *J. Cell Biol.*, **81**, 446–452.
de Silva, M., Hazleman, B. L., Page Thomas, D. P. and Wraight, P. (1979). *Lancet*, **1**, 1320–1322.
Deamer, D. and Bangham, A. D. (1976). *Biochim. Biophys. Acta*, **443**, 629–634.
Delattre, J. (1979). *J. Fr. Biophys. et Med. Nucl.*, **3**, 3–12.
Demel, R. A. and de Kruyff, B. (1976). *Biochem. Biophys. Acta*, **457**, 109–132.
Dimitriadis, G. J. (1979). *Nucleic Acids Res.*, **6**, 2697–2705.
Dimitriadis, G. J. and Butters, T. D. (1979). *FEBS Lett.*, **98**, 33–36.
Dousset, J. C., Dousset, N., Soula, G. and Douste-Blazy, L. (1979). *Lyon Pharmaceutique*, **30**, 83–91.
Engelhard, V. H., Guild, B. C., Helenius, A., Terhorst, C. and Strominger, J. L. (1978a). *Proc. Nat. Acad. Sci. USA*, **75**, 3230–3234.
Engelhard, V. H., Strominger, J. L., Mescher, M. and Burakoff, S. (1978b). *Proc. Nat. Acad. Sci. USA*, **75**, 5688–5691.
Enoch, H. G. and Strittmatter, P. (1979). *Proc. Nat. Acad. Sci. USA*, **76**, 145–149.
Esser, A. F., Bartholomew, R. M., Parce, J. W. and McConnell, H. M. (1979). *J. Biol. Chem.*, **254**, 1768–1770.
Finkelstein, M. C. and Weissmann, G. (1979). *Biochim. Biophys. Acta*, **587**, 202–216.
Forman, J. and Finkelstein, R. A. (1977). *J. Immunol.*, **118**, 1655–1658.
Fraley, R. T., Fornari, C. S. and Kaplan, S. (1979). *Proc. Nat. Acad. Sci. USA*, **76**, 3348–3352.
Fry, D. W., White, J. C. and Goldman, I. D. (1978). *Anal. Biochem.*, **90**, 809–815.
Gardas, A. and Macpherson, I. (1979). *Biochim. Biophys. Acta*, **584**, 538–541.
Geiger, B. and Schreiber, A. D. (1979). *Clin. Exp. Immunol.*, **30**, 149–154.
Gerlier, D., Sakai, F. and Doré, J-F. (1980). *Br. J. Cancer*, In press.
Gersoude, K. and Nicolau, C. (1979). *Blut*, **39**, 1–7.
Gregoriadis, G. (1979). In *Drug Carriers in Biology and Medicine* (ed. G. Gregoriadis) Academic Press, pp. 287–341, London, New York, San Francisco.
Gregoriadis, G. (1980). *Pharmacology and Therapeutics*, In press.
Gregoriadis, G. and Davis, C. (1979). *Biochem. Biophys. Res. Comm.*, **89**, 1287–1293.
Gregoriadis, G., Neerunjun, E. D., Meade, T. W., Goolamali, S. K., Weereratne, H. and Bull, G. M. (1979). In *Enzyme Therapy in Genetic Diseases. Birth Defects: Original Articles Series.* In press.
Gruenberg, J., Coral, D., Knupfer, A. L. and Deshusser, J. (1979). *Biochem. Biophys. Res. Comm.*, **88**, 1173–1179.
Gutman, Y., Lichtenberg, D., Cohen, J. and Boonyaviroj, P. (1979). *Biochem. Pharmacol.*, **28**, 1209–1211.
Hafeman, D. G., Parce, J. W. and McConnell, H. M. (1979). *Biochem. Biophys. Res. Comm.*, **86**, 522–528.
Hashimoto, A. and Kawada, J. (1979). *Endocrinol. Japan.*, **26**, 337–344.
Helenius, A., Morein, B., Fries, E., Simons, K., Schirrmacher, V., Terhorst, C. and Strominger, J. L. (1978). *Proc. Nat. Acad. Sci. USA*, **75**, 3846–3850.
Higgins, T. J., Sabatino, A. P., Remold, H. G. and David, J. R. (1979). *J. Immunol.* In press.
Hoekstra, D. and Scherphof, G. (1979). *Biochim. Biophys. Acta*, **551**, 109–121.

Hoekstra, D., Van Renswoude, J., Tomasini, R. and Scherphof, G. (1980). *Membrane Biochem.* In press.
Hosick, H. L. (1979). *Exp. Cell Res.*, **122**, 127–136.
Huang, L. and Kennel, S. J. (1979). *Biochemistry*, **18**, 1702–1707.
Huang, R. T. C., Wahn, K. Klenk, H. D. and Rott, R. (1979). *Virology*, **97**, 212–217.
Hudson, L. D. S., Fiddler, M. B. and Desnick, R. J. (1979). *J. Pharm. Exp. Therap.*, **208**, 507–514.
Humphries, G. M. K. (1979). *J. Immunol.*, **123**, 2126–2132.
Humphries, G. M. K. and McConnell, H. M. (1977). *Proc. Nat. Acad. Sci. USA*, **74**, 3537–3541.
Humphries, G. K. M. and McConnell, H. M. (1979). *J. Immunol.*, **122**, 121–126.
Hwang, K. J. and Mauk, M. R. (1977). *Proc. Nat. Acad. Sci. USA*, **74**, 4991–4995.
Juliano, R. L. (1978). *Can. J. Physiol. Pharmacol.*, **56**, 683–690.
Kaye, S. B. and Richardson, V. J. (1979). *Cancer Chemother. Pharmacol.*, **3**, 81–85.
Kirby, C., Clarke, J. and Gregoriadis, G. (1980). *Biochem. J.*, **186**, 591–598.
Klareskog, L., Banck, G., Forsgren, A. and Peterson, P. A. (1978). *Proc. Nat. Acad. Sci. USA*, **75**, 6197–6201.
Klein, I., Moore, L. and Pastan, I. (1978). *Biochim. Biophys. Acta*, **506**, 42–53.
Kosloski, M. J., Rosen, F., Milholland, R. J. and Papahadjopoulos, D. (1978). *Cancer Res.*, **38**, 2848–2853.
Koszinowski, U., Gething, M. J. and Waterfield, M. (1977). *Nature*, **267**, 160–163.
Kriss, J. P. and Mehdi, S. Q. (1979). *Proc. Nat. Acad. Sci. USA*, **76**, 2003–2007.
Krupp, L., Chobanian, A. V. and Brecher, P. I. (1976). *Biochem. Biophys. Res. Comm.*, **72**, 1251–1258.
Kunitake, T. and Okanata, Y. (1977). *J. Am. Chem. Soc.*, **99**, 3860.
Kurrie, R., Wagner, H., Röllinghoff, M. and Rott, R. (1979). *Eur. J. Immunol.*, **9**, 107–111.
Leserman, L. D., Weinstein, J. N., Blumenthal, R., Sharrow, S. O. and Terry, W. D. (1979). *J. Immunol.*, **122**, 585–591.
Littman, D. R., Cullen, S. E. and Schwartz, B. D. (1979). *Proc. Nat. Acad. Sci. USA*, **76**, 902–906.
Mannino, R. J., Allebach, E. S. and Strohl, W. A. (1979). *FEBS Lett.*, **101**, 229–232.
Matthews, B., Dray, S., Widholm, J. and Ostro. M. (1979). *Planta*, **145**, 37–44.
Mauk, M. R. and Gamble, R. C. (1979). *Anal. Biochem.*, **94**, 302–307.
McCullough, H. N. and Juliano, R. L. (1979). *J. Nat. Cancer Inst.*, **63**, 727–731.
Morein, B., Helenius, A., Simons, K., Kaarianen, L. and Schirrmacher, V. (1978). *Nature*, **276**, 715–718.
Mortara, R. A., Quina, F. H. and Chaimovich, H. (1978). *Biochem. Biophys. Res. Comm.*, **81**, 1080–1086.
Nicolson, G. L. and Poste, G. (1978). *J. Supramolec. Struct.*, **8**, 235–245.
Olson, F., Hunt, C. A., Szoka, F. C., Vail, W. J. and Papahadjopoulos, D. (1979). *Biochim. Biophys. Acta*, **557**, 9–23.
Osborne, M. P., Richardson, V. J., Jeyasingh, K. and Ryman, B. E. (1979). *Int. J. Nucl. Med. Biol.*, **6**, 75–83.
Pagano, R. E. and Weinstein, J. N. (1978). *Ann. Rev. Biophys. Bioeng.*, **7**, 435–468.
Papahadjopoulos, D. (1979). *Ann. Rep. Medic. Chem.*, **14**, 250–260.
Portal, A., Durm, F., Aubert, P. (1979). *Nouv. Presse Med.*, **8**, 1749–1752.
Poste, G. and Kirsh, R. (1979). *Cancer Res.*, **39**, 2582–2590.
Poste, G., Kirsh, R. and Fidler, I. J. (1979a). *Cell. Immunol.*, **44**, 71–88.
Poste, G., Allen, H. and Matta, K. L. (1979b). *Cell. Immunol.*, **44**, 89–98.

Poste, G., Kirsh, R., Fogler, W. E. and Fidler, I. J. (1979c). *Cancer Res.*, **39**, 881–892.
Poste, G., Lyon, N. C., Macauder, P., Porter, C. W., Reeve, P. and Bachmeyer, H. (1980). *Biochim. Biophys. Acta.* In press.
van Renswoude, A. J. B. M., Westenberg, P. and Scherphof, G. L. (1979). *Biochim. Biophys. Acta.*, **558**, 22–40.
Rhoden, V. and Goldin, S. M. (1979). *Biochemistry*, **18**, 4173–4176.
Richards, R. L., Gewurz, H., Siegel, J. and Alving, C. R. (1979). *J. Immunol.*, **122**, 1185–1189.
Richardson, V. J., Jeyasingh, K., Jewkes, R. F., Ryman, B. E. and Tattersall, M. H. N. (1978). *J. Nucl. Med.*, **19**, 1049–1054.
Roitt, I. (1977). *Essential Immunology*, Blackwell, Oxford, p. 166.
van Rooijen, N. and van Nieuwmegen, R. (1978). *Stain Technology*, **53**, 307–310.
Rustum, Y. M., Dare, C., Mayhew, E. and Papahadjopoulos, D. (1979). *Cancer Res.*, **39**, 1390–1395.
Sakai, F., Gerlier, D. and Doré, J.-F. (1980). *Br. J. Cancer.* In press.
Scherphof, G., Roerdink, F., Waite, M. and Parks, J. (1978). *Biochim. Biophys. Acta*, **542**, 296–307.
Scherphof, G., Morselt, H., Regts, J. and Wilschut, J. C. (1979). *Biochim. Biophys. Acta*, **556**, 196–207.
Schieren, H., Rudolph, S., Finkelstein, M., Coleman, P. and Weissmann, G. (1978). *Biochim. Biophys. Acta*, **542**, 137–153.
Schuster, B. G., Neidig, M., Alving, B. M. and Alving, C. R. (1979). *J. Immunol.*, **122**, 900–905.
Segal, A. W., Black, C. D. V. and Gregoriadis, G. (1975). *Clin. Sci. Mol. Med.*, **49**, 99–106.
Shaw, I. H., Knight, C. G., Page Thomas, D. P., Phillips, N. C. and Dingle, J. T. (1979). *Br. J. Exp. Path.*, **60**, 142–150.
Shinozawa, S., Tsutsui, K. and Oda, T. (1979a). *Experientia*, **35**, 1102–1103.
Shinozawa, S., Araki, Y. and Oda, T. (1979b). *Res. Comm. Chem. Pathol. Pharmacol.*, **24**, 223–232.
Sinha, D. and Karush, F. (1979). *Biochem. Biophys. Res. Comm.*, **90**, 554–560.
Smith, L. M., Parce, J. W., Smith, B. A. and McConnel, H. M. (1979). *Proc. Nat. Acad. Sci. USA.* **76**, 4177–4179.
Strejan, G. H., Smith, P. M., Grant, C. W. and Surlan, D. (1979). *J. Immunol.*, **123**, 370–378.
Sugamura, K., Shimizu, K. and Bach, F. H. (1978). *J. Exp. Med.*, **149**, 276–287.
Surolia, A. and Bachhawat, B. K. (1977). *Biochim. Biophys. Acta*, **497**, 760–765.
Szoka, F. and Papahadjopoulos, D. (1978). *Proc. Nat. Acad. Sci. USA*, **75**, 4194–4198.
Torchilin, V. P., Goldmacher, V. S. and Smirnov, V. N. (1978). *Biochem. Biophys. Res. Comm.*, **85**, 983–990.
Torchilin, V. P., Khan, B. A., Smirnov, V. N. and Haber, E. (1979). *Biochem. Biophys. Res. Comm.*, **89**, 1114–1119.
Turner, M. J. and Sanderson, A. R. (1978). *Biochem. J.*, **171**, 505–508.
Uchida, T., Kim, J., Yamaizumi, M., Miyake, Y. and Okada, Y. (1979). *J. Cell Biol.*, **80**, 10–20.
Weinstein, J. N., Magin, R. L., Yatvin, M. B. and Zaharko, D. S. (1979). *Science*, **204**, 188–191.
Wilson, T., Papahadjopoulos, D. and Taber, R. (1979). *Cell*, **17**, 77–84.

Wisse, E., Van der Meulen, J., De Bruyn, F., Roerdink, F. and Scherphof, G. (1978). *J. Ultramicroscopy*, **3**, 146–147.

Yasuda, T., Dancey, G. F. and Kinksky, S. C. (1977). *J. Immunol.*, **119**, 1863–1867.

Yasuda, T., Tadakuma, T., Pierce, C. W. and Kinsky, S. C. (1979). *J. Immunol.*, **123**, 1535–1539.

Yatvin, M. B., Weinstein, D. N., Dennis, W. H. and Blumenthal, R. (1978). *Science*, **202**, 1290–1293.

Young, S. P., Baker, E. Huehns, E. R. (1979). *Brit. J. Haematol.*, **41**, 357–363.

Zierenberg, O. and Betzing, H. (1979). *Arzneim. Forsch.*, **29**, 494–498.

Zinkernagel, R. M. (1978). *Immunol. Rev.*, **42**, 224–270.

Subject Index

ABA-tyr-PE, 358
N-acetyl cysteine, 77
Actinomycin-D, 29, 32, 38, 48, 49, 71, 91, 94, 141, 142, 221–4, 228, 244
  chemotherapeutic effect of liposomal, 221
  effect of liposomal, on actinomycin-D-resistant cells, 223, 224
  effect of liposomal, on DNA directed RNA synthesis, 48
  effect of liposomal, on RNA synthesis, 223
  entrapment in aqueous phase of liposomes, 221, 222
  entrapment in lipid phase of liposomes, 221, 222
  lysosomotropic action by liposomal, 49
  mode of action of liposomal, in partially hepatectomized rats, 49
  mode of action of liposomal, in tumour-bearing mice, 49
  survival of tumour-bearing mice treated with liposomal, 49, 244
Actinomycin-D-resistant cells, interaction with liposomal actinomycin-D, 38
Adsorption, 104
  as mechanism of liposome uptake by cells, 103–11, 162
  as mechanism of vesicle interaction with cells, 121–38
  evidence for, 104, 121–38
Aggregated IgM, in targeting of liposomes, 163, 164

Alanyl alanine, 92
Alanyl glycine, 92
Albumin, 27, 32, 34, 56, 67, 183, 188, 199, 333, 340
  catabolism of liposomal, by hepatocytes in vitro, 203
  effect on leakage of liposomes, 195
  effect on liposomal stability, 180, 183
  fate of liposomal, after intravenous injection, 187, 188
  retention of steroids by liposomes in presence of, 313
  uptake of liposomal, by isolated hepatocytes, 201
[^{125}I]Albumin, 187, 189, 193, 194, 203
[^{131}I]Albumin, 167, 168, 171
Albumin spheres, in diagnostic medicine, 330
D-amino acid oxidase, 66
L-amino acid oxidase, 66
Amphotericin B, disruption of liposomes with, 158
Amyloglucosidase, 45, 156, 172
[^{3}H]Amyloglucosidase, 167, 168
1-anilino-8-napthalene sulphonate, 90
8-anilino-1-napthalene sulphonate, 350
Anti-AKR-A cell, 69
Antibiotics, 38
Antibodies, 61, 212
  effect of liposomal, on clearance of liposomes from blood, 334
  use of liposomal in targeting, 61
Antibody–complement-mediated attack nucleated cells, 360
  on erythrocytes, 360
Anti-coxsackie A-21 virus, 70

Anti-fibroblast, 69
Antigens, 45
  synthetic, in liposomes, 357
  synthetic, in study of immunogenicity, 357
Anti-α-glucosidase, 70
Anti-α-glucosidase antibodies, 37
AntiHeLa cell, 69
Anti-lymphocyte, 70
Antimetabolites, 141
Anti-Meth 'A' cell, 69
Antimony potassium tartrate, 74
Anti-6C3HED cell, 69
Anti-thyroglobulin, 70
α_1-antitrypsin, 68
Antiviral antibody, 249
  protection of cells by, 249
1-β-D-arabinofuranosylcytosine, 49, 73
  chemotherapeutic effect of liposomal, 221, 222
  mode of action of liposomal, in tumour-bearing mice, 49
  protection of liposomal, from deoxycytidine deaminase, 50
1-β-D-arabinofuranosylcytosine-5'-triphosphate, 73, 142
Arsenazo 111, 103
Asparaginase, 51
L-asparaginase, 50, 95, 154, 156
  in treatment of L-asparagine-dependent lymphosarcoma, 154
  survival of tumour-bearing mice with liposomal, 50
  tumour regression in mice treated with liposomal, 50
Aspergilus niger amyloglucosidase, 65
ATPase, 340
$(Mg^{2+} + Ca^{2+})$-ATPase, 67
$(Na^+ + Ka^+)$-ATPase, 156
Azaguanine, 222
  chemotherapeutic effect of liposomal, 222
8-azaguanine, 30, 73, 91, 93, 96
8-azaguanine chloramil, charge transfer complex, 93
8-azaguanine 3,5 dinitrobenzoyl-n-butylamide, charge transfer complex, 93
8-azaguanine vitamin B$_{12}$ complex, 93

Bacillus subtilis α-amylase, 65
BAL, 77

BCNU, 73
Benzyl penicillin, 180
Bifurcation, of cell membrane with vesicles, 136
Black lipid films, in study of the effect of reactive lysis on membrane conductance, 371
Black lipid membranes, 6
Bleomycin, 27, 73, 91, 103, 164, 333
  uptake of liposomal, by animal tumours, 46
  uptake of liposomal, by human tumours, 48
Bordetella pertussis, 55
  synergistic acting with liposomal antigens, 55, 57
Bovine carbonic anhydrase, 67
Bovine β-glucurnidase, 67

Calcium, 40
  contraction of actomyosin-containing microfilaments by, 137
  role in vesicle fusion, 137, 138
  structural changes of cell membrane by, 137, 138
6-carboxyfluorescein, 29, 30, 32, 33, 76, 93, 114, 119, 133
  a market for interacting with cells, 114–16
  effect of pH on leakage from vesicles, 115
Catalase, 66, 154
  in treatment of catalase deficient mice, 154
[^{14}C]cefazolin, 165
Cell membrane, internalization of, 135
Chelating agents
  desferrioxamine, 267
  diethylenetriaminepentaacetic acid, 267
  2,3-dimercaptopropanol, 267
  ethylenediaminetetraacetic acid, 267
  methods for entrapment in liposomes, 270–2
  D-penicillamine, 267
  structure, 270
  toxic effects, 267–8
  toxicity of liposomal, 277, 278
Chloranil, 30
Cholesterol
  effect in cortisol ester incorporation in liposomes, 306

effect in solute retention by liposomes, 304

effect on complement fixation by lecithin–hapten mixtures, 364, 365

effect on IgG binding capacity of hapten-bearing liposomes, 361–3

effect on liposomal stability, 27–9

effect on retention of cortisol esters by liposomes, 307

effect on retention of cortisol octanoate by liposomes, 308

effect on the biodegradability of, 332

effect on the permeability of liposomes, 332

maximum amount incorporated into phosphatidylcholine liposomes, 349

role in lipid structure, 88

role in membranes, 349–50

α-chymotrypsin, 68

Cis-dichlorobiscyclopentylamine platinum (II), 47, 74

tumour uptake of liposomal, 47

9-*cis*-retinaldehyde, 76

11-*cis*-retinaldehyde, 76

11-*cis*-retinol, 76

Clostridium perfringens neuraminidase, 65

Colchicine, 29, 53, 74

Complement activation, 360

Complement fixation, 363–4

by natural lipid haptens, 364

Complement pathway, activation by liposomes, 165

Cortisol, 75, 306

Cortisol acetate, 306

Cortisol cyclohexyl ester, 306

Cortisol esters

effect of albumin on retention by liposomes, 313

effect of cholesterol in incorporation in liposomes, 306–9

effect of ester chain length on retention by liposomes, 310

Cortisol octanoate, 75, 309

effect of transition temperature of liposomal phospholipid in retention of, 309

Cortisol palmitate, 75

Cortisol phosphate, 306

Cortisol succinate, 306

[^{3}H]cortisol, 310

[^{3}H]cortisol esters, 305

[^{3}H]cortisol octanoate, 308, 310, 312

[^{3}H]cortisol palmitate, 310, 312

Creatinine phosphokinase, 67

Crithidia fasciculata, interaction with liposomes, 53

CrO_4^{2-}, 158, 159

Cyclic AMP, 35, 74, 91, 92, 140

effect of liposomal, on cell growth, 141

Cyclic nucleotides, 103

Cysteamine, 42, 77

Cytochalasin B

effect on capping, 129

effect on endocytosis of, 116

effect on uptake of liposomes by cells, 162

inhibition of fusion by, 137

Cytochrome *c*, 69, 95, 156

Cytochrome d-b$_5$, 95

Cytochrome oxidase, 67, 156

Cytosine arabinoside, 141, 224, 241, 244

survival of tumour-bearing mice treated with, 224

survival of tumour-bearing mice treated with liposomal, 224

uptake of liposomal, by cells, 224

Cytotoxic drugs, 133

Daunomycin, 29, 49, 73

DNA-bound, 49

Dehydrostreptomycin, 52, 74

Deoxyglucose, effect on endocytosis of liposomes, 161

Desferrioxamine, 54, 77, 271, 274, 293

use of liposomal, in metal storage conditions, 54

[^{59}Fe]desferrioxamine, 273

Desialylated fetuin, 61, 69

Dextran, 71

Dextranase, 42, 65, 95, 156, 170

Dibucaine, 75

Dicetyl phosphate, in immunopotentation with liposomes, 55

^{99m}Tc–Sn–diethylene triamine pentaacetic acid, 168

3, 3 dioctadcyloxacarbocyanine, 130

All-*trans*-1,6-diphenyl-1,3,5-hexatriene, 93

Diphtheria toxoid, 55, 68, 335
  antibody response to liposomal, 55
Discoid structures, formation from
    liposomes in presence of high
    density lipoproteins, 197
Dithiothereitol, 77
DNA, 29
  from calf thymus, 70
  from Ehrlich ascites cells, 71
  from λ phage, 71
  from SV40 virus, 71
DNP-Cap-PE, 55, 358
  antibody-forming ability of cell
    suspensions from guinea pigs
    immunized with liposomal, 358
Drug-carriers
  cells, 25
  macromolecules, 25
  properties of, 26
  synthetic particles, 25
  viruses, 25
Drug resistance
  circumvention with liposomes, 38, 39
  of tumour cells, 141
  overcoming with liposomal drugs,
    141–3
DTPA, 53, 77, 271, 272, 277, 278, 281,
    288–95
  toxicity *in vivo*, 281
CaNa$_3$DTPA, 277
[^{45}CaNa$_3$]DTPA, 274
^{99m}Tc-DTPA, 77

EDTA, 54, 55, 77, 92, 171, 181, 228,
    271, 277–82, 285–7
  cellular distribution of liposomal, 282,
    285–7
  hepatic subcellular distribution of
    liposomal, 287
  tissue distribution of free, 284
  tissue distribution of liposomal, 282,
    283
  toxicity *in vivo*, 281
  use of liposomal in metal storage
    conditions, 54
[^{14}C]EDTA, 168, 271, 273, 282, 283,
    286, 287
2-[^{14}C]EDTA, 274
Electron paramagnetic resonance
    spectroscopy
  in study of phase transition of
    liposomes, 348

information obtained by, 352
interpretation of data from, 352–5
uses in liposomes, 352
Endocytosis
  as mechanism for liposome uptake by
    cells, 34, 48, 103–18, 160–2
  electron microscopic evidence for,
    122–7
  evidence for, 34, 104, 111
Enzyme replacement therapy
  glycogen storage disease type II, 42
  immunological reactions, 42
  liposomes in, 42
  side effects, 42
Enzymes
  methods for entrapment in liposomes,
    155–60
  problems after direct infusion, 154
  use of liposomal, for treatment of
    enzyme deficiency model
    conditions, 170
Ergosterol, 39, 76
Erwinia asparaginase, 65
Erwinia L-asparaginase, 50
Erythrocyte ghosts, as carrier of
    enzymes, 155
Erythrocyte major sialoglycoprotein, 69
Escherichia coli asparaginase, 66
Ethanolamine-labelled EDTA complex,
    54
Exchange diffusion
  evidence for, 118–20
  mechanism for interaction of vesicles
    with cells, 118–20

Feline β-galactosidase, 66
Ferritin, 68
Fetuin, 69
  use of desialylated lipsomal in
    targeting, 61
Floxuridine, 72
Fluidity, effect of liposomal, in
    interaction of liposomes with cells,
    161
Fluorescein-consugated antibodies, 170
5-fluorouracil, 72
Forssman antigen, 76
Fragment Ag diphtheria toxin, 69
β-fructofuranosidase, hepatic
    intracellular distribution of
    liposomal, 169
β-D-fructofuranosidase, 156, 169

Fusion
  as mechanism of liposome uptake by
    cells, 34–6, 103–11, 121–38,
    160–2
  change in cell surface morphology
    after, 126
  electron microscopic evidence for,
    122–7
  evidence for, 34, 35, 104, 121–38
  freeze-fracture studies of, 126, 127
  microinjection techniques, 139
  molecular mechanism of, 135–8
  of cells by vesicles, 131–3
  role of calcium, 137

β-galactosidase, 155, 156
Gangliosides, 95
Gaucher's disease, 154
  glucocerebroside : β-glucosidase, 44
  treatment with liposomal
    glucocerebroside : β-glucosidase,
    44
Gel–liquid crystalline transition
  temperature, 309
Glucocerebrosidase, 156
Glucocerebroside : β-glucosidase, 44
Glucose, 103, 158, 159, 163, 327, 328,
  367
  release from liposomes in
    complement fixation studies,
    368–70
D-glucose, 159
[³H]D-glucose, 157, 162
Glucose oxidase, 66, 156
Glucose 6-phosphate dehydrogenase,
  156
α-Glucosidase, inhibiting of hepatic,
  with liposomal anti-α-glucosidase
  antibodies, 212
β-glucosidase, 155
Glucuronidase, 33
β-glucuronidase, 156, 169, 173
  hepatic intracellular distribution of
    liposomal, 169
Glutamate, 76
Glutathione, 76
Glycogen storage disease type II
  treatment with liposomal
    amyloglucosidase, 45
  use of liposomes in treatment of, 172
Glycolipid extract from vescular
  stomatitis virus, 68

Glycophorin, 349
  selective concentration in liposomal
    membranes, 349
Gold
  elimination through faeces, 294
  treatment of poisoning with liposomal
    DTPA, 293, 294

Haemagglutinin, 56
Halobacterium halobium, 68
Heavy metal chelators, 38
Hepatitis-B surface antigen, 56, 78
  antibodies to liposomal, 56, 57
Hepatocytes
  culture of, 201
  interaction of liposomes with, 201–5
  mechanism for uptake of liposomes
    by, 203
  uptake of liposomal albumin by, in
    the presence of serum, 203–5
Hexokinase, 156
Hexosaminidase, 103
  use in treatment of Tay–Sachs
    disease, 154
Hexosaminidase A, 156, 159, 163, 164,
  216
High-density lipoproteins
  association of liposomal lecithin with,
    196–9
  effect on liposomal stability, 183
  fate of liposomal lecithin bound 6,
    199–201
Histamine, 76
Horseradish peroxidase, 32, 65, 94,
  103, 123, 140, 158, 159, 171, 183,
  188, 190, 191, 192, 199, 216, 250
  localization of free, after intravenous
    injection, 189
  localization of liposomal, after
    intravenous injection, 188–93
  morphological observations after
    injection of liposomal, 190–3
Human glucocerebroside : β-glucosidase,
  66
Human hexosaminidase A, 66
Human IgG, 217
5-hydroxytryptamine, 75, 95

IgG, 139, 339
  against coxsackie virus A-21,
    protection of ML cells from virus
    injection by, 139
  in targeting of liposomes, 163, 164

IgG immunoglobulin, 69
Immune RNA, 70
Immunogenicity, mechanisms for, 355–9
Immunoglobulins, 339, 362
    in targeting of liposomes, 163, 164
    liposomal, in liposome targeting, 339
$^{111}In^{3+}$, 78
^{111}In-bleomycin, 29, 31, 33, 46, 47, 48, 73
$rI_n rC_n$, 38, 144
    use of liposomal, for protection of
        cells against virus challenge, 144
$[^{14}C]rI_n·[^3H]rC_n$, 144
Influenza virus haemagglutinin and
    neuraminidase, 65
Influenza virus split products, 56
Influenza virus subunits, antibodies to
    liposomal, 56
Insulin, 58, 59, 61, 69, 91, 94
    absorption of liposomal by gut, 59
    effect of liposomal lipid composition
        on glucose lowering effect, 58
    levels in blood after oral
        administration of liposomal, 59
    mode of action of liposomal, 60
    orally given liposomal, 58
    survival of liposomal in stomach, 59
Interferon, 68
    induction by liposomal
        polynucleotides, 144
    induction *in vivo*, by liposomal
        poly(I):poly(C), 256
    induction with liposomal
        polynucleotides, 38
    in serum after treatment with
        liposomal poly(I):poly(C), 256
Interferon inducers, 38
Intracellular distribution
    of liposomal contents after uptake by
        cells, 164
    of liposomes after intravenous
        injection, 167
Inulin, 76, 180, 183
$[^{14}C]$inulin, 171
$[^3H]$inulin, 161, 195
Invertase, 27, 28, 42, 140, 170
    see also β-Fructofuranosidase
Ionophores, action in liposomes, 90

Large unilamellar liposomes, 111, 144
    advantages in use of, 143–5
    entrapment of large molecules in, 144

freeze-fracture electron micrograph, 11
    methods of preparation, 143–4
    reconstitution of proteins in, 348
Lead
    content of mouse tissues after
        treatment with liposomal DTPA,
        291
    elimination from mouse skeleton, 292
    in nuclei of mouse kidney after
        treatment with liposomal DTPA,
        293
    treatment of poisoning, with
        liposomal DTPA, 291–3
Leakage
    of chelating agents from liposomes,
        273, 274
    of liposomal agents in presence of
        serum, 165
    of liposomal drugs after
        intramuscular injection, 165
    of liposomes after contact with
        plasma, 193–5
    of liposomes in blood, 180, 181
    of liposomes in presence of serum,
        223
    of liposomes *in vivo*, 223
Lecithin
    as liposomal marker, 199
    clearance of liposomal, from
        circulation, 184, 185
    fate of liposomal, after intravenous
        injection, 187, 188, 199
    transfer of liposomal, to albumin,
        195, 196
    treatment, with liposomal antimonials,
        52
Leishmaniasis, treatment with liposomal
    antimonials, 52
Lesch–Nyhan syndrome, 154
Lipoic acid, 76
Liposome-associated substances. *See
    under* specific names of substances
Liposome-entrapped cytotoxic drugs in
    treatment of experimental tumours,
    141–3
Liposome-entrapped enzyme
    in alleviation of model storage
        condition, 140
    uptake by enzyme deficient cells, 140
Liposome-incorporated drugs,
        mechanism of action in treatment
        of rheumatoid arthritis, 303

Liposomes
  see also Vesicles
  advantages in use as carriers of
    chelating agents, 269, 287, 288
  aggregation with divalent metals, 90
  alteration of permeability of, 331–3
  animal species injected with, 65–78
  antibody-complement-mediated
    immune attack on, 359
  applications in biology, 36, 37, 39, 40
  applications in medicine, 41–62
  aqueous volume, 155
  as carriers of enzymes, 160–2
  as carriers of orally given drugs, 57
  as immunological adjuvants, 55–7
  as interferon inducers, 38
  autoradiography of tissues after
    injection of, 183
  binding of macromolecules on surface
    of, 90
  biphasic clearance from circulation,
    184
  biphasic clearance *in vivo*, 168
  by intraperitoneal route, 339
  by subcutaneous route, 339
  cell types exposed to, 65–78
  charge transfer complex in, 96
  clearance from plasma after
    intravenous injection, 167, 169
  coating with heat aggregated
    immunoglobulins, 111
  complement fixation studies with,
    363–72
  criteria for, as diagnostic tools, 326, 329
  criteria for entrapment in, 157, 158
  crossing of capillaries by, 337–9
  degradation in tissues after
    intravenous injection, 186
  determination of size, 272
  diagnostic uses *in vitro*, 327–9
  diagnostic uses *in vivo*, 329–41
  disruption by amphotericin B, 158
  disruption by nystatin, 158
  disruption by Triton X-100, 158
  distribution of liposomal markers in
    cancer patients, 172
  drug entrapment in, 87–98
  drug-targeting, 26
  effect of antibodies on rate of
    clearance from blood, 334
  effect of charge on clearance from
    blood, 30, 334

  effect of charge on uptake by cells *in
    vitro*, 252
  effect of charge on uptake by tissues,
    31
  effect of cholesterol content on
    stability, 28
  effect of cholesterol on leakage of,
    242
  effect of cholesterol on rate of
    clearance from blood, 334
  effect of complement components on,
    361
  effect of erythrocytes on stability, 29
  effect of fluidity on complement
    fixation by IgG, 366, 367
  effect of lipid composition of, on *in
    vivo* fate, 166
  effect of lipoproteins on stability, 29
  effect of multiple antigen
    incorporation on immunological
    adjuvant properties of, 358, 359
  effect of pH on drug entrapment in, 96
  effect of phospholipids on immune
    lysis of, 370
  effect of plasma constituents on
    leakage of, 193–5
  effect of polyene antibiotics on, 9
  effect of route of administration on *in
    vivo* fate, 166
  effect of saponin, 2, 4
  effect of serum on stability of, 181
  effect of size of
    methotrexate-containing, on
    survival of tumour-bearing mice,
    243
  effect of size on clearance from
    blood, 30, 185, 229, 258, 275
  effect of size on clearance of, 168
  effect of size on *in vivo* fate, 166
  effect of size on tissue distribution,
    275
  effect of size on uptake by tissues, 31,
    186
  effect of sonication on, 16
  effect of sterols on, 9
  effect of surface charge on, 4
  effect of surface charge on clearance
    from circulation, 184, 185
  effect of surface charge on clearance
    of, 168
  effect of surface charge on solute
    entrapment, 159

Liposomes (*continued*)
effect of surface charge on tissue distribution, 259–60
effect of surface charge on uptake by tissues, 186
effect of surface ligands on *in vivo* fate of, 167
effect on adenylate cyclase, 37
effect on catecholamines, 37
effect on cellular cholesterol, 38
effect on cyclic AMP, 37
effect on glucose distribution, 37
effect of homovanillic acid, 38
electron micrograph of, 3
electron microscopic studies, 33
electron microscopic studies after injection, 32
elimination from blood, 30
endocytosis by cells, 38
endocytosis by polymorphonuclear lymphocytes, 111
endocytosis of, 26
evidence for endocytosis by cells, 34
evidence for fusion with cells, 34, 35, 36
examination by electron spin resonance, 10
examination by light scattering, 11
examination by microcalorimetry, 10
examination by nuclear magnetic resonance, 10
examination by X-ray diffraction, 11
extent of drug entrapment in, 92–5
factors influencing stability *in vivo*, 180
fate after injection into animals, 27
fate after intracerebral injection, 234–8
fate after intraperitoneal injection, 32, 33, 166, 233, 234
fate after intravenous injection, 30, 32, 166
fate after oral administration, 166
fate after subcutaneous administration, 166
fate of protein-containing liposomes *in vivo*, 26
fluorescent markers in, 89, 90
for introduction of enzymes into cells, 140
for introduction of non-permeable materials into cells, 140–2
fusion with cells, 38
fusion with divalent metals, 90
half-life in plasma after injection, 168
hydrogenation of, 90
immune lysis in absence of liposomal proteins, 368
immune lysis, of, 367–72
immunogenicity of sphingomyelin-containing, 357
immunological adjuvant effect of, 335
immunological hazards, 173
immunopotentation in tumour rejection, 57
in antimicrobial therapy, 38, 51–3
in cancer chemotherapy, 45–51, 221–4
in cancer patients, 171
in clinical trial, 171
in complement-induced immune lysis studies, 327–9
in Gaucher's disease, 44
in genetic engineering, 39
in glycogen storage disease type II, 45
in immunopotentation, 55–7
in lysosomal storage diseases, 42–5
in metal storage diseases, 38, 53–5
in myocardial infarction, 61
in treatment of fungal diseases, 53
in treatment of leishmaniasis, 52
in treatment of malaria, 53
in treatment of Pompe's disease, 172
in treatment of solid tumours, 51
in treatment of trypanosomiasis, 53
in treatment of viral diseases, 53
in tumour-bearing mice, 33
in vivo fate of, 166–71
incorporation of radionuclides in, 330, 331
incorporation of synthetic antigens in, 357
injection into cancer patients, 48
injection into partially hepatectomized rats, 48
interacting positive and negative vesicles, 40
interaction of cells *in vitro*, 26
interaction of molecules with, 89
interaction of positive and negative vesicles, 41
interaction with blood constituents, 226
interaction with hepatocytes, 201–5

interaction with lipoproteins *in vivo*,
165
interaction with plasma proteins, 31
intracellular distribution after
intravenous injection, 169
intracellular distribution in liver, 33
intramuscular injection of, 50
intraperitoneal injection of, 49
intravenous infection of, 27
Kolmer Syphilis Test with, 364, 365
latency of entrapped enzymes, 26, 27
leakage *in vivo*, 226
leakage of drugs from, 29
leakage of entrapped agents from,
165
lipid composition of, 88, 92–5
lipid composition used, 65–78
localization in tissues, 31
localization in tumours, 61
lysosomotropic action of, 38
mechanisms for interaction with cells,
160–2
mechanisms for uptake by cells, 340
methodology for enzyme entrapment,
155–60
methods for preparation of, 326, 327
molecular sieve chromatography of,
15
molecular structure of, 89
morphological observations after
intravenous injection, 170–1
optimal conditions for drug
entrapment in, 87–98
parameters influencing target
recognition, 61
penetration through membranes, 32
permeability of, 45
permeability to albumin, 333
permeability to bleomycin, 333
permeability to penicillin G, 333
permeability to $^{99m}TcO_4$, 332
preparation from plasma, 335
preparation of polyribonucleotide
containing, 251–4
prodrugs in drug entrapment in, 96
properties of, 8, 9
properties of large unilamellar, 348
properties of small unilamellar, 348
radiolabelled, 27
selective modulation of fluidity of, 90
size of, 220
stability in circulation, 28, 30, 180–4
stability in presence of blood, 27, 28,
30
stability in presence of serum, 28, 30
stability *in vitro*, 28
stability *in vivo*, 27, 28, 167, 333
sterilization of, 341
steroid retention by, 304–15
studies with electron paramagnetic
resonance, 352
subcutaneous injection of, 49
surface ligands as means for targeting,
163, 164
targeting of, 60–2, 163–5, 336–41
targeting with aggregated
immunoglobulin, 216
tests for stability, 272, 273
tissue distribution after intravenous
injection, 166, 170, 171, 182
tissue distribution of, 46
toxicity, 172, 173, 275–8
toxicity after intracerebral injection,
235
toxicity *in vitro*, 254, 255
uptake by hepatic parenchymal cells,
31, 32, 186, 187
uptake by Kupffer cells, 31, 32
uptake by spleen, 31
uptake by tissues, 168, 169
uptake by tumours, 46
use of spin labels in study of, 352–5
visualization in liver of newborn rats,
213–16
volume of aqueous phase, 91
Liver, uptake of liposomes by, 31, 32
Low density lipoproteins, association
of liposomal lecithin with, 196–9
Lymph nodes, uptake of liposomes by,
32
Lysodeictus lysozyme, 65
Lysolecithin, role in cell-vesicle fusion,
138
Lysosomal storage diseases
animal models, 42
feline GM_1 gangliosidosis, 42
lysosomal enzymes in, 42
Lysosomes
catabolism of liposomes in, 34
endocytosis by cells, 43
interaction with liposomes, 104,
105
uptake of liposomes by, 26, 33
Lysozyme, 95, 155, 156, 158

α_2-Macroglobulins, after injection of liposomes, 44
Macromolecules, 37
Macrophages, release of contents in cholesterol-rich liposomes by, 350
Macrovesicles
    formation of, 17
    multilayer periodicity of, 17
Malaria, treatment with liposomal drugs, 53
α-Mannosidase, 156, 169
    Jack bean, 65
Mechlorethamine, 73
Meglumine antimoniate, 74
Melphalan, 29, 73
6-Mercaptopurine, 30, 73, 91, 92, 96
6-Mercaptopurine chloranil charge transfer complex, 92
6-Mercaptopurine 3,5-dinitrobenzoyl-n-butyl-amide charge transfer complex, 92
6-Mercaptopurine 3,5-dinitrobenzoyl-phosphatidylethanolamine charge transfer complex, 93
6-Mercaptopurine vitamin B_{12} complex, 93
Mercury, treatment, poisoning, with liposomal DTPA, 293
Metal poisoning, problems in chelating therapy, 266–7
Metaphase chromosomes, 39, 71
Methotrexate, 27, 29, 72, 91, 92, 103, 180, 223–46, 333
    assay with dihydrofolate reductase, 232
    breakdown of liposomal in blood, 230, 232
    chemotherapeutic effect of liposomal, 241–4
    chemotherapeutic index of liposomal, 243
    distribution of liposomal, in brain after intracerebral injection, 235–8
    effect of liposomal, on cells *in vitro*, 238–40
    effect of serum on leakage from liposomes, 242
    extent of entrapment in liposomes, 226
    fate of liposomal, after intracerebral injection, 234–8

fate of liposomal, after intraperitoneal injection, 233, 234
fate of liposomal, *in vivo*, 223
leakage of liposomal, in presence of serum, 226, 227
pharmacokinetics of liposomal, in monkey after intravenous injection, 228–32
preparation of liposomal, 224–8
survival of tumour-bearing mice after intraperitoneal injection of liposomal, 241–4
survival of tumour-bearing mice after intravenous injection of liposomal, 242
uptake of liposomal, by cells *in vitro*, 240
uptake of liposomal, by tissues *in vivo*, 231
urinary excretion of liposomal, after intravenous injection, 230, 231
[^{3}H] Methotrexate, 168
Microcapsules as carrier of enzymes, 154
Micro-organisms, 145
Micropinocytosis, as mechanism of vesicle uptake by cells, 117
Microvesicles. *See* Small unilamellar liposomes
Monovalent cations, 228
mRNA, 39, 70
Multilamellar liposomes, 12
    action of local and general anaesthetics on, 14
    amino acid permeabilities of, 14
    as immunological adjuvants, 13
    as means of depleting plasma cell membranes of sterols, 14
    as model for study of complement lysis of erythrocytes, 14
    as stimulants of interferon production, 13
    attachment of viruses and viral fragments to, 14
    effect of lytic reagents on, 13
    effect of surface charge on cation and anion permeability of, 13
    effect of temperature on uptake by cells, 118
    entrapment of enzymes in, 13
    freeze-fracture electron micrograph, 1

interaction with basic polypeptides, 14
interaction with monosodium urate, 14
interaction with retinal and retinaldehyde, 14
interaction with thyroid hormones, 14
susceptibility to hydrolysis by phospholipases, 13
Mycobacterium, synergistic acting with liposomal antigens, 55
Myelin figures, as artefacts in electron microscopy, 182, 193

Neuraminidase, 56, 181
effect of liposomal, on blood N-acetylneuraminic acid, 181
hepatic intracellular distribution of liposomal, 169
Neuraminidase (*Clostridium perfringens*), 156
Neuraminidase (Influenza virus), 156, 169
N-4-nitrobenz-2-oxa-1,3-1,3-diazole phosphatidylethanolamine, 130
Nitroblue tetrazolium, 77, 170, 183
Non-specific, 70
Noradrenalin, 95
Norepinephrine, 75
Nystatin, disruption of liposomes with, 158

17β-oesteradiol, 75
Organelles, 145
^{99m}Tc-Sn-oxine, 78

Parenchymal cells
preparation from liver, 189
uptake of liposomal albumin by, 189
uptake of liposomes by hepatic, 171, 183, 186
Parethoxycaine derivatives, 75
Penicillamine, 77
D-penicillamine, 271
[^{45}Ca]D-penicillamine, 274
Penicillin, 52, 94, 165, 223, 228
clearance of liposomal, from blood, 52
tissue distribution of liposomal, 52
Penicillin G, 74
Pepstatin, 37, 76
Permeability
of cells, 104–9
of liposomes, 104–9, 331–3

Peroxidase, 156
Peroxidase deficiency, 154
Photobleaching techniques, in study of cell–vesicle interaction, 130
Phthalyltetrathioacetic acid, 274, 293
Plasmodium falciparum, 78
Plasmodium falciparum mature segmenters, 56
Plutonium
elimination from mouse skeleton, 289
elimination from tissues, 53
elimination through faeces, 290
elimination through urine, 290
treatment of poisoning with liposomal DTPA, 289–92
Polio virus, 144
Polio virus resistant cells, interaction with liposomal polio virus, 39
Polio virus RNA, 145
Polio virus type 1, 78
Polio virus virions, 145
infection of cells by liposomal, 145
Polyacrylamide gel particles, as carrier of enzymes, 154
Polyalanine, effect of liposomal on clearance of liposomes from blood, 334
Polyamino acids, 340
Polyglutamic acid, 29
Poly(I), 70, 94
Poly(I):Poly(C), 70, 94, 250, 251, 253–62
biological activity of liposomal in animals, 256–63
fate of liposomal, after intraperitoneal injection, 258, 259
fate of liposomal, after intravenous injection, 257–62
interferon induction in cells by liposomal, 254–6
protection of cell with liposomal, from virus infection, 254–6
tissue distribution of liposomal, after intravenous injection, 257–62
[^{14}C]Poly(I):poly(C), 168
Poly-1-alanine, 71
Poly-1-leucine, 71
Polylysine, effect of liposomal, on clearance of liposomes from blood, 334
Poly-1-lysine, 71, 95
Polynucleotides, 133

Poly-1-phenylalanine, 71
Poly-L-phenylalanine, 167
Polyribonucleotides, entrapment in liposomes, 251
Poly-L-tyrosine, 167
Polyuridilic acid, 71, 233, 251
  protection of liposomal, *in vitro* and *in vivo*, 233
Polyvinylpyrrolidone, 31, 32, 34, 57, 71
  excretion of liposomal into faeces, 58
[^{125}I]Polyvinylpyrrolidone, 166
Pseudomonas cytochrome oxidase, 66
Pyranine, 89, 96

Radioactive pharmaceuticals, uses in associating with liposomes, 329
Radionuclides, methods for incorporating in liposomes, 330, 331
^{86}Rb$^+$, 78, 165, 223, 226
Retinol, 39
Rheumatoid arthritis
  occurrence, 299, 300
  treatment of, 300–2
Rhodopsin, 94, 339
Ribonuclease, 95
Ricinus communis lectin, 69
RNA, 39, 95
rRNA, 70

S$_9$ bacteriothodopsin, 68
Saponin, synergistic action with liposomal antigens, 57
Scanning
  of animals injected with radiolabelled liposomes, 335–8
  of mice after injection of liposomes, 46, 47
Semliki Forest virus glycoproteins, 65
Semliki Forest virus spike glycoproteins, 56
Sendai virus, 78
Sendai virus spike proteins, 65
Sialoglycoprotein, 340
  in targeting of liposomes, 164, 165
  of mammalian erythrocytes, 95
Sindbis virus, 78
Small unilamellar liposomes, 15, 111, 114, 119, 120
  dielectric properties of, 17
  differential permeability to ions, 16

effect of temperature on uptake by cells, 118
freeze-fracture electron micrograph, 109
fusion of cells by, 17
fusion of microvesicles to each other, 17
fusion with cells, 17
high resolution NMR spectroscopy, 17
inside–outside distributions of phospholipids, 17
partial specific volume of, 17
reconstitution of membrane enzymes, 17
Smectic mesophases. *See* Liposomes
Sodium, 40
^{22}Na$^+$, 78, 165, 223, 226
Sodium antimony gluconate, 52
Sodium azide, effect of, on endocytosis of liposomes, 161
Sodium salicylate, 75
Sodium stibogluconate, 74
Sodium sulphite, 77
Soya bean trypsin inhibitor, 68, 157, 159
Spin labels
  as epitopes of lipid haptens and conjugated proteins, 351
  in binding of TEMPO-specific anti-bodies to liposomes, 361
  in study of *in vivo* fate of liposomes, 166
  in study of kinetic and structural properties of liposomes, 350–5
  incorporation into liposomes, 351
  structure, 351, 352
Spleen, uptake of liposomes by, 31, 32
Staphylococcus aureus, killing with liposomal antibiotics, 52
Steroids
  adverse reactions after treatment with, 300–2
  in treatment of rheumatoid arthritis, 300–2
Sucrose, 103, 114, 144, 180, 183
[^{14}C]Sucrose, 194
[^{35}S]Sulphate, 304
Staphyloccocal α-toxin, 69
Surface charge, effect of liposomal, on interaction of liposomes with cells, 161

Synovial fluid
  effect on retention of steroids by
    liposomes, 310–15
  effect on stability of liposomal
    steroids, 312
  in rheumatoid arthritis, 310–11

Targeting
  aggregated immunoglobulin as surface
    ligand for, 163
  of liposomes, 163–5
Tay–Sach's disease, 154
Technetate, 151
Technetium, 103
^{99m}Tc, 48, 61, 330
^{99m}TcO$_4$, 77, 228, 332, 335, 336, 339
  effect of liposomal liquid composition
    on release of entrapped, 332
^{99m}TcO$_4^-$, 166
Tempocholine, 328
Tempocholine chloride, 166
Testicle, uptake of liposomes by, 32
Testosterone, 75
Tetracaine, 75, 94
2,2,6,6-Tetramethyl piperidine-1-oxyl,
  348
Thyroglobulin, 69
Thyrotropin, 69
Thyroxine, 75
Toxicity
  of liposomes, 213, 235, 275
  of liposomes in drugs, 64
  of liposomes in rats, 64
Triiodothyronine, 75
Triton X-100, disruption of liposomes
  with, 158
tRNA, 70
Trypanosomiasis, treatment with
  liposomal drugs, 53
Tubocurarine, 75
Tumour-bearing animals, injection with
  liposomes, 33

Urease, 66

Vesicles, 103
  advantages in use as drug carriers,
    139
  as drug carriers, 138–45
  capping in cells after interactions
    with, 128, 129
  cellular membrane surface after
    fusion with, 121
  effect of charge on interaction with
    cells, 106
  effect of cholesterol on permeability
    of, 108
  effect of cytochalasin B on
    endocytosis of, 116
  effect of fluidity on endocytosis of,
    116
  effect of fluidity on permeability of,
    107
  effect of metabolic inhibitors on
    endocytosis of, 111, 113, 117
  effect of metabolic inhibitors on fusion
    with cells, 113
  effect of synthetic lecithin
    components on permeability of,
    108, 109
  effect of temperature on endocytosis
    and fusion of, 118
  effect of temperature on endocytosis
    of, 116, 117
  effect on cell permeability, 104–9
  electronmicroscopic evidence for
    fusion with cells, 122–7
  elution of adsorped, 130, 131
  endocytosis by *Acanthamoeba
    castellanii*, 112
  endocytosis by diploid fibroblasts, 112
  endocytosis by lymphocytes, 112
  exchange of components with cells,
    103–11
  extent of association with cells, 121
  fusion of cells by, 131–3
  fusion with cells, 133–5
  fusion with Sendai virus, 112
  lateral mobility in cell membranes
    after interaction with, 129–30
  markers of, for study of interaction
    with cells, 103
  mechanisms of interaction with cells,
    103–11
  methodology, 15
  micropinocytosis of, 117
  molecular mechanism for fusion with
    cells, 135–8
  permeability in presence of protein,
    106, 107
  permeability in presence of serum, 106
  phospholipid exchange with cells,
    118–20

Vesicles (*continued*)
  single walled, 15
  subcellular fractionation of cells after
    interaction with, 127, 128
  transfer of cellular markers by, 120
  transfer of protein onto cell
    membrane by, 130
Vinblastine, 29, 73
Viral nucleic acids, 133
Viruses
  fusion with cells, 137

interaction with cells during infection,
  250
Vitamin A, 76
Vitamin B_6, 76
Vitamin B_{12} complexes of purine
  antagonists, 96
Vitamin C, 76
Vitamin K, 76, 94

Yeast invertase, 65